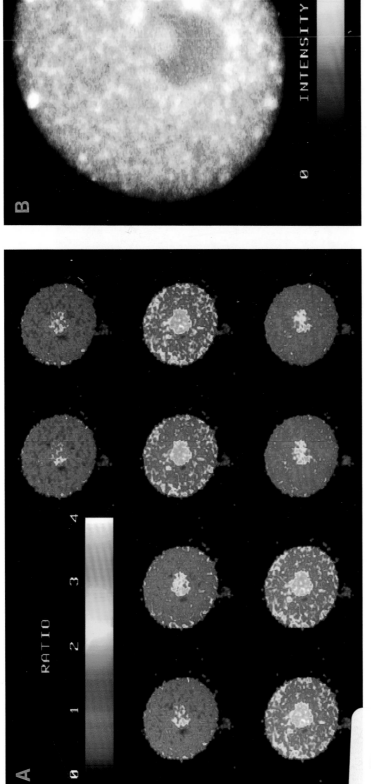

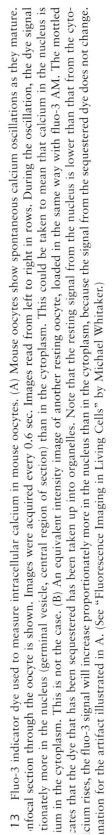

13 Fluo-3 indicator dye used to measure intracellular calcium in mouse oocytes. (A) Mouse oocytes show spontaneous calcium oscillations as they mature. A confocal section through the oocyte is shown. Images were acquired every 0.6 sec. Images read from left to right in rows. During the oscillation, the dye signal is proportionately more in the nucleus (germinal vesicle, central region of section) than in the cytoplasm. This could be taken to mean that calcium in the nucleus is higher than in the cytoplasm. This is not the case. (B) An equivalent intensity image of another resting oocyte, loaded in the same way with fluo-3 AM. The mottled image indicates that the dye that has been sequestered has been taken up into organelles. Note that the resting signal from the nucleus is lower than that from the cytoplasm. As cytoplasmic calcium rises, the fluo-3 signal will increase proportionately more in the nucleus than in the cytoplasm, because the signal from the sequestered dye does not change. This is the explanation for the artifact illustrated in A. (See "Fluorescence Imaging in Living Cells" by Michael Whitaker.)

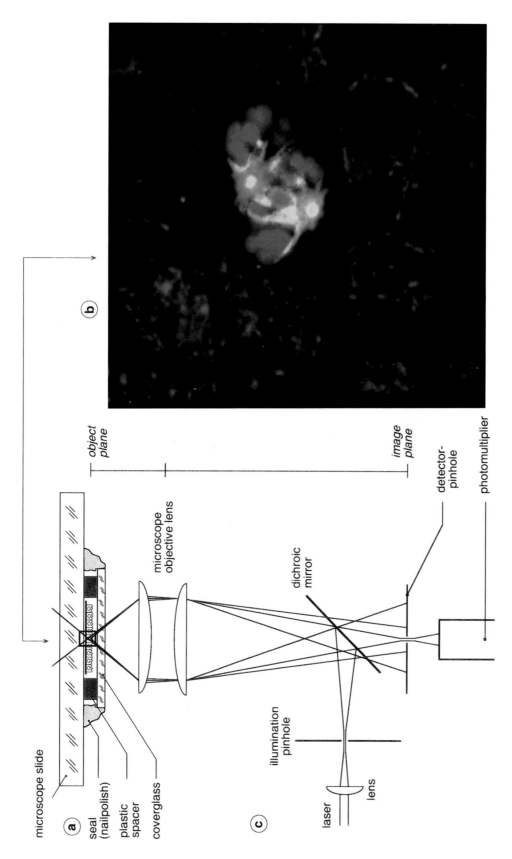

COLOR PLATE 14 Cytoskeleton and nuclei of MDCK cells with accompanying confocal microscope configuration. (a) The mounted sample of MDCK cells grown on permeable filter supports is in the object plane. The apical membrane of MDCK cells is oriented toward the microscope objective. (b) A single *x/y* image of a prometaphase MDCK cell is surrounded by interphase cells. The microtubules were stained with anti-β-tubulin antibody (green). The chromatin (red) and centrioles (yellow dots visible at the center of the microtubule asters) were visualized with propidium iodide and anti-γ-tubulin antibody, respectively. The centrioles of the interphase cells are not visible as they are in a different focal plane than in the mitotic cell. (c) The principal configuration of a confocal fluorescence microscope. (See "Confocal Microscopy of Polarized MDCK Epithelial Cells" by Sigrid Reinsch and Ernst Stelzer.)

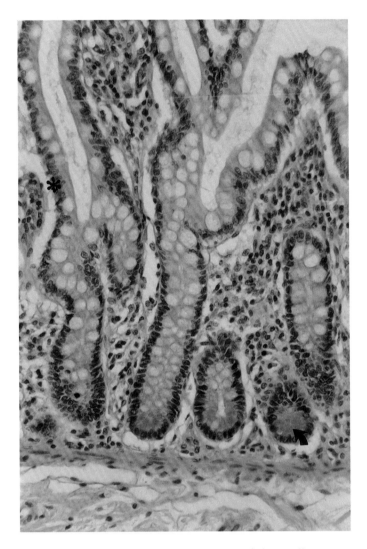

COLOR PLATE 15 Micrograph section of the small intestine stained with Mayer's hematoxylin–eosin. Note the dark blue staining of nuclei, particularly in the columnar epithelium (*), and the intense red staining of the cytoplasm of the Paneth cells situated in the deeper parts of the intestinal crypts (arrow). (See "Mayer's Hematoxylin–Eosin: An example of Common Histological Staining Method" by Hans Lyon.)

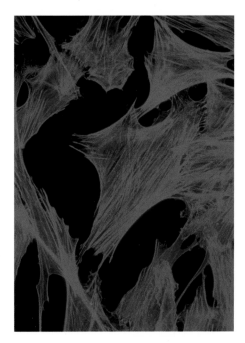

COLOR PLATE 16 Actin stress fibers in rat mammary cell line revealed by staining with rhodamine-labeled phalloidin (×400). (See "Immunofluorescence Microscopy of Cultured Cells" by Mary Osborn.)

COLOR PLATE 17 Microtubules in the monkey CV-1 cell line revealed by staining with antibodies to tubulin (×400). (See "Immunofluorescence Microscopy of Cultured Cells" by Mary Osborn.)

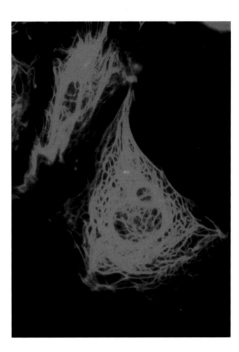

COLOR PLATE 18 Keratin filaments in the rat kangaroo PtK2 cell line revealed by staining with antibodies to keratin (×600). (See "Immunofluorescence Microscopy of Cultured Cells" by Mary Osborn.)

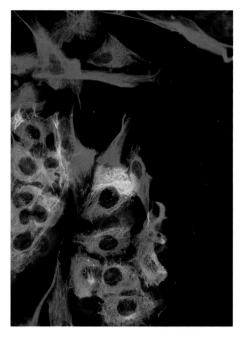

COLOR PLATE 19 Artificial mixture of cells from the human breast carcinoma cell line MCF-7 stained with an antibody to keratin and an FITC-labeled second antibody (in green) and the human fibroblast cell line HS27 stained with the V9 antibody to vimentin (in red). Note that each cell type contains only a single intermediate filament. The yellow color results from MCF-7 and HS27 cells that lie over each other (×150). (See "Immunofluorescence Microscopy of Cultured Cells" by Mary Osborn.)

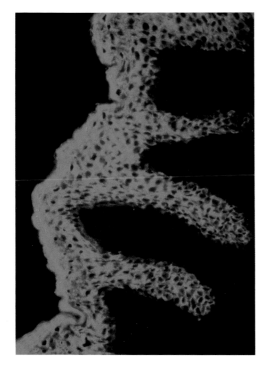

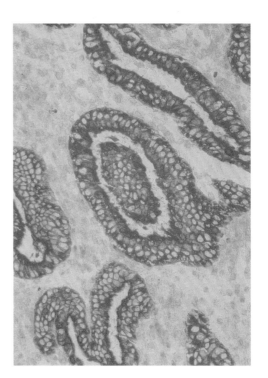

COLOR PLATE 20 Frozen section of human skin stained with KL1 keratin antibody with FITC-labeled second antibody. Only the epidermis is stained (×150). (See "Immunocytochemistry of Frozen and of Paraffin Tissue Sections" by Mary Osborn and Susanne Isenberg.)

COLOR PLATE 21 Frozen section of human uterus is stained with KL1 keratin antibody in the alkaline phosphatase–antialkaline phosphatase technique. Only the epithelial cells are positive (×150). (See "Immunocytochemistry of Frozen and of Paraffin Tissue Sections" by Mary Osborn and Susanne Isenberg.)

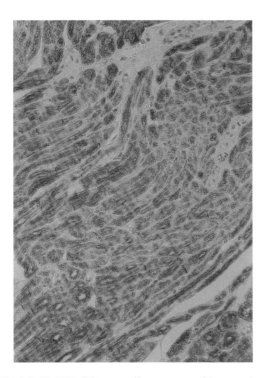

COLOR PLATE 22 Paraffin section of human heart stained with antibody after microwave fixation with the desmin DER 11 antibody in the streptavidin–biotin technique. Note striations. Nuclei are counterstained blue (×150). (See "Immunocytochemistry of Frozen and of Paraffin Tissue Sections" by Mary Osborn and Susanne Isenberg.)

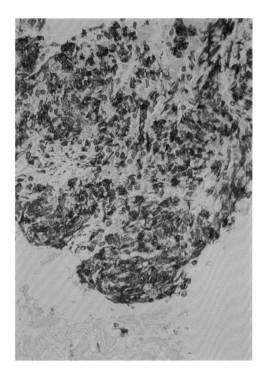

COLOR PLATE 23 Frozen section of human rhab-domyosarcoma stained after microwave treatment with desmin antibody DEB 5 and with peroxidase-labeled second antibody. Brown tumor cells are positive for desmin. Nuclei are counterstained blue (×160). (See "Immunocytochemistry of Frozen and of Paraffin Tissue Sections" by Mary Osborn and Susanne Isenberg.)

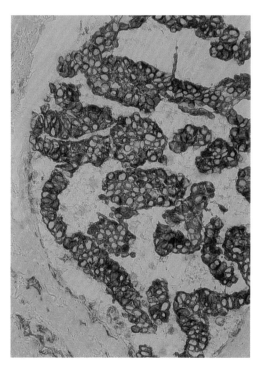

COLOR PLATE 24 Frozen section of human breast carcinoma stained with the keratin KL1 antibody and with peroxidase-labeled second antibody. Brown tumor cells are positive for keratin. Nuclei are counterstained blue (×150). (See "Immunocytochemistry of Frozen and of Paraffin Tissue Sections" by Mary Osborn and Susanne Isenberg.)

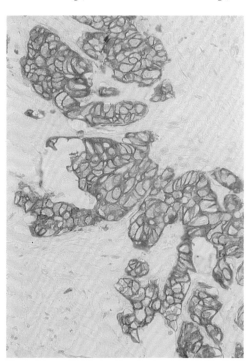

COLOR PLATE 25 Paraffin section of human breast carcinoma stained after microwave treatment with ker-atin KL1 antibody in the streptavidin–biotin technique. Red tumor cells are keratin positive. Nuclei are counter-stained blue (×150). (See "Immunocytochemistry of Frozen and of Paraffin Tissue Sections" by Mary Osborn and Susanne Isenberg.)

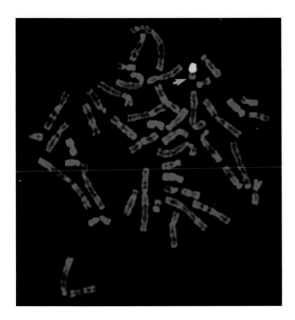

COLOR PLATE 26 Chromosome Painting. (See "Chromosome Painting Using Degenerate Oligonucleotide-Primed Polymerase Chain Reaction-Amplified, Flow-Sorted Human Chromosomes" by Nigel P. Carter.)

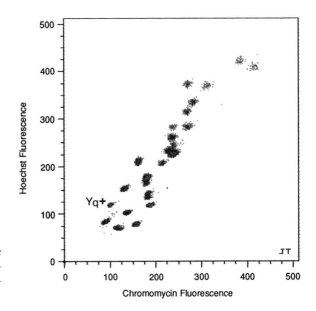

COLOR PLATE 27 Chromosome Painting. (See "Chromosome Painting Using Degenerate Oligonucleotide-Primed Polymerase Chain Reaction-Amplified, Flow-Sorted Human Chromosomes" by Nigel P. Carter.)

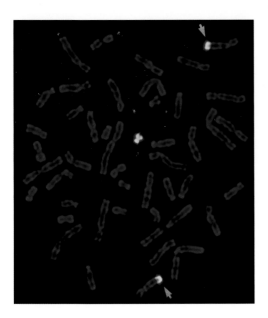

COLOR PLATE 28 Chromosome Painting. (See "Chromosome Painting Using Degenerate Oligonucleotide-Primed Polymerase Chain Reaction-Amplified, Flow-Sorted Human Chromosomes" by Nigel P. Carter.)

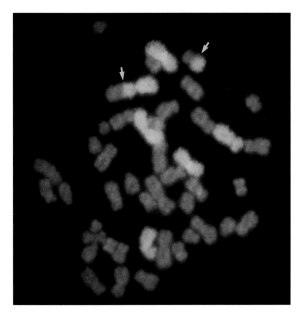

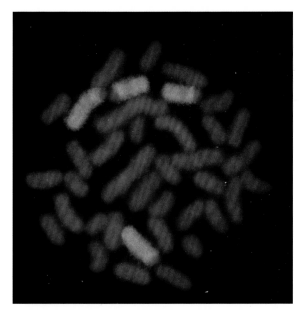

COLOR PLATE 29 A human peripheral blood lymphocyte in metaphase hybridized with a biotinylated probe for chromosomes 1, 3, and 4 simultaneously. Bound probe was detected with two layers of fluorescein-conjugated avidin. Note the presence of a reciprocal translocation (arrows). (See "Fluorescence *in Situ* Hybridization of Human and Mouse DNA Probes to Determine the Chromosomal Contents of Cell Lines and Tumors" by James D. Tucker, John W. Breneman, Denise A. Lee, Marilyn J. Ramsey, and Roy R. Swiger.)

COLOR PLATE 30 Lymphocyte chromosomes from a mouse homozygous for a Robertsonian (6.7) translocation. This cell was painted with probe for chromosomes 2 and 8. Note that the chromosomes are uniformly labeled except for the centromere region, which consists of repetitive DNA that is not present in this probe (Breneman *et al.*, 1993). (See "Fluorescence *in Situ* Hybridization of Human and Mouse DNA Probes to Determine the Chromosomal Contents of Cell Lines and Tumors" by James D. Tucker, John W. Breneman, Denise A. Lee, Marilyn J. Ramsey, and Roy R. Swiger.)

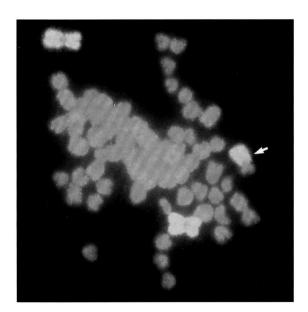

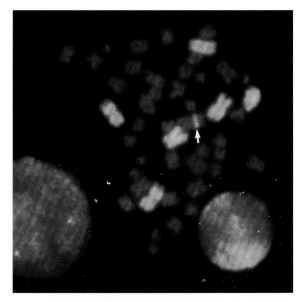

COLOR PLATE 31 Probe for mouse chromosomes 2 and 8 was used to paint this heteroploid mouse lung fibroblast. There are two apparently normal Robertsonian (2.8) chromosomes, as well as a portion of either chromosome 2 or 8 (arrow). (See "Fluorescence *in Situ* Hybridization of Human and Mouse DNA Probes to Determine the Chromosomal Contents of Cell Lines and Tumors" by James D. Tucker, John W. Breneman, Denise A. Lee, Marilyn J. Ramsey, and Roy R. Swiger.)

COLOR PLATE 32 A human lymphocyte in metaphase painted with SpectrumOrange probe for chromosomes 1, 2, and 4. The arrow marks the presence of a small insertion of painted material into an otherwise unpainted chromosome. (See "Fluorescence *in Situ* Hybridization of Human and Mouse DNA Probes to Determine the Chromosomal Contents of Cell Lines and Tumors" by James D. Tucker, John W. Breneman, Denise A. Lee, Marilyn J. Ramsey, and Roy R. Swiger.)

CELL BIOLOGY

A LABORATORY HANDBOOK

VOLUME 2

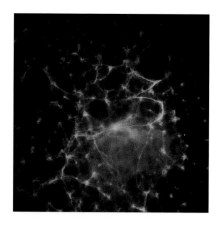

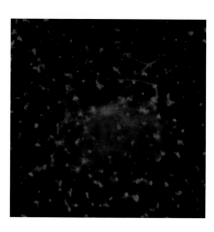

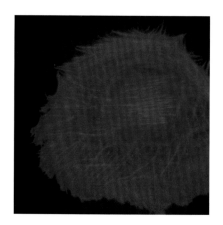

ACADEMIC PRESS

San Diego   New York   Boston
London   Sydney   Tokyo   Toronto

CELL
BIOLOGY

A LABORATORY HANDBOOK

Edited by

JULIO E. CELIS

Danish Centre for Human Genome Research
Aarhus, Denmark

VOLUME 2

Cover Photograph for Volume 2: TC7 cells treated with Cytochalasin B
and stained with rhodamine-labeled phalloidin. Courtesy of J. E. Celis.

Academic Press, Inc.
A Division of Harcourt Brace & Company
525 B Street, Suite 1900, San Diego, California 92101-4495

United Kingdom Edition published by
Academic Press Limited
24-28 Oval Road, London NW1 7DX

Library of Congress Cataloging-in-Publication Data

Celis, J. E. (Julio E.)
    Cell biology / Julio E. Celis.
        p.   cm.
    Includes indexes.
     ISBN 0-12-164714-5 (set). -- ISBN 0-12-164715-3 (v. 1). -- ISBN
0-12-164716-1 (v. 2). -- ISBN 0-12-164717-X (v. 3)
     1. Cytology-Laboratory Manuals.   I. Title.
QH583.2.C45   1994
574.87' 078--dc20   94-27690
                                                   CIP

PRINTED IN THE UNITED STATES OF AMERICA
94 95 96 97 98 99 DO 9 8 7 6 5 4 3 2 1

CONTENTS OF VOLUME 2

Contents of Other Volumes   xiii
Contributors to Volume 2   xxiii

 ## PART 4
MICROSCOPY TECHNIQUES

Section A
Light Microscopy   **3**

Phase-Contrast, Nomarski (Differential-Interference) Contrast
and Dark-Field Microscopy: Black and White and
Color Photomicrography   5
Dieter Brocksch

Reflection Interference Microscopy   15
Jürgen Bereiter-Hahn and Pavel Vesely

Using Interference Microscopy to Study Cell Behavior   25
Graham A. Dunn and Daniel Zicha

Section B
Fluorescence Microscopy   **35**

Fluorescence Imaging in Living Cells   37
Michael Whitaker

Practical Laser-Scanning Confocal Light Microscopy: Obtaining Optimal Performance from Your Instrument   44
James B. Pawley and Victoria E. Centonze

Caged Fluorescent Probes for Monitoring Cytoskeleton Dynamics   65
Timothy J. Mitchison, Kenneth E. Sawin, and Julie A. Theriot

Section C
Video Microscopy   **75**

Video-Enhanced Contrast Microscopy   77
Dieter G. Weiss

Section D
Confocal Microscopy   **87**

Confocal Microscopy of Polarized MDCK Epithelial Cells   89
Sigrid Reinsch and Ernst H. K. Stelzer

Real-Time Confocal Microscopy and Cell Biology   96
Alan Boyde, Colin Gray, and Sheila Jones

Section E
Electron Microscopy   **103**

Fixation of Cells and Tissues for Transmission Electron Microscopy   105
Arvid B. Maunsbach

Embedding of Cells and Tissues for Ultrastructural and Immunocytochemical Analysis   117
Arvid B. Maunsbach

Negative Staining   126
Andreas Bremer and Ueli Aebi

Whole-Mount Electron Microscopy of the Cytoskeleton: Negative Staining Methods   135
J. Victor Small and Monika Herzog

Glycerol Spraying/Low-Angle Rotary Metal Shadowing   140
Andreas Bremer, Markus Häner, and Ueli Aebi

Rapid Freezing of Biological Specimens for Freeze-Fracture and Deep Etching   148
Nicholas J. Severs and David M. Shotton

Freeze Fracture and Freeze Etching   157
David M. Shotton

Use of Ultrathin Cryo- and Plastic Sections for
Immunoelectron Microscopy   168
Norbert Roos and Gareth Griffiths

Cryo-Transmisson Electron Microscopy of Thin
Vitrified Sections   177
Nathalie Sartori and Laurée Salamin Michel

Preparation Methods for Quantitative X-Ray Microanalysis of
Intracellular Elements in Ultrathin Sections for Transmission
Electron Microscopy: The Freeze-Dry, Resin-Embed Route   186
Hugh Y. Elder and Stuart M. Wilson

High-Resolution Scanning Electron Microscopy in
Cell Biology   193
Terence D. Allen and Martin W. Goldberg

PART 5
MICRODISSECTION TECHNIQUES

Microdissection-Based Techniques for the Determination of
Cell Proliferation in Gastrointestinal Epithelium: Application to
Animal and Human Studies   205
Robert A. Goodlad

Micromanipulation of Chromosomes Using Laser
Microsurgery (Optical Scissors) and Laser-Induced Optical
Forces (Optical Tweezers)   217
Michael W. Berns, Hong Liang, Gregory J. Sonek, and Yagang Liu

Microdissection of Chromosomes and Microcloning   228
Uwe Claussen and Bernhard Horsthemke

PART 6
HISTOCHEMISTRY

Mayer's Hematoxylin–Eosin: An Example of a Common
Histological Staining Method   239
Hans Lyon

Selected Enzyme Staining in Histochemistry   245
Joseph Chayen and Lucille Bitensky

PART 7
ANTIBODIES

Section A
Production of Antibodies   255

Production of Polyclonal Antibodies in Rabbits   257
Christian Huet

Production of Mouse Monoclonal Antibodies   269
Ariana Celis, Kurt Dejgaard, and Julio E. Celis

Production of Human Monoclonal Antibodies via Fusion
of Epstein–Barr Virus-Transformed Lymphocytes
with Heteromyeloma   276
Miroslaw K. Gorny

Rapid Production of Antibodies in Chicken and Isolation
from Eggs   282
Harri Kokko, Ilpo Kuronen, and Sirpa Kärenlampi

Section B
Purification and Labeling of Immunoglobulins   289

Purification of Immunoglobulins   291
Christian Huet

Conjugation of Fluorescent Dyes to Antibodies   297
Benjamin Geiger and Tova Volberg

Section C
Antibody Specificity   303

Determination of Antibody Specificity by Western Blotting
and Immunoprecipitation   305
Julio E. Celis, Jette B. Lauridsen, and Bodil Basse

Western Blotting and Ligand Blotting Using Enhanced
Chemiluminescence and Radioiodine Detection   314
Amandio Vieira, Robert G. Elkin, and Karl Kuchler

Enzyme-Linked Immunosorbent Assay   322
Hedvig Perlmann and Peter Perlmann

A Simple Solid-Phase Mutual Inhibition Assay Using
Biotinylated Antigen for Analyzing the Epitope Specificities of
Monoclonal Antibodies   329
Masahide Kuroki

DNA Immunoprecipitation: Application to Characterization of
Target Sequences for a Human Centromere DNA-binding
Protein (CENP-B)   335
Kenji Sugimoto

PART 8
IMMUNOCYTOCHEMISTRY AND VITAL STAINING OF CELLS

Immunofluorescence Microscopy of Cultured Cells   347
Mary Osborn

Immunofluorescence Microscopy of the Cytoskeleton: Double
and Triple Immunofluorescence   355
Monika Herzog, Annette Draeger, Elisabeth Ehler, and J. Victor Small

Immunocytochemistry of Frozen and of Paraffin
Tissue Sections   361
Mary Osborn and Susanne Isenberg

Fluorescent Labeling of Nascent RNA in the Cell Nucleus
Using 5-Bromouridine 5′-Triphosphate   368
Derick G. Wansink, Alison M. Motley, Roel van Driel, and Luitzen de Jong

Labeling of Endocytic Vesicles Using Fluorescent Probes for
Fluid-Phase Endocytosis   375
Esther L. Racoosin and Joel A. Swanson

Labeling of the Endoplasmic Reticulum with DiOC$_6$(3)   381
Mark Terasaki

Use of Fluorescent Analogs of Ceramide to Study the Golgi
Apparatus of Animal Cells   387
Richard E. Pagano and Ona C. Martin

Vital Staining of Mitochondria with Rhodamine 123 and of
Acidic Organelles with Acridine Orange   394
Julio E. Celis and Kurt Dejgaard

PART 9
INTRACELLULAR MEASUREMENTS

Measuring Membrane Potential in Single Cells with
Confocal Microscopy   399
Leslie M. Loew

Measurement of Cytosolic pH in Single Cells by Dual-
Excitation Fluorescence Spectrometry: Simultaneous
Visualization Using Hoffman Modulation Contrast Optics   404
Robert Romanek, Ori D. Rotstein, and Sergio Grinstein

PART 10
CYTOGENETICS AND *IN SITU* HYBRIDIZATION

Basic Cytogenetic Techniques: Culturing, Slide Making,
and G-Banding   415
Chih-Lin Hsieh

Production of Viable Hybrids between Adherent Cells   422
Doris Cassio

Microcell-Mediated Chromosome Transfer: Selective Transfer
and Retention of Single Human Chromosomes into Recipient
Cells of Choice   428
Michael J. Anderson and Eric J. Stanbridge

Microcell Transfer of Chromosomes from Mitotic Cells   435
Elton Stubblefield and Mark Pershouse

Chromosome Painting Using Degenerate Oligonucleotide-
Primed Polymerase Chain Reaction-Amplified, Flow-Sorted
Human Chromosomes   442
Nigel P. Carter

Fluorescence *in Situ* Hybridization of Human and Mouse
DNA Probes to Determine the Chromosomal Contents of Cell
Lines and Tumors   450
*James D. Tucker, John W. Breneman, Denise A. Lee, Marilyn J. Ramsey,
and Roy R. Swiger*

In Situ Hybridization Applicable to Abundantly Expressed
mRNA Species   459
Roeland W. Dirks, Frans M. van de Rijke, and Anton K. Raap

In Situ Hybridization of Frozen Sections Using
^{35}S-Riboprobes   466
Daniel Carrasco and Rodrigo Bravo

In Situ Detection of Human Papillomavirus DNA after
Polymerase Chain Reaction Amplification   477
Gerard J. Nuovo

Accurate Quantitation of mRNA Species by Polymerase Chain
Reaction and Solid-Phase Minisequencing   488
Ann-Christine Syvänen and Leena Peltonen

CONTENTS OF OTHER VOLUMES

VOLUME 1

PART 1: TISSUE CULTURE AND ASSOCIATED TECHNIQUES

Section A: General Techniques

General Procedures for Tissue Culture   5
Ariana Celis and Julio E. Celis

Development of Serum-Free Media and Methods for Optimization of
Nutrient Composition   18
David W. Jayme and Dale F. Gruber

Testing Cell Cultures for Microbial and Viral Contaminants   25
Robert J. Hay

Section B: Primary Cultures from Embryonic Tissues

Primary and Extended Culture of Embryonic Mouse Cells:
Establishment of a Novel Cell Culture Model of Apoptosis
and Neural Differentiation   45
Deryk T. Loo and Carl W. Cotman

Tissue Culture of Embryonic Stem Cells   54
Martin Evans

Isolation and Culture of Germ Cells from Mouse Embryo   68
Massimo De Felici

Section C: Cultures of Specific Cell Types

Epithelial Cells

Cultivation of Human Epidermal Keratinocytes with a 3T3 Feeder Layer   83
Fiona M. Watt

Growth of Human Keratinocytes in Serum-Free Medium   90
John P. Daley and Jean M. Donovan

Isolation of Hepatocytes   96
Per O. Seglen

Isolation and Culture of Oval Cells from Carcinogen-Treated Rats   103
Pablo Steinberg

In Vitro Culture of Mouse Fetal Choroid Plexus Epithelial Cells   109
Elizabeth Stadler, Tim Thomas, and Marie Dziadek

Isolation and Culture of Type II Pulmonary Epithelial Cells   116
Stephen R. Rannels and D. Eugene Rannels

Mesenchymal Cells

Maintenance of Human Diploid Fibroblast-like Cells in Culture   124
Robert T. Dell'Orco

Isolation of Osteoclasts and Osteoclast Plasma Membranes   128
Miep Helfrich, Takuya Sato, Ken-ichi Tezuka, Masayoshi Kumegawa,
Stephen Nesbitt, Michael Horton, and Patricia Collin-Osdoby

Culturing of Human Umbilical Vein and Dermal Microvascular
Endothelial Cells   142
Eyðfinnur Olsen

Neuroectodermal Cells

Isolation and Proliferation of Adult Mammalian Central Nervous System
Stem Cells   148
Brent A. Reynolds, Catherine Leonard, and Samuel Weiss

Hemopoietic Cells

Clonal Cultures *in Vitro* for Hemopoietic Cells Using Semisolid
Agar Medium   153
Gregory R. Johnson

Gonads

Properties of Isolated Sertoli Cells   159
Pierre S. Tung and Irving B. Fritz

Culture of Ovarian Granulosa Cells: Calcium Imaging at the Single-
Cell Level   170
Jorge A. Flores and Johannes D. Veldhuis

Section D: Cell Separation Techniques

Isolation of Peripheral Blood Mononuclear Cells and Identification
of Human Lymphocyte Subpopulations by Multiparameter
Flow Cytometry   179
Marianne Hokland, Hanne Jorgensen, and Peter Hokland

Purification of Functionally Active Epidermal Langerhans Cells Using
Immunomagnetic Beads   185
Jenny Morris and Anthony Chu

Section E: Model Systems to Study Differentiation

Nonterminal and Terminal Adipocyte Differentiation of Murine 3T3 T
Mesenchymal Stem Cells   193
Hanlin Wang, Dawn B. Sturtevant, and Robert E. Scott

Cell Systems for *ex Vivo* Studies of Myogenesis: A Protocol for the
Isolation of Stable Muscle Cell Populations from Newborn to
Adult Mice   199
Christian Pinset and Didier Montarras

Induction of Cell Differentiation in Human HL-60 Promyelocytic
Leukemia Cells: Quantitation of a Myeloid Specific Antigen MRP-8/MRP-
14 Protein Complex   207
*Shinichi Murao, Mamoru Nakanishi, Seiya Matsumoto, Norifumi Ueda,
and Eliezer Huberman*

Differentiation of Murine Erythroleukemia Cells (Friend Cells)   213
Victoria M. Richon, Richard A. Rifkind, and Paul A. Marks

Cultured PC12 Cells: A Model for Neuronal Function
and Differentiation   218
Kenneth K. Teng and Lloyd A. Greene

Growing Madin-Darby Canine Kidney Cells for Studying Epithelial
Cell Biology   225
Kai Simons and Hilkka Virta

In Vitro Studies of Epithelium-to-Mesenchyme Transitions   232
Ana Maria Vallés, Jean Paul Thiery, and Brigitte Boyer

Section F: Immortalization of Cells

Inducible Immortalization of Cells from Transgenic Mice Expressing
Simian Virus 40 under *lac* Operon Control   245
Ruth Epstein-Baak

Immortalization of Rat Ventral Prostate Epithelial Cells Using Simian
Virus 40 T Antigen   251
Debra A. Gordon and Roger L. Miesfeld

Section G: Cell Cycle Analysis

Cell Cycle Analysis by Flow Cytometry   261
Zbigniew Darzynkiewicz

Preparation of Synchronous Populations of Mammalian Cells in Specific
Phases of the Cell Cycle by Centrifugal Elutriation   272
R. Curtis Bird, Shiawhwa Su, and Gin Wu

Synchronization of Normal Diploid and Transformed Mammalian Cells   282
*Gary S. Stein, Janet L. Stein, Jane B. Lian, Thomas J. Last, Thomas Owen,
and Laura McCabe*

Synchronization of Transformed Human Amnion Cells by
Mitotic Detachment   288
Julio E. Celis and Peder Madsen

Stimulation of DNA Synthesis in Quiescent 3T3 Cells   294
Theresa Higgins and Enrique Rozengurt

Section H: Cytotoxic Assays

Quantitative Determination of Compound Cytotoxicity in Proliferating
Cells: Monitoring DNA Synthesis by [^{3}H]Thymidine Incorporation   305
Kathy May

Section I: Senescence, Programmed Cell Death, and Others

Serial Propagation of Human Fibroblasts for the Study of Aging at the
Cellular Level   313
Vincent J. Cristofalo, Roberta Charpentier, and Paul D. Phillips

Morphological Criteria for Identifying Apoptosis   319
John F. R. Kerr, Clay M. Winterford, and Brian V. Harmon

Use of the Terminal Transferase DNA Labeling Reaction for the
Biochemical and *in Situ* Analysis of Apoptosis   330
Jonathan L. Tilly

Growth and Induction of Metastasis of Mammary Epithelial Cells   338
Barry R. Davies and Philip S. Rudland

Measurement of Cell–Cell and Cell–Extracellular Matrix Interactions:
A Quantitative Cell Attachment Assay   345
Thomas E. Lallier

Section J: Electrophysiological Methods

Patch-Clamp Recording   355
James L. Rae and Richard A. Levis

Section K: Histocultures

Three-Dimensional Sponge-Gel Matrix Histoculture:
Methods and Applications   367
Robert M. Hoffman

Section L: Other Cell Types

Anthropoda

Primary Culture of *Drosophila* Embryo Cells   383
Paul M. Salvaterra and Izumi Hayashi

Caenorhabditis elegans

Laboratory Cultivation of *Caenorhabditis elegans* and Other
Free-Living Nematodes   389
Ian M. Caldicott, Pamela L. Larsen, and Donald L. Riddle

Protozoa

Cultivation of *Tetrahymena Cells*   398
Yoshio Watanabe, Osamu Numata, Yasuhiro Kurasawa, and Mariko Katoh

Acanthamoeba castellanii: A Model System for Correlative Biochemical
and Cell Biological Studies   405
Ivan C. Baines and Edward D. Korn

Fungi

Cell Biological, Molecular Genetic, and Biochemical Methods to
Examine *Dictyostelium*   412
Sandra K. O. Mann, Peter N. Devreotes, Susannah Eliott, Keith Jermyn,
Adam Kuspa, Marcus Fechheimer, Ruth Furukawa, Carol A. Parent,
Jeffrey Segall, Gad Shaulsky, Philip H. Vardy, Jeffrey Williams,
Keith L. Williams, and Richard A. Firtel

Large-Scale Culture of *Physarum:* A Simple Method for Growing Several
Hundred Grams of Plasmodia   452
Kazuhiro Kohama, Ryoki Ishikawa, and Mitsuo Ishigami

Plants

Induction of Regeneration-Competent Monocot Callus   456
Roberta H. Smith and Shyamala Bhaskaran

Isolation, Culture, and Plant Regeneration from Protoplasts   462
German Spangenberg and Ingo Potrykus

PART 2: VIRUSES

Propagation and Purification of Polyoma and Simian Virus 40   471
Roland Sahli and Peter Beard

Construction and Propagation of Human Adenovirus Vectors   479
Mary Hitt, Andrew J. Bett, Ludvik Prevec, and Frank L. Graham

Tissue Culture Techniques for the Study of Human Papillomaviruses in
Stratified Epithelia   491
Craig Meyers, Mark G. Frattini, and Laimonis A. Laimins

Growth and Purification of Murine Leukemia Virus   500
Jette Lovmand, Anders H. Lund, and Finn Skou Pedersen

PART 3: ORGANELLES, CELLULAR STRUCTURES, MACROMOLECULES, AND FUNCTIONAL ASSAYS

Purification of Rat Liver Golgi Stacks   509
Paul Slusarewicz, Norman Hui, and Graham Warren

Preparation and Purification of Post-Golgi Transport Vesicles from
Perforated Madin-Darby Canine Cells   517
Lukas A. Huber and Kai Simons

Purification of Clathrin-Coated Vesicles from Bovine Brain, Liver, and
Adrenal Gland   525
Robert Lindner

Functional Identification of Membranes Derived from the Rough
Endoplasmic Reticulum of Yeast   531
Christopher M. Sanderson and David I. Meyer

Isolation of Yeast Mitochondria and Study of Mitochondrial
Protein Translation 538
Johannes M. Herrmann, Heike Fölsch, Walter Neupert, and Rosemary A. Stuart

Inclusion of Proteins into Isolated Mitochondrial Outer
Membrane Vesicles 545
Andreas Mayer, Arnold Driessen, Walter Neupert, and Roland Lill

Isolation of Peroxisomes 550
Alfred Völkl and H. Dariush Fahimi

Purification of Secretory Granules from PC12 Cells 557
Jane C. Stinchcombe and Wieland B. Huttner

Preparation of Synaptic Vesicles from Mammalian Brain 567
Johannes W. Hell and Reinhard Jahn

Purification and Reconstitution of the Ca^{2+}-ATPase of Red Blood Cells 575
Paolo Gazzotti and Ernesto Carafoli

Isolation of Focal Adhesions from Cultured Cells 584
Markus Niederreiter and Mario Gimona

Isolation of Laminins from Tumor Sources and from Normal Tissues 589
Mats Paulsson and Anders Lindblom

Isolation of Centrosomes from Cultured Animal Cells 595
Mohammed Moudjou and Michel Bornens

Preparation of Yeast Spindle Pole Bodies 605
Michael P. Rout and John V. Kilmartin

Preparation of Nuclei and Nuclear Envelopes, Identification of an
Integral Membrane Protein Unique to the Nuclear Envelope 613
Einar Hallberg

Preparation of Cytoplasts and Karyoplasts from HeLa Cell Monolayers 619
Julio E. Celis and Ariana Celis

Isolation and Visualization of the Nuclear Matrix, the Nonchromatin
Structure of the Nucleus 622
Jeffrey A. Nickerson, Gabriela Krockmalnic, and Sheldon Penman

Preparation of U Small Nuclear Ribonucleoprotein Particles 628
Sven-Erik Behrens, Berthold Kastner, and Reinhard Lührmann

Rapid Preparation of hnRNP Core Proteins and Stepwise Assembly of
hnRNP Particles *in Vitro* 641
Mei Huang and Wallace M. LeStourgeon

Preparation of Ribosomes and Ribosomal Proteins from Cultured Cells 657
Jean-Jacques Madjar

Preparation of Proteasomes 662
Keiji Tanaka and Akira Ichihara

Small-Scale Preparation of Nuclear Extracts from Mammalian Cells 668
Kevin A. W. Lee, Kenn Zerivitz, and Göran Akusjärvi

Purification of DNA Using Guanidine Thiocyanate and Isobutyl
Alcohol Fractionation 674
James E. Nelson, Mohamed Khidhir, and Stephen A. Krawetz

Single-Step Method of Total RNA Isolation by Acid–
Guanidine Phenol Extraction   680
Piotr Chomczynski

VOLUME 3

PART 11: TRANSFER OF MACROMOLECULES AND SMALL MOLECULES

Microinjection of RNA and DNA into Somatic Cells   3
Monika Graessmann and Adolf Graessmann

Microinjection of Proteins into Somatic Cells: Needle Microinjection
and Scrape Loading   16
Yu-Li Wang

Computer-Automated Capillary Microinjection of Macromolecules
into Living Cells   22
Rainer Pepperkok, Rainer Saffrich, and Wilhelm Ansorge

Syringe Loading: A Method for Inserting Macromolecules into Cells
in Suspension   30
Mark S. F. Clarke and Paul L. McNeil

Electroporation of Cells   37
*Stefan Herr, Rainer Pepperkok, Rainer Saffrich, Stefan Weimann,
and Wilhelm Ansorge*

Electroporation of Antibodies into Mammalian Cells   44
Ratna Chakrabarti and Sheldon M. Schuster

Virus (Sendai Virus Envelopes) Mediated Gene Transfer   50
Yasufumi Kaneda

Liposomes in Drug Targeting   58
Gregory Gregoriadis

Electroporation-Mediated DNA Transfer to Tobacco Protoplasts for
Transient Gene Expression Assays   67
Geert Angenon, Willy Dillen, and Marc Van Montagu

Electroporation-Mediated DNA Delivery to Embryos of
Leguminous Species   72
Willy Dillen, Marc Van Montagu, and Geert Angenon

Permeabilization by α-Toxin and Streptolysin O   77
Gudrun Ahnert-Hilger

Introduction of Small Molecules into Cells Using a Transient Cell
Permeabilization System   83
Curtis J. Henrich

Microinjection of RNAs into *Xenopus* Oocytes   88
Glenn Matthews

PART 12: CLONING OF EMBRYOS, TRANSGENICS, AND GENE TARGETING

Cloning Rabbit Embryos by Nuclear Transplantation   99
Philippe Collas

Production of Transgenic Mice by Pronuclear Microinjection   106
Jon W. Gordon

Gene Targeting by Homologous Recombination in Embryonic
Stem Cells   112
Miguel Torres and Ahmed Mansouri

Transgenic Plants: *Agrobacterium*-Mediated Transformation of the
Diploid Legume *Lotus japonicus*   119
Kurt Handberg, Jiri Stiller, Thomas Thykjær, and Jens Stougaard

PART 13: CELL-FREE EXTRACTS, PERMEABILIZED CELL SYSTEMS, AND EXPRESSION SYSTEMS

Preparation and Use of Translocating Cell-Free Translation Extracts
from *Xenopus* Eggs   131
Glenn Matthews

A Permeabilized Cell System to Study Peroxisomal Protein Import 140
Martin Wendland

Baculovirus Expression Vector System: Production and Isolation of
Recombinant Viruses   148
Linda A. King, Susan G. Mann, Alison M. Lawrie, and Robert D. Possee

Expression of Recombinant Proteins in the Vaccinia Virus
Expression System   155
Henrik Leffers

PART 14: PROTEINS

Section A: Protein Determination

Protein Determination   169
Martin Guttenberger

Section B: Preparation of Tagged Proteins and Others

Controlled Radioiodination of Proteins   181
Michael J. Rudick

Cell Surface Biotinylation Techniques   185
Chiara Zurzolo, André Le Bivic, and Enrique Rodriguez-Boulan

Assays for Cellular Protein Binding and Ligand Internalization   193
Kim Vettenranta, Guojun Bu, and Alan L. Schwartz

Identification of Cell Surface Binding Proteins via Covalent
Crosslinking   199
Guojun Bu and Alan L. Schwartz

Section C: Gel Electrophoresis

One-Dimensional Sodium Dodecyl Sulfate-Polyacrylamide Gel
Electrophoresis   207
Julio E. Celis and Eyδfinnur Olsen

Nondenaturing Polyacrylamide Gel Electrophoresis (NPAGE) as a
Method for Studying Protein Interactions   218
Daniel Safer

High-Resolution Two-Dimensional Gel Electrophoresis of Proteins:
Isoelectric Focusing and Nonequilibrium pH Gradient
Electrophoresis (NEPHGE)   222
Julio E. Celis, Gitte Ratz, Bodil Basse, Jette B. Lauridsen, and Ariana Celis

High-Resolution Two-Dimensional Electrophoresis of Proteins Using
Immobilized pH Gradients   231
Angelika Görg

Mini Two-Dimensional Gel Electrophoresis   243
Mario Gimona, Barbara Galazkiewicz, and Markus Niederreiter

Two-Dimensional Gel Analysis of Posttranslational Modifications   249
Scott D. Patterson and James I. Garrels

Detection of Protein Kinase Activity after Renaturation of Proteins
Transferred from Sodium Dodecyl Sulfate-Polyacrylamide Gels
to Membranes   258
Deborah A. Shackelford, Richard Y. Yeh, and Justin A. Zivin

Zymography of Proteases   264
Christian Paech and Teresa Christianson

Electroelution of Proteins from Two-Dimensional Gels   272
Julio E. Celis, Gitte Ratz, and Bodil Basse

Monitoring Sodium Dodecyl Sulfate Contamination   276
Michael Arand, Thomas Friedberg, and Franz Oesch

Section D: Staining

Ultrasensitive Silver-Based Stains for Protein Detection   281
Carl R. Merril, Janet E. Joy, and G. Joseph Creed

Detection of Subpicogram Quantities of Protein in
Polyacrylamide Gels   288
Andrew Wallace and Hans Peter Saluz

Section E: Overlay Techniques and Others

Blot Overlay Assay: A Method to Detect
Protein–Protein Interactions   301
Aaron W. Crawford and Mary C. Beckerle

Calcium Overlay Assay   309
Hans Jürgen Hoffmann and Julio E. Celis

Blot Overlay Assay for the Identification of GTP-Binding Proteins   313
Pavel S. Gromov and Julio E. Celis

Two-Dimensional Gel-Based Mapping of *in Situ* Crosslinked
GTP-Binding Proteins   317
Marcus E. Peter and Lukas A. Huber

Protein-Blot Analysis of Glycoproteins and Lectin Overlays   323
Shoshana Bar-Nun and Jonathan M. Gershoni

Purification of Lectins and Determination of Their
Carbohydrate Specificity   332
Halina Lis, David Belenky, Aaron Rabinkov, and Nathan Sharon

Two-Dimensional Northwestern Blotting   339
Kurt Dejgaard and Julio E. Celis

In Vivo Genomic Footprinting with Dimethyl Sulfate   345
Jean-Pierre Jost and Hans Peter Saluz

Section F: Microsequencing and Other Techniques

Internal Amino Acid Sequencing of Proteins Recovered from
One- or Two-Dimensional Gels   359
Joël Vandekerckhove and Hanne H. Rasmussen

Amino-Terminal Protein Sequence Analysis   369
Heinz Nika and Ruedi Aebersold

Sequencing Peptides Derived from the Class II Major
Histocompatibility Complex by Tandem Mass Spectrometry   380
*John R. Yates, III, Ashley L. McCormack, James B. Hayden,
and Michael P. Davey*

Mass Spectrometry: Detection and Characterization of
Posttranslational Modifications   389
Beth L. Gillece-Castro

Plasma Desorption Mass Spectrometry of Peptides and Proteins   399
Peter Roepstorff

Methods Optimization for the Analysis of Peptides Using
Capillary Electrophoresis   405
Michael Albin and John E. Wiktorowicz

Section G: Amino Acid Analysis

Amino Acid Analysis on Microscale from Electroblotted Proteins   417
Friedrich Lottspeich, Christoph Eckerskorn, and Rudolf Grimm

Phosphopeptide Mapping and Phosphoamino Acid Analysis on
Cellulose Thin-Layer Plates   422
Peter van der Geer, Kunxin Luo, Bartholomew M. Sefton, and Tony Hunter

PART 15: APPENDICES

Cell and Tissue Culture Media: History and Terminology   451
Dale F. Gruber and David W. Jayme

Representative Cultured Cell Lines and Their Characteristics   459
Robert J. Hay

Working Safely with Radioactivity   471
Richard W. Davies

Suppliers List   479
Index   499

CONTRIBUTORS TO VOLUME 2

Numbers in parentheses indicate the pages on which the authors' contributions begin.
Affiliations listed are current.

UELI AEBI (126, 140), M. E. Müller Institute for Microscopy, Biocenter, University of Basel, CH-4056 Basel, Switzerland

TERENCE D. ALLEN (193), CRC, Department of Structural Cell Biology, Paterson Institute for Cancer Research, Christie Hospital National Health Service, Manchester M20 9BX, United Kingdom

MICHAEL J. ANDERSON (428), Ludwig Institute for Cancer Research, La Jolla, California 92093

BODIL BASSE (305), Institute of Medical Biochemistry and Danish Centre for Human Genome Research, Aarhus University, DK-8000 Aarhus C, Denmark

JÜRGEN BEREITER-HAHN (15), Cinematic Cell Research Group, Johann-Wolfgang-Goethe-Universität, Frankfurt am Main, D-60054 Frankfurt/M, Germany

MICHAEL W. BERNS (217), Beckman Laser Institute and Medical Clinic, University of California, Irvine, Irvine, Calfornia 92715

LUCILLE BITENSKY (245), Unit of Cellular Pharmacology and Toxicology, Robens Institute of Health and Safety, University of Surrey, Guildford GU2 5XH, Surrey, United Kingdom

ALAN BOYDE (96), Department of Anatomy and Developmental Biology, University College London, London WC1E 6BT, United Kingdom

RODRIGO BRAVO (466), Bristol-Myers Squibb Pharmaceutical Research Institute, Princeton, New Jersey 08543

ANDREAS BREMER (126, 140), Department of Cell Biology, Duke University Medical Center, Durham, North Carolina 27710

JOHN W. BRENEMAN (450), Biology and Biotechnology Research Program, Lawrence Livermore National Laboratory, Livermore, California 94551

DIETER BROCKSCH (5), Carl Zeiss Application Laboratory, 73446 Oberkochen, Germany

DANIEL CARRASCO (466), Bristol-Myers Squibb Pharmaceutical Research Institute, Princeton, New Jersey 08543

NIGEL P. CARTER (442), Department of Pathology, University of Cambridge, Cambridge CB2 1QP, United Kingdom

DORIS CASSIO (422), URA CNRS 1343, Institut Curie, Bât 110, Université de Paris-Sud, 91405 Orsay, Cedex, France

ARIANA CELIS (269), Institute of Medical Biochemistry and Danish Centre for Human Genome Research, Aarhus University, DK-8000 Aarhus C, Denmark

JULIO E. CELIS (269, 305, 394), Institute of Medical Biochemistry, and Danish Centre for Human Genome Research, Aarhus University, DK-8000 Aarhus C, Denmark

VICTORIA E. CENTONZE (44), IMR, Madison, Wisconsin 53706

JOSEPH CHAYEN (245), Unit of Cellular Pharmacology and Toxicology, Robens Institute of Health and Safety, University of Surrey, Guildford GU2 5XH, Surrey, United Kingdom

UWE CLAUSSEN (228), Institut für Humangenetik und Anthropologie, Universität Jena, D-07740 Jena, Germany

KURT DEJGAARD (269, 394), Institute of Medical Biochemistry, and Danish Centre for Human Genome Research, Aarhus University, DK-8000 Aarhus C, Denmark

LUITZEN DE JONG (368), E. C. Slater Institute, University of Amsterdam, 1018 TV Amersterdam, The Netherlands

ROELAND W. DIRKS (459), Department of Cytochemistry and Cytometry, Leiden University, 2333 AL Leiden, The Netherlands

ANNETTE DRAEGER (355), Institute of Molecular Biology, Austrian Academy of Sciences, A-5020 Salzburg, Austria

GRAHAM A. DUNN (25), MRC Muscle and Cell Motility Unit, King's College London, London WC2B 5RL, United Kingdom

ELISABETH EHLER (355), Institute of Molecular Biology, Austrian Academy of Sciences, A-5020 Salzburg, Austria

HUGH Y. ELDER (186), Institute of Physiology, University of Glasgow, Glasgow, G12 8QQ, Scotland, United Kingdom

ROBERT G. ELKIN (314), Department of Animal Sciences, Purdue University, West Lafayette, Indiana 47907

BENJAMIN GEIGER (297), Department of Chemical Immunology, The Weizmann Institute of Science, Rehovot 76100, Israel

MARTIN W. GOLDBERG (193), CRC Department of Structural Cell Biology, Paterson Institute for Cancer Reseach, Christie Hospital NHS Trust, Manchester M20 9BX, United Kingdom

ROBERT A. GOODLAD (205), Histopathology Unit, Imperial Cancer Research Fund, 35–43 Lincoln's Inn Fields, London WC2A 3PN, United Kingdom

MIROSLAW K. GORNY (276), New York University Medical Center, Department of Pathology, New York, New York 10016

COLIN GRAY (96), Department of Anatomy and Developmental Biology, University College London, London WC1E 6BT, United Kingdom

GARETH GRIFFITHS (168), European Molecular Biology Laboratory, D-69012 Heidelberg, Germany

SERGIO GRINSTEIN (404), Division of Cell Biology, Hospital for Sick Children, Toronto, Canada M5G 1X8

MARKUS HÄNER (140), M. E. Müller Institute for Microscopy, Biocenter, University of Basel, CH-4056 Basel, Switzerland

MONIKA HERZOG (135, 355), Institute of Molecular Biology, Austrian Academy of Sciences, A-5020 Salzburg, Austria

BERNHARD HORSTHEMKE (228), Institut für Humangenetik, Universitätsklinikum Essen, D-45147 Essen 1, Germany

CHIH-LIN HSIEH (415), Molecular and Clinical Cytogenetics Laboratory, Department of Pathology, Stanford University Medical Center, Stanford, California 94305

CHRISTIAN HUET (257, 291), Centre National de la Recherche Scientifique, Bureau Formation, 91198 Gif-sur-Yvette Cedex, France

SUSANNE ISENBERG (361), Max Planck Institute for Biophysical Chemistry, D-37018 Göttingen, Germany

SHEILA JONES (96), Department of Anatomy and Developmental Biology, University College London, London WC1E 6BT, United Kingdom

SIRPA KÄRENLAMPI (282), Department of Biochemistry and Biotechnology, University of Kuopio, SF-70211 Kuopio, Finland

HARRI KOKKO (282), Department of Biochemistry and Biotechnology, University of Kuopio, SF-70211 Kuopio, Finland

KARL KUCHLER (314), Department of Molecular Genetics, University and Biocenter Vienna, A-1030 Vienna, Austria

MASAHIDE KUROKI (329), First Department of Biochemistry, School of Medicine, Fukuoka University, Fukuoka 814–01, Japan

ILPO KURONEN (282), Department of Biochemistry and Biotechnology, University of Kuopio, SF-70211 Kuopio, Finland

JETTE B. LAURIDSEN (305), Institute of Medical Biochemistry and Danish Centre for Human Genome Research, Aarhus University, DK-8000 Aarhus C, Denmark

DENISE A. LEE (450), Biology and Biotechnology Research Program, Lawrence Livermore National Laboratory, Livermore, California 94551

HONG LIANG (217), Beckman Laser Institute and Medical Clinic, University of California, Irvine, Irvine, California 92715

YAGANG LIU (217), Beckman Laser Institute and Medical Clinic, University of California, Irvine, Irvine, California 92715

LESLIE M. LOEW (399), Department of Physiology, University of Connecticut Health Center, Farmington, Connecticut 06030

HANS LYON (239), Department of Pathology 134, Hvidovre Hospital, University of Copenhagen, DK-2650 Hvidovre, Denmark

ONA C. MARTIN (387), Department of Embryology, Carnegie Institution, Baltimore, Maryland 21210

ARVID B. MAUNSBACH (105, 117), Department of Cell Biology, Institute of Anatomy, Aarhus University, DK-8000 Aarhus C, Denmark

TIMOTHY J. MITCHISON (65), Department of Pharmacology, University of California, San Francisco, California 94143

ALISON M. MOTLEY (368), E. C. Slater Institute, University of Amsterdam, 1018 TV Amersterdam, The Netherlands

GERARD J. NUOVO (477), Department of Pathology, SUNY at Stony Brook, Stony Brook, New York 11794

MARY OSBORN (347, 361), Max Planck Institute for Biophysical Chemistry, D-37018 Göttingen, Germany

RICHARD E. PAGANO (387), Department of Embryology, Carnegie Institution, Baltimore, Maryland 21210

JAMES B. PAWLEY (44), Zoology Department ERB, Madison, Wisconsin 53706

LEENA PELTONEN (488), Department of Human Molecular Genetics, National Public Health Institute, Mannerheimintie 166, SF-00300 Helsinki, Finland

HEDVIG PERLMANN (322), Department of Immunology, Stockholm University, S-106 91 Stockholm, Sweden

PETER PERLMANN (322), Department of Immunology, Stockholm University, S-106 91 Stockholm, Sweden

MARK PERSHOUSE (435), Department of Neuro-Oncology, The University of Texas, Houston, Texas 77030

ANTON K. RAAP (459), Department of Cytochemistry and Cytometry, Leiden University, 2333 AL Leiden, The Netherlands

ESTHER L. RACOOSIN (375), Department of Biochemistry and Molecular Pharmacology, Harvard Medical School, Boston, Massachusetts 02115

MARILYN J. RAMSEY (450), Biology and Biotechnology Research Program, Lawrence Livermore National Laboratory, Livermore, California 94551

SIGRID REINSCH (89), European Molecular Biology Laboratory, D-69012 Heidelberg, Germany

ROBERT ROMANEK (404), Division of Cell Biology, Hospital for Sick Children, Toronto, Canada M5G 1X8

NORBERT ROOS (168), Electronmicroscopical Unit for Biological Sciences, University of Oslo, N-0316 Oslo, Norway

ORI D. ROTSTEIN (404), Department of Surgery, Toronto General Hospital, Toronto, Canada M5G 2C4

LAURÉE SALAMIN MICHEL (177), Département Analyse Ultrastructurale, Université de Lausanne, Bâtiment de Biologie, CH-1015 Lausanne-Dorigny, Switzerland

NATHALIE SARTORI (177), Département Analyse Ultrastructurale, Université de Lausanne, Bâtiment de Biologie, CH-1015 Lausanne-Dorigny, Switzerland

KENNETH E. SAWIN (65), Department of Biochemistry, University of California, San Francisco, San Francisco, California 94143

NICHOLAS J. SEVERS (148), Department of Cardiac Medicine, National Heart and Lung Institute, London SW3 6LY, United Kingdom

DAVID M. SHOTTON (148, 157), Department of Zoology, University of Oxford, Oxford OX1 3PS, United Kingdom

J. VICTOR SMALL (135, 355), Institute of Molecular Biology, Austrian Academy of Sciences, A-5020 Salzburg, Austria

GREGORY J. SONEK (217), Beckman Laser Institute and Medical Clinic, University of California, Irvine, Irvine, California 92715

ERIC J. STANBRIDGE (428), Department of Microbiology and Molecular Genetics, University of California, Irvine, Irvine, California 92717

ERNST H. K. STELZER (89), European Molecular Biology Laboratory, D-69012 Heidelberg, Germany

ELTON STUBBLEFIELD (435), Department of Neuro-Oncology, The University of Texas, Houston, Texas 77030

KENJI SUGIMOTO (335), Laboratory of Biochemistry, Department of Agricultural Chemistry, University of Osaka Prefecture, Sakai, Osaka 593, Japan

JOEL A. SWANSON (375), Department of Cell Biology, Harvard Medical School, Boston, Massachusetts 02115

ROY R. SWIGER (450), Biology and Biotechnology Research Program, Lawrence Livermore National Laboratory, Livermore, California 94551

ANN-CHRISTINE SYVÄNEN (488), Department of Human Molecular Genetics, National Public Health Institute, SF-00300 Helsinki, Finland

MARK TERASAKI (381), Laboratory of Neurobiology, NINDS, National Institutes of Health, Bethesda, Maryland 20892

JULIE A. THERIOT (65), Whitehead Institute, Cambridge, Massachusetts 02139

JAMES D. TUCKER (450), Biology and Biotechnology Research Program, Lawrence Livermore National Laboratory, Livermore, California 94551

FRANS M. VAN DE RIJKE (459), Department of Cytochemistry and Cytometry, Leiden University, 2333 AL Leiden, The Netherlands

ROEL VAN DRIEL (368), E. C. Slater Institute, University of Amsterdam, 1018 TV Amersterdam, The Netherlands

PAVEL VESELY (15), Institute of Molecular Genetics, AS CR, Prague, The Czech Republic

AMANDIO VIEIRA (314), Department of Molecular Genetics, University and Biocenter Vienna, A-1030 Vienna, Austria

TOVA VOLBERG (297), Department of Chemical Immunology, The Weizmann Institute of Science, Rehovot 76100, Israel

DERICK G. WANSINK (368), E. C. Slater Institute, University of Amsterdam, 1018 TV Amersterdam, The Netherlands

DIETER G. WEISS (77), Universität Rostock, Lehrstuhl für Tierphysiologie, D-18055 Rostock, Germany

MICHAEL WHITAKER (37), Department of Physiology, University College London, London, WC1E 6BT, United Kingdom

STUART M. WILSON (186), Institute of Physiology, University of Glasgow, Glasgow, G12 8QQ, Scotland, United Kingdom

DANIEL ZICHA (25), MRC Muscle and Cell Motility Unit, King's College London, London WC2B 5RL, United Kingdom

PART **4**

MICROSCOPY TECHNIQUES

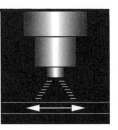

SECTION A

Light Microscopy

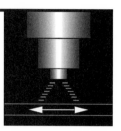

Phase-Contrast, Nomarski (Differential-Interference) Contrast, and Dark-Field Microscopy: Black and White and Color Photomicrography

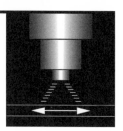

Dieter Brocksch

I. Introduction

Cell biology and light microscopy constitute a suitable combination for scientific studies in experimental cell research. Under optimum conditions it turns each single (living) cell into a test tube and permits the analysis of biologically relevant and important material at the cellular level.

Most cells under investigation have a typical diameter of around 20 μm and most of them are colorless and translucent and, therefore, hardly visible. Various microscopical contrasting techniques like phase contrast, with or without suitable natural and artificial probes such as fluorochromes and labeled antibodies, offer multiple methods for biological analysis under the light microscope, enabling even live biological processes to be visualized at the cellular level.

Scientific light microscopy started with the discovery of protozoa by Leeuwenhoek in the year 1674. The cell theory of Schleiden and Schwann followed in 1835. Twenty-two years later, in 1857, Kölliker reported mitochondria in muscle cells. In the year 1879 Flemming observed the mitotic behavior of chromosomes in animal cells. By 1876 Ernst Abbe had optimized the microscope and analyzed the effects of diffraction on image formation. The optical design of a light microscope by Abbe enabled Carl Zeiss in 1886 to produce microscopes and objective lenses with which microscopists of those days could resolve structures at the theoretical limits of visible light. Zernicke invented the phase-contrast technique in 1932. The first movie on cell division using phase-contrast was made at the Zeiss Application Laboratory in 1943. Twenty years after Zernike's invention the differential-interference-contrast (DIC) technique was developed by Nomarski.

Today's light microscope equipped with standard optical components is able to resolve details 0.2 μm apart. The suitable maximum microscope magnification at the eyepiece is 1000-fold the numerical aperture (NA) of the objective lens used. The product of the magnification factors of the objective lens and the eyepiece, and any intermediate tube and optovar factors, should not exceed this value.

To observe living cells and other unstained translucent specimens in the light microscope, the techniques of phase-contrast, Nomarski (differential-interference) contrast, and, to a certain extent, dark-field microscopy are used. With light microscopes equipped for bright field, in general, only colored or stained biological specimens can be visualized. Some of these microscopical contrasting techniques are described here with special emphasis on the microscope configuration and optical

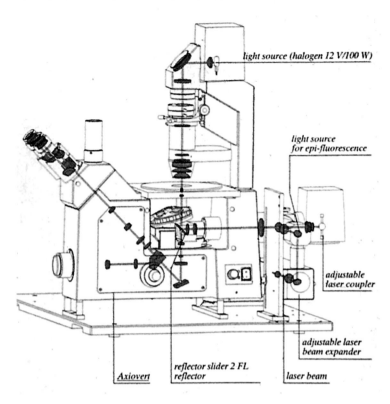

light source (halogen 12 V/100 W)

light source
for epi-fluorescence

adjustable
laser coupler

adjustable laser
beam expander

Axiovert

reflector slider 2 FL
reflector

laser beam

FIGURE 1   Scheme and components of the light path in the Axiovert inverted microscope additionally equipped for laser and mercury are epifluorescence illumination.

components. For a more detailed physical explanation of the nature of light, please refer to standard handbooks dealing with microscopes and optical methods (Michel, 1950; Bradbury *et al.*, 1989; Slayter and Slayter, 1992; Bradbury, 1994).

The documentation of light microscope images is changing from conventional microscope photomicrography to TV-based equipment due to the rapid development of video technology. Black and white and color photomicrography, however, are still widely used and to date are unsurpassed in overall image quality and resolution.

II. Materials and Instrumentation

A. GENERAL CONFIGURATIONS AND COMPONENTS OF A LIGHT MICROSCOPE

The most important technical requirement to perform unlimited light microscopy with all available contrasting techniques is the carefully chosen microscope (Fig. 1). In the basic microscope configuration, bright field and phase contrast should be available from the beginning. The microscope should include a vertically adjustable centerable condenser, lamp housing with collector optics and iris diaphragm, and a field stop to enable Köhler illumination of the specimen. Köhler illumination results in an evenly illuminated object field without reflections or glare in the image and minimum heating of the specimen. A future microscope upgrade for Nomarski (differential-interference) contrast, dark field, epifluorescence illumination, and other microscope techniques like polarization can be achieved simply by adding the necessary optical components to the existing microscope stand, without needing to purchase a new microscope.

Depending on the experimental design and on how the biological material is prepared and presented for the microscopical examinations, an inverted or upright microscope is chosen. For nearly all cell culture work and experiments on living cells the inverted microscope is favored. The reason is that most of these cells are growing attached to the bottom of cell culture vessels like plastic petri dishes or specifically designed cell chambers. The specimen has to be observed from below and illuminated from above using the features of an inverted microscope (stable, three-point mounted, fixed stage), the specimen being focused with the moving nosepiece bearing the objective lenses. Applications using fixed cells (e.g., histocyto-chemistry) and fixed or living tissue sections (e.g., brain slices for patch-clamp studies) need, to a certain extent, upright microscopes to perform proper microscopy. The conventional upright microscope focuses the specimen plane by moving the stage up, while keeping the nosepiece with the objective lenses at a fixed stable position. In the specific case of manipulation experiments on thick living tissue slices in electrophysiology (patch-clamp), a modified upright microscope with the features of an inverted microscope is necessary: fixed stage and movable nosepiece with specific water immersion objective lenses.

The light source for transmitted light illumination should be powerful enough (e.g., 100 W halogen) to fulfill the light demands for all applicable microscopic techniques, especially for the light-demanding technique Nomarski (differential-interference) contrast at high magnification.

Several types of microscope stages are available, depending on the experimental design in use: simple x/y stages, which move the specimen; heating stages including an x/y object guide to maintain cell culture temperatures; gliding stages for free (rotational) movement of the specimen; and motorized (scanning) stages with step resolutions of 250 nm to be driven by software programs.

To fulfill the various demands for documentation—video technique and photo-micrography—and quantification—photometry and image analysis—the microscope stand used should offer several ports to permit attachment of documentation and measurement devices simultaneously. Different binocular phototubes and side ports are available. At the present time, the maximum number of such attachable devices that can be mounted on the inverted microscope Axiovert TV is five: one small format camera and four TV cameras or measurement units at the various optical exits.

B. INFINITY COLOR-CORRECTED OPTICS

In recent years, microscope manufacturers have moved toward infinity color-corrected objectives. All objective lenses of this type possess an image distance which is corrected for infinity. The fully corrected intermediate image is generated by the tube lens. The space between objective lens and tube lens is the range with infinite image distance. The infinite image distance space offers great advantages for trans-mitted light and epifluorescence illumination in cell biology: single filters and com-plete fluorescence filter sets mounted into reflector sliders, optovar lenses, analyzers, compensators, and other optical components can be inserted without change in image quality. All other necessary microscope components like condensers and eye-pieces are adapted to the infinity optics system.

1. Microscope Condenser Systems

In transmitted light the condenser system is the partner of the objective lens and should have similar optical capabilities. As a guideline the numerical aperture of the condenser should match the numerical aperture of the objective lens used. As already mentioned the condenser system in the light microscope has to be vertically adjustable and centerable. Together with the field stop in the microscope stand, an evenly illuminated object field can be obtained in transmitted light illumination by achieving Köhler illumination according to the manufacturer's instructions. Depending on the quality and the number of lenses the different condenser systems offer various numerical apertures which can be changed and defined by opening and closing the condenser diaphragm to match the numerical aperture of the objective lens. The maximum numerical aperture for condenser systems is 1.4 and is available for upright and inverted microscopes. In addition to conventional condenser systems, inverted microscopes offer long-working-distance (LD) condensers. LD condenser systems provide ample space between specimen/stage plane and condenser front lens to accommodate large chambers (e.g., tissue culture flasks) or to perform micromanipulation experiments on living cells. By increasing this distance one has to accept an optical compromise: extremely long working distances (around 70 mm) are possible only with low- and medium-power objective lenses (from 5× to 40×) in bright field and phase contrast and without optimum setting and alignment according to the Köhler illumination. The medium-range LD condenser offers less working distance (about 20 mm) but higher numerical aperture. Therefore, even high-power objective lenses can be used to a certain extent. Another advantage of this condenser type is that it permits the use of Nomarski (differential-interference) contrast with a quite large working distance.

2. Objective Lenses

The features of the objective lens determine the overall performance of the light microscope. Image brightness is proportional to the square of the numerical aperture, $(NA)^2$, and the theoretical resolution of the microscope is directly related to the numerical aperture: $d_{\min} = 0.61\lambda/NA_{objective}$, according to Rayleigh's criterion.

Two major groups of objective lenses are available: the conventional "dry" objective lenses and immersion objective lenses. In the "dry" type air is present between the front lens and the specimen. "Dry" objective lenses are subdivided into objective lenses corrected for cover glass thickness and the already mentioned LD objective lenses, which are corrected for thicker glass or plastic petri dishes, and offer working distances of 2 mm or longer. Therefore, LD objective lenses are used mainly in cell culture applications. The immersion objective lens requires immersion fluids like oil, glycerine, and water. Using these immersion fluids, which have refractive indices higher than that of air, higher numerical apertures are obtained, which results in better resolution and increased image brightness.

On the basis of the glass material used for the lenses, the number of lenses per objective, the calculated lens form, and the coating of the lenses, all available objective lenses are classified into several groups, depending on their transmission in the ultraviolet region of the spectrum, their correction for chromatic aberration, and their flatness of field. The appropriate objective lens has to be selected very carefully with respect to the experiment, the applied method, and the probe material. Experiments using UV light ($\leq$230 nm) for the examination (UV microscopy) require an objective lens of the Ultrafluar type, as these lenses consist of quartz material for highest possible transmission of light. Work in the near-UV range ($\leq$330 nm), such as in intracellular [Ca^{2+}] measurements using the fluorochrome fura-2, does not require expensive quartz lenses but still needs an objective lens of the Fluar type with high transmission in that light range. In fluorescence microscopy in which fluorochromes emitting in the visible range of light from around 400 nm to about 700 nm are used, the Plan-Neofluar lens shows the best performance regarding light transmission, color correction, and flat field. Apochromats have an extremely flat field and high color correction for exact photomicrography without light intensity problems. LD-Achroplan lenses give satisfying light transmission for fluorescence microscopy, flat-field performance for photography, and enough working distance to be used in cell culture and micromanipulation experiments. Water immersion lenses are useful for work on tissue slices in electrophysiology (patch-clamp) using upright microscopes.

Most of the described objective lenses are available in two versions: the so-called bright-field version, which can be used for bright-field and dark-field microscopy, as well as for Nomarski (differential-interference) contrast and the epifluorescence illumination technique, and the phase-contrast version, which contains an additional phase annulus lens for phase-contrast microscopy, making it a little less well suited for fluorescence and DIC techniques.

All except a few objective lenses are parfocal. Thus, objective lens changes do not require extensive refocusing of the specimen plane, focused objects remaining in focus within micrometer precision.

3. Eyepieces

The eyepiece is used to observe the real intermediate image formed within the microscope by the objective lens. Its optical function is to magnify the intermediate image, and, in many microscopes, to complete the chromatic aberration correction of the objective lens. The eyepiece magnification factor, together with the objective lens factor, gives the total magnification of the light microscope in the eyepiece's field of view: $magnification_{microscope} = magnification_{objective} \times magnification_{eyepiece}$, unless additional optical components, such as an optovar, are included in the light path. Several types of eyepieces exist: simple eyepieces without any correction capabilities, eyepieces for people wearing eyeglasses, and eyepieces with focusable eye lenses to compensate bad eyesight to a certain extent. In all these eyepieces, reticules for photomicrography, measurement, and counting can be inserted.

III. Procedures

A. PHASE-CONTRAST MICROSCOPY

Structures of flat unstained specimen such as living cells cannot be well visualized using a light microscope equipped only for bright-field microscopy. Object details are not differentiated by their light-transmitting capacity but by their refractive indices. Light passing through such an unstained specimen does not alter the amplitude, which would result in a change of light intensity, but is varied in its phase as it encounters organelles of differing refractive indices. The human eye is only able to detect differences in light intensity, not differences in phase. The purpose of the phase-contrast technique (Fig. 2) is simply explained as the artficial transfer of these phase differences into brightness (intensity) differences. To accomplish this, the light that has passed the specimen must be altered by using an additional optical component, a phase annulus, in the objective lens. A fixed annular phase ring is mounted in the condenser system, and is imaged by the condenser and the phase-contrast objective lens into the exit pupil of the objective. At this place a semi-opaque phase annulus is placed that covers barely the image of the annular phase ring. This annulus both attenuates the undeflected light and advances its phase by $\lambda/4$ (90°). All other components of the microscope are exactly the same as the corresponding components for bright-field microscopy.

Since, by the nature of refractive deflection of light by a transparent object, deflected light rays emerging from the specimen have already been retarded in phase by $-\lambda/4$ ($-90°$), this 90° phase advance of the undeflected rays by the phase annulus now makes the deflected and undeflected beams 180° out of phase, as required for destructive interference. When these rays combine in the primary image plane, phase contrast is generated in areas of nonuniform refractive index. The resulting bright-

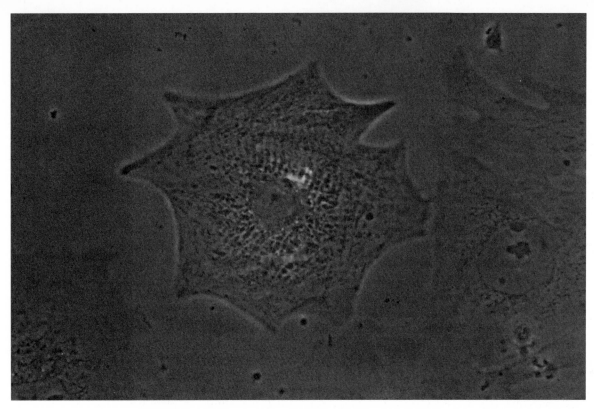

FIGURE 2 Living heart muscle cell in phase contrast (objective lens Plan-Neofluar 100×/ 1.3 oil Ph3).

ness differences are clearly visible to the human eye. For example, when light passes the relatively thick and dense cell nucleus, more light will be diffracted than by the nearby thin and nearly translucent cell cytoplasm. Therefore, in phase-contrast microscopy the nucleus will appear darker than the surrounding cytoplasm.

The adjustment of the phase-contrast setup is easy. The selected phase annulus in the condenser system should match the phase number of the objective lens. For example, the objective lens labeled Ph2 needs a phase ring with the number 2 in the condenser system. With the help of a centering telescope or, in some microscopes, inbuilt Bertrand optics, the bright annular illumination transmitted by the phase ring in the condenser and the dark phase annulus of the objective lens are made visible. The lateral position of the phase ring in the condenser is adjusted until it is concentric with and completely contained within the phase annulus of the objective lens. This procedure results in a properly set phase contrast. Changing to objective lenses with other phase rings (1 or 3) requires a change of the condenser phase ring as well with a check for its correct alignment.

B. NOMARSKI (DIFFERENTIAL-INTERFERENCE) CONTRAST MICROSCOPY

As for phase contrast, the DIC technique in transmitted light also permits visualization of a flat unstained specimen, but with the addition of a three-dimensional "shadowcast" appearance (Fig. 3). The specimen can be somewhat thicker and have a greater difference in refractive indices than the phase-contrast specimen. The physical principles and operation of the DIC optics are totally different from those of phase contrast and are technically far more complicated.

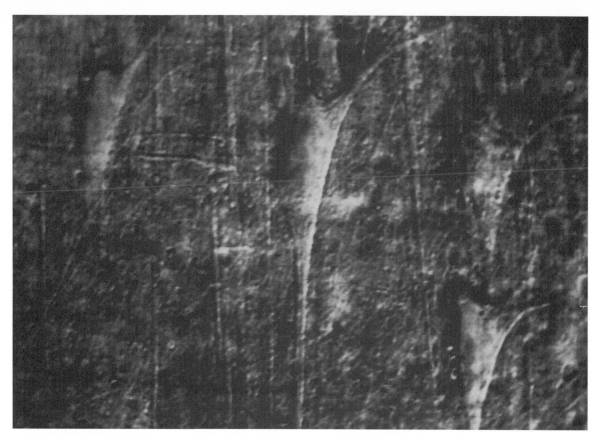

FIGURE 3 Living cells of a brain section in Nomarski (differential-interference) contrast under infrared light observation (objective lens Achroplan 40×/0.75 W).

First, polarized light is used. In addition to the objective lens, four optical components are necessary to perform Nomarski (differential-interference) contrast: polarizer, DIC prism, DIC slider, and analyzer.

In the transmitted light path a polarizer is mounted directly in front of the condenser system, causing the light to be linearly polarized. In the condenser itself a cemented quartz Wollaston prism, or DIC prism, is placed. This prism splits each light wave into two waves with two different polarization vibration directions (x and y), which diverge at a very small angle. The condenser optics aligns the two waves to both be parallel to the optical axis of the microscope. The lateral spacing of the two waves is in the order of magnitude of micrometers and does not exceed the limit of resolution. Thus no double image occurs in the eyepiece. The two light waves, which are initially identical in phase, are projected through adjacent regions of the specimen. The phase specimen now induces path differences at the two waves according to its thickness and refractive indices. A second Wollaston prism, the DIC slider, situated at (or near) the back focal plane of the objective, is used to recombine these two waves into a single beam. The two vibration planes (x and y) still exist. At the end, the light beam passes a second polarizing element, the analyzer, which is mounted at right angles to the orientation of the polarizer before it forms the DIC image in the eyepiece. The analyzer transforms the two perpendicular waves into two waves with a common vibration plane, thereby enabling them to interfere. The path difference between the x and y waves is responsible for more or less transmitted light. A path difference with the value of 0 results in no transmitted light by the analyzer. Maximum light is transmitted if the path difference is half the

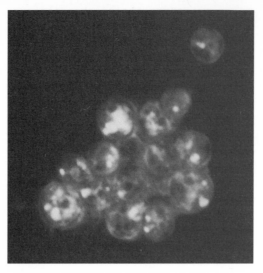

FIGURE 4   Plant protoplasts under dark-field observation (objective lens Achrostigmat 10×/0.25 Ph1).

wavelength. By these means, different regions of the specimen appear bright or less bright in contrast to the mid-grey of the background.

To modify and optimize the image contrast, the DIC slider, the second Wollaston prism in the light pathway, has a longitudinal fine adjustment to alter the path difference, which affects the brightness of the image. The setting of the DIC slider generates a positive or negative shadowcast appearance of the specimen details, one edge having a bright border and the opposite edge, a dark border. This gives an artifactual three-dimensional impression of the specimen.

A proper microscope setup for the DIC technique is achieved by first aligning all optical components according to the Köhler illumination rules. A second step is to check the correct crossed position of polarizer and analyzer without the DIC prism in the condenser, without the DIC slider in the objective nosepiece, and without the specimen: a dark image is the result. The Wollaston prisms are then inserted at 45° to its polarizer, and adjusted for optimal contrast. Note that the DIC sliders and prisms are specific for particular objective lenses. The numerical aperture indicated on the DIC elements has to match the numerical aperture of the objective lens.

C. DARK-FIELD MICROSCOPY

In dark-field microscopy, the illuminated object appears bright against the black background (Fig. 4). By means of a large central opaque stop in the condenser, direct axial illumination of the specimen is prevented, the illuminating rays of light coming only from the side, at an angle that exceeds the collecting angle of the objective lens. As a consequence, only light scattered by parts of the object enters the objective lens. This results in an extraordinarily high contrast of the specimen. It is even possible to visualize particles in the specimen whose sizes are considerably smaller than the resolution of the microscope, although their shape cannot be detected.

The simplest optical configuration for dark-field microscopy uses a phase-contrast condenser together with a bright-field (non-Ph) objective lens. The annular stop of the condenser has to be larger than the exit pupil of the objective lens, for example, a Ph3 phase ring in the condenser and a 10×/0.3 objective lens. The specimen is then illuminated by a cone of light with an angle of the inner aperture larger than the collecting aperture of the objective lens. Specimen areas with no specific structures or empty spaces appear dark. The scattered or diffracted light from the specimen enters the objective lens and forms the dark-field image.

Specific dark-field condenser systems are also available, with a numerical aperture higher than the numerical aperture of the objective lens used. To facilitate reduction of the observation aperture to below that of the annular illumination, objective lenses with an inbuilt iris diaphragm are recommended.

Setting up Köhler illumination for dark-field microscopy is a little more difficult and tricky than for bright-field illumination because of the low imaging quality of these condensers. Only practice and the advice of an already experienced person solve this problem. As only scattered light is detected by the objective lens, all optical surfaces, especially the condenser front lens, the specimen, and the objective front lens, must be extremely clean. Dirty surfaces produce additional scattered light which does not come from the specimen but just increases the brightness of the image background. For an optimum dark-field image, the condenser aperture and field diaphragm of the transmitted light path must be fully open.

D. BLACK AND WHITE AND COLOR PHOTOMICROGRAPHY

For photomicrographic documentation the light microscope has to be equipped with optical exits offering a defined intermediate image plane where camera systems can be attached. Two camera types are available to take micrographs from the specimen. One type is represented by the well-known reflex cameras from various manufacturers, which include all necessary elements like shutter and light measurement device for the calculation of exposure time. In many microscopes reflex cameras can be mounted directly on the microscope stand via so-called T-adapters. In others, additional optical components are required to project the intermediate image to the film plane, for which technical advice should be sought from a representative of the microscope manufacturer. The second type of camera is exemplified by the specialized microscope camera systems produced by microscope manufacturers. Besides attachable camera systems, there are true photomicroscopes with all the necessary camera elements to generate micrographs of the specimen built in.

The main differences between reflex cameras, microscope camera systems, and photomicroscopes are flexibility and performance. Most reflex cameras offer automatic exposure only up to around half a minute, which requires a lot of battery energy. Not all reflex cameras allow the operator to expose several times onto the same image to perform multiple exposures after double- or triple-staining procedures. Microscope camera systems and photomicroscopes offer features including automatic exposure time determinations with integral and point measurement, serial exposure with different exposure times, Schwarzschild effect compensation, and PC control via interfaces.

For all photomicrographic systems two filters are important: an interference green filter for black and white photography and a conversion filter (3200–5500°K) for color photography. In black and white photomicrography the green filter gives a slightly increased contrast in the image. The conversion filter is used to vary the color temperature of the light source to a higher temperature to allow daylight color film to be used in color micrography without color changes in the photographed specimen. In addition, neutral density filters to attenuate light intensities and color-compensating filters to avoid color distortion (Schwarzschild effect) at long-duration exposures may be necessary.

Today, nearly any film material can be used without significant limitation. The image resolution and brilliance of the photograph are, to a certain extent, related to the film speed. High-speed film material shows a little more grain structure and, therefore, a weaker image compared with the sharp and crisp images of low-speed film material. The film speed has to be chosen according to the microscopical contrasting technique and the experimental design: bright-field microscopy on a stained specimen allows the use of a low-speed film; fluorescence microscopy on living or fixed specimen in most cases requires a high-speed film.

To produce good high-quality images a beginner must practice and should contact experts in the field to avoid wasting time. A very good handbook on the topic has been published by the Eastman Kodak Company (Delly, 1988).

IV. Conclusion

No list of recipes for the configuration of light microscopes will match all the individual needs for the innumerable experimental designs. Therefore, the purchase of a light microscope has to be well considered. An exact and farsighted definition of all the required optical components for different experiments is absolutely necessary in order not to waste money. Contact the representatives of the microscope manufacturers to discuss the microscope project, to obtain all the necessary help to solve the optical part in the experimental design, and to be informed about the newest developments in light microscopy.

Despite all the efforts of the microscope manufacturers, physical and optical laws set limits beyond which a specifically desired optical solution cannot be reached with 100% satisfaction. And remember, the image in the field of view is only as good as the specimen.

REFERENCES

Bradbury, S. (1994) "An Introduction to the Optical Microscope" (revised edition). Royal Microscopical Society, Microscopy Handbook No. 1. Bios Scientific Publisher, Oxford.
Bradbury, S., Evennett, P. J., Haselmann, H., and Piller, H. (1989) "Dictionary of Light Microscopy." Royal Microscopical Society, Microscopy Handbook No. 15. Oxford Univ. Press, London/New York.
Delly, J. G. (1988) "Photography through the Microscope." Eastman Kodak Co., Rochester.
Michel, K. (1950) "Die Grundlagen der Theorie des Mikroskops." Wissenschaftliche Verlagsgesellschaft, Stuttgart.
Slayter, E. M., and Slayter, H. S. (1992) "Light and Electron Microscopy." Cambridge Univ. Press, London/New York.

Reflection Interference Microscopy

Jürgen Bereiter-Hahn and Pavel Vesely

I. Introduction

Reflection microscope arrangements are extensively used to study surface topography of opaque objects and of specimens transmitting light. The resolution in z axis of these methods by far exceeds the lateral resolution of a light microscope, reaching the nanometer range. The *relative reflectivity* (RI), defined as the ratio of photon fluxes reflected from the object and from the background depends on the differences in refractive indices of the media forming a boundary. The reflectivity R (fraction of incident light intensity that is reflected at a boundary) of one optical interface is described for homogeneous, absorption-free, transparent and isotropic media by the Fresnel equations:

For normal incidence,

$$R_0 = \left(\frac{n_0 - n_1}{n_0 + n_1}\right)^2 \tag{1}$$

In the case of reflection at an optically denser medium ($n_1 > n_0$), a phase shift of π results for the reflected *amplitude r* (the calculated value of intensity R corresponds to the product of an amplitude and its conjugated complex value $\bar{r}$).

For oblique incidence, reflection depends on the relative orientation of the reflecting plane and the polarization plane of the incident light:

$$R_\perp = +\frac{\sin^2(\varphi_0 - \varphi_1)}{\sin^2(\varphi_0 + \varphi_1)} \tag{2}$$

$$R_\parallel = +\frac{\tan^2(\varphi_0 - \varphi_1)}{\tan^2(\varphi_0 + \varphi_1)} \tag{3}$$

with

φ_0 = angle of incidence
$\varphi_1 = \arcsin[(n_0/n_1)\sin \varphi_0]$ = angle of refraction as a function of the angle of incidence dependent on the adjacent refractive indices
$R_\perp, R_\parallel$ = reflectivity referring to vertical and parallel polarized light, respectively.

At angles of incidence $\varphi_0 \leq 25°$ (under some conditions even more) the simple Fresnel equation for normal incidence can be used without causing major errors in the calculation of reflectivity. If reflectivity calculations are based on RI the error introduced by this simplification is diminished.

Living as well as fixed cells attached to a plain surface can be investigated using reflection-type microscopes. The resulting image is determined by the RI at different areas of the cell and by interferences of the light reflected at different boundaries

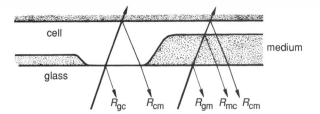

FIGURE 1 Schematic representation of the main reflecting interfaces in a cell preparation on a cover glass. The thick arrows indicate the incident beams; the thin arrows, the reflected beams with the relative intensity R. The suffixes indicate the optical media forming the interface. The phase of R_{mc} is shifted for $\lambda/2$ at the reflecting surface. (Reproduced, with permission from Bereiter-Hahn *et al.* (1979).)

(Fig. 1). Considering the dominance of interferences, microscope arrangements visualizing the reflections delineated in Fig. 1 have been termed interference reflection microscopy (IRM), reflection interference microscopy (RIM), reflection interference contrast microscopy (RIC), or reflection contrast microscopy (RCM). To us RIM seems to be the logically most convincing term and correctly emphasizes the fact that this type of interference microscopy is based on light *reflections*. It is a more general term than RIC which, in addition, denominates the fact that in some cases contrast-enhancing precautions are taken (i.e., presence of a ring-shaped diaphragm). Therefore these two terms will be used throughout this description.

The technical difficulties in RIM arise from the very small differences in the refractive index of cytoplasm and the surrounding medium. The reflections at cell surfaces are in the range of about 0.4% of the incident light. Therefore, high intensities of illumination and/or very sensitive recording devices have to be used. Furthermore, RIM images are sensitive to unwanted reflections in the optical system. The principle dates back to the surface contact microscope described by Ambrose (1956), who coupled a glass slide with cells to a 60° prism and illuminated the upper surface of the glass slide at an angle greater than the critical angle. Thus, the light is totally internally reflected at the glass/water interface. At those zones of cells that make close contact with the surface of the glass, the difference in refractive indices is smaller, thus allowing the beam to evanesce from the glass surface into the cytoplasm. The light may be scattered and enter the objective lens which was positioned above the cell. In this case the image field appears completely dark at all clean and cell-free areas (due to total reflection), whereas regions where cells adhere closely to the glass are brightly illuminated.

Curtis (1964), also using an upright microscope stage and almost normal incidence of the intensely collimated illuminating light beam, termed this technique *interference reflection microscopy*. Ploem (1975) combined epi-illumination through the objective lens and the use of polarized light, a Stach's stop (ring-shaped illuminating aperture), and a rotatable quarter wavelength plate. The polarizing system was designed to exclude light reflected in the optical system (see legend to Fig. 2); Stach's aperture allows conical illumination of the specimen and thus increases the contrast of fine surface structures (oblique illumination). In addition, this aperture allows illumination at a known and defined angle of incidence (corresponding to a certain range of the illuminating numerical aperture).

II. Materials and Instrumentation

A. GENERAL ARRANGEMENTS

RIM can be performed with any microscope stage, upright or inverted. The specific requirements are an analyzer and epi-illumination equipment, including a strong

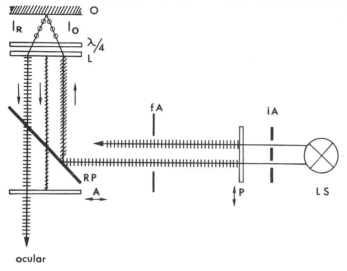

FIGURE 2 Diagram of the Leitz–Ploem reflection contrast system as it was realized on a Diavert inverted microscope stand. Light from a mercury arc lamp (LS) is collimated by a collimation lens (not shown), and then penetrates a ring-shaped illuminating aperture (iA), which is projected to the back focal plane of the objective by a second collimating lens (not shown). By passing a polarizer (P) the light becomes linearly polarized. A field-limiting aperture (fA) is focused via the objective in the object plane. A semireflecting plate (RP) directs the beam to the objective lens (L) without any change in polarization. The light is projected on the object (O), where it has the intensity I_O. A quarter-wavelength plate ($\lambda/4$) with its slow axis 45° to the polarizer's direction causes circular polarization of the illuminating beam and linear polarization of the reflected beam (I_R), but with a 90° difference in the direction of polarization. Therefore, I_R penetrates the analyzer (A) crossed to the polarizer. Light reflected from the lens surfaces (beam exemplified between the main paths) with unaltered polarization does not cross the analyzer. To simplify the diagram, only one part of the light beam penetrating the iA is followed. (Reproduced, with permission, from Bereiter-Hahn *et al.* (1979).)

light source (typically a mercury arc lamp HBO 100 or similar), filter to obtain monochromatic light, polarizing filter, central or ring-shaped diaphragm (optional) to increase contrast (for RIC), a semireflecting mirror, and an oil immersion objective with quarter-wavelength plate which can be rotated in front of the lens. The arrangement of the components and the ray paths is shown in Fig. 2.

The optimum device produced so far (but no longer commercially available) consists of a Diavert inverted research microscope (Leica, Wetzlar) equipped with a 100-W or 200-W mercury arc lamp, a polarizer, and a second collimating lens in the incident illuminator stand (Fig. 2). The system can be adapted to most of the common research microscopes equipped with epifluorescence. Prins *et al.* (1993) tested a variety of microscopes for their RIM performance (Table I).

Oil immersion polarization optics (free of internal tension) with magnifications between 40× and 100× are recommended. Immersion is essential to obtain good pictures of low-reflecting specimens. Tension-free optics are necessary to work with polarized light. If phase optics are used, the virtual size of the dark central part of the ring-shaped illuminating aperture should exceed the outer diameter of the phase ring (seen with an auxiliary eyepiece). Then the influence of the phase ring on the reflection contrast image is negligible. Combined phase-reflection optics allow an easy comparison of phase and RIC images of a cell simply by changing illuminating systems. Illuminating ring-shaped apertures can be prepared photographically on document film, taking pictures of black (india ink) rings of the desired geometry and enlarging the negatives onto another film with very steep gamma.

TABLE I

Microscope	Objective[a]	Polarization block
Leica Aristoplan or Diaplan	1	Pol block (513734)[b]
Leitz Diavert or Orthoplan	1	Pol block (513791)
Nikon Optiphot or Labophot	1	IGS block MXA 20138
Olympus BH2-RFCA	1	HM-IGS block (3284)
Zeiss Axioplan (infinite optics),	2	IGS block (487960)
Axiovert (inverted microscope)		UV-barrier filter (467860-9903)

[a] (1) Leica NPL 50 × NA 1.00 oel imm kontr phaco 2 (559206), Leica NPL 100 × NA 1.30 oel imm kontr phaco 2 (559207), or Zeiss Antiflex-Neofluar 63 × NA 1.25 oil (421800). (2) Zeiss Antiflex Plan-Neofluar 63 × NA 1.25 oel ph3 (440469). In addition to these objectives and polarizing filters, light deflectors must be introduced to avoid reflections from the far surfaces of the specimen (see Section V).

[b] Ordering numbers in parentheses.

If quantitative evaluation is envisaged monochromatic light must be used for illumination. For living cells, orange or near-infrared light is recommended because short wavelengths (including green light) cause severe photodamage during prolonged illumination with strong intensities. The most favorable filter combination comprises a heat-reflecting filter, a UV-absorbing filter, and a long-pass filter with its edge at 580 nm (e.g., K580 from Schott) in combination with a mercury arc lamp. This lamp has a strong emission band at 589 nm. This band is easily selected by this cheap filter combination. Animal cells have negligible absorption in this spectral range (a cytochrome a absorption band at 614 nm is very weak). Near infrared is even less hazardous; however, electronic imaging systems are needed for visualization.

B. SPECIFIC INSTRUMENTATION

1. Total Internal Reflection Fluorescence

Total internal reflection fluorescence (TIRF) is achieved by adaptation of Ambrose's surface contact microscope (see above) to fluorescence illumination. The cells are attached to a prism (the prism may be connected to a cover glass using a thin film of immersion oil); the angle of incidence can be varied by moving a mirror. In this case the illumination is coming from one side only, rather than being conical. The angle of total reflection characteristic for the glass/medium interface is chosen. At areas where molecular contacts are formed, the local difference in refractive indices is smaller, allowing the light to evanesce toward the specimen for a certain distance. This evanescent light can be used to excite fluorochromes and thus allows one to study specifically fluorescent molecules in close proximity to the reflecting interface. Variation of the angle of incidence provides the possibility to calculate the distance of the fluorochrome from the glass surface. For a review see Axelrod (1990); detailed theoretical guidelines have been developed by Gingell *et al.* (1987).

2. Integration of RIM in Confocal Laser-Scanning Microscopy

Most modern confocal laser-scanning microscopes allow a reflection image of the specimen to be obtained. In this case contrast problems are minimized because of the spotlike illumination and the confocal diaphragm in front of the photomultiplier. A further advantage of confocality is the possibility of optical sectioning, which is preserved also in the reflection mode. It is easier to apply and it gives a larger viewing field. A broader range of objectives, including water immersion objectives, can be used. One system has been developed (Olympus with Lasertec 1LM11 confocal microscope) that allows study of fast movements at video rate (Vesely *et al.*, 1993). The main disadvantage of confocal laser-scanning microscopy reflection imaging lies in the lack of a clearly defined illuminating aperture (provided by the ring-shaped aperture); the whole angular spectrum contributes to image generation. As a consequence it is almost impossible to achieve quantitative data on topography, cell/glass distances, or refractive index of cytoplasm. These disadvantages can be overcome by decreasing the numerical aperture of the objectives, i.e., by an iris aperture at the back focal plane, restricting the illuminating beam down to almost normal incidence.

III. Applications and Image Interpretation

The theoretical background of image interpretation has been developed by Gingell (1981), Gingell and Todd (1979), Beck and Bereiter-Hahn (1981), and Bereiter-Hahn *et al.* (1979). The two main fields of application of RIM are to study surface topography of cells and membrane dynamics and contrast enhancement of cells after various staining procedures.

A. SURFACE TOPOGRAPHY AND MEMBRANE DYNAMICS

RIM is used to view cells in culture adhering to a plane glass surface. If it is assumed that the cytoplasm is optically homogeneous, three optical interfaces may occur (Fig. 1): glass/culture medium, medium/cell, cell/medium (two thin layers on top of the glass). In areas where the cells are intimately attached to the glass, the glass/medium interface is replaced by a glass/cytoplasm interface (one thin layer on the glass). Light beams reflected from the various interfaces may interfere with each other. The resulting intensities depend on the differences in optical path lengths and the RI at the boundaries. Sufficient coherence length of the illuminating light is a prerequisite which is fulfilled by high-pressure mercury lamps.

Thus the topography of both the cellular surfaces may be revealed by a typical pattern of interference fringes, that of the upper surface (the culture medium facing) and that of the lower cell surface (facing the glass surface). As far as interference fringes appear, an estimation of the distances can be made because the distance between adjacent constructive (bright line) and destructive (dark lines) interferences corresponds to a quarter wavelength (the phase difference between adjacent maxima and minima corresponds to $\lambda/2$, but the light must pass the layer twice before interfering). Therefore, the geometrical difference of layer thickness (d) between adjacent maxima and minima is given by

$$d = \lambda \cos \beta / 4n \qquad (4)$$

where d is the thickness of the layer between maxima and minima of adjacent interference fringes, λ is the wavelength of light in a vacuum, n is the refractive index of the layer, and β is the angle of incidence of the illuminating beam (normal incidence: $\cos \beta = 1$).

Zones of close contact of the cells to the glass appear dark gray, *focal contacts* almost black. Their brightness does not change considerably by changing either the

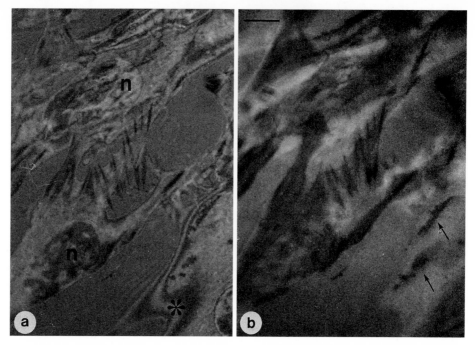

FIGURE 3 RIC images of living PtK2 cells attached to a glass slide viewed at different angles of conical illumination determined by a ring-shaped aperture: (a) 22° (mean angle of incidence), (b) 40°. Diavert microscope, objective 100×. Bar = 10 μm. The appearance of those cell regions that are in molecular contact with the glass surface is almost the same at the two angles of incidence (i.e., focal contacts—arrows in a, spotlike contacts—arrows in b). The gray values of all those zones that are further apart from the glass result from interferences. These change because of angle-dependent optical path differences. At the lower angle of incidence we look more into the depth. The separation of the lower cell surface from the glass is indicated by interference fringes (asterisks in a). There appears to be less interference at higher angles of incidence (b); therefore the image appears clearer and which cellular parts are over or under another cell can easily be seen. This relationship cannot be deduced from image a. Asterisk in a marks an area where the cell distance to the glass increases. n, Nucleus.

wavelength or the angle of illumination (Fig. 3). Calculations of the cell/glass distances from these intensity distributions (which can be quantified by photometry) are restricted to cells of known cortical cytoplasm refractive index. The uncertainty of this value prohibits any accurate calculations of cell/glass distance based on intensity measurements at a single wavelength. Evaluation is only possible in steps of λ/4, where the phase difference can be directly recorded, or with a two-wavelength system. The same applies to the determination of the refractive index of cytoplasm when the distance from the cell to the glass is not known (Bereiter-Hahn *et al.*, 1979).

RIM allows us to follow very small changes and differences in thickness of cytoplasmic lamellae (Beck and Bereiter-Hahn, 1981). For instance, at an angle of incidence of 30° and orange light (589 nm) in cytoplasm with a refractive index of 1.4, a geometrical difference in cell thickness of 0.1 μm is sufficient for maximum interference contrast [from maximum brightness to a minimum (or vice versa)]. Thus, very small deviations of boundaries in the z axis are revealed by RIM (Fig. 4). Good examples are the flickering movements of erythrocyte membranes or the vivid activities at the surface of nuclei in living cells. This potential has not been used adequately.

If cells are homogeneously attached to a glass surface, the upper cell surface of which relatively smooth and the angle of incidence is known, the volume of the

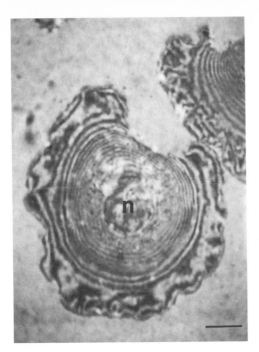

FIGURE 4 Single *Xenopus* tadpole epidermis cell in culture, viewed with RIC, objective 100×, mean angle of incidence 22°. These cells are closely attached to the glass; therefore the interference lines delineate the upper surface topography which is well resolved in the peripheral lamella. The concentric lines marking the cell body can be used to determine cell volume. For this purpose the focus should be slightly more toward the top of the cell. The bright spots close to the cell center are areas where the cells do not adhere properly. n, Nucleus. Bar = 10 μm. (Photograph courtesy of R. Strohmeier.)

cells can be determined using Eq. (4). The method works well with epithelial cells which normally fulfill the condition of smooth adherence to the glass. The upper cell surface is best revealed using an angle of incidence $0° \leq 22°$. The surface profile is delineated by the course of interference rings (Fig. 4). The cell volume comprises a stack of disks with a thickness equal to the thickness difference between the interference lines [according to Eq. (4)]. The areas delineated by each interference line are measured (e.g., using an interactive image analyzing system). Multiplication of the single areas by the thickness difference gives the volume of each of the "disks." The total of the "disk" volumes is the cell volume. For correct calculations the refractive index of the cytoplasm has to be known. This is of particular importance when osmotic volume changes are to be followed.

To determine the refractive index, the cells are immersed in solutions of different concentrations of bovine serum albumin in saline. The albumin content is varied by mixing two solutions of different concentrations, as is done for density centrifugation. The cells are viewed using a phase-contrast microscope and the BSA concentration is increased until the contrast of the cytoplasm disappears. At this point the refractive index of the immersion medium equals that of the cytoplasm. Then the refractive index of the medium can immediately be measured with an Abbé refractometer.

B. CONTRAST ENHANCEMENT OF STAINED CELLS

Many stained biological specimens show an increase in contrast when viewed in reflected light. Membrane surfaces, chromosomes, and cytoskeletal elements have been viewed using RIM. In general, if staining gives only a weak signal in bright-field microscopy, contrast enhancement using reflection microscopy should be considered. Two fields of application seem to survive the competition with other methods, visualization of immunogold and immunoperoxidase–diaminobenzidine staining and Coomassie blue staining of actin fibers.

Because of their high refractive index, gold particles (<15 nm) can be visualized in reflected light, preferentially when illuminated at the wavelength of Rayleigh scattering (green light in the case of gold). This method can be extended to ultrathin sections (Prins *et al.,* 1993). These authors recommend coating of the slide with gelatin–chromalum to enhance tissue visualization or with aminosilane to enhance electrostatic sticking of the sections. In the case of ultrathin sections those appearing silvery to white on the surface of the water bath of the sectioning knife provide optimal contrast in RIM. Specimens are embedded in immersion oil with a refractive index matching that of glass ($n = 1.52$) to obtain optimum contrast for the tissue staining.

IV. Procedures

A. ALIGNMENT OF OPTICS

The procedures for RIM depend on the type of microscope used. With a normal upright microscope stand, cells can be grown or left incubating for some time on a clean coverslip or all other plane surfaces suitable for cell attachment, and water immersion objectives may be used for access through the liquid to the cell. With this arrangement, specific precautions have to be taken to avoid reflections from the far glass/air interface (the one opposing the cell adhesion surface).

With an inverted microscope unwanted reflections can be avoided more easily. In this case the cells have to be attached to a coverslip and optimal imaging is achieved with oil immersion objectives. In all cases Köhler's illumination has to be fulfilled.

Steps

1. Insert specimen into the microscope.

2. Focus as usual, preferentially using phase contrast.

3. Switch to epi-illumination: the half-reflecting mirror is introduced; a high-pressure mercury or xenon lamp has to be centered. Use filters for heat reflection, UV stop, and wavelength selection.

4. Center the field aperture (in epi-illumination mode).

5. Insert an auxiliary telescope (Amici–Bertrand lens) instead of one ocular, which allows observation of the back focal plane of the objective lens to which the light source is conjugated (Fig. 3). The correct position of the light arc and the collector can be seen after insertion of the polarizer and the analyzer (in a position corresponding to that shown in Fig. 2) the quarter-wavelength plate (in front of the objective) has to be moved into the correct position (45° to the plane of polarization): The correct position is reached when the dark cross disappears (maximum brightness at the back focal plane).

6. If possible, insert a Stach stop now and center it on the optical axis of the objective lens.

7. Replace the auxiliary telescope with the ocular. A good IRM image should be obtained.

For taking pictures, the photographic camera should be loaded with a high-speed film yielding small grain [e.g., Kodak Tmax film, developed for instance in a two-step developer like Emofin (Tetenal)].

B. AUXILIARY ELECTRONIC INSTRUMENTS

RIM images are not very bright, especially if the illumination is restricted to a narrow angular band by a Stach stop and to a certain wavelength. An "intensified" CCD camera (from, e.g., Hamamatsu, Photometrics, or Proxitronic) is of unvaluable help. The best results are obtained when the camera is connected to a frame grabber which allows on-line image subtraction and image averaging. [An example is the AT-FS100 series of Imaging Technologies Inc., distributed by Stemmer. Many commercial systems for image analysis also include this option. The market is changing very fast in this field.] The subtraction eliminates the effects of uneven illumination and small dust particles and thus increases contrast. Image averaging may be helpful to reduce noise at low light levels. Furthermore electronic imaging opens the wide field of image analysis and video recording. RIM images of appropriate specimens, if well adjusted, are of excellent contrast. RIM therefore provides a very good basis for automatic specimen detection.

V. Pitfalls

The main problem with RIM and RIC may be unsatisfactory contrast. If all the precautions described above have been considered, the main reason is reflections from the object side far from the illuminating objective. If living cells are investigated in an inverted microscope addition of culture medium (thus thickening of the layer of culture medium above the cells) improves contrast. This layer of culture medium should be about 3 mm thick to be sure that no light is reflected from the highly reflecting boundary to air. Another possibility has been described for the work with upright microscopes by Prins et al. (1993) that works as well with inverted microscopes: A plano-convex lens (Milles Griot, 01LPX 005 or 01LPX 011) or a right-angle prism (Milles Griot, 01PRS 007, 01RPS 009, or 01RPS 011) is attached (by immersion oil) to the glass surface of the specimen which is not in contact with the objective. These light deflectors prevent reflections (because there is no longer a reflecting interface) and the light reflected at the free sides of the plano-convex lens or the prism does not fall back into the objective. For thin specimens (free surface closer than about 3 mm to the front of the objective) the use of such a light deflector is a must.

REFERENCES

Ambrose, E. J. (1956) A surface contact microscope for the study of cell movements. *Nature* **178**, 1194.

Axelrod, D. (1990) Total internal reflection fluorescence at biological surfaces. *Noninvasive Techniques Cell Biol.* **9**, 93–127.

Beck, K., and Bereiter-Hahn, J. (1981) Evaluation of reflection interference contrast microscope images of living cells. *Microsc. Acta* **84**, 153–178.

Bereiter-Hahn, J., Fox, C. H., and Thorell, B. (1979) Quantitative reflection contrast microscopy of living cells. *J. Cell Biol.* **82**, 767–779.

Curtis, A. S. G. (1964) The mechanism of adhesion of cells to glass. *J. Cell Biol.* **20**, 199–215.

Gingell, D. (1981) The interpretation of interference reflexion images of spread cells: Significant contributions from thin peripheral cytoplasm. *J. Cell Sci.* **49**, 237–247.

Gingell, D., Heavens, O. S., and Mellor, J. S. (1987) General electromagnetic theory of total internal reflection fluorescence: The quantitative basis for mapping cell–substratum topography. *J. Cell Sci.* **87**, 677–693.

Gingell, D., and Todd, I. (1979) Interference reflection microscopy: A quantitative theory for image interpretation and its application to cell–substratum separation measurement. *Biophys. J.* **26**, 507–526.

Opas, M., and Kalnins, V. I. (1985) Multiple labeling of cellular constituents by combining surface reflection interference and fluorescence microscopy. *Exp. Cell Biol.* **53**, 241–251.

Ploem, J. S. (1975) Reflection-contrast microscopy as a tool for investigation of the attachment of living cells to a glass surface. *In* "Mononuclear Phagocytes in Immunity, Infection and Pathology" (R. von Furth, ed.), pp. 405–421. Blackwell, Oxford.

Prins, F. A., Bonnet, J., and Velde Cornelese-ten, I. (1993) Reflection contrast microscopy of ultrathin sections in immunocytochemical localization studies: A versatile technique bridging electron microscopy with light microscopy. *Histochemistry* **99**, 417–429.

Vesely, P., Jones, S. J., and Boyde, A. (1993) Video-rate confocal reflection microscopy of neoplastic cells: Rate of intracellular movement and peripheral motility characteristic of neoplastic cell line (RSK4) with high degree of growth independence in vitro. *Scanning* **15**, 43–47.

Using Interference Microscopy to Study Cell Behavior

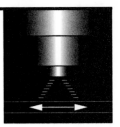

Graham A. Dunn and Daniel Zicha

I. Introduction

The aim of analyzing cell behavior in culture is usually to determine the characteristic patterns of translocation and dynamic morphology of specific cell types under set conditions. This often requires the statistical analysis of large quantities of data and a major problem is how to get these data into a computer. Images of living cells obtained by conventional methods of microscopy, such as phase contrast or differential interference contrast (DIC), are very unsuitable for interpretation by computer. Here we show how the recently developed method of *phase-stepping interferometry* can be applied to transmission interference microscopy to obtain images in which the intensity is linearly related to the distribution of nonaqueous cellular material. These are directly interpretable by computer and a further benefit is that the amount of cellular material can be accurately quantified.

II. Materials and Instrumentation

A. CULTURE REQUIREMENTS

It is important for interference microscopy that the culture chamber have good optical properties and good dimensional stability. We use bacteria-counting chambers of the Helber type which can be obtained without rulings (Z3 special unruled) from the manufacturer (Weber Scientific International Ltd.). Cells are best cultured on a rigid coverslip, such as a No. 3, which is unlikely to become distorted during assembly of the chamber. For quantitative interference microscopy, the cells should never be seeded densely, as a cell-free region must always appear in the image to serve as a reference background. The buffering of the culture medium must be suitable for closed systems and we use media containing Hanks' saline which equilibrates with a bubble of air left in the chamber. Culture temperature during interference microscopy may be maintained by a thermally controlled warm air blower although certain precautions may need to be observed (see Section V).

B. HORN INTERFERENCE MICROSCOPE

Transmission interference microscopes vary enormously in design and capabilities but are quite similar in principle. The ideal design for cell biology is most closely approached by the Horn interference microscope (Leitz, Wetzlar), which essentially

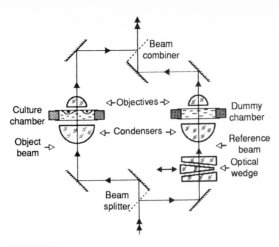

FIGURE 1   Schematic diagram of the Horn interference microscope.

comprises two precisely matched conventional microscopes placed side by side with parallel optical axes (Fig. 1). The illuminating beam of light is split into two beams of which only one, the **object beam,** passes through the culture chamber; the other, the **reference beam,** passes through a cell-free dummy chamber. The two beams are recombined after leaving the objectives which results in the **interference** of the two wavefronts and leads to the variations in color and intensity that constitute the image. With monochromatic illumination, the distribution of intensity in the image is determined by the distribution of the **phase difference** between the two wavefronts. This phase difference depends on how much the object beam has been slowed down by the higher refractive index encountered on passing through a cell. The intensity distribution is thus directly related to the distribution of cellular material (see Section IV).

The conventional method of measuring the phase difference at any chosen point in the image of a cell is to adjust the phase of the reference beam using a calibrated optical wedge until the intensity at the chosen point matches that of the cell-free background. With the advent of fast digital image processors and the method of phase stepping, however, it is now feasible to measure the phase difference introduced by the cells on a point-by-point basis across the whole image. The theory of phase stepping (Creath, 1988) states that the distribution of phase difference may be calculated using the information provided by the intensity distribution in images obtained at only three different settings of the background phase. To implement this it is convenient if the host computer can control the background phase automatically. In the Horn microscope, this is adjusted by rotating a micrometer head which drives the optical wedge, and Fig. 2 shows how this may be coupled to a stepper motor for automatic control.

C. JAMIN–LEBEDEFF INTERFERENCE OPTICS

In the Jamin–Lebedeff interference optics for Zeiss (Oberkochen) microscopes, the object and reference beams pass through the same condenser and objective, and beam isolation is achieved by orthogonal polarization rather than by physical separation. The main disadvantage of this arrangement is the presence of a blurred and astigmatic secondary image or ghost image which is shifted laterally from the primary image by about one-third of the field width. This severely restricts the use of the microscope on extended objects but is not too limiting for the study of isolated cells. A second complication of having polarized beams can arise if the specimen is

FIGURE 2   A stepper motor coupled to the precision wedge drive of the Horn microscope. Note the spring leaf coupling which allows some longitudinal movement.

birefringent. Nevertheless, the Jamin–Lebedeff system is intrinsically more stable and easier to adjust than the Horn and has the advantage that compensators designed for polarizing microscopy can be used.

The simplest way of implementing phase stepping with the Jamin–Lebedeff system is to change the background phase by the method of **Sénarmont compensation,** which consists of rotating the analyzer in the presence of a specially oriented quarter-wave retardation plate (Dunn and Zicha, 1993). One eighth of a rotation of the analyzer gives a phase shift of $\pi/2$ radians. Figure 3 shows how a stepper motor can be coupled to the main drive shaft of a Zeiss analyzer, after disassembling the control knob and vernier scale, to achieve computer control.

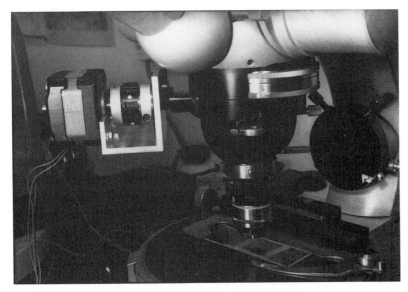

FIGURE 3   A stepper motor coupled to the main drive shaft of a Zeiss analyzer after disassembly of the control knob and vernier scale.

D. JENAPOL INTERPHAKO SHEARING-INTERFERENCE MICROSCOPE

To our knowledge, the Jenapol microscope with Interphako attachment (Carl Zeiss, Jena) is the only transmission interference microscope suitable for cell biology that is currently manufactured. The instrument is unusual in that the beam enters an interferometer only after leaving the objective. Here the two wavefronts are shifted laterally with respect to each other by a variable shear distance so that a single object in the specimen plane gives rise to two images which are identical except that phase retardations in one image correspond to phase advances in the other. This arrangement is very stable and easily adjusted but, as with the Jamin–Lebedeff microscope, the secondary image presents a problem when viewing extended objects. Another disadvantage is that the image resolution is relatively poor because the illuminating numerical aperture must be severely reduced in the shear direction using either a slit diaphragm or an array of parallel slits.

The background phase can be controlled by an knob coupled to a shaft encoder to give an accurate electronic readout, and although we have not yet adapted such an instrument for automatic phase stepping, it should present no problems. Zeiss is currently developing in Jena a software package called Jenamap for implementing phase stepping on the Jenapol.

E. VIDEO CAMERAS

Charge-coupled device (CCD) cameras which incorporate solid-state photodetector arrays are a major improvement over conventional video cameras for quantitative interference microscopy, as they have a lower geometric distortion and better photometric properties. We use the Sony XC-77CE miniature monochrome video camera with a CCD array of 756×581 pixels. For photometric work, the AGC should be switched off and the gamma set to 1.0. These cameras may be obtained with a control box incorporating gain and offset controls (Optivision Ltd.), though this is not usually necessary if the image processing board has a computer-controllable video amplifier.

F. IMAGE PROCESSORS

Image capturing and processing boards that fit into a standard slot in a PC AT-compatible host computer are now quite common and generally cheaper than standalone systems. With video microscopy of cultured cells, the individual video frames are often quite noisy because the intensity of illumination must be kept low to avoid cellular damage. The first requirement of the image board, therefore, is that it should be able to average frames acquired at video rate. Until recently, this required a frame grabber and processor board, such as the DT2867 (Data Translation Inc), which can perform frame averaging at video rate. With the introduction of the EISA standard 32-bit bus, an alternative for time-lapse recording is now to use a much cheaper board such as the Matrox Magic (Matrox Ltd.) which can capture and send frames at video rate, for averaging between exposures, to a suitable host computer with a sufficiently large memory. For phase stepping, a second requirement is that three averaged images must be acquired in rapid succession during each exposure.

The computer system should also embody hardware and software for showing both live and stored digitized images in pseudocolor coding and for computing a histogram of the distribution of gray-level values in a stored image. A large hard disk and some bulk storage device such as a tape streamer will be necessary for storing and archiving sequences of images.

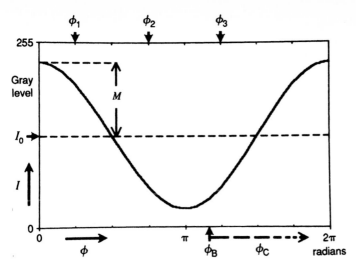

FIGURE 4   Plot of I against ϕ over the range 0 to 2π radians.

G. AUXILIARY INSTRUMENTATION

The computer must also have some means for controlling the stepper motor for automatically adjusting the background phase difference. We use the parallel data port to send signals to a purpose-built controller, although commercial controller boards that fit PC AT slots are now available. The parallel port can also send a signal that operates a shutter to prevent unnecessary illumination of the cells between exposures.

III. Procedure

A. SETTING UP THE MICROSCOPE

Steps

1. The microscope is first adjusted according to the manufacturer's instructions for the particular instrument in use. With the Horn or Jamin–Lebedeff systems, the setting of the illuminating numerical aperture is a compromise between low aperture for accurate phase determination and high aperture for optimal lateral resolution. In the case of the Horn or Jenapol instruments, the interference fringes should be expanded to achieve a moderately uniform background (homogeneous field), whereas there is no alternative to the homogeneous field setting with the Jamin–Lebedeff system. White tungsten or polychromatic mercury illumination should be used to ensure that the background interference color lies within the first order.

2. The illumination is next switched to monochromatic green light by introducing a filter to isolate the 546-nm mercury line and the light path of the microscope is diverted from the eyepieces to the video camera.

3. The following adjustments are best made by continuously sampling the mean gray-level value in a small region of the cell-free background of the digitized image from the frame grabber. Figure 4 shows how the intensity, I, at a single pixel varies sinusoidally as the phase difference, ϕ, between object and reference beams is increased by turning the stepper motor drive. The video amplifier gain and offset controls should be adjusted so that the mean intensity, I_0, is approximately halfway through the intensity range of the digitizer, a gray-

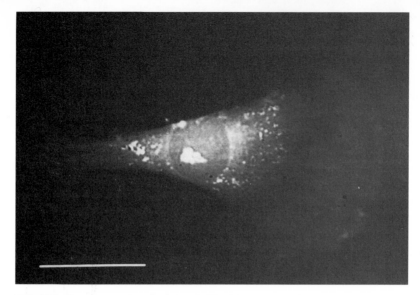

FIGURE 5 Image of a chick heart fibroblast captured using the Jamin–Lebedeff system without phase stepping. Bar = 20 μm.

level value of 128 in our case, and the modulation, M, is about 80% of I_0. This gives a safety margin if a drift in some parameter such as the lamp intensity occurs during an image recording session. Viewing the image in pseudocolor coding and/or using a histogram function help to ensure that these adjustments are approximately correct across the whole image background.

4. For qualitative work, the value of ϕ in the background should be set to just over π radians as marked by the arrow ϕ_B in Fig. 4. This gives the optimal contrast of bright cells on a dark background. The reason is that the additional ϕ introduced by well-spread cells in culture rarely extends beyond the range indicated by the broken arrow ϕ_C; and I increases almost linearly as ϕ increases within this range (see Brown and Dunn, 1989). Figure 5 shows an image of a chick heart fibroblast acquired at this setting. Such images are not suitable for the precise quantitation of cellular material; however, because the setting of ϕ_B and the other two variables, I_0 and M, can vary across the image plane and with time. Phase stepping circumvents these problems by calculating ϕ directly at each location in the image.

B. PHASE STEPPING

Steps

1. The procedure for phase stepping is to acquire three images in rapid succession with the value of ϕ in the background set to $\pi/4$, $3\pi/4$, and $5\pi/4$ radians, respectively, as marked by the arrows ϕ_1, ϕ_2, and ϕ_3 in Fig. 4.

2. Sufficient frame averaging should be used to eliminate noticeable noise in acquiring each image.

3. It is not necessary to set the background phase precisely to $\pi/4$ before acquiring the first image, as any error can be corrected during postprocessing, but it is necessary to ensure that the phase steps are precisely $\pi/2$. The number of stepper motor pulses required for this may be calculated in the case of Sénarmont compensation, but must be found by experiment in the cases of the Horn or Jenapol instruments.

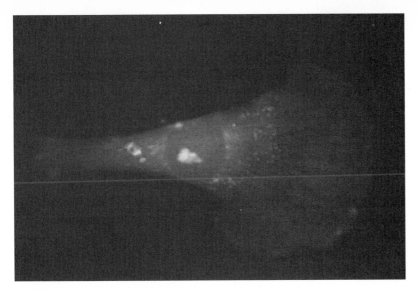

FIGURE 6 ϕ-Encoded image of the same cell as in Fig. 5.

4. The stepper motor should finally be returned to the $\pi/4$ setting which requires its reversal except in the case of Sénarmont compensation.

5. The entire procedure is controlled by the host computer which also opens the light shutter during the period of image acquisition.

6. The next stage is to calculate the phase angle at each pixel location by eliminating the unknown variables I_0 and M. For any pixel location whose intensities in the three images are I_1, I_2, and I_3, the equation relating these to ϕ is given by Creath (1988) as $\tan(\phi) = (I_3 - I_2)/(I_1 - I_2)$. The two-argument arctangent function available in many computer languages should be used to solve this equation to obtain ϕ over the full range of 0 to 2π radians.

7. By coding this range of values as integers covering the full range of 256 image gray levels, a final image may be constructed that represents the distribution of ϕ in the specimen (Dunn and Zicha, 1993).

8. The ϕ-encoded image of our example fibroblast is shown in Fig. 6 and it can be seen that blemishes caused by dust contamination have disappeared because variations in intensity due to variations in I_0 or M have been eliminated.

C. RECORDING SEQUENCES OF IMAGES

Steps

1. The time taken for the acquisition of each set of three images constitutes an exposure and this should be short enough to freeze any motion of the cells. A theoretical minimum is set by the time taken for three video frames which is a little under one-eighth of a second but, in practice, an exposure is usually much longer because of the time taken by frame averaging and phase stepping.

2. The time interval between exposures is used to calculate the ϕ distribution from the three acquired images and to store the resulting ϕ-encoded image on hard disk. The calculation of ϕ may be speeded up 50 times or more using integer arithmetic. Instead of calling the arctangent function, a small lookup table is used to specify the encoded ϕ over the range 0 to 32 gray levels, and a nest of

three binary decisions determines within which octant ϕ lies (details supplied on request).

3. With our present system, the exposure time is 1.64 sec and the maximum rate of recording is 12 exposures per minute which generates data at the rate of about 300 Mb per hour. This rate of image acquisition is quite adequate for the time-lapse recording of slowly moving objects such as fibroblasts in culture. The TIFF 5.0 format is convenient for storing images, and one of several data compression techniques may be used to reduce the required storage space.

D. POSTPROCESSING AN IMAGE SEQUENCE

The cell-free areas of each ϕ-encoded image serve as a reference surface and the images should ideally be adjusted so that this surface is uniformly encoded for a ϕ value of zero.

Steps

1. The ϕ-encoded images are unusual in that the gray levels represent a circular measure, with 0 and 255 being adjacent values. This confers the great advantage that each image can be adjusted, by "rotating" the gray levels using modular arithmetic, so that the cell-free areas have a modal gray level of zero. This eliminates any drift in the background phase setting of the microscope and enables even the relatively unstable Horn microscope to be used for long-term recording.

2. For accurate quantitation it may be necessary further to process each image to compensate for any tilting or warping of the wavefront during recording. This may be done by applying a biquadratic or bicubic transformation to the gray levels of each image so that the background closely matches that of the first image in the regions of overlap.

3. A further refinement is to flatten the reference plane by subtracting from each image an estimate of the cell-free background obtained from all images of the sequence. For each pixel location, the modal value of its gray level throughout the sequence is generally a good estimate of the value to subtract.

4. A final stage of postprocessing is **object recognition,** which consists of automatically determining which regions of each image represent cells using, as the main criterion, the connectivity of pixels with gray levels above a threshold value. The gray level of the cell-free background may then be set to zero, as in Fig. 6, to eliminate any residual noise and to reduce dramatically the storage space required for compressed images.

IV. Comments

All the material constituents of the cell, whether in solution or not, slow down the object beam to approximately the same extent (within a few percent) for a given dry mass of material within the cross-sectional area of the beam. An areal density of nonaqueous matter of 3 pg for each square micrometer of the cell gives a phase retardation of 2π radians or one wavelength of green light (Davies *et al.,* 1954). As cells in culture very rarely exceed this mass density, the ϕ-encoded images are an accurate representation of the mass distribution of cellular material.

Having the dynamic changes in the distribution of cellular material available in machine-readable form opens up a wide range of possibilities for the automatic analysis of cell growth and behavior. In our laboratory, the analysis of an image sequence usually starts by taking the moments of each cell (Brown and Dunn, 1989). Moments are two sequences of numbers, the areal moments and the mass moments, that can together describe the size, location, orientation, shape, and mass distribution of a cell. Areal and mass moments of order zero give, respectively, the total spread area of a cell and its total mass. The position of the geometric centroid or of the true mass centroid may be obtained from the first-order areal and mass moments. Moments of successively higher orders describe the cell's shape and mass distribution to any required degree of accuracy.

The ϕ-encoded images are also suitable for studying the dynamics of intracellular motility. The minimal intracellular flow required to account for a given change in dry mass distribution may be calculated using **finite-element analysis** (Brown and Dunn, 1989). This analysis can result in images of a cell showing the velocity and direction of the minimal flow, the magnitude and direction of the mass flux, and the distribution of the kinetic energy of this minimal flow. Integrating kinetic energy over the whole cell gives a single measure of the non-steady-state intracellular activity.

V. Pitfalls

Care must be taken to ensure that the mechanism of phase stepping does not introduce any spurious effects such as a lateral misalignment of the three captured images or a change in overall image intensity due to polarization effects. The gamma controls of the CCD camera must be adjusted so that the contrast transfer function is linear and this may be checked by examining the histogram of a ϕ-encoded image of a fringe field, which should give a uniform distribution. Factors that are likely to give rise to stability problems, such as stage heaters, arc lamps, and video amplifiers, should be switched on well in advance of a recording session. In choosing an area of the culture to record, care must be taken to avoid the likelihood of secondary images overlapping the primary images of the cells of interest during the recording period. The Horn microscope does not have this problem but it is particularly susceptible to air currents, and shields should be fitted around the objectives and condensers, especially if warm-air stage heating is used.

REFERENCES

Brown, A. F., and Dunn, G. A. (1989) Microinterferometry of the movement of dry matter in fibroblasts. *J. Cell Sci.* **92**, 379–389.
Creath, K. (1988) Phase-measurement interferometry techniques. *In* "Progress in Optics" (E. Wolf, ed.), Vol. XXVI, pp. 349–393. North-Holland, Amsterdam.
Davies, H. G., Wilkins, M. H. F., Chayen, J., and La Cour, L. F. (1954) The use of the interference microscope to determine dry mass in living cells and as a quantitative cyto-chemical method. *J. Microsc. Sci.* **95**, 271–304.
Dunn, G. A., and Zicha, Z. (1993) Phase-shifting interference microscopy applied to the analysis of cell behaviour. *In* "Cell Behaviour: Adhesion and Motility" (G. Jones, C. Wigley, and R. Warn, eds.), SEB Symposium No. 47, 91–106.

SECTION **B**

Fluorescence Microscopy

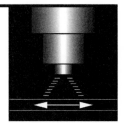

Fluorescence Imaging in Living Cells

Michael Whitaker

I. Introduction

Fluorescent molecules can be detected at low concentrations inside cells using low-light-level detectors. This is because they light up against what is in theory a very black background; however, the detection limit is set not by technology, but by the fact that cells themselves contain endogenous fluorescent molecules that fluoresce weakly. The fluorescent groups (fluorophores) used in fluorescence microscopy in living cells are chosen for their brightness (quantum yield). The lowest detectable concentrations for the usual fluorophores is around 1 μM.

Fluorescent molecules are used as *tags* or *indicators*. A fluorescent tag is attached to a protein and can be used to localize the protein in a living cell and to follow changes in localization in response to stimuli. Most proteins can be tagged *in vitro* using reactive fluorophores such as fluorescein isothiocyanate. A fluorescent indicator works like intracellular litmus paper and changes its color or brightness in response to a change in the cell. Usually, indicators are used to measure the concentrations of small ions, such as Ca^{2+}, H^+, Mg^{2+}, and K^+ (Tsien, 1989), or to measure membrane potential. These indicators are specially designed fluorophores of around 500–1000 Da. The catalog and bulletins produced by Molecular Probes Inc. (Haughland, 1992) contain information about these sorts of fluorescent probes and include bibliographies. They are a very useful and informative introduction to the vast range of fluorophores available. Other indicators are based on fluorescent proteins whose fluorescence changes when the protein changes conformation. Proteins are not naturally very fluorescent, so the indicator proteins are modified *in vitro* by attaching bright fluorophores. These protein indicators are not for the most part commercially available and must be made or obtained at the source from the investigator who has constructed them.

Many fluorescent probes do not readily cross the cell membrane. This is a useful property, as permeant probes quickly diffuse out of cells; however, impermeant probes must be introduced into cells by microinjection or transient permeabilization. This limits their utility in many cell types. Roger Tsien invented a way of introducing some normally impermeant molecules into cells using acetoxymethyl (AM) esters. Many molecules are impermeant because they have charged groups. Some classes of charged groups (e.g., carboxylate, phosphate) can be neutralized by esterification. They are then cell permeant. The trick works because there are esterases in the cell cytoplasm that convert the esters back to the free acid. The free acid is impermeant and is trapped inside the cell. There are other fluorophores that can be trapped using similar principles.

Fluorescent molecules can be visualized using low-light cameras or confocal microscopy. The naked eye and photographic film will not take you very far. Using fluorescence techniques requires some familiarity with the principles of operation

Cell Biology: A Laboratory Handbook Copyright © 1994 by Academic Press, Inc. All rights of reproduction in any form reserved.

of cameras and computers. However, most of the large companies that market microscopes sell good photometric systems that are designed on a turnkey principle, so that it is now possible for anyone with a knowledge of the rudiments of physics and chemistry and an interest in the techniques to use quantitative fluorescence microscopy in living cells.

A bigger problem is the existence of numerous artifacts of technique. A rule of thumb might be that if you see what others see, then you can be reasonably confident of your interpretation, but if you see something new, it is an artifact. This is certainly our experience and a significant number of papers in the field of fluorescence indicator imaging report artifacts that are taken as real.

II. Materials and Instrumentation

Fluorescent molecules

Fluorescence probes can be obtained from Molecular Probes Inc. (Haughland, 1992).

Digital imaging fluorescence microscopes

For $20,000 to 30,000, you can now buy a sensitive camera, computer, and software as a package. The important element is the camera, as computing is now cheap. There is no need to buy a more expensive piece of equipment. The main choice is between intensified cameras and charge-coupled device (CCD) cameras. The terminology is now a little confusing, as most modern video cameras are CCD based. The difference is that intensified cameras use sensitive photocathode technology, usually with video output, and CCD cameras use digital photon capture and readout. The advantage of the intensified cameras is that they interface easily with video-based image processing hardware and software. Signal averaging is done in the computer. The advantage of CCD cameras is that averaging is done in the camera. There is little to choose between them at present for most applications. CCD cameras have very low noise when images are acquired over minutes and so are preferable for very long exposures, but most cells change on a time scale of 0.1– 10 sec, so that in practice there is no great advantage in using CCD technology. Princeton Instruments and Photek sell CCD cameras and Photonic Science sells intensified cameras and software. Applied Imaging, Improvision, and most other commercial fluorescence imaging systems use intensified cameras (Jovin and Arndt-Jovin, 1989). The image processing software should be able to add, subtract, multiply, and divide images pixel by pixel; 512×512 is a standard image format. The hardware and software must permit the storage of as many images as possible in memory. This is not a trivial requirement, as a 512×512 image occupies 0.25 Mbyte. Disk-based storage alone is too slow to permit the rapid acquisition of images. An optical disk drive (WORM or erasable) is essential for storage and archival.

Confocal fluorescence microscopes

The major microscope companies (Zeiss, Leica, and also Bio-Rad) all market laser-scanning fluorescence microscopes. At the moment, computer-assisted laser-scanning microscopes are preferable because they have the highest detection sensitivity and come equipped with the image processing hardware and software that is necessary for image analysis and interpretation. One difficulty with confocal imaging is that many good fluorophores can only be excited in the ultraviolet, whereas standard confocal microscopes are fitted with visible-wavelength lasers. There are good reasons for this: ultraviolet lasers are large, cumbersome, and expensive to run and any ultraviolet confocal microscope must have special optics corrected for chromatic aberration in the ultraviolet.

Microinjection systems

For microinjection, manipulators, microelectrode holders, a good research microscope, a pressure source, and micropipettes are required. Zeiss can provide all this. It is cheaper to use a Nikon microscope and Narishige manipulators, with a Picospritzer electrically actuated pressure system and a simple micropipette puller from Kopf, Palmer, or Clarke Electromedical. Manual expulsion of the pipette contents into the cell using the oil-drop method (Hiramoto and Nakano, 1988) is a useful alternative to high-pressure microinjection, especially for peptides and proteins.

III. Procedures and Comments

A. LOADING CELLS WITH FLUORESCENT DYES

1. AM and Other Esters

Cells may be loaded in suspension or attached to glass or plastic. Very-thin-bottomed petri dishes (Bachoffer) are essential if petri dishes are used on the microscope, as the high-numerical-aperture lenses used in fluorescence microscopy have too short a working distance to bring a cell into focus through conventional plastic petri dishes. Cells vary in their capacity to accumulate and hydrolyze AM and other esterified fluorophores.

Steps

1. To a cell suspension or cell monolayer, add AM ester to a final concentration of 5 μM from a 5 mM stock in DMSO.

2. Incubate for 15 min (at 25°C for mammalian cells).

3. Wash twice with 10-fold excess volume and incubate for a further 15 min (at 37°C for mammalian cells).

4. Check efficacy of loading. If too great, reduce concentration and time of step 1. If too little, then go to step 5.

5. Increase AM ester concentration by 5 μM and add both ester and Pluronic F-127 (to a final concentration of 0.2% from 20% (w/v) DMSO stock made by warming to 40°C for 20 min) with stirring to the vortex before applying to fresh cells. Incubate for 15–30 min, then go to step 2.

2. Verifying Uptake and Hydrolysis

The esters must be completely hydrolyzed to act as indicators. Hydrolysis can be checked by comparing the fluorescence spectrum of the dye in the cells with the fluorescence spectra of the ester and free acid forms of the dye.

Steps

1. Release dye from cells using 0.1% Triton X-100.

2. Determine relevant (excitation or emission) spectrum of released dye in a spectrofluorometer. This is best done at saturating levels of dye ligand (e.g., 1 mM free calcium for fura-2).

3. Compare shape of spectrum with standard spectra of the ester and free forms of the dye, under the same conditions as 1. A mixed spectrum indicates incomplete hydrolysis.

4. Compare amplitude of released dye signal with amplitude of known concentration of standard to determine cell concentration of dye (C_{cell}).

If the cell volume is known, the concentration of dye in the cells can also be estimated.

$$C_{cell} = \frac{F_{sam}}{F_{std}} \times C_{std} \times \frac{V_{sam}}{V_{cell}}$$

where

C_{std} = dye concentration of standard
V_{sam} = volume of dye sample
V_{cell} = volume of cells sampled
F_{sam} = fluorescence amplitude of sample
F_{std} = fluorescence amplitude of standard

3. Microinjection

Micropipettes can be backfilled with as little as 0.5 μl of injectate by using filament capillary glass tubing (Clarke Electromedical). The solution can be placed in the shank of the pipette using fine plastic tubing and a Hamilton syringe. Fine tubing can easily be made by drawing out a yellow Gilson pipette tip after heating to melting in a flame. For some applications, the tip of the pipette will fill if simply dipped in solution.

Steps

1. Construct an electrode holder from aluminum so that drawn micropipettes are held at 45°, tip up. An array of 2-mm holes drilled to a depth of 10 mm is adequate.

2. Place holder in a deep petri dish with lid and add 10 μl dimethylamino-nitromethylsilane to the bottom of the dish.

3. Bake in oven for 30 min at 175°C. Remove lid in fume hood as vapor is toxic.

Protein is more easily injected from silanized micropipettes. Use an inverted microscope. The most difficult part of microinjection is finding the pipette tip in the field without breaking it on the substrate: focus above the cells by 1 mm or more and find the tip there, then gradually lower both the tip and the plane of focus toward the cells.

When using high-pressure microinjection, it is important to use repetitive (0.5-Hz) pressure pulses to keep the solution in the tip of the pipette free from contamination from the bathing solution. With skill, it is possible to impale a cell and inject a pulse of solution within this 0.5-Hz rhythm. Automated injection systems, for example, that from Zeiss, require little skill. Manual injection (Hiramoto and Nakano, 1988) uses an oil droplet at the tip of the pipette to protect the contents from contamination as the pipette approaches the cell.

B. ACQUIRING IMAGES

1. Adjusting the Detector Sensitivity

Most video image acquisition systems are based on 8-bit pixels. This reflects the dynamic range and gray-scale resolution of video cameras. It is important to set the sensitivity of the system to avoid saturation of the detector by the strongest signals that will occur during an experiment. Gross saturation is usually obvious and experiments that show it can be seen and discarded; however, even a signal at a mean 90% saturation will have pixels that saturate. This will not be obvious, but the data will nonetheless be quantitatively meaningless (Bolsover *et al.*, 1993). Aim for a maximum mean 75% saturation of the detector.

2. Background Subtraction

If fluorescence data are to be used quantitatively, then the signal that is measured must come solely from the dye within the cells. Cells have intrinsic fluorescence and if this amounts to more than a few percent of the dye signal, quantitative estimates, particularly those involving ratio images, can be badly in error. The best way to avoid the problem is to use highly fluorescent dyes. Background subtraction for cell autofluorescence is rarely useful, as the background image to be subtracted must be taken from the cell before the dye is introduced. As the cell must not be moved between acquisition of the background image and the experiment, the technique cannot be used with AM loading. It is difficult even with microinjection.

3. Image Acquisition Rate

The rate of image acquisition should be matched to the speed of the changes in fluorescence distribution and intensity that are observed or expected. Acquiring images at too fast a rate has two disadvantages: (1) the amount of image averaging in time is reduced, with a resultant increase in signal–noise ratio; (2) the number of images that must be stored and processed increases. The slowest step in fluorescence imaging is image analysis. One second's recording at video rates generates 30 images and 7 Mbyte of data; one minute's recording, 180 images and 420 Mbyte of data. Most image acquisition hardware and software permit averaging: if they do not permit real-time averaging on-line, they are of no use for fluorescence imaging.

With ratiometric dyes, it is almost essential to ratio on-line during an experiment, with display of the ratio image, so that the experimenter sees what is happening as it happens. Few systems can do this at video rates, but for the reasons given above, this is not necessarily a disadvantage.

C. ANALYZING DATA

1. Ratiometric Analysis

Some questions in fluorescence imaging are answered by measuring simple intensity changes: For example, does the localization of a fluorescent probe change during an experiment? Other questions are more subtle: Is the increase sensed by an indicator proportionately greater in the nucleus than the cytoplasm? A ratio method is necessary to answer the latter sort of question, as the resting distribution of the signal is very unlikely to be uniform. Ratio dyes offer the best solution: one (unchanging signal) gives the dye concentration, the other (changing) signal senses the change within the cell. Alternatively, two dyes can be used simultaneously (Lipp and Niggli, 1993): the active partner sensing a change, the passive partner controlling for dye distribution. The dyes must be identical in their cellular distribution if this technique is to work. This is most easily achieved if the dyes are linked to a large molecule like dextran (Berger and Brownlee, 1993). If nothing in the cell moves during an experiment, then a ratio can be generated by dividing each experimental image, point by point, by a control image taken before the experiment.

2. Quantitative Display

Quantitative information from imaging experiments is usually displayed as a pseudocolor image, because the relative color discrimination of human vision is far better than its relative intensity discrimination. The rainbow scale is best (Color Plate 13), in that it is well known, easily interpreted, and continuous. A useful rule is that data should undergo only linear transformations, unless a nonlinear but monotonic relation is theoretically appropriate, as, for example, in obtaining calcium concentrations from ratiometric calcium dyes (Tsien and Harootunian, 1990). Another rule that should never be broken is always to display a calibration scale with an image. Without a scale, an image is quantitatively meaningless.

IV. Pitfalls

Fluorescence imaging pitfalls are discussed in detail by Bolsover *et al.* (1993).

A. RESOLUTION

Fluorescent microscopes do not have good z-axis resolution. This is now generally appreciated and the problems can be solved by using image deconvolution (Monck *et al.*, 1993) or confocal microscopy. However, poor z-axis resolution also generates poor resolution in the x and y axes (Bolsover *et al.*, 1993). This leads, for example to halo, where the fluorescence image of a cell is larger than its bright-field counterpart. It is very important to realize that limitations of the fluorescence microscope lead to loss of xy resolution for any signal that is not localized to the plane of focus. Even with high-numerical-aperture lenses, xy resolution is no better than 0.5 times cell thickness (Bolsover *et al.*, 1993). In a round 10-μm cell, the resolution of the image will be 5 μm.

B. DYE DISTRIBUTION ARTIFACTS

Several types of dye distribution artifacts lead to false conclusions about relative increases in different regions of the cell (Bolsover *et al.*, 1993). The most common, both in practice and in the literature, is dye uptake into cellular organelles. If the organelles are not uniformly distributed, then the relative change in dye signal from different parts of the cell will be nonuniform, even if the signal that the dye is responding to is uniform. This artifact is described elsewhere (Bolsover *et al.*, 1993; Gillot and Whitaker, 1993) and illustrated in Color Plate 13, where uptake of dye into organelles makes it appear that the increase in nuclear calcium concentration is greater than the increase in cytoplasmic calcium during a calcium transient. In fact, the calcium transient is spatially uniform both inside and outside the nucleus.

REFERENCES

Berger, F., and Brownlee, C. (1993) Ratio confocal imaging of free cytoplasmic calcium gradients in polarising and polarised *Fucus* zygotes. *Zygote* **1**, 9–16.

Bolsover, S. R., Silver, R. A., and Whitaker, M. J. (1993) Ratio dye imaging of Ca_i and pH_i. *In* "Electronic Light Microscopy" (D. Shotton, ed.), pp. 181–210. Liss, New York.

Gillot, I., and Whitaker, M. J. (1993) Imaging calcium waves in eggs and embryos. *J. Exp. Biol.*, **184**, 213–219.

Haughland, R. (1992) "Handbook of Fluorescent Probes and Research Chemicals," pp. 113–122. Molecular Probes, Eugene, OR.

Hiramoto, Y. and Nakano, Y. (1988) Micromanipulation studies of the mitotic apparatus in sand dollar eggs. *Cell Motil. Cytoskel.* **10**, 172–184.

Jovin, T. M., and Arndt-Jovin, D. J. (1989) Luminescence digital imaging microscopy. *Annu. Rev. Biophys. Biophys. Chem.* **18**, 271–308.

Lipp, P., and Niggli, E. (1993) Ratiometric confocal Ca^{2+}-measurements with visible wavelength indicators in isolated cardiac myocytes. *Cell Calcium* **14**, 359–372.

Monck, J. R., Oberhauser, A. F., Keating, T. J., and Fernandez, J. M. (1993) Thin-section ratiometric Ca^{2+} images obtained by optical sectioning of fura-2 loaded mast cells. *J. Cell Biol.* **116**, 749–759.

Tsien, R. Y. (1989) Fluorescent probes of cell signalling. *Annu. Rev. Neurosci.* **12**, 227–253.

Tsien, R. Y. (1990) Laser scanning confocal microscopy at video rates (30 frames/sec) with dual wavelength emission rationing for quantitative imaging of intracellular messengers. *Proc. R. Microsc. Soc.* **25**, S52.

Tsien, R. Y., and Harootunian, A. T. (1990) Practical design criteria for a dynamic ratio imaging system. *Cell Calcium* **11**, 93–109.

Practical Laser-Scanning Confocal Light Microscopy: Obtaining Optimal Performance from Your Instrument

James B. Pawley and Victoria E. Centonze

I. Introduction

Light microscopy experienced a rebirth in the early 1980s when it was discovered that significant advantages could be gained by applying advanced video techniques to conventional light microscopy. These advances were highlighted by the work of Allen and Allen (1983) and Inoue (1986). The essence of their contribution was to point out (a) that electronic imaging sensors are considerably more sensitive and linear in their response to light than is photographic film, and (b) that the capabilities of the hardware then becoming available for real-time digital image processing were sophisticated enough to improve substantially the visibility of features in electronically recorded light microscope images.

As a result, microscopes with attached, digitally processed video systems became capable of displaying interpretable images of features that were either too low in intensity or too low in contrast to be seen by unenhanced microscope systems.

Although the spatial resolution of these electronically enhanced light microscopes inevitably remained far less than that of the electron microscope, they had the tremendous advantage that they could be used to study specimens that were alive or at least metabolically active. In addition, the ability to make visible, features that were very low in contrast or intensity permitted the observer to detect the location and motion of structures that were considerably smaller than the limit of light optical resolution.

During this same period other developments related to the specific staining of biological specimens also occurred. In immunology, the development of the techniques for producing monoclonal antibodies made it possible to produce fluorescent probes with extremely high specificity (Wang and Taylor, 1989, pp. 87–102). More recently, the techniques of genetic engineering have made it possible to label nucleic acid sequences with fluorescent markers with the same specificity that the monoclonal antibody technique makes possible for labeling proteins. These and other techniques for labeling biological material with specific fluorescent stains are reviewed by Wang and Taylor (1989) and Herman and Jacobson (1989).

As a result of these developments, the sophisticated techniques of digital electronic imaging were being applied to the light microscopic study of living specimens incorporating fluorescent analogs of specific proteins, thus making them visible when present at the plane of focus of a fluorescence microscope. The remaining major limitation was that, although biological specimens were three dimensional (3D), the conventional light microscope imaged only a single 2D plane. In addition, unless the specimen was first sliced into very thin sections, the image of this plane was often confused by the presence of the fuzzy outlines of out-of-focus structural features located in planes above or below the plane of focus. As a result, it was difficult for the microscopist to fully appreciate the 3D architecture of the specimen.

In this article, we describe the important features of the laser-scanning confocal microscope (LSCM) and provide some examples demonstrating some of its capabilities. We then describe a number of aspects of the instrument that may be unfamiliar to the conventional light microscopist but are essential to the proper use of this instrument. In this part of the article, the underlying principle is that the major obstacle to obtaining optimal confocal data is the problem of bleaching. *Bleaching* is the term used to describe the fact that, under intense illumination, all dye molecules eventually lose their ability to fluoresce. Because the laser is such a bright source of light, it is possible to bleach the specimen 100 or even 1000 times faster with an LSCM than with a conventional fluorescence microscope unless due care is paid to the adjustment of the controls. It is therefore essential to operate the LSCM in such a way that the dose of light striking the specimen is never more than the minimum needed to see the object of interest.

II. The Confocal Microscope: Its Features and Operation

Central to the confocal approach to microscopy is the idea of focusing a point source of light into a point within the specimen and then imaging the light signal emitted from this point back through the objective, which focuses it onto a small aperture or pinhole behind which is located a photodetector (Fig. 1). The pinhole is optically conjugate to both the source and to the focused spot in the specimen (i.e., all three planes are mutually in focus). Of course, because of diffraction, the spot focused in the specimen is actually not a point but an Airy disk having a size inversely proportional to the numerical aperture (NA) of the objective and of the wavelength (λ) of the light. An image of this Airy disk is produced at the plane of the pinhole and the pinhole should be the correct size to permit most of it to pass through to the photodetector.

The disadvantage of the confocal imaging system outlined so far is that it only produces an image of a single point. To make a 2D image, either the specimen or the light beam must be scanned in the $x-y$ plane. In 1957, when the confocal principle was first used for microscopic imaging, the specimen was mechanically scanned using a pair of tuning forks arranged at 90° to each other and the image was displayed on a long-persistence cathode-ray tube which was scanned in synchrony with the forks (Minsky, 1957, 1988). When confocal imaging was next proposed in 1968, scanning was accomplished by passing the illuminating and emitted light through opposite sides of a symmetrical variation of the rotating Nipkow disk, as is discussed by Alan Boyde, Colin Gray, and Sheila Jones elsewhere in this volume. Two, diametrically opposed patches of the holes in this disk were brought into optical registration using a series of mirrors so that one set of holes served as sources and the other set became the detector pinholes (Petran *et al.*, 1968). This approach produces a real-time confocal image that can be seen with the naked eye; however, because only about 1% of the light from the mercury arc light source passes the disk, it does not produce a very bright image of a fluorescent specimen.

This problem was solved in the 1980s with the introduction of instruments that employed a laser light source to solve the intensity problem and thereby permit confocal imaging of biological specimens that had been treated with highly specific

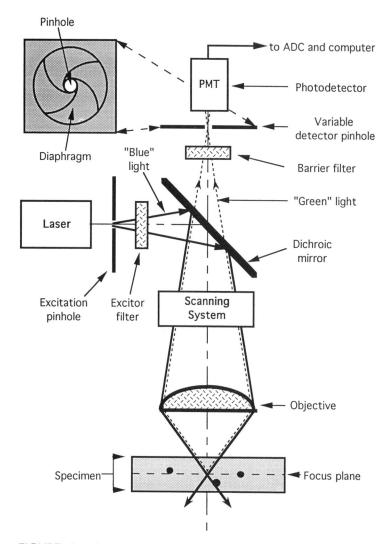

FIGURE 1 Block diagram of the optical components of a laser-scanning confocal microscope: short-wavelength "blue" light from the laser passes through an excitor pinhole and filter and is then reflected by the dichroic mirror into the objective lens. The lens focuses it into a spot within the specimen. Some of the "green" fluorescent light from the specimen returns through the objective. Because of its longer wavelength it passes through the dichroic and barrier filters and is brought to a focus at the plane of the detector pinhole. The fluorescent light originating from the plane of focus passes through the pinhole to the detector, whereas that from other planes is out of focus at the pinhole plane and so is selectively excluded from the detector.

fluorescent stains. It is this type of instrument that is now widely used for biological confocal studies (Brakenhoff *et al.,* 1979; White *et al.,* 1987; Pawley, 1990). In most commercially available systems, light from a laser is scanned over the image plane in a rectangular pattern or raster, by two, orthogonal galvanometer-driven mirrors located in aperture planes of the microscope. The data recorded at each point in the raster are stored as a number in a computer memory and then displayed as a proportional intensity at the appropriate location on a video monitor.

The advantages and disadvantages of each scanning method are summarized in Table I.

The advantage of the confocal method of image formation is that light emitted or scattered from planes other than the focus plane will be out of focus when it reaches the pinhole plane. As a result, most of it will not pass through the aperture,

TABLE I Features of Confocal Light Microscopes

Feature	Stage scanning	Disk scanning	Laser scanning
Light source	Laser, discrete λ	Hg arc, "white" light	Laser, discrete λ
Beams	One	100–500	One
Scan speed (limited by)	Slow (specimen mass)	Very fast (disk speed)	Medium (galvan. resp.)
Advantages	On-axis optics	"Real-time" image	Best fluorophore quantitation
	Transmitted light operation possible	"White" light	
		High detector QE	Normal operation of microscope possible
	Data stored digitally	No fluorophore saturation	Data stored digitally
Disadvanages	Very slow	Insufficient	Saturation
	Shakes specimen	fluorophore	Bleaching
	Hard-to-"find"	illumination	Slow scanning speed
	specimen	Fixed pinhole size	No real-time imaging
	High detector noise	High mirror losses	

and, to the extent that this happens, any image produced from the detected signal will be characteristic of only a single plane within the specimen. For this reason the confocal microscope is said to make "optical sections."

Figure 2 shows the effect of this pinhole. The two images show the same specimen of rose leaf tricomb viewed with the same confocal microscope but while, in the left image, the entire specimen is illuminated with exciting light and the signal is collected in a manner that mimics film, the right image is collected using confocal laser illumination and a detector pinhole to produce an optical section.

The thickness or z resolution, δ_z, of this optical section was defined by Brakenhoff (Brakenhoff *et al.*, 1979), assuming a very small detector pinhole diameter, as

$$\delta_z = \frac{2\lambda}{n(\sin^2\alpha)} \tag{1}$$

where, n is the index of refraction of the medium, and α is the half-angle of the cone of light accepted by the objective.

Confocal imaging requires that the optical system for excitation remain aligned with that for detection so that both are focused on a single point in the specimen. This is greatly simplified if one uses epi- rather than transillumination because, in this case, light for both illumination and recording passes through the same objective lens and also through the same part of the specimen. For this reason, most of the confocal microscopes now available use epi-illumination. Although this precludes the use of those contrast techniques that depend on coherent interactions between the illumination and the specimen, such as phase or interference contrast, it works very well with fluorescent or backscattered light. Fortunately, fluorescent specimens, especially those in which intense staining is confined to only a very small volume fraction, are often those best suited to study with confocal techniques because they can yield 3D data sets that produce easily interpretable, 3D images.

It is also possible to use the confocal microscope to produce epi-illuminated, dark-field images using the light that is scattered back or reflected from optical inhomogeneities in the specimen. However, because in this case the light detected has the same wavelength as the illumination, a dichroic mirror can no longer be used to ensure that the stray light produced by reflections from the optical components of the system does not reach the detector. In some early instruments, this reflected light appears as a series of bright circles in the center of the image, but now these can be removed using polarization techniques (Fig. 3) (Pawley *et al.*, 1993).

The backscattered-light signal is produced "free" in the sense that it can be

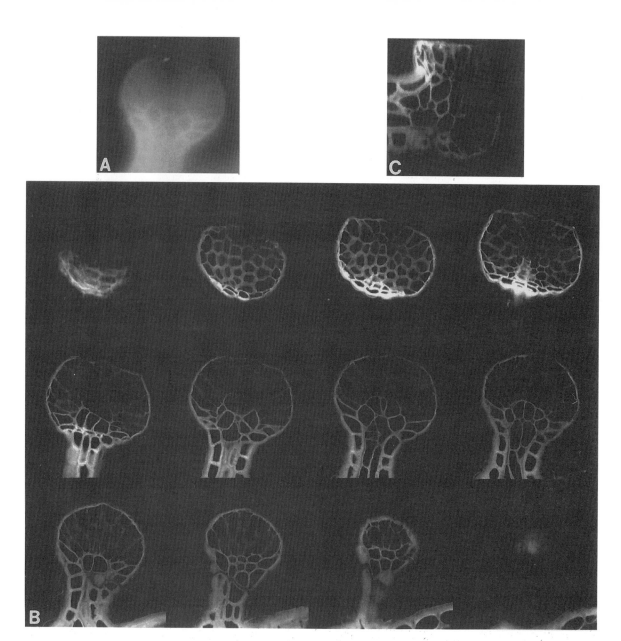

FIGURE 2 Effect of the confocal pinhole. (A) Image of a rose leaf tricomb stained with a rhodamine fluorescing dye. The image was made with the laser turned off and using a normal, nonconfocal, epifluorescence Hg arc source to excite the fluorescence. The signal was collected using the scanning mirrors and the PMT of the confocal microscope with a large pinhole size. This setup mimics the imaging process present in a conventional light microscope. (B) Series of 12 selected image planes through the tricomb collected confocally with a normal pinhole setting. Image 6 corresponds to the same focus plane shown in A. The reduction in out-of-focus flare is clearly visible in the confocal images. (C) An x–z scan of the tricomb. It was made by holding the normal, vertical (Y) scanning mirror stationary and stepping the focus control motor instead. As a result the signal for each line is collected at a different height along a vertical plane within the specimen, and the resulting image appears as though one was viewing the specimen from the side. From this image it is easy to see that the tricomb is being distorted by the pressure of the coverslip on the top (upper) surface.

obtained without interfering in any way with the collection of the fluorescent signal. Therefore, it is wasteful not to collect it for the information that it provides about unstained cellular structures that scatter light. Figures 4A and 4B are stereo projec-

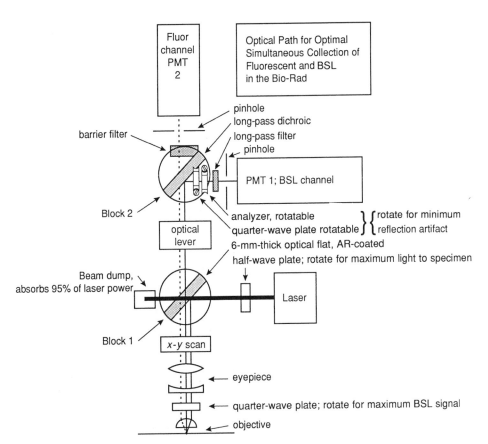

FIGURE 3 Diagram of a system to permit simultaneous collection of fluorescent and back-scattered light (BSL) on the Bio-Rad MRC-500/600 while using polarization techniques to suppress reflections from the optical components. Block 1 contains a laser line filter followed by a beam splitter consisting of a 6-mm-thick Pyrex optical flat, antireflection (AR) coated on its rear (upper) side. A half-wave plate after the laser is used to rotate the laser polarization so that 0.8–5% of the laser light is reflected down the optic axis and through a quarter-wave plate between the ocular and the objective. Almost all of the returning BSL and fluorescent light passes through the Pyrex beam splitter to block 2, where the BSL and fluorescent signals are separated with a dichroic mirror. The long wave signal passes to PMT 1 via an emission filter. Signal at the excitation wavelength passes through a quarter-wave plate and analyzer (both rotatable) and a laser line filter to PMT 2. The orientation of the half-wave plate is adjusted to give maximum light from the objective; then the rotatable elements in block 2 are adjusted to eliminate spurious reflections. Finally, the quarter-wave plate in the microscope body is rotated to produce the maximum BSL signal from a living cell.

tions made from a series of 15 single-plane images of a cheek cell that had been stained with acridine orange. The left images were made by simply adding up the intensity values at each corresponding pixel and then dividing the total by the number of planes. The right images were also made by adding pixel intensities, but, in this case, each image was translated 2 pixels to the right before it was added to the sum of the planes added up so far (Cox and Sheppard, 1983). The stereo pair in Fig. 4A was made using light backscattered by the cell; that in Fig. 4B was made, simultaneously, using fluorescent light.

A. THREE-DIMENSIONAL IMAGING

Because each 2D image shows *only* the location of fluorescent or scattering features in a single optical section, it is relatively easy to build up a 3D image by

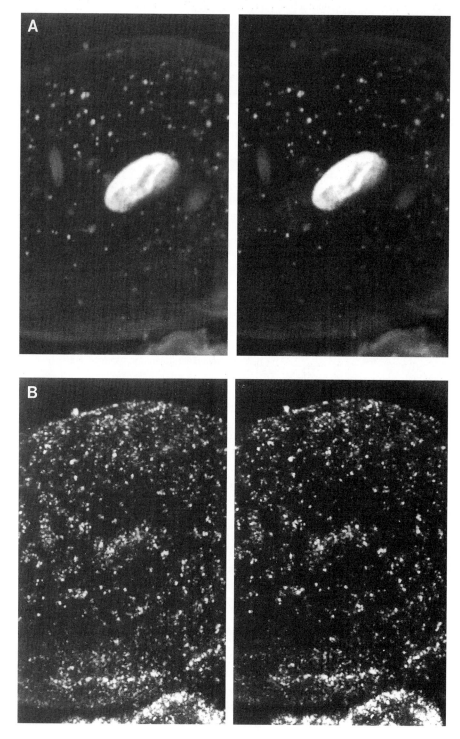

FIGURE 4   Stereo pairs made, as described in the text, using a 2-pixel shift between planes on a stack of 15 images acquired simultaneously using the BSL/fluor system shown in Fig. 3. The specimen is a living cheek cell in saliva stained with acridine orange.

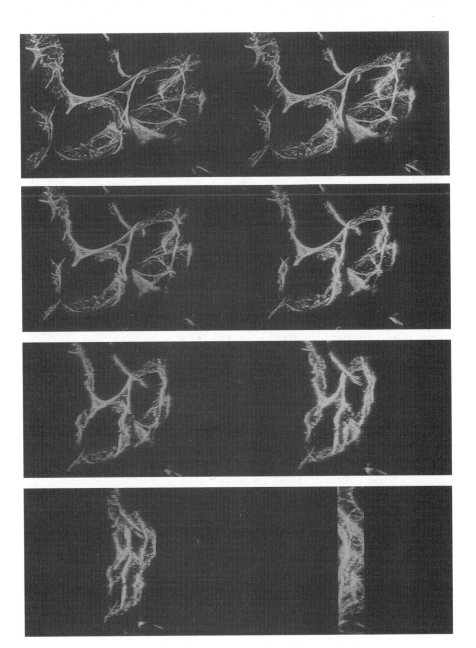

FIGURE 5 Rotation series produced using the Bio-Rad Thru-View 3-D Reconstruction software. The eight images show projections through the data set along angles that are 12.50 apart. They can be viewed as a series of four stereo pairs, each having a mean tilt of 250 with respect to its neighbors. The specimen of autofluorescent human lung was provided by Professor Whimster, King's College, London.

collecting similar data from adjacent focus planes throughout any specimen that is reasonably transparent. This can be done by driving a focus motor from the same computer that is used to drive the mirrors and store the data. By collecting a 2D image at 10 to 100 adjacent focus planes that are 0.3–3 μm apart within the specimen, a 3D intensity data set can be produced. This can ultimately be viewed either as a stereo pair made by adding up or "projecting" the data along two axes about 10° apart (Cox and Sheppard, 1983) (Fig. 4) or as a rotating "object" on the video screen of a 3D computer graphics display system (Pawley, 1990, pp. 141–150) (Fig. 5).

There are two other methods for mapping the 3D density distribution of fluorescent stains in microscopic specimens. The most direct approach involves mechanically sectioning the specimen, recording images from each section, and then digitizing these images so that they can be assembled and displayed by a computer in much the same way as was once common with serial section images from the transmission electron microscope. Unfortunately, this procedure is both tedious and rather ineffective. The sections become distorted and disoriented during the sectioning process and so the resulting images are very difficult to align. In the other approaches, the specimen remains undeformed and intact, and so the alignment of the entire data stack depends only on the mechanical precision of the scanning and focusing mechanisms of the microscope.

The second method for obtaining 3D intensity data from intact microscopical specimens is often referred to as the wide-field method. It uses a cooled-CCD 2D image detector attached to a conventional epifluorescence microscope to acquire sequentially a set of extremely precise images at adjacent focus planes throughout the volume of interest. In this case, each image contains data from both in-focus and out-of-focus planes. Computer deconvolution algorithms are used to remove the effects of the latter and produce images that contain only in-focus data (Pawley, 1990, pp. 141–150).

At present, this nonconfocal approach has several practical advantages. In particular, it can use a wide range of dyes that are excited in the UV. Such dyes are often more robust and efficient than those excited with visible light. Although it is possible to use a UV laser with a confocal microscope (Bliton *et al.,* 1993) it is an endeavor associated with considerable practical difficulty and expense. In addition, as the cooled-CCD detectors collect data in parallel rather than serially, as does the photomultiplier tube (PMT) in the laser confocal instrument, the wide-field instrument is not limited by saturation of the fluorescent dye (as discussed below) and illumination intensity can be increased to provide images more rapidly.

It is argued by some (Pawley, 1990, pp. 151–161) that the image deconvolution approach to 3D microscopic imaging is superior to the confocal approach because the confocal pinhole excludes photons which, although not originating from the plane of focus, may still carry relevant information regarding the stain density in adjacent planes, and that this information can be retrieved by image processing.

The extent to which this out-of-focus "signal" carries real structural information or only noise is a debatable point and the answer seems to depend strongly on the stain distribution present in a specific specimen. However, even if digital image processing can effectively subtract the average value of the out-of-focus background signal in each voxel and leave only the in-focus signal (which seems unlikely), the statistical error associated with this remainder will be proportional to the square root of the *total* recorded signal and hence higher than that associated with a confocal measurement of the in-focus signal alone (see Section IIIA). This problem will be exacerbated as the fraction of light originating from the in-focus plane decreases.

It should also be remembered that the deconvolution approach cannot be used to produce a single optical section from a single wide-field image. The deconvolution algorithm can only be applied to a series of wide-field images obtained at known and closely spaced focus positions. It also requires an accurate knowledge of the point-spread function of the objective lens in use and, if possible, the way that this changes over the image plane and as the focus plane moves farther into the specimen. Finally, it should be pointed out that the same deconvolution algorithms can be applied to data that have been collected in a confocal microscope. All parties now agree that this approach will probably yield the best possible solution of all (Shaw and Rawlins, 1991).

B. IMAGING DEPTH

An important aspect of any microscope used for making 3D images is how far
below the surface of the specimen it can obtain useful data. The most obvious
limitation is the mechanical one imposed by the finite working distance of the
objective: once the objective touches the specimen surface, it cannot be focused to
yet deeper planes.

Unfortunately, the opacity and optical inhomogeneity of the specimen usually
impose more stringent limits. To the extent that the illuminating beam is either
scattered or absorbed as it passes through the upper layers of the specimen, it will
fail to reach a plane of focus located farther into the specimen. Likewise, "signal"
light that is scattered or absorbed between the focus plane and the detector cannot
be measured.

Finally, any optical inhomogeneity in the specimen between the focus plane and
the objective will defocus both the beam of incident illumination and the light of
the returning signal. This will tend to increase the effective size of the focused spot
that is returned to the pinhole, causing some of the light not to reach the detector
as it should. To the extent that this defocusing action is the result of immersion of
the specimen in a liquid (water?) with an index-of-refraction other than that for
which the objective is corrected (oil?), the objective will no longer be corrected for
spherical aberration, especially at high numerical aperture (Hell *et al.*, 1993). This
lack of correction produces a serious reduction in spatial resolution, which gets
rapidly worse as one focuses further into the specimen (even 5 or 10 μm). In
mismatched specimens, spherical aberration is the major reason that the signal
intensity decreases so rapidly with depth into the specimen: the defocusing has the
effect that most of the signal from the plane of focus no longer gets through the
pinhole.

All three of these effects reduce the fraction of the signal that is detected as the
focus plane is pushed progressively further into the specimen. In addition, the last
mechanism also reduces the spatial resolution. Unless the specimen is highly transparent and has a uniform index of refraction matched to the objective, these three
factors usually place a practical limit to the effective penetration depth of the confocal light microscope which is much more stringent than that posed by the working
distance. When using an immersion objective on a biological specimen that is only
lightly stained and has been "cleared" by replacing the water with an imbibing
medium with an index of refraction that is matched to the objective and also close
to that of the solid components of the cell, the useful penetration depth can be
several hundred micrometers, but on less ideal specimens it is usually much less.
On the other hand, even deeper penetration is sometimes possible if the microscope
is used at lower magnification with a dry objective lens of lower numerical aperture
because the defocusing effects of the specimen are much less serious at low numerical
apertures.

III. Pitfalls of Practical Confocal Microscopy

As with any type of sophisticated instrument, best results can be obtained only
if the operator uses the microscope correctly. Many aspects of proper confocal
practice are either similar or identical to those that govern the operation of the
conventional light microscope. There are, however, two controls, one contrast effect,
and one optical effect that are unique to the confocal microscope. These four sub-
jects—pixel size, pinhole size, fluorescence saturation, and chromatic magnification
error—are discussed below following a brief outline of the limitations imposed on
confocal imaging by photon statistics.

The fundamental principle underlying your consideration of these matters should be the desire to maximize photon efficiency. To minimize the effect of bleaching, we must get as much information as possible from every photon that strikes the specimen.

A. STATISTICAL CONSIDERATIONS IN CONFOCAL MICROSCOPY

The photomultiplier tube (PMT) detector used in most laser confocal microscopes is extremely sensitive. It is capable of producing one recordable event for every four to five photons striking it, and as long as it does not get too warm and is shielded from all sources of extraneous light, it has almost no dark current. Using the fast photon counting mode now found on some instruments, useful images can be recorded in which the brightest 2D picture element (pixel) may represent only 25 counts (100 photons) and the dimmest pixel may represent only 2 counts (8 photons).

Even though this performance is impressive, it is important to remember that the visibility of features in any image is limited by a relationship between the contrast intrinsic to the signal from the feature and the statistical uncertainty associated with the number of photons detected from each pixel in the image. Although statistical limitations affect all image-forming systems (and indeed all scientific observations), this topic is discussed here because it may be unfamiliar in the context of imaging. When one records a fluorescent image on photographic film, the number of photons involved is so much greater and the chance of detecting an individual photon is so much less that the topic of photon statistics is seldom explicitly considered. In the discussion that follows, *contrast* refers to a measure of the variation of the signal intensity within the image. It can be thought of as the ratio of the light intensity of the brightest pixel in the specimen to that of the dimmest and should be about 100:1 in a well-stained specimen.

The term *photon statistics* recognizes the fact that a beam of light is actually composed of photons which, as elementary particles, are governed only by Poisson statistics. If one supposes that after many measurements, the mean brightness of a given pixel is found to be 25 counts, random statistical variations ensure that the actual number counted on any given measurement will be in the range of plus or minus one standard deviation from this mean value only 67% of the time. In Poisson statistics, the standard deviation is simply the square root of the mean as long as the mean is not too small, so 67% of the measurements will be in the range of 20–30 counts/pixel and 33% of the measurements will be outside this range!

As a practical matter, a feature that is 1 pixel in size will be recognizable or "visible" to a human observer as being above the statistical "noise" present in the surrounding pixels only if it differs from the mean of the background by 5 standard deviations. In the case noted above, the 25-count feature would be visible only if the average background signal level was about one count per pixel. In other words, the staining of the bright pixel must be about 25 times that of its surroundings if it is to be visible. Fortunately, most features of interest cover more than 1 pixel and, in these circumstances, it is the total number of counts recorded for the whole feature that is relevant to its visibility. As a result, images containing several gray levels can be usefully recorded with no more than 25 counts in the brightest pixel (Fig. 6).

The limitations imposed by counting statistics on feature visibility are immutable and are not affected by linear image processing. Therefore, when imaging specimens having a staining contrast that is lower than 25:1, it is often necessary to average a number of scans to produce a useful image. This process does not literally "remove the noise"; it merely permits more photons to be used and this reduces the statistical variations in each of the 256,000 intensity measurements that make up a 512

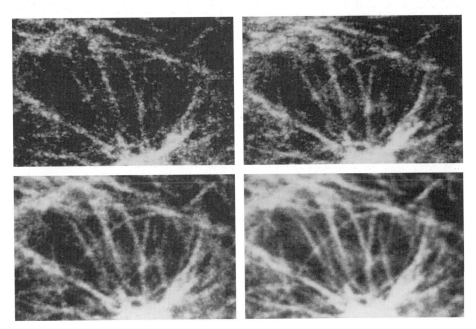

FIGURE 6 Four images made of the same part of a cell labeled with an FITC-conjugated antibody against tubulin, using the Bio-Rad MRC-600 microscope with an ND 4 (10,000:1) filter in front of the laser and with the data collected in the fast photon counting mode. In the top left image, the brightest area represents 16 counts/pixel, whereas the pixels over the microtubules represent about 7–9 counts/pixel. The top right has two times this exposure, the bottom left four times, and the bottom right is an analog image. Clearly, linear features such as microtubules can be recognized even at very low doses. The fast photon counting technique permits optimal extraction of data from the PMT signal when the signal levels are low. Figure 8 shows the bleaching rate of a specimen subjected to this much light.

$\times$ 512-pixel image. Because this process obeys Poisson statistics, $S/N = n/\sqrt{n} = \sqrt{n}$, counting four times as many photons will double S/N, and one will be able to detect features in the image having only half as much contrast. S/N can always be improved by counting more photons but this requires either additional exposure of the specimen to the laser light and therefore more bleaching and phototoxicity or better quantum efficiency (QE) in the detector. Quantum efficiency is a measure of the fraction of photons striking the detector that actually contribute to the signal. It is discussed in some detail by Pawley (1994), and some information on the optimal detectors for the different types of confocal microscope is listed in Table II.

B. PIXEL SIZE

The term *pixel,* introduced earlier, refers to that area of a digital image over which the intensity can be accurately represented by a single number. Normally, each horizontal line of the rectangular scanning raster is divided into either 512, 768, or 1024 subdivisions and each of these subunits represents one pixel. The area of the specimen that is represented by a single pixel depends both on the magnification of the objective and on the adjustment of the zoom setting. The zoom setting controls the magnitude of the current waveforms supplied to the scanning mirrors, and, hence, the size of the raster scanned on the specimen. Smaller currents make the light beam scan over smaller areas of the specimen, producing a higher magnification in the final image as displayed on the computer screen. Larger scan currents produce lower magnification as the raster scanned over the specimen is larger in area.

TABLE II Optimal Photon Detectors for Confocal Microscopes

Feature	Stage scanning	Disk scanning	Laser scanning
Present Advantages	PMT Fast Low dark current	Cooled CCD High QE: 60–80% Large dynamic range Parallel, 2D readout	PMT Fast Low dark current
Limitations	Low QE: 3–20% depending on wavelength	Dark current leakage Electronic noise Slow readout (1–5 sec/frame)	Low QE: 3–20% depending on wavelength
Future Optimized for low signal	Few-element CCD?	Cooled CCD QE = 60–80% Well size = $10^4 e$ Noise = $1e$/pixel Readout speed = 10^6 pixels/sec	Few-element CCD?

Although the ability to arbitrarily change the magnification in this way is usually seen as a great convenience in terms of being able to fit the scanned area to the size of the object of interest, there can be hidden costs associated with the incautious use of this control. As there is a fixed ratio between the size of the raster and the size of an individual pixel, adjusting the zoom control changes the area of the specimen represented by a single intensity value; however, not all possible pixel sizes are capable of recording digital data that retain all of the information present in the original analog image. The Nyquist sampling theorem states that, if the information content of an image is to be retained when a continuous, analog signal from the photodetector is digitized, then the diameter of the area represented by each sampling interval, or pixel (referred to the specimen), must be at least 2.8 times smaller than the optical resolution limit of your system (in x, y, and z).

The optical resolution limit in the $x-y$ plane, δ_{xy}, is set by the Abbé equation:

$$\delta_{xy} = \frac{0.61\lambda}{\text{NA}} \tag{2}$$

This implies that for each λ and objective lens used, there is an "optimal" setting for the zoom control. Equation (1) sets the relationship between δ_z and NA in a similar manner and this value of δ_z should then be used to choose the interplane sampling interval in 3D data sets. Taking 200 nm as a typical value for δ_{xy} for a high-resolution, NA 1.4 objective, a pixel diameter of 200/2.8 = 70 nm is needed to properly sample the data in the $x-y$ plane, and an interplane spacing of 200 nm would adequately sample data in the z direction.

C. PINHOLE SIZE

The diameter of the aperture in front of the photodetector is usually adjustable so that it can be adjusted to match the size of the image of the Airy disk in the pinhole plane that the objective lens projects back from the excited spot in the specimen (Fig. 7). The diameter of this disk is directly proportional to the magnification and, through the Abbé equation, is inversely proportional to the NA of the objective. The area of the central spot of the Airy disk increases by a factor of more than 12 if, for instance, a 10×, NA 0.5 lens is replaced by a 100×, NA 1.3 lens. As the signal that passes through the aperture is generally proportional to its area,

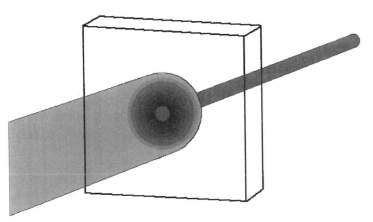

FIGURE 7 Relation between the size of the Airy disk and the diameter of the pinhole: Light from the objective comes from the left. The pinhole should be sized to permit the central maximum of the Airy disk to pass through to the detector.

incorrect adjustment of the pinhole size can significantly reduce the effective sensitivity of the microscope.

There is a second constraint on the choice of pinhole size. Because almost all of the light originating at the plane of focus will pass through a properly aligned pinhole which is the size of the central spot of the Airy disk, one might expect that there could be no reason for ever wanting to use any other aperture size. However, the diameter of the pinhole also affects the spatial resolution of the microscope, both in the $x-y$ plane and in z. If the pinhole is made very small, the $x-y$ resolution of the instrument can be improved by about 40% over that set by the Abbé limit. As the pinhole is made larger so that it accepts a reasonable amount of light, the resolution drops. When it equals the diameter of the Airy disk, almost all of the light originating from the focus plane is accepted, while a 10% gain in $x-y$ resolution is still realized. When it is opened still more, significant amounts of light originating from either above or below the focus plane begin to reach the detector and this reduces the optical sectioning effect while providing even more photons.

Therefore, depending on the particulars of the experiment, it may be preferable either to close the pinhole down to improve spatial resolution or to open it up to collect more signal at somewhat reduced resolution. The latter strategy can be particularly useful when viewing sensitive living specimens because, as these will usually not tolerate the multiple exposures needed to image many closely spaced planes, the reduction in the z resolution is not a serious penalty.

For most specimens, the best compromise between sensitivity and spatial resolution is found by setting the aperture to be equal to the diameter at which the Airy disk reaches 50% of its peak intensity. At this setting, about 80% of the light from the plane of focus will reach the detector and the $x-y$ resolution will still be about 20% better than that produced by the same optics when used in a nonconfocal manner. Basic calculations regarding pinhole diameter and starting values for the Bio-Rad MRC-600 and Molecular Dynamics instruments are included in Table III.

D. BLEACHING

Bleaching occurs whenever a dye is exposed to light. In fixed cells, the rate of bleaching can be markedly reduced by immersing the specimen in a solution containing an antioxidant that minimizes the concentration of free oxygen. These antioxidants can be dissolved in the many types of mounting media available (Harris, 1986). A commonly used mounting medium is buffered glycerol, composed of 90%

TABLE III Relationship between Optimal Pinhole Diameter and Other Instrumental Variables[a]

Manufacturer: Objective lens magnification (NA 1.3):	Bio-Rad/MRC-600 ($M_x = 57$)			Molecular Dynamics ($M_x = 5$)		
	40×	60×	100×	40×	60×	100×
Total magnification with 1.25× fluor module	2850×	4275×	7127×	250×	375×	625×
Spot size at pinhole plane (mm)	0.57	0.85	1.4	50 μm	75 μm	125 μm
Pinhole setting						
Bio-Rad, 0 (in)–15 (out)	0	1	2			
Molecular Dynamics				50 μm	75 μm	125 μm

[a] The optimal pinhole size, d_p, is defined by the equation $d_p = Md_s$, where d_p is the diameter of the pinhole, d_s is the diameter of the focused spot in the specimen, and M is the total magnification of the optical system in between. M includes the magnification of the objective (M_{obj}), of any accessories such as DIC of wide-field fluorescence modules (M_{access}, usually 1.25× each), and of any additional coupling optics such as talon lenses and eyepieces (M_x). The table lists correct settings for the Bio-Rad MRC-600 ($M_x = 57$ w/standard, 8× eyepiece) and the Molecular Dynamics ($M_x = 5$) confocal microscopes, assuming an objective of NA = 1.3 and blue light producing $d_p = 0.2$ μm.

glycerol in 10% phosphate-buffered saline (PBS), pH 7.4. Suggested antioxidants for fixed specimens include 1,4-Diazbicyclo[2.2.2]octane (DABCO, Johnson et al., 1982; Langanger et al., 1983) at a concentration of 100 mg/ml; p-phenylenediamine (Johnson and Nogueira Araujo, 1981; Johnson et al., 1982) at a concentration of 1 mg/ml; and n-propyl gallate (Giloh and Sedat, 1982) at a concentration of 1 mg/ml. An antioxidant that can be used with living material is ascorbic acid. This should be added to the culture medium the day before the experiment and then added fresh just prior to observation. A suggested concentration range is 1–100 μM but should be adjusted so that it does not perturb the physiology. Though antioxidants greatly reduce the problem of bleaching, they do not eliminate it.

To a first approximation, bleaching of a fluorescent dye is proportional to the intensity of the light flux to which the dye is exposed multiplied by the duration of the exposure. If either the pinhole size or the zoom are set incorrectly, the specimen may have to be subjected to a much higher light level than should be necessary to produce an image of a given statistical quality. Although the photodetectors used in confocal microscopes are substantially more sensitive than photographic film, bleaching of the dye is often considered to be a more serious problem in confocal microscopy. There are several possible reasons for this perception:

1. The entire specimen is exposed to the laser illumination even though data are being collected from only a single plane.

2. If 20–50 images are collected from different planes to produce a 3D data set, the dye in the specimen in exposed to 20–50 times more illumination than would have been necessary to record a single plane.

3. The laser represents a light source that is 10^4 to 10^6 times brighter than a mercury source. At low zoom magnification, the scanning mirrors spread this light over the rastered area. As the total amount of light passing through the specimen is not affected by the zoom setting, the intensity seen by the dye is proportional to (zoom mag)^2, so scanning above the Nyquist limit (mentioned above) rapidly, and unnecessarily, increases the rate at which the dye is bleached. This is in contrast to normal wide-field fluorescence where, in general, dose to the specimen does not increase with image magnification because it is limited by the

brightness of the mercury source. In other words, the laser makes rapid bleaching possible, though fortunately(!) not unavoidable.

4. In a misguided attempt to obtain the ultimate in spatial resolution, the user may use pinhole settings that are unrealistically small. The pinhole on the Bio-Rad MRC-600 can be set anywhere between 0.6 and 8 mm in diameter. The difference in area, and hence signal, is about 1:180. The small increase in resolution available is seldom worth such a drastic reduction in signal.

These points are even more important when examining living specimens containing fluorescent substances where the exciting illumination inevitably produces both bleaching and cytotoxicity. Exposing the specimen to more laser power than is absolutely required to make an acceptable image is likely to reduce the biological reliability of the data. In other words, even though using more light may make the image appear more distinct, it will also increase the damage to the object that the image is supposed to represent and, hence, make the data less biologically reliable (Herman and Jacobson, 1989, pp. 173–181).

Circumstances may require small deviations from the benchmark settings of the zoom control and pinhole size given above but this should be done only after considering the potential cost in terms of biological reliability.

E. FLUORESCENCE SATURATION

Generally speaking, light interacts with biological specimens in a linear fashion. In other words, if two times more illumination is used, two times more signal is produced or two images of a given statistical quality can be recorded in the amount of time required to record one at the lower intensity. This happens because the interaction between the specimen and the light does not depend on the intensity of the light flux. Unfortunately, the intensities present in the laser confocal microscope are so high that the fluorescent process can become nonlinear (White *et al.*, 1987; Pawley, 1990, pp. 27–39, 169–178). The process by which a fluorescent molecule absorbs and then reemits a photon takes a finite amount of time. For instance, the emission from fluoroscein is reduced to $1/e$ after about 4 nsec. At the light flux level present when 1 mW of laser power is focused into a 200-nm-diameter spot, the intensity is sufficient to drive almost all of the fluoroscein molecules near the focus point into the excited state. While in the excited state, these molecules will not efficiently absorb additional photons from the exciting light beam. As a result, additional input light cannot lead to more fluorescent output and the dye is said to be "saturated." This nonlinear process has several important implications:

1. Operating at (or even within a factor of 10 of) saturation levels produces data that are nonlinear, distorting the intensities recorded in the image and making the data useless for quantitative image analysis.

2. As most photodamage processes do not saturate, operating near saturation produces relatively more photodamage for the amount of data that is obtained.

3. As the degree of saturation depends on the intensity of the incident light flux, saturation losses are highest at the focus plane where the light beam is narrowest. As a result, an image recorded under conditions that saturate the dye tends to record, as signal, relatively more light from planes that are out of focus. This degrades the *z* resolution.

Saturation can be avoided by using less input power; however, as the rate at which data are produced from the specimen is proportional to the excitation intensity, dye saturation places an absolute limit on the rate at which fluorescence information

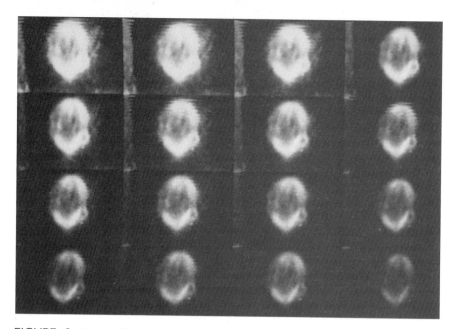

FIGURE 8 Series of confocal images collected of a single plane of an FITC-stained mitotic figure in a sea urchin. The specimen was subjected to the same amount of light between each image. The total light flux deposited by the 16th image in the lower right corresponds to 2000 scans at the illumination level needed to make the top left image in Fig. 5. This demonstrates that bleaching need not be a serious limitation in confocal microscopy.

can be obtained. As the light flux varies with (spot diameter)$^{-2}$, this limit is most severe when the instrument is operating at high spatial resolution (high NA) because this implies a smaller focused spot.

Fortunately, many fluorescent specimens produce adequate images using as little as a few microwatts of laser power, especially if the instrument is operating in a fast photon counting mode. At these levels, it may be possible to make thousands of images before the specimen bleaches (Fig. 8).

(The power of the laser in most systems is about 10 mW, but this is considerably reduced by optical losses and ND filters before it strikes the specimen.)

Because of saturation, one cannot expect both to scan the beam rapidly (for instance, at TV scan rate) and to produce a statistically well-defined, fluorescent, confocal image in a single scan time, unless one also reduces the number of pixels and, therefore, the field of view of each image; i.e., saturation effects place an absolute limit on the number of large-field, high-resolution images that can be obtained from a fluorescent specimen in a given amount of time.

F. CHROMATIC MAGNIFICATION ERROR

The focal length, f, of an objective changes slightly with wavelength. Although an achromatic objective has the same focal length for two wavelengths and an apochromatic objective is corrected for three or four wavelengths, there are still small changes in f at intermediate wavelengths. These are the source of the red or blue halos visible at the periphery of the field of view when a bright-field image is viewed in a conventional light microscope. These are relatively innocuous in normal epifluorescence microscopy because, in this case, a large area of the specimen is illuminated simultaneously and the final fluorescent image is not affected by whether or not the ray that excites a specific dye molecule passes through the objective lens in exactly the same way as does the fluorescent ray leaving it.

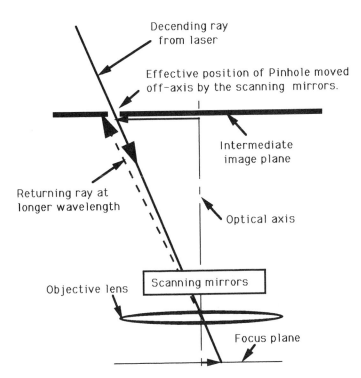

FIGURE 9 The effect of chromatic magnification error on signal level in the confocal microscope. The focal length, and hence the magnification, of any optical system changes with wavelength. Consequently, an off-axis ray of short-wavelength light will not follow the same path as that of a ray of longer-wavelength light originating from the same point. In the laser-scanning confocal microscope, the scanning mirrors are supposed to deflect both the source and the detector pinhole off-axis by the same amount; however, this will not happen (and the image will be darker away from the axis), if the optical system has high chromatic aberration and the system is used for fluorescence, because the exciting and emitting wavelengths may be very different. The problem can be reduced only by using optical systems that are highly corrected for chromatic aberration and by using the field of view as near to the axis as possible.

The confocal microscope is much less forgiving (Pawley, 1990, pp. 27–39). If the exciting and emitted rays do not exactly coincide, the returning light will not pass through the detector aperture (Fig. 9). The image will appear dark is those areas of the image where this misalignment occurs. All the average microscopist can do to reduce this problem is to use only objective lenses having the highest possible chromatic aberration correction and to make sure that these lenses are used correctly.

Two other points are worth mentioning in regard to this second point.

1. In many older microscopes, it was common to correct chromatic aberration in the eyepiece. Objectives from such microscopes that are not used in conjunction with the appropriate correcting eyepieces will demonstrate totally unacceptable levels of chromatic aberration. Generally, one should use only modern, highly corrected objectives for fluorescence confocal microscopy.

2. The magnitude of the displacement caused by the chromatic magnification error is generally proportional to the distance that the point in the image is away from the optical axis. Therefore, the effect will be less severe if imaging is restricted to an area near the center of the field of view.

In addition to the considerations listed above and others listed in Pawley (1990), the instrumentation used for confocal microscopy is far less forgiving than that used for normal light microscopy. Therefore, the operator must take much more care to maintain the optical system at peak performance:

1. Eliminate mechanical vibration, particularly vertical motion between the objective and the specimen, which is far more evident in confocal than in conventional light microscopy.

2. Be sure that the photodetector is shielded from all sources of stray light.

3. Keep the instrument cleaned, aligned, and tested.

Table IV summarizes the performance of a laser-scanning confocal microscope if these precautions are observed.

IV. Summary: The Ultimate Light Microscopy System?

At a fundamental level, there is truth in the saying "To observe is to disturb." This is particularly true of observation of living systems, especially those that have been fluorescently labeled. From this viewpoint, it follows that the best observation system is that which extracts the most information from each photon that strikes the specimen. From a practical point of view, extracting the maximum information from each photon has two aspects: actually detecting each photon in the signal and doing so under conditions that provide as much data about the specimen as possible.

Fortunately, the PMT detector used in most laser-scanning confocal microscopes is at least as good a detector for low signals as that used in video microscopy. However, as the confocal microscope is able to localize each detected photon in three dimensions rather than just two, it extracts more information from each event.

In addition, using a confocal microscope, it is relatively easy to detect and record simultaneously up to four independent signals: fluorescent signals at two different wavelengths, backscattered light, and nonconfocal, transmitted light. Though a similar feat is theoretically possible using nonconfocal instrumentation, it has not yet been done, and in practice, it would be very difficult, if not impossible, to preserve proper pixel alignment between four images recorded on cooled-CCD sensors.

In addition, as noted above, it is more effective to prevent the light emanating from adjacent planes from reaching the detector than it is to "remove" such light later using the 3D image deconvolution procedure. On the other hand, the deconvolution algorithms will provide their best performance when applied to confocal data sets.

For this reason, confocal imaging seems likely to find increasing application in the field of biological microscopy. As the performance of the instrumentation available for performing it begins to approach theoretical limits, it seems certain that confocal microscopy will indeed be found to be the "ultimate" microscopic technique for viewing either living or fixed and stained specimens in three dimensions.

ACKNOWLEDGMENTS

This work was supported by Grant DIR-90-17534 from the U.S. National Science Foundation and Grant DRR-570 from the National Institutes of Health to the Integrated Microscopy Laboratory, Madison, Wisconsin.

TABLE IV Limits in Confocal Microscopy

	Parameters	Limit value
Spatial limits		
Sample rate		
Spatial	Pixel size (Nyquist limit)	x–y 50–80 nm
	Interplane spacing	z 150–1000 nm
	Continuous horizontal scan	"Oval" pixel
Temporal	Image sampled sequentially	Scan time
Optical resolution		
X	Eq. (1), NA, λ, pinhole size	140–200 nm
Y	Eq. (1), NA, λ, pinhole size, oval pixel	140–200 nm
Z	Eq. (2), NA, λ, pinhole size	500–700 nm
Feature position error	Optical distortion	<1% field[a]
	Mirror position error	<1 part in 10^6 [a]
	Vibration in x–y plane	<40 mm[a]
	Vibration in z direction	<150 nm[a]
	Optical misalignment (referred to specimen)	<40 nm[a]
Intensity limits		
Specimen limits:	Fluorescence saturation	<1.0 mW at specimen[a]
	Bleaching/toxicity	Degrades specimen
Intensity, n	Poisson statistics of photons (limits detectable contrast)	S/N t = $\sqrt{n}$
Lost signal (%)	Absorption (in objective, accessory optics)	30–60[b]
	Mirror losses	10–80[b]
	Misfocus/uncorrected objective aberrations	10–80[b]
	Detector quantum efficiency	50–99[b]
	Digitizing errors (improper signal integration)	0–75[b]
Total possible signal loss (%)		≤99.996[b]
Dark signal	PMT noise	300–3000 c/sec
	Stray light	≪PMT noise[a]

[a] These values represent levels above which the listed parameters will begin to reduce performance.
[b] The values listed are realistic and are similar to those listed in Pawley (1990, p. 29) but, fortunately, not inevitable. Significant practical improvements can be and have been made in this area.

REFERENCES

Allen, R. D., and Allen, N. S. (1983) Video-enhanced microscopy with video frame memory. *J. Microsc.* **129**, 3–17.

Bliton, C., Lechleiter, J., and Clapham, D. E. (1993) Optical modifications enabling simultaneous confocal imaging with dyes excited by ultra-violet and the visible-wavelength light. *J. Microsc.* **196**, 15–26.

Brakenhoff, G. J., Blom, P., and Barends, P. (1979) Confocal scanning light microscopy with high aperture immersion lenses. *J. Microsc.* **117**, 219–232.

Cox, I. J., and Sheppard, C. J. R. (1983) Digital image processing of confocal images. *Image Vision Comput.* **1**, 53.

Giloh, H., and Sedat, J. W. (1982) Fluorescence microscopy: Reduced photobleaching of rhodamine and fluorescein protein conjugates by n-propyl gallate. *Science* **217**, 1252–1255.

Harris, J. P. (1986) Cytology and immunocytochemistry. *In "Methods in Cell Biology,"* Vol. 27, pp. 243–262. Academic Press, San Diego.

Hell, S., Reiner, G., Cremer, C., and Stelzer, E. H. K. (1993) Aberrations in confocal fluorescence microscopy induced by mismatches in refractive index. *J. Microsc.* **169,** 391–405.

Herman, B., and Jacobson, K. (eds.) (1989) "Optical Microscopy for Biology," Proceedings of the International Conference on Video Microscopy held in Chapel Hill, North Carolina, June 4–7 1989, pp. 1–641. Wiley–Liss, New York.

Inoue, S. (1986) "Video Microscopy." Plenum Press, New York.

Johnson, G. D., Davidson, R. S., McNamee, K. C., Russel, G., Goodwin, D., and Holbrow, E. J. (1982) Fading of immunofluorescence during microscopy: A study of the phenomenon and its remedy. *J. Immunol. Methods* **55,** 231–242.

Johnson, G. D., and Nogueira Araujo, G. M. (1981) A simple method of reducing the fading of immunofluorescence during microscopy. *J. Immunol. Methods* **43,** 349–350.

Langanger, G., De Mey, J., and Adam, H. (1983) 1,4-Diazobicyclo(2,2,2)-octane (DABCO) retards the fading of immunofluorescence preparations. *Mikroskopie* **40,** 237–241.

Minsky, M. (1957) U.S. Patent No. 3013467: microscopy apparatus.

Minsky, M. (1988) Memoir on inventing the confocal scanning microscope. *Scanning* **10,** 128–138.

Pawley, J. B. (ed.) (1990) "Handbook of Biological Confocal Microscopy." Plenum Press, New York.

Pawley, J. B. (1994) The sources of noise in three-dimensional microscopical data sets. *In* "Three Dimensional Confocal Microscopy: Volume Investigation of Biological Specimens" (J. Stevens, ed.) Academic Press, New York.

Pawley, J. B., Amos, W. B., Dixon, A., and Brelje, T. C. (1993) Simultaneous, non-interfering, collection of optimal fluorescent and backscattered light signals on the MRC-500/600. *Proc. Microsc. Soc. Am.* **51,** 156–157.

Petran, M., Hadravsky, M., Egger, D., and Galambos, R. (1968) Tandem-scanning reflected-light microscope. *J. Opt. Soc. Am.* **58,** 661–664.

Shaw, P. J., and Rawlins, D. J. (1991) The point spread function of a confocal microscope: Its measurement and use in deconvolution of 3D data. *J. Microsc.* **163,** 151–165.

Wang, Y-L, and Taylor, D. L. (eds.) (1989) "Methods in Cell Biology," Vols. 29 and 30. Academic Press, New York.

White, J. G., Amos, W. B., and Fordham, M. (1987) An evaluation of confocal versus conventional imaging of biological structures by fluorescence light microscopy. *J. Cell Biol.* **105,** 41–48.

Caged Fluorescent Probes for Monitoring Cytoskeleton Dynamics

Timothy J. Mitchison, Kenneth E. Sawin, and Julie A. Theriot

I. Introduction

The cytoskeleton consists of microtubules and actin filaments, which are noncovalent polymers of the proteins tubulin and actin, together with intermediate filaments. In many cell types both microtubules and actin filaments are highly dynamic, with polymerization and depolymerization occurring at the polymer ends. Polymerization dynamics are intimately involved in the function of the filaments. For example, polymerization of microtubules at kinetochores is tightly coupled to chromosome movement, and polymerization of actin filaments is tightly coupled to movement of the pathogenic bacterium *Listeria* through the cytoplasm. For microtubules, the predominant form of exchange between monomer and polymer appears to be dynamic instability of plus ends, whereas for actin filaments *in vivo*, the predominant exchange mechanism has not yet been elucidated. Monitoring cytoskeleton dynamics is a first step toward understanding both how cytoskeletal filaments function in a particular motile system and how their spatial organization is controlled.

Fluorescence microscopy provides a sensitive, specific method for following molecules inside living cells. Labeling a filament population uniformly with a fluorochrome such as rhodamine can reveal dynamic behavior of isolated filaments, but cannot reveal filament turnover or movement in situations where filaments are packed together closer than the resolution of the light microscope (ca. 0.2 μm). Such packing is common in motile assemblies such as microtubules in mitotic spindles or actin filaments in lamellipodia. To infer filament dynamics in such assemblies requires an anisotropic label distribution, whose pattern can be followed with time. The classic method for generating anisotropic fluorescent marks is photobleaching. An intense pulse of light at the adsorption wavelength of the fluorochrome is delivered to a specific region, usually from a laser, resulting in local bleaching. The chemistry is poorly characterized, but probably involves generation of chemically active oxygen species that attack and chemically modify the fluorochrome. This chemistry is likely to cause degree of damage to the labeled protein, with polymer breakage and motor-protein arrest among the possible consequences.

We have developed photoactivation of fluorescence as an alternative technology for filament marking. In this technique tubulin or actin monomers are labeled with caged fluorochromes *in vitro* and then incorporated into the cytoskeleton by injection into living cells or addition to reconstituted cytoskeletal assemblies *in vitro*. Local irradiation with 360-nm light triggers an efficient photocleavage reaction with quantum yields around 0.1, generating the active fluorochrome (Fig. 1). The main advantages over photobleaching are (1) the defined, less toxic photochemistry and (2) the signal-to-noise advantage of following a bright mark on a dark background. The main disadvantages are (1) the increased size and hydrophobicity of currently available caged fluorescent probes compared with conventional fluorochromes, (2)

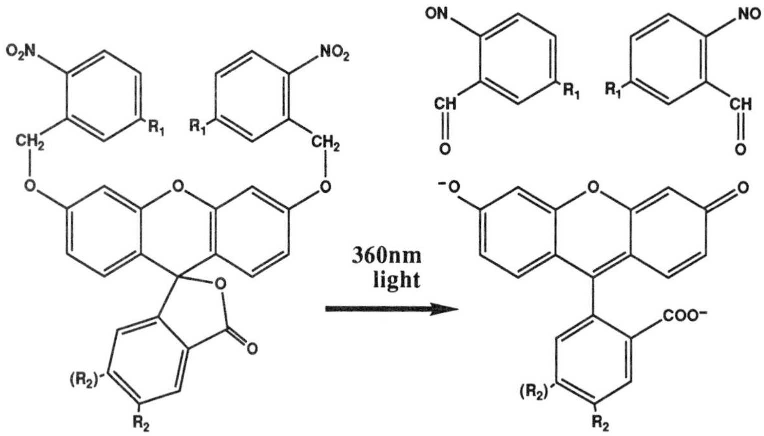

FIGURE 1 Photoactivation of caged fluorescein. Caged fluorescein (left) is nonfluorescent due to trapping of the xanthene chromophore in its lactone tautomer form. Irradiation with 360-nm light leads to release of the nitrobenzyl caging groups as nitrosoaldehydes. A substituted fluorescein (right) is formed. For R groups, see Fig. 2.

the fact that imaging in two fluorescent channels may be required to image both the mark and the whole cytoskeleton, and (3) the possible chemical toxicity of the nitrosoaldehyde side product. At present, applications of the photoactivation method are limited by the limited range of available probe chemistries, so and this article focuses on the properties, limitations, and synthesis of currently useful caged fluorochromes.

II. Caged Fluorochrome Chemistry

To date we have made photoactivable derivatives of three fluorochromes: fluorescein (Figs. 1–4), resorufin (Figs. 5 and 6), and rhodamine (Fig. 7). All the probes use photocleavage of O-nitrobenzyl derivatives in the long-wavelength UV for activation. The caged fluorescein and rhodamine probes are nonfluorescent because the fluorochrome is trapped in its lactone tautomeric state. Caged resorufin is nonfluorescent because the nitrobenzyl ether group causes a blue shift and quenching of the chromophore.

For labeling cytoskeletal polymers (or other proteins) to study dynamics we need to optimize several properties of the caged fluorescent probe molecule:

1. Low or zero fluorescence of caged form
2. Chemical stability, and photochemical stability below the uncaging wavelength, of the caged form of the probe
3. Small size and hydrophilic character of caged form to minimize perturbation of labeled protein
4. Choice of thiol and amine coupling chemistries
5. Good light adsorption and fluorescence yield of the uncaged form of the probe
6. Good photostability of uncaged form

Our first caged fluorochrome, C2CF (Fig. 2), is satisfactory on points 1, 2, and 5, but unsatisfactory for most proteins on point 3. An exception is tubulin, which polymerizes and depolymerizes relatively normally after labeling with this molecule.

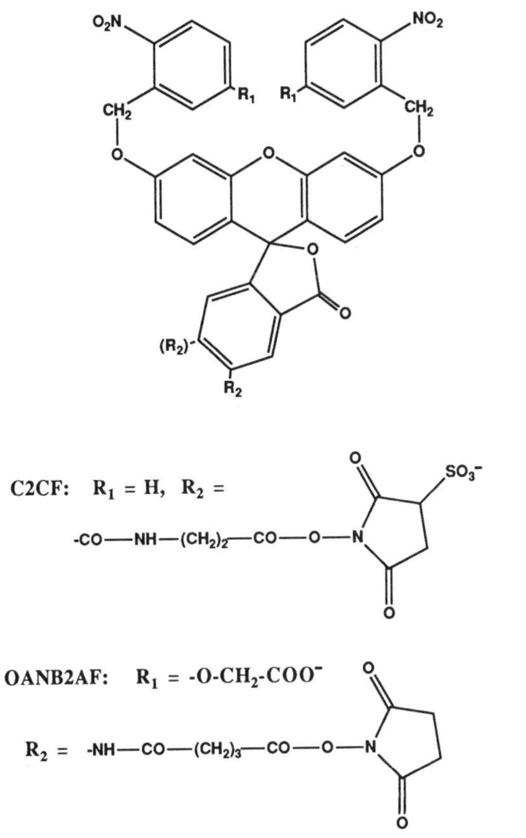

FIGURE 2 Caged fluorescein structures. These active ester probes react with lysine amino groups on proteins. Thiol-reactive iodoacetate derivatives have also been prepared. For carboxyfluorescein derivatives (C2CF), F_2 is a mixture of isomers at the two positions shown. For aminofluorescein derivatives, R_2 is at the unique position shown.

C2CF is too hydrophobic for labeling most proteins, including actin. To address this problem we synthesized OANB2AF, which has negative charges on the caging group and is water soluble (Figs. 2 and 3). This probe, attached to dextran to which nuclear localization peptides were subsequently attached, made a useful lineage tracer in *Drosophila* embryos (Vincent and O'Farrell, 1992). OANB2AF should be suitable for labeling most proteins, though these applications have yet to be extensively explored. Antibodies labeled with 2–4 mole/mole OANB2AF still bind to cellular antigens efficiently and specifically. OANB2AF can easily be prepared as a thiol-reactive iodoacetate derivative by substituting iodoacetic anhydride for the NHS ester in step 9 of Fig. 3.

Preparation of a functional, caged fluorochrome-labeled actin derivative was accomplished with caged resorufin (Fig. 5), presumably because of the smaller size and less hydrophobic character of this probe compared with C2CF. Caged resorufin–actin was used to make a number of observations on actin dynamics. An experiment in which the filaments in the tail of a moving *Listeria* bacterium are marked is shown in Fig. 6. This experiment revealed that the actin filaments induced by the bacterium are stationary in the cytoplasm and are highly dynamic, depolymerizing with a half-life of less than a minute.

Although useful for studying actin dynamics, caged resorufin suffers problems with respect to points 2 and 6 above. The electron-deficient resorufin monoether ring system is subject to nucleophilic attack by thiols (Afanas'eva *et al.*, 1974). We have found that caged resorufin is slowly inactivated by reaction with gluta-thione under physiological conditions, forming a product that photoactivates to

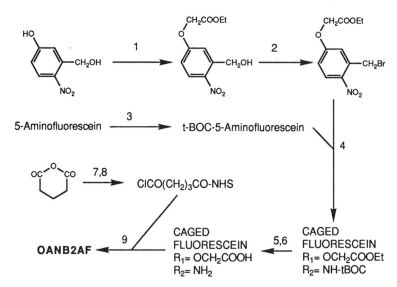

FIGURE 3 Synthesis of OANB2AF. Conditions: (1) $BrCH_2COOC_2H_5$, K_2CO_3, acetone, reflux 12 hr; product recrystallized from CH_2Cl_2/petroleum ether. (2) $SOBr_2$/pyridine/CH_2Cl_2, reflux 1 hr; product recrystallized from CH_2Cl_2/petroleum ether. (3) t-Butyl-pyrocarbonate (excess), DMF, 25°C, 24 hr; product recrystallized from ethyl acetate/CH_2Cl_2. (4) Ag_2O, benzene:THF 2:1, reflux 18 hr; product purified on silica gel column in petroleum ether:acetone 2:1. (5) 5 M KOH:THF:CH_3OH 1:10:10, 25°C, 10 min. (6) CF_3COOH, 25°C, 20 min. (7) N-Hydroxysuccinimide, THF, 25°C, 2 hr. (8) $COCl_2$, THF, 25°C, 12 hr; product used directly or recrystallized from CH_2Cl_2/petroleum ether. (9) 2,6-Lutidine, DMSO, 25°C, 10 min; product collected by precipitation with 0.5 M citric acid at 0°C and centrifugation.

a blue, nonfluorescent chromophore, presumably a thiol adduct. In practice caged resorufin–actin has a half-life of 0.5–2 h *in vivo*, decaying to a form that is nonfluorescent and will not photoactivate to a fluorescent molecule (L. Cramer and T. J. Mitchison, unpublished results). Actin seems to protect the caged fluorochrome, as caged resorufin-labeled dextran decays more quickly.

The most recent synthetic development is caged rhodamine (Fig. 7). This probe should prove superior on points 5 and 6 and reasonable on the other points. The α-carboxy caging groups used in this probe confer both faster photoactivation and increased water solubility compared with simple nitrobenzyl carbamate derivatives. Caged rhodamine is still in the testing stage, but it has the potential to be the most useful probe yet.

III. Synthetic Notes

Synthesis of C2CF is described by Mitchison (1989). OANB2AF is synthesized as diagrammed in Fig. 3. Detailed lab protocols for all syntheses are available on

FIGURE 4 Poleward microtubule flux in the mitotic spindle visualized by local uncaging of C2CF–tubulin. Top and bottom panels show phase-contrast images of the mitotic spindle in a newt lung cell injected in metaphase and early anaphase, respectively. This cell was injected with C2CF–tubulin in prometaphase. The middle four panels show fluorescence in the fluorescein channel (excitation 490 nm, emission 510 nm) after photoactivating with a bar normal to the spindle axis. The time in minutes relative to the photoactivation pulse is shown in the bottom right corner of each panel. The spindle pole is marked with an arrow. Note that marked segments of kinetochore microtubules move steadily poleward, indicating poleward subunit flux. At the same time the segments decrease in brightness as a result of microtubule turnover. For details, see Mitchison and Salmon (1992).

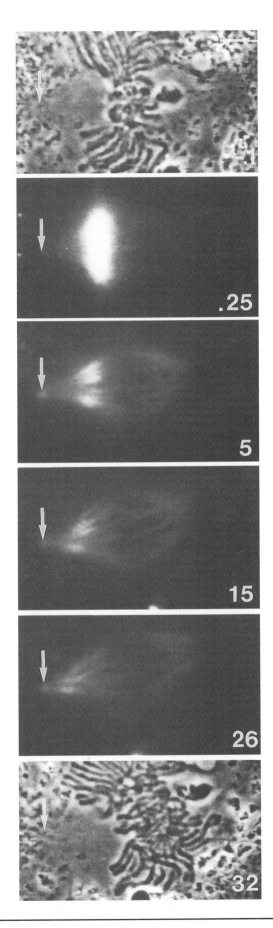

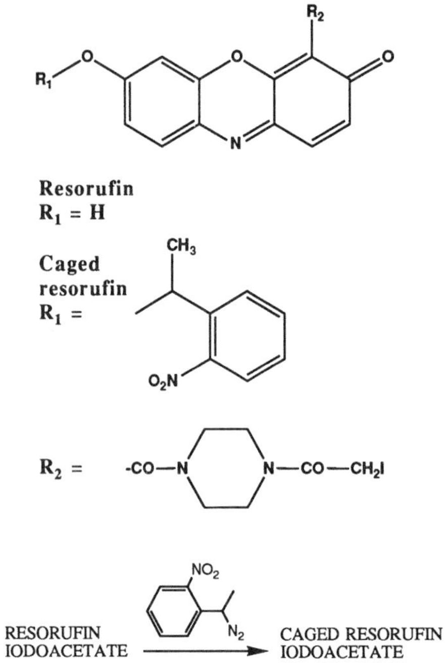

Resorufin
R_1 = H

Caged
resorufin
R_1 =

CH₃ (written as CH$_3$)

O_2N

R_2 = -CO—N⟩⟨N—CO—CH$_2$I

RESORUFIN
IODOACETATE ⟶ CAGED RESORUFIN
IODOACETATE

NO$_2$

N$_2$

FIGURE 5 Caged resorufin. This compound has been used for following actin dynamics. Synthesis is by reaction of resorufin–iodoacetate with 2-diazo-2-(2-nitrophenyl)-ethane.

request. For both caged fluoresceins, the bisalkylation of the fluorescein phenolic hydroxyls (step 4 in Fig. 3) is the key reaction, and it proceeds in rather low yields. The problem is that alkylation of the second phenolic hydroxyl is in competition with alkylation of the o-carboxyl group. Basic conditions promote formation of the ketocarboxy tautomer over the phenol-lactone tautomer, favoring the side reaction. Formation of the bisphenoxyether is achieved under conditions developed by Krafft *et al.* (1988), using silver oxide in a hydrophobic solvent system. C2CF is prepared with the hydrophilic N-hydroxysulfosuccinimide as the leaving group of the active ester. This group makes the probe sufficiently water soluble to allow labeling. Simple NHS esters are easier to make but are not water soluble. Synthesis of caged resorufin, described by Theriot and Mitchison (1991), uses the diazo chemistry of Walker *et al.* (1989) applied to commercial resorufin iodoacetate (Boehringer-Mannheim). Optimal synthesis of caged Q-rhodamine is still under development. The key step is reaction of carboxy-Q-rhodamine with the appropriate protected chloroformate under basic conditions.

IV. Protein Labeling

Tubulin is labeled with C2CF according to a published procedure (Hyman *et al.*, 1991) in which the lysine-reactive probe is added to stabilized microtubules at pH 8.6 and then the labeled tubulin is subject to two cycles of polymerization/ depolymerization to select out active subunits. Recently we have modified this procedure as follows [abbreviations as in Hyman *et al.* (1991)]: (1) The first polymerization step before labeling was promoted with 10% DMSO (v/v) rather than 33% glycerol. (2) Labeling was for 60 min at 37°C. (3) For depolymerization steps, microtubule pellets were resuspended in a minimal volume of IB (50 mM K-glutamate, 0.5 mM MgCl$_2$, pH 6.5) and sonicated carefully until the suspension was no longer turbid. For repolymerization after cold spin, cold supernatants were supplemented with 0.2 vol 5× BRB80 to favor polymerization. These modifications gave

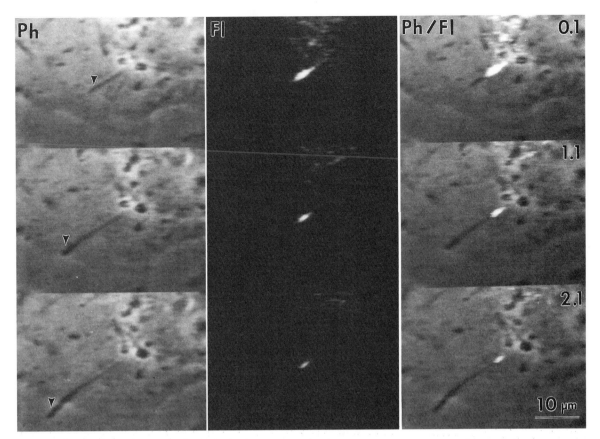

FIGURE 6 Analysis of *Listeria* motility by photoactivation of caged resorufin–actin. The Ph column shows phase-contrast visualization of a *Listeria monocytogenes* bacterium (arrowhead) moving through the cytoplasm of a PtK2 cell that was injected with caged resorufin–actin. The bacterium is propelled by a "comet tail" of actin filaments visible in the phase-contrast image. The FI column shows fluorescence in the resorufin channel (excitation 580 nm, emission 600 nm) after photoactivation of a region of the tail immediately behind the bacterium. The Ph/FI column shows an overlay of the two images. Time in minutes after photoactivation is indicated for each row. Note that the marked actin filaments are stationary while the bacterium moves, indicating that actin filaments are continually nucleated and released during movement. Decreasing fluorescence intensity with time indicates filament depolymerization. For details, see Theriot *et al.* (1992).

improved yield and stoichiometry (0.6 mole C2CF/mole tubulin dimer) relative to previous methods. Photoactivation of C2CF–tubulin in mitotic spindles revealed poleward flux of microtubules (Fig. 4).

Actin is labeled with caged resorufin iodoacetate according to a published procedure (Theriot and Mitchison, 1991). Presumably this results in alkylation of the reactive residue Cys-374. Caged resorufin-labeled actin polymerizes and depolymerizes normally *in vitro* and incorporates normally into the actin cytoskeleton *in vivo*. As caged resorufin is slowly inactivated by exposure to thiols, it is important to keep the concentration of DTT low after the labeling step.

V. Microscopy

Imaging marks made on the cytoskeleton by photoactivation of fluorescence in living cells has the same general instrument requirements as conventional *in vivo* fluorescence observations. These include a fluorescence microscope equipped with

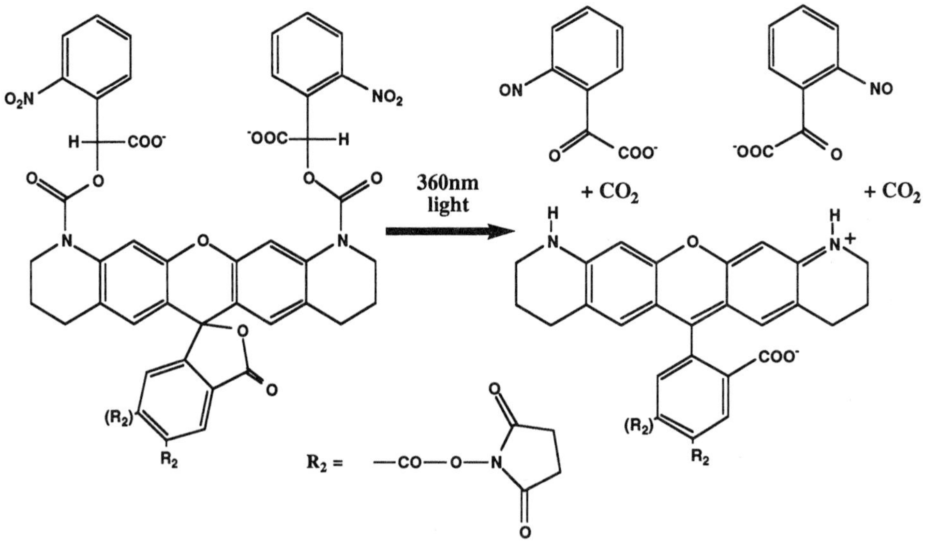

FIGURE 7 Caged Q-rhodamine. The rhodamine derived from 7-hydroxyquinoline (Q-rhodamine) can be caged as the biscarbamate shown. Photolysis releases 2 moles of a nitroso-ketone. The resulting unstable carbamic acid derivative rapidly loses 2 moles of CO_2. The active rhodamine is then generated by the same type of tautomeric shift shown for fluorescein in Fig. 1. Caged Q-rhodamine holds considerable promise as a bright, photostable, water-soluble, caged fluorochrome. Q-Rhodamine in aqueous solution excites at 540 nm and emits at 560 nm with a high quantum efficiency. It is considerably more photostable than fluorescein, behaving similarly to tetramethylrhodamine in both fluorescence and photobleaching properties.

high-numerical-aperture objective lenses, a sensitive electronic camera system, and computer-controlled shutters on the illumination pathways. Although photoactivation of a mark on microtubules does not cause detectable perturbation of spindle function, photobleaching of the resulting fluorescence by the observation light can damage the spindle. Low light levels are thus essential. To be safe, photobleaching of the activated zone should be kept below 5% of the total signal. To determine the level of photobleaching caused by observation light, it is convenient to photoactivate the whole cell and measure its fluorescence as a function of the number of illumination pulses. We have mostly used an ISIT camera in conjunction with image averaging to obtain images. Photoactivation requires a focused beam of long-wavelength UV light for activation in addition to the full-field epi-illumination used to observe the activated signal. We have used the 360-nm line from a 100-W mercury arc lamp for activation, focused onto a variable slit in a conjugate image plane. A detailed description of our apparatus has been published (Sawin *et al.*, 1993). The nitrobenzyl rings of the caged fluorochromes adsorb light in the range 200–400 nm. In practice, photoactivation is best triggered by light in the range 340–400 nm, with the shorter wavelength governed by transmission of the microscope optics and possible cellular damage. Alternative light sources for photoactivation include a small pulsed dye laser, or a cadmium laser operating in the range 340–400 nm, or a high-power, short-pulse titanium–sapphire laser operating at 700–760 nm to activate by two-photon adsorption. The last method should in principle give much better *z* resolution of the marked zone, both from the two-photon effect and because longer-wavelength light is scattered less in biological specimens. Two-photon activation is likely to be the method of choice for photoactivation deep in embryos or other thick systems.

VI. Image Analysis

Two types of information can be extracted from the behavior of a photoactivated area of the cytoskeleton followed over time. Movement of filaments can be detected, and its rate quantitated. Filament turnover can also be determined by measuring the decrease in fluorescence intensity in the marked zone due to diffusion of free subunits after depolymerization. To test whether photobleaching contributes to the observed signal decay it is advisable to measure apparent turnover rates at different levels of observation light, as turnover rate should be independent of this parameter. The ability to detect filament movement depends on movement rate relative to turnover rate. For example we were able to detect poleward movement of microtubules in the kinetochore fibers of tissue culture cells, which turn over slowly (half-life approximately 200 sec), but not in astral microtubules in the same spindles, which turn over quickly (half-life approximately 30 sec) (Mitchison and Salmon, 1992). Astral microtubules may in fact flux, but we cannot detect significant mark movement in the available time window. Increasing the spatial resolution of measurement, for example, with a cooled-CCD camera, would improve our ability to detect movement.

VII. Future Developments

To increase our understanding of cytoskeleton dynamics two types of development are needed. First, we need novel caged fluorochrome probes with improved photostability of the activated form to allow more precise quantitation of *in vivo* dynamics. Second, we need to dissect the biochemical regulation of dynamics using *in vitro* systems, particularly for the actin cytoskeleton where we currently cannot account for rapid dynamics using existing models. Novel caged fluorochromes would also open up new areas of investigation, including dynamic behavior of less abundant proteins in cells, long-term lineage tracing in embryos, and analysis of junctional communication in embryos. We hope that improved and modified probe chemistries will open up these areas in the near future.

ACKNOWLEDGMENTS

We thank R. Haugland, D. Trentham, and R. Tsien for chemistry advice. This work was funded by NIH Grant GM-39565 and by scholarships from the Searle Foundation and Packard Foundation to T.J.M.

REFERENCES

Afanas'eva, G. B., Viktorova, T. S., Pashkevich, K. I., and Postovskii, I. Y. (1974) Research on the chemistry of phenoxazines. VII. Reactions and properties of resorufin and some of its derivatives. *Chem. Heterocyclic Compounds* **10**, 302–306.
Hyman, A. A., Drexel, D., Kellog, D., Salser, S., Sawin, K., Steffen, P., Wordeman, L., and Mitchison, T. J. (1991) Preparation of modified tubulins. *In "Methods in Enzymology"* (R. B. Vallee, ed.), Vol. 196, pp. 478–485. Academic Press, San Diego.
Krafft, G. A., Sutton, W. R., and Cummings, J. P. (1988) Photoactivable fluorophores. 3. Synthesis and photoactivation of fluorogenic difunctionalized fluoresceins. *J. Am. Chem. Soc.* **110**, 301–303.
Mitchison, T. J. (1989) Polewards microtubule flux in the mitotic spindle. *J. Cell Biol.* **109**, 637–652.
Mitchison, T. J., and Salmon, E. D. (1992) Kinetochore fiber movement contributes to anaphase-A in newt lung cells. *J. Cell Biol.* **119**, 569–582.

Sawin, K. E., Theriot, J. A., and Mitchison, T. J. (1993) Photoactivation of fluorescence as a probe for cytoskeletal dynamics in mitosis and cell motility. *In "Fluorescent and Luminescent probes for Biological Activity"* (W. T. Mason, ed.), pp. 405–419. Academic Press, San Diego.

Theriot, J. A., and Mitchison, T. J. (1991) Actin microfilament dynamics in locomoting cells. *Nature* **352**, 126–131.

Theriot, J. A., Mitchison, T. J., Tilney, L. G., and Portnoy, D. A. (1992) The rate of actin-based motility of intracellular *Listeria monocytogenes* equals the rate of actin polymerization. *Nature* **357**, 257–260.

Vincent, J. P., and O'Farrell, P. H. (1992) The state of engrailed expression is not clonally transmitted during early *Drosophila* development. *Cell* **68**, 923–931.

Walker, J. W., Reid, G. P., and Trentham, D. R. (1989) Synthesis and properties of caged nucleotides. *In "Methods in Enzymology"* (S. Fleischer and B. Fleischer, eds.), Vol. 172, pp. 288–301. Academic Press, San Diego.

SECTION C

Video Microscopy

Video-Enhanced Contrast Microscopy

Dieter G. Weiss

I. Introduction

Video contrast enhancement is a technique that considerably improves images obtained by a large variety of video-based imaging systems used in light, electron, and confocal microscopy. It requires a camera system with manually adjustable "gain" and "offset" (also called pedestal or black level by some manufacturers). Much better results are obtained if digital image processing can be applied in addition. In light microscopy, the most striking image improvements are possible if the technique is applied to images obtained by polarized light methods. The principle and the equipment required are described in detail elsewhere (Weiss *et al.,* 1989; Weiss and Maile, 1993).

II. Strategy of Image Generation

Video contrast enhancement of microscopic images obtained using bright-field, dark-field, anaxial illumination, fluorescence, reflected light confocal, or fluorescence confocal optics, rather than differential interference contrast (DIC), is very straightforward. It is performed by following the steps in Table I with the exception of step 4.

Much more striking image improvement is usually gained with DIC and polarization microscopy, but special attention and some explanation are required for step 4. Allen *et al.* (1981a,b) and Inoué (1981, 1989) simultaneously described procedures of video contrast enhancement for polarized-light techniques which differed considerably in their approach but yielded very similar results. Although this is not the place to judge which one is more appropriate, we have to distinguish clearly between the two strategies to avoid confusion.

Allen named his techniques "Allen video-enhanced contrast" differential interference contrast and polarization (AVEC-DIC and AVEC-POL respectively) microscopy. The AVEC techniques involve the introduction of additional bias retardation by setting polarizer and analyzer relatively far away from extinction, to gain a high specimen signal. Allen suggested the use of a de Sénarmont compensator setup (Bennett, 1950) which consists of a quarter-wave plate (specific for the wavelength used) in front of a rotatable analyzer. In DIC microscopy, alternatively but less accurately, the desired bias retardation can also be introduced by shifting the adjustable Wollaston prism. Allen recommended a bias retardation of one-quarter to one-ninth of a wavelength away from extinction, with one-ninth as the best compromise between high signal and minimal diffraction anomaly of the Airy pattern (Allen *et al.,* 1981b). The enormous amount of stray light introduced at such settings is removed by an appropriately large setting of analog and/or digital offset. In AVEC

TABLE I Steps in AVEC-DIC Microscopy

Step	Manipulation	Result
1[a] M[b]	Focus specimen	Image appears
2 M	Adjust microscope correctly for Köhler illumination	Image improves
3 M	Open iris diaphragm fully	Optical image becomes too bright
4 M	Set compensator up to 20° from extinction[c]	Optical image worsens
5 C	Analog-enhance by manually adjusting gain and offset	High-contrast TV image with often disturbing mottle pattern appears
6 M	Defocus or move specimen laterally out of field of view	Object disappears, mottle remains
7 P	Average and store mottle image, then subtract mottle image from incoming video images	Absolutely homogeneous, light gray ("empty") image appears
8 M	Return specimen to focal plane	Clear image appears; if contrast is weak go to step 9
9 P	Contrast-enhance digitally (histogram stretching)	Contrast becomes optimal; if pixel noise is high go to step 10
10 P	Use rolling or jumping averaging or digital filtering	Clear, low-noise, and high-contrast image appears

[a] Before step 1, one should set the "brightness" and "contrast" controls of the monitor showing the processed image to their intermediate positions because the degree of enhancement will not be adequate in the recorded sequence if the monitor had been adjusted to an extreme setting. To use VEC microscopy to its full extent make sure that the microscope objective and condenser front lenses are absolutely clean (check at least once daily) and that the lamp is always optimally adjusted and centered.

[b] The manipulations are performed at the microscope (M), camera control (C), or image processor (P), respectively.

[c] Particles need to appear in DIC microscopy images as if illuminated from above, i.e., with their bright part up, while vacuoles have the opposite shadows. If this is not the case, the camera has to be rotated 180° or the compensator or Wollaston prism has to be set to the opposite side with respect to the extinction position.

Reprinted, with permission, from Weiss and Maile (1993).

microscopy the amount of light required for saturation of the video camera can be adjusted by setting the de Sénarmont compensator or the Wollaston prism further away from extinction, thereby gaining a higher signal but also admitting more stray light. It is most desirable to obtain saturation at a retardation of about one-ninth of a wave (20°) if the microscope–camera–illumination combination does permit it, as this setting provides the best resolution (Hansen et al., 1988). Further opening of the crossed polarizers beyond 20° will rarely improve the image further, but it may introduce amounts of stray light no longer manageable by offset. See Weiss and Maile (1993) for more detailed explanation.

The technique recommended by Inoué, which in this article is called IVEC microscopy for distinction, aims to optically reduce stray light and diffraction anomaly arising from curved lens surfaces and other sources by employing extremely strain-free objectives and the special rectifying lenses developed by Inoué (1961). The latter are commercially available only for few microscopes (some lines of Nikon) and are expensive. Inoué's special optimized microscope (Inoué, 1986) is used at a polarizer setting very close to extinction, which cannot be used for VEC microscopy with many other instruments because insufficient light is passed for near saturation of the video camera.

Thus, in IVEC microscopy, stray light is not admitted, as the polarizers stay close to extinction and the special rectifying optics further reduce the stray light. Consequently filters to reduce brightness are not required. On the contrary, a very bright arc lamp, ideally with a fiberoptic illuminator, is necessary to saturate the camera. The AVEC technique, on the other hand, electronically improves primary optical images characterized by low contrast and relatively high stray light content, arising from a "nonoptimal" optical arrangement. In IVEC microscopy no compromise is made regarding the optics, and consequently less demanding electronic steps are required to rescue the image. The AVEC technique is, however, one that can be used with any good research microscope equipped with commercial film polarizers. The steps required for image generation and improvement by VEC microscopy are summarized in Table I and explained below. They include procedures different from those used in conventional microscopy, which are, however, required for the highest resolution and visualization of subresolution objects. The procedure described is that for AVEC-DIC (see below), but if DIC is not required, step 4 should simply be omitted.

Steps 1–5 of the procedure given here yield the final image, if digital processing is not possible, or if only analog enhancement is required. In this situation, analog enhancement has to be stopped just before the mottle or uneven illumination becomes annoying. Analog shading correction and other types of analog image improvement may be applied, if the camera control unit offers them. The use of a light scrambler and meticulous cleaning of the inner optical surfaces of the microscope and especially the lens surfaces in the projecting system to the camera (eyepiece and camera lens) usually help considerably in permitting high levels of analog enhancement.

III. Sample Preparation

In VEC microscopy the same samples can be used as in conventional light microscopy. Live cells from tissue cultures should preferentially be grown on a cover glass. The specimen's region of interest should be close to the cover glass surface, where the best image is obtained. If the highest magnifications are intended, it may be that the optics can be adjusted for Köhler illumination only at this surface and a few tens of micrometers below (upright microscope), as high-magnification objectives are usually designed for optical imaging of objects at a distance of 170 μm from the front element. Thus, for work with oil immersion objectives it is recommended that a No. 0 cover glass (80–120 μm thick) be used instead of a normal No. 1 cover glass (approx 170 μm thick), as this permits a greater working distance within the specimen. Note, however, that because the oil immersion objective will now be focusing through water, rather than glass, spherical aberration will be introduced. The use of immersion oils of differing refractive indices is recommended to overcome this problem. Alternatively for imaging deep within an aqueous specimen, a water immersion objective may be employed to overcome the problem.

Aqueous samples have to be prevented from drying out by completely sealing the cover glass to the microscope slide. Nail polish may be used for this, or if a live specimen, such as microtubules, extruded cytoplasm, or cultured cells is being observed, VALAP is recommended. This consists of equal parts by weight of vaseline, lanolin, and paraffin (MP 51–53°C); it liquefies at around 65°C. It may be applied around the cover glass with a cotton-tip applicator or fine paint brush, and rapidly hardens. If the specimen is in suspension, sample volumes of no more than 5–7 μl should be used with 22 × 22-mm cover glasses, to produce very thin specimens (ca. 10 μm thick) for best image quality.

If working with an inverted microscope, the specimen slide has to be inverted for fitting to the microscope with the cover glass underneath. With most microscope stages this will interfere with the VALAP sealant, and flat positioning of the slide

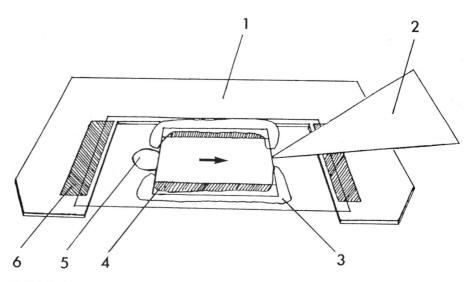

FIGURE 1 Slide preparation suitable for superfusion of live cells or suspension specimens: (1) metal frame; (2) filter paper wick; (3) VALAP sealant; (4) adhesive tape spacer; (5) drop of medium to replace the original medium; (6) adhesive tape. Reprinted, with permission, from Weiss *et al.* (1990).

will not be possible. Instead, use of a metal frame the size of a regular slide and 0.8 to 1 mm thick to hold a sandwich of two cover glasses of dissimilar sizes is recommended (Schnapp, 1986; Weiss *et al.*, 1989, 1990) (Fig. 1).

If a thicker specimen, such as tissue slices, vibratome sections, or nerve bundles, is to be observed, only DIC or anaxial illumination (Kachar, 1985) techniques are recommended. Only the first 10 or 20 μm closest to the objective will yield good images, as the image quality degrades quickly if one focuses deeper into the tissue. The opacity of tissue can be greatly reduced when infrared (IR) or near-infrared light is used (Dodt and Zieglgänsberger, 1990).

IV. Generation of the Image

Step 1: Focusing the specimen.

We find the specimen preferably by looking through the oculars or, alternatively, by looking at reduced magnification at the monitor. Only if the entire specimen consists of subresolution-size material (density gradient fractions, microtubule suspensions, unstained EM sections) will it be difficult to find the specimen plane. Use a relatively dark setting of the condenser diaphragm and/or polarizers or prisms and look for contaminating larger particles. If there are none, routinely apply a fingerprint to one corner of the specimen side of the cover glass and use this for focusing.

Step 2: Adjusting Köhler illumination.

After finding a coarse setting for the illumination, the desired plane for the specimen is selected exactly. Then the condenser is finely adjusted, but now in relation to the image on the monitor (make sure the light is reduced to avoid damage to the camera!). The field diaphragm must be centered on the monitor and opened until it becomes just invisible. If the field diaphragm is opened too much, most microscope–camera adapter tubes or high-power projectives and oculars will create a very annoying central hot spot. If this persists at the adjustment for proper illumination, closing the projective diaphragm or inserting a self-made diaphragm cutting the

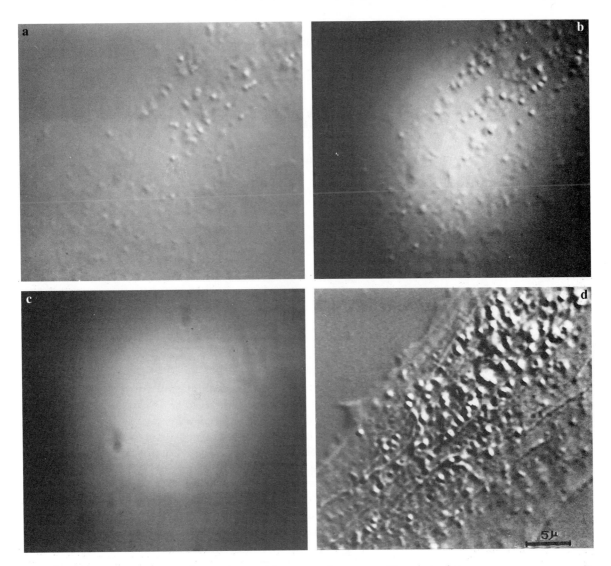

FIGURE 2 VEC microscopy of a specimen with very weak contrast. The steps of image generation and improvement in VEC microscopy are demonstrated using a live cultured cell containing a large number of subresolution-size organelles. a to c demonstrate analog contrast enhancement, and d, digital background subtraction and digital contrast enhancement. (a) In focus, not enhanced; (b) in focus, analog-enhanced; (c) out of focus, with mottle; (d) in focus, mottle subtracted. Microscope: Reichert–Leica Polyvar; processor: Hamamatsu C-1966 Photonic Microscope System. Bar = 5 μm.

peripheral light at the microscope exit usually helps. Note that at the high magnifications and numerical apertures used here, Köhler illumination has to be readjusted once the focus is changed more than a few micrometers.

As we will apply extreme contrast enhancement later, we have to start out with as even an illumination setting as possible. Proper centering of the lamp and setting of the collector lens are therefore important. At high magnifications as much light as possible needs to be collected. Some workers have therefore used critical illumination, that is, focusing the light source onto the specimen plane, instead of Köhler illumination (Schnapp, 1986). This is counter to good microscopical practice and can lead to very uneven illumination because the filament or arc will be superimposed onto the image of the specimen and, subsequently, has to be subtracted digitally by mottle subtraction. Critical illumination might be useful, however, in those cases where the illuminating light is made extremely homogeneous by light scrambling with a light fiber device (Inoué, 1986; Schnapp, 1986; Ellis, 1985) (available from Technical Video Ltd.).

Step 3.

Open the condenser diaphragm fully to use the highest possible numerical aperture to obtain highest resolution. Also, any iris diaphragm of the objective should be fully opened. Be careful to protect the camera from too high light intensity prior to this step. The result of opening the condenser diaphragm will usually be that the optical image worsens because it becomes too bright and flat for the eye. This setting will result in a small depth of focus, especially with DIC (optical sections of 0.3 μm or less with 100× oil objectives). If a large depth of focus is required (e.g., viewing dilute suspensions), the condenser diaphragm can be closed down as desired but preferably not smaller than one-fourth of the aperture of the objective.

Step 4. (polarized light techniques only).

Set the polarizer (AVEC-POL) or the main prism or compensator (AVEC-DIC) to about $\frac{1}{9}\lambda$, i.e., one-ninth of a wavelength. The optical image, that is, the image seen in the oculars, will disappear due to excessive stray light. The illumination may have to be reduced to protect the camera (but not by closing diaphragms).

If you have the accessories for de Sénarmont compensation as recommended by Allen *et al.* (1981a,b), set them at 20° off extinction. The basic setup for de Sénarmont compensation is as follows: Remove both Wollaston prisms and quarter-wave plate from the light path; set analyzer and polarizer to best extinction; insert quarter-wave plate at 0° (best extinction); insert Wollaston prisms and set the adjustible one to best symmetrical extinction (if possible, check with a phase telescope for symmetry of the pattern); use the rotatable analyzer as compensator and set it as desired (one-ninth of a wave is 20°, one-quarter is 45°).

If you do not have such a calibrated system, first determine the distance between extinction (0°) and maximum brightness (90° or one-half of a wavelength) by moving the adjustable Wollaston prism; then estimate and select the ninth of a wave or 20° position. Many microscopes equipped with DIC for biological applications do not allow a phase shift of 90° and some may not even allow 20°, because for observation by eye phase shifts of a few degrees already yield good contrast. Microscope manufacturers will, however, have the proper parts in their mineralogy programs.

At this point you have to make sure that the camera receives the proper amount of light to work near its saturation end. Some manufacturers have red and green LEDs built in to indicate this. Otherwise you should see a moderately modulated image on the monitor; a *very* flat or no image indicates insufficient light. In this case redo the illumination adjustments, possibly while observing the image on the screen to improve, remove any diffusers from the microscope, or go to brighter lamp types. Opening the crossed polarizers beyond 20° will not improve the image. If you have excessive light, reduce it in the case of adjustable lamp types or, with arc lamps, use neutral-density gray or other filters or go a few degrees closer to extinction.

In IVEC microscopy stray light is not admitted; that is, the polarizers stay close to extinction and the special rectifying optics further reduce the straylight. Filters to reduce brightness will not be required, but much brighter lamps will most probably be necessary to saturate the camera.

Step 5: Analog enhancement.

Increase the gain on the camera to obtain good contrast. Then apply offset (pedestal). Always stop before you lose parts of the image that become too dark or too bright. Repeat this procedure several times, if necessary and helpful. Make sure that the monitor for watching the changes is not set to extreme contrast or brightness, and is terminated properly (75-ohm setting). Analog enhancement improves the contrast of the specimen but unfortunately also emphasizes dust particles, uneven illumination, and optical imperfections. These artifacts, called "mottle," are superimposed on the image of the specimen and may in some cases totally obscure it (see Fig. 2). Disturbing contributions from fixed pattern noise (mottle) or excessive amounts in unevenness of illumination (see Fig. 2b) can be tolerated if digital enhancement is performed later.

If digital processing is not possible stop enhancement just before the mottle or uneven illumination becomes annoying. Apply analog shading correction and other types of analog image improvement if your camera control unit offers these features. Thorough cleaning of the inner optical surfaces of the microscope, the oculars, and the camera lens usually results in images that allow the application of considerably higher analog contrast enhancement.

Finding dust: When the imaged dust particles or the mottle pattern rotate when the camera head is rotated, they are in the optical path before the camera, while the immobile dust is to be found on the camera face plate. Rotate the ocular or camera objective lens to find dust located there. Dust should be removed with a low-pressure air gun or an optical cleaning brush. If this does not help use lens paper or a fat-free cotton-tip applicator (wooden stick, not plastic) with ethanol or ether (in the fume hood only!). Work from the center to the periphery in a circular fashion while carefully avoiding to apply pressure. Dust or mottle that is defocused if the specimen is defocused is part of the specimen.

Step 6: Finding a "background" scene.

Try removing the specimen laterally out of the field of view or (when using DIC) defocus to render it just invisible (preferably toward the cover glass). The result is an image containing only the imperfections of your microscope system (mottle pattern) (see Fig. 2c). This step may not be satisfactory, however, with such techniques as phase contrast or bright field.

Step 7: Background (mottle) subtraction.

Store, that is, freeze, the mottle image, preferably averaged over several frames, and subtract it from all incoming video frames.

Step 8.

When returning the specimen to the focal plane, you should see an absolutely even and clean image, which may, however, be weak in contrast. If there are regions "missing" that are gray and flat, there is too much contrast in the raw image to perform proper background subtraction. Reduce gain, adjust offset, and repeat the procedure (see Fig. 2d).

Step 9.

Perform digital enhancement in a similar manner to step 5; that is, alternate between stretching a selected range of gray levels (setting "width") and shifting the image obtained up and down the scale of gray levels (setting "level") until a pleasing result is found. If available on your equipment, display the gray level histogram and select the upper and lower limits, which are to be defined as bright white and saturated black, respectively. If the image is noisy (pixel noise) go to step 10.

Step 10.

Use an averaging function in a rolling (recursive filtering) or jumping mode over two or four frames. This will allow the observation of movements in your specimen, but very fast motions and noise due to pixel fluctuations will be averaged out.

Averaging over a larger number of frames will filter out all undesired motion such as distracting Brownian motion of small particles in suspension. The image will then contain the immobile parts of the object exclusively.

Please note that not all image processors are capable of performing background subtraction and rolling average simultaneously. In this case, averaging generally yields the better image improvement for low light applications (fluorescence), whereas background subtraction is more advantageous in VEC microscopy, although this should be determined experimentally.

Step 11.

A number of procedures for spatial filtering are available that can be used to reduce noise, to enhance edges of objects, or to reduce shading. Some image processors offer such filters at video rate so that live sequences can be accentuated by filtering prior to recording.

Step 12.

For publication purposes, pictures may be photographed or filmed off the video screen by observing special procedures and hints which are discussed in detail by Inoué (1986, Chap. 12) and Weiss *et al.* (1989). Alternatively, video printers can be used that are available with near-photographic or, at higher cost, photographic quality.

V. Interpretation of the Images

Unlike in EM images, which truly resolve the submicroscopic objects depicted, the sizes of objects seen by AVEC-DIC microscopy may not necessarily reflect their real size. When AVEC-DIC is used the limit of true resolution is shifted to almost one-half of that obtained conventionally. Objects smaller than the limit of resolution, that is, 100–250 nm, depending on the optics and the wavelength of light used, are inflated by diffraction to the size of the resolution limit. The orientation of birefringent objects may also somewhat affect their apparent thickness if they are oriented at angles very close to 45° or 135°. Whereas the size of the image does not enable a decision on whether one or several objects of a size smaller than the limit of resolution are present, the contrast sometimes permits this judgment to be made. A pair of microtubules would, for example, have the same thickness as a single one, but the contrast would be about twice as high. If large numbers of subresolution objects are separated by distances of less than 200 nm from each other (e.g., vesicles in a synapse), they will remain invisible, but they will be clearly depicted if they are separated by more than the resolution limit.

Also remember that if in-focus subtraction or averaging is used, the immobile or the moving parts of the specimen, respectively, may have been *completely* removed from the image.

REFERENCES

Allen, R. D., Allen, N. S., and Travis, J. L. (1981a) Video-enhanced contrast, differential interference contrast (AVEC-DIC) microscopy: A new method capable of analyzing microtubule-related motility in the reticulopodial network of *Allogromia laticollaris. Cell Motil.* **1,** 291–302.

Allen, R. D., Travis, J. L., Allen, N. S., and Yilmaz, H. (1981b) Video-enhanced contrast polarization (AVEC-POL) microscopy: A new method applied to the detection of birefringence in the motile reticulopodial network of *Allogromia laticollaris. Cell Motil.* **1,** 275–288.

Bennett, H. S. (1950) Methods applicable to the study of both fresh and fixed materials. The microscopical investigation of biological materials with polarized light. *In* "Handbook of Microscopical Technique" (C. E. McClung, ed.), pp. 591–677. Harper & Row (Hoeber), New York.

Dodt, H. U., and Zieglgänsberger, W. (1990) Visualizing unstained neurons in living brain slices by infrared DIC-video microscopy. *Brain Res.* **537**, 333–336.

Ellis, G. W. (1985) Microscope illuminator with fiber optic source integrator. *J. Cell Biol.* **101**, 83a.

Hansen, E. W., Conchello, J. A., and Allen, R. D. (1988) Restoring image quality in the polarizing microscope: Analysis of the Allen video-enhanced contrast method. *J. Opt. Soc. Am.* **A5**, 1836–1847.

Inoué, S. (1961) Polarizing microscope. *In* "The Encyclopedia of Microscopy" (G. L. Clark, ed.), pp. 480–485. Reinhold, New York.

Inoué, S. (1981) Video image processing greatly enhances contrast, quality, and speed in polarization-based microscopy. *J. Cell Biol.* **89**, 346–356.

Inoué, S. (1986) "Video Microscopy." Plenum Press, New York.

Inoué, S. (1989) Imaging of unresolved objects, superresolution, and precision of distance measurement with video microscopy. *In* "Methods in Cell Biology" (D. L. Taylor and Y-L. Wang, eds.), Vol. 30, ch 3, pp. 85–112. Academic Press, New York.

Kachar, B. (1985) Asymmetric illumination contrast: A method of image formation for video light microscopy. *Science* **277**, 766–768.

Schnapp, B. J. (1986) Viewing single microtubules by video light microscopy. *In* "Methods in Enzymology" (R. B. Vallee, ed.), Vol. 134, pp. 561–573. Academic Press, New York.

Shotton, D. (1993) "Electronic Light Microscopy." Wiley–Liss, New York.

Weiss, D. G., and Maile, W. (1993) Principles, practice, and applications of video-enhanced contrast microscopy. *In* "Electronic Light Microscopy" (D. Shotton, ed.), pp. 105–140. Wiley–Liss, New York.

Weiss, D. G., Maile, W., and Wick, R. A. (1989) Video microscopy. *In* "Light Microscopy in Biology. A Practical Approach" (A. J. Lacey, ed.), pp. 221–278. IRL Press, Oxford.

Weiss, D. G., Meyer, M., and Langford, G. M. (1990) Studying axoplasmic transport by video microscopy and using the squid giant axon as a model system. *In* "Squid as Experimental Animals" (D. L. Gilbert, W. J. Adelman, Jr., and J. M. Arnold, eds.), pp. 303–321. Plenum Press, New York.

SECTION **D**

Confocal Microscopy

Confocal Microscopy of Polarized MDCK Epithelial Cells

Sigrid Reinsch and Ernst H. K. Stelzer

I. Introduction

Confocal laser-scanning microscopy combined with sophisticated image processing techniques allow the cell biologist to explore the three-dimensional infrastructure of the cell (van Meer *et al.*, 1987; White *et al.*, 1987; Wijnaendts-van Resandt *et al.*, 1985). Here we present techniques for sample preparation including fixation, immunofluorescence staining, and filter postfixation and mounting. These techniques have been optimized to preserve the three-dimensional structure of the epithelial kidney cell line (MDCK-II) grown on permeable filter supports and to allow detection of the cytoskeleton, organelles, and nuclei (Fig. 1; Color Plate 14). The protocols described herein have been adapted and modified from Bacallao and Stelzer (1989).

II. Materials and Instrumentation

1. Cells grown on permeable (Costar, 24 mm) polycarbonate filters.
2. Six- or twelve-well tissue culture dishes for fixation and washing steps.
3. Ten-centimeter plastic dish with lid as a humidified incubation chamber for immunofluorescence: Place a strip of wet Whatman filter paper around the outside edge and a piece of Parafilm in the bottom of the chamber (can be held in place with double-stick tape).
4. Glass slides.
5. Coverslips, 24 × 24 mm, No. 1 thickness.
6. Plastic spacers (~3 mm × 7 mm × 30–50 μm, cut from heavyweight plastic bags like those in which tissue culture dishes are supplied).
7. Clear acrylic nail varnish.

Solutions

1. *Phosphate-buffered saline without Ca^{2+}–Mg^{2+} (PBS$^-$):* For washing filters during fixation and immunofluorescence.

2. *40% Paraformaldehyde:* Paraformaldehyde stock solution is based on the description by Robertson *et al.* (1963). Add 40 g of paraformaldehyde (Merck) to 100 ml of H_2O. While continuously stirring, heat the mixture to >67°C. Add a

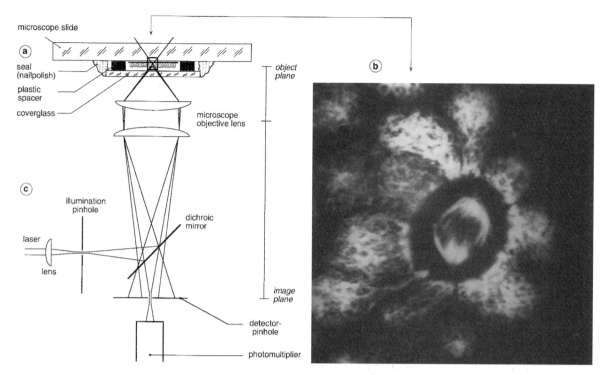

FIGURE 1 Microtubule cytoskeleton of MDCK cells with accompanying confocal microscope configuration. (a) In the object plane is the mounted sample of MDCK cells grown on permeable filter supports. The apical membrane of MDCK cells is oriented toward the microscope objective. (b) A single x/y image of a metaphase MDCK cell surrounded by interphase cells. The microtubules were stained with anti-β-tubulin antibody. The apical dense network of microtubules is clearly seen in the interphase cells. (c) The principal configuration of a confocal fluorescence microscope.

few drops of 6 N NaOH to dissolve the paraformaldehyde. Divide into aliquots and store at −20°C.

3. *Fixative:* In this two-step fixation protocol, 40% paraformaldehyde is diluted to 2–4% into two different buffers:

    a. *80 mM K-Pipes (pH 6.5), 5 mM EGTA, 2 mM MgCl$_2$:* Final concentrations are given; make as a 5× stock, filter-sterilize, and store at 4°C.

    b. *100 mM NaB$_4$O$_7$ (pH 11), 0.2% saponin (Sigma):* Titrate sodium borate (100 mM) to pH 11.0 by adding 6 N NaOH. Add saponin along with paraformaldehyde just before use.

Immediately prior to use, thaw aliquots of 40% paraformaldehyde by warming in a water bath (do not allow to boil). Dilute the paraformaldehyde to 2–4% in both the K-Pipes (diluted from 5× stock to 1×) and sodium borate buffers. Bring the pH of the K-Pipes buffer to 6.5 with 1 N HCl after the paraformaldehyde has been added.

4. *Quench solution:* 1 mg/ml NaBH$_4$ (Sigma) in PBS⁻, pH 8.0. Store NaBH$_4$ desiccated, preferably under N$_2$. Add a few drops of 6 N NaOH to PBS⁻ to adjust to pH 8.0.

5. *Immunofluorescence blocking, washing, and antibody dilution buffer:* PBS containing 0.2% fish skin gelatin (Amersham).

6. *DNase-free RNase:* Bring RNase H (Sigma) to 1 mg/ml in PBS (pH 7.0).

Incubate at 95°C for 15 min to inactivate the DNase. Aliquot and store at −20°C.

7. *Propidium iodide (PI):* Store as a 5 mg/ml stock solution in DMSO at −20°C. Dilute the stock to 0.05 μg/ml in 10 mM Tris, pH 7.6, 150 mM NaCl for use.

8. *Mounting medium:* 50% glycerol/2× PBS/0.1% NaN$_3$/100 mg/ml 1,4-diazabicyclo[2.2.2]octane (DABCO, Sigma).

III. Procedures

A. FIXATION

The pH-shift paraformaldehyde fixation is a variation of the method described by Berod *et al.* (1981).

Steps

1. Pour off the medium in the apical well of the filter.

2. Dip the filters in 80 mM K-Pipes, pH 6.5, 5 mM EGTA, 2 mM MgCl$_2$ prewarmed to 37°C.

3. Add 3 ml 3% formaldehyde in 80 mM K-Pipes, pH 6.5, 5 mM EGTA, 2 mM MgCl$_2$ to the basal chamber of the filter in a six-well dish, and add 2 ml fixative on the apical surface of the cells. Incubate the cells with agitation on a rotary table at room temperature for 5 min.

4. Remove the formaldehyde/K-Pipes solution. Add 3 ml 3% formaldehyde in 100 mM NaB$_4$O$_7$ (pH 11) to the basal side and 2 ml to the apical side of each filter. Incubate with agitation on a rotary table at room temperature for 10 min.

5. Weigh out two 10-mg aliquots of NaBH$_4$ for each filter to conical tubes with a screw cap.

6. Remove the fixation solution. Wash the filters by successively dipping the filters in three beakers containing PBS.

7. Dissolve an aliquot of NaBH$_4$ in 10 ml PBS, pH 8.0 (final concentration of NaBH$_4$ should be 1 mg/ml). Rotate the solution briefly and add the solution to the apical (2 ml) and basal (3 ml) portions of the filters. Incubate for 15 min while shaking the filters on a rotary table (longer incubations are not harmful). Repeat this step once more using a fresh solution of NaBH$_4$/PBS$^-$, pH 8.0.

8. Wash the filters by successively dipping them in three beakers containing PBS. The filters can be stored overnight at 4°C or longer if azide is added to the PBS. As formaldehyde crosslinks can reverse with time, the longer the sample is stored, the more it will deteriorate.

9. Permeabilize the sample with PBS/0.1% Triton X-100 if internal antigens of the cell are to be observed. For staining of only surface antigens, omit this step. Wash for 5 min in PBS.

B. IMMUNOFLUORESCENCE STAINING

In this procedure fish skin gelatin (FSG) is used as a blocking agent instead of albumin.

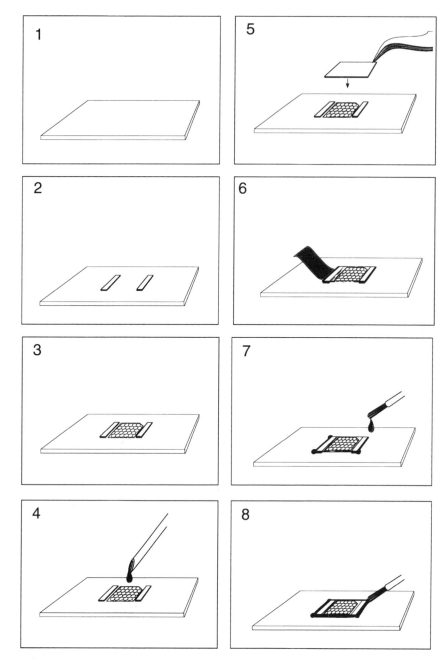

FIGURE 2

Steps

1. Cut the filter from the plastic holder. Be sure to note the side of the filter on which the cells are layered. Cut the filter into squares using a sharp scalpel or fine scissors and keeping the filter wet with PBS while cutting. A good method of ensuring that the cell side of the filter can be readily identified is to cut a notch in the upper right corner (Fig. 2). The filter is cut into squares, as this tends to give a flat field of cells after mounting. Dividing a filter into wedges with one rounded edge causes the filter to ripple during mounting of the specimen and results in cells oriented vertically and horizontally in the same focal plane.

2. Wash the filter squares in PBS containing 0.2% FSG and the appropriate

percentage of detergent in a six-well plate. All washes are in 3 ml of solution, at room temperature, with agitation. Unless otherwise stated, the filters are washed for 15 min after every change of washing buffer.

3. Place a 50-μl drop of the first antibody diluted in PBS containing 0.2% FSG on the Parafilm in the humidified chamber. (The volume of antibody solution depends on the size of the filter square; use more or less depending on the size.)

4. Place a filter square, cell side down, on the antibody solution. Add additional antibody solution to the top of filter. Cover the petri dish to form a small, humidified chamber. The edges of the dish can be sealed with Parafilm to ensure that the antibody solution does not evaporate during the incubation.

5. Incubate at 37°C for at least 1 hr (for specimens thinner than 10 μm, 35 min is adequate). The incubation can also be done overnight at room temperature.

6. Wash the filter three times with PBS containing 0.2% FSG.

7. Add the second antibody as described for the first antibody and repeat steps 5 and 6.

8. Incubate 5 min in PBS containing 0.1% Triton X-100.

9. Wash twice in PBS for 5 min each time.

The filter squares are ready for mounting or for staining with propidium iodide to detect DNA.

C. DNA STAINING WITH PROPIDIUM IODIDE

Propidium iodide (PI) stains both DNA and RNA. It excites maximally at 536 nm and has an emission maximum of 617 nm. Rhodamine filter sets can be used to observe PI-stained samples. This protocol includes an RNase digestion step, to decrease the cytoplasmic background from RNA. The amount of PI to use varies with the confocal setup used (i.e., the particular filters and laser lines used) and the intensity of the fluorescein signal of the other antibody. If the signal from the PI bleeds into the fluorescein channel, stain with a lower concentration of the dye and/ or for shorter times. We have also successfully combined propidium iodide staining with staining for γ-tubulin using a Texas red or rhodamine secondary antibody. This allows simultaneous visualization of nuclei and centrosomes in one epifluorescence channel on the confocal microscope. This is only useful for antigens with discrete localization, well separated from the nucleus.

Steps

1. Incubate with RNase (1 mg/ml in PBS pH 7.0) for 30 min at room temperature.

2. Incubate with 40 μl of propidium iodide (0.05–0.2 μg/ml in 10 mM Tris, pH 7.6, 150 mM NaCl) for 30 min at room temperature.

3. Wash in PBS three times for 5 min.

D. MOUNTING THE SAMPLE

Refer to Fig. 2.

Steps

1. Use a clean, dust-free slide to mount the samples.

2. Place two plastic spacers (approximately 3 × 7 mm × 30–50 μm) on a

microscope slide to make support mounts for a coverslip. Most research institutes have mechanical workshops with a micrometer which can be used to measure the thickness of the plastic used to make spacers. The spacers should be only 10–15 μm thicker than the sample (for MDCK cells plated on Costar polycarbonate filters, 20 μm (cell height) + 10 μm (filter thickness) = 30 μm).

3. Place the filter square on the slide between the two spacers, making sure that the cells face up.

4. Place a drop of mounting medium (50% glycerol, 2× PBS, 0.1% NaN_3, 100 mg/ml DABCO) on the filter.

5. Carefully place the coverslip over the filter. Avoid trapping air bubbles in the specimen mount.

6. Aspirate the excess mounting medium or wick the excess away with tissue.

7. Place a drop of clear acrylic nail polish in each corner of the coverslip and allow it to harden briefly.

8. Seal the coverslip to the slide with additional nail varnish. The specimen should be viewed within 24–48 hr, as these are not permanent mounts. Semipermanent samples can be made by postfixing the filter for 30 min with 4% paraformaldehyde in PBS at room temperature, followed by quenching with 50 mM NH_4Cl in PBS for 15 min.

IV. Comments

In general, thick samples like MDCK cells grown on filter supports require more concentrated antibodies for immunofluorescence than flat samples grown on glass coverslips. First titrate the antibody on cells grown on coverslips, and then try doubling the optimal concentration for the incubation on filter-grown cells. In particular, we found that especially for abundant antigens like tubulin, it is important to apply antibody solution to both sides of the filter and to incubate overnight. We often add fresh primary antibody the following morning and incubate for an additional hour at 37°C before continuing with the washing steps and secondary antibody application. Formaldehyde fixation is not permanent; the crosslinks slowly reverse in aqueous buffers. Therefore, the samples should be stained and observed within a short period of fixation. For immunofluorescence staining with two antigens, it is important to titrate the antibody staining such that the signals in the two channels are fairly equivalent; then bleed-through from one channel to the other is less likely to occur. This is also dependent on the optical characteristics of the epifluorescence filters. We found that a 3% solution of paraformaldehyde was adequate for preserving both the structures and antigenic determinants of a wide variety of cell organelles, e.g., microtubules, centrosomes, Golgi apparatus, zonula occludens, and bromodeoxyuridine incorporated into DNA (Reinsch and Karsenti, 1994; Bacallao et al., 1989; Stelzer et al., 1988). The specific problems of observing thick specimens in a confocal fluorescence microscope are discussed elsewhere (Hell et al., 1993).

REFERENCES

Bacallao, R., Antony, C., Dotti, C., Karsenti, E., Stelzer, E. H. K., and Simons, K. (1989) The subcellular organization of MDCK cells during the formation of a polarized epithelium. *J. Cell Biol.* **109**, 2817–2832.
Bacallao, R., and Stelzer, E. H. K. (1989) Preservation of biological specimens for observation in a confocal fluorescence microscope and operational principles of confocal fluorescence

microscopy. *In* "Methods in Cell Biology," Vol. 31, pp. 437–452. Academic Press, San Diego.

Berod, A., Hartman, B. K., and Pujol, J. F. (1981) Importance of fixation in immunohisto-chemistry: Use of formaldehyde solutions at variable pH for the localization of tyrosine hydroxylase. *J. Histochem. Cytochem.* **29**, 844–850.

Hell, S., Reiner, G., Cremer, C., and Stelzer, E. H. K. (1993) Aberrations in confocal fluores-cence microscopy induced by mismatches in refractive index. *J. Microsc.* **169**, 391–405.

Reinsch, S. and Karsenti, E. (1994) Orientation of spindle axis and distribution of plasma membrane proteins during cell division in polarized MDCKII cells. *J. Cell Biol*, in press.

Robertson, J. D., Bodenheimer, T. S., and Stage, D. E. (1963) Ultrastructure of Mauthner cell synapses and nodes in goldfish brains. *J. Cell Biol.* **19**, 159–199.

Stelzer, E. H. K., Bomsel, M., and Bacallao, B. (1988) Confocal fluorescence microscopy of epithelial cells. *In* "Optical Microscopy for Biology" (B. Herman and K. Jacobson, eds.), pp. 45–57. Wiley–Liss, New York.

Van Meer, G., Stelzer, E. H. K., Wijnaendts-van Resandt, R. W., and Simons, K. (1987) Sorting of lipids in epithelial (MDCK) cells. *J. Cell Biol.* **105**, 1623–1635.

White, J. G., Amos, W. B., and Fordham, M. (1987) An evaluation of confocal versus conventional imaging of biological structures by fluorescence light microscopy. *J. Cell Biol.* **105**, 41–48.

Wijnaendts-van Resandt, R. W., Marsman, H. J. B., Kaplan, R., Davoust, J., Stelzer, E. H. K., and Stricker, R. (1985) Optical fluorescence microscopy in three dimensions: Microto-moscopy. *J. Microsc. (Oxford)* **138**, 29–34.

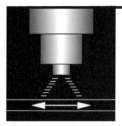

Real-Time Confocal Microscopy and Cell Biology

Alan Boyde, Colin Gray, and Sheila Jones

I. Introduction

Video-rate (or faster) confocal scanning light microscopy (CSLM) may have advantages in the investigation of both live and fixed cells. A few years ago, it would have been a daunting prospect to find any form of CSLM, never mind one that scans so fast that the scanning is no longer intrusive. At the time of this writing, slow-scan CSLMs could be found in all well-equipped cell biology laboratories, where they are used to exploit the power of spot-focused laser light in exciting fluorescence from an immunotag. Confocality, or the property of focusing an apertured detector on the same small volume that is most intensely irradiated at the crossover of the optical beam, is in fact not the most important advantage of the commercially distributed slow CSLMs. This is because the cell biologist is so used to working with isolated cells (or sections) which are physically thin that there is no imperative need for optical sectioning. Even a marginal improvement in axial resolution (the same thing as a small reduction in the depth of field) will suffice for much work.

This is not true when working with bulk tissues, including views into the living animal (vital microscopy), and for work with thick tissue slices and organ culture. True confocal microscopy then has advantages that are truly revolutionary.

The original idea of biological CSLM was to enable the user to do the minimum in specimen preparation. All standard approaches apply, but with special provisos and considerations concerning the choice of instrument and objective lens.

II. Definition

Taken literally, real time would mean a continuous image formation process that could be visualized at any time. As the process is scanning, then such a real image does not exist at any one time, but it may exist within such a short time interval as to make no practical difference. What is this time interval? The cine frame interval or the TV frame interval is commonly accepted to satisfy the definition "real time."

Disk scanning confocal microscopes (originally called tandem scanning microscopes) give frame rates very much faster than those of TV and cine. Information can be sampled from a point or a line at a high frequency in a conventional slow-scan instrument. We do not include such xT, yT, or zT scans in the present working definition.

III. Advantages

Compared with confocal systems, which cannot be considered to be real time, the main advantages are realized if we are looking at moving cells or rapidly moving parts of cells. We can also scan more fields per unit time and thus more efficiently scan through and across the sample.

With fixed cells, another advantage can ensue from being able to through-focus rapidly, obtaining digital images from which the maximum brightness at each pixel in a through-focus pass can be determined and thus used to generate both *max* intensity (all in focus) and *map* images. Because the axial (vertical or z) resolution is excellent in confocal microscopy, the vertical resolution of such a mapping procedure depends on the number of z levels sampled. If many measurements have to be made, then fast scanning is an important advantage. The mapping method provides the means to measure the volumes of (metal-coated, freeze-dried) cells on flat substrates.

Some disk scanning microscopes can produce a frame rate so fast that the specimen can also be scanned rapidly in z (through focus) at the same time it is scanned very rapidly in the x−y plane. This gives rise to an instantaneous and controlled increase in the depth of field. A further important advantage for rapid scanning comes from minimizing the beam damage to the sample for photosensitive samples.

IV. Objective Lenses

You may examine any standard light microscopical preparation, but the optical sectioning property of a confocal microscope depends on the numerical aperture (NA) of the lens, which will, in most practical configurations, be both the condensor (illuminating) and objective (collecting, detecting) lens. Cell biologists used to working with the high contrast but poor resolving power of phase-contrast microscopy must face several facts:

1. An existing supply of lenses may not suffice.
2. Plastic dish bottoms are too thick for the short working distance (WD) of high-NA lenses.
3. It is messy to use immersion media (oil or glycerine) with inverted microscopes and conventional tissue culture plasticware.
4. Coverslips are highly recommended over culture plasticware.
5. Coverslip thickness is important for water immersion lenses, or no no-coverslip (NCS) water immersion (WI) lenses must be used.
6. WI objectives are essential if one is interested in a true image more than 10 μm deep to the coverslip.
7. Optical sectioning with epi-illumination means that the optical path length is doubled.
8. The longitudinal chromatic aberration of the lens is important, both for fluorescence CSLM with any type of instrument and for reflection work with instruments illuminated with conventional white light sources.

V. Choice of Real-Time Confocal Microscope

There are several different means of obtaining rapid scanning that satisfy the criterion that only unit volumes in the sample be illuminated and synchronously "detected." There are some important shortcuts. It is not absolutely necessary, in practice, that the illuminated points be separated in both directions: efficient working instruments have been produced that use a line of illumination such as would be produced by imaging a slit into the focal plane in the specimen, and/or use a line of detectors such as a linear CCD array or a slit detector. It is now commonly accepted that slit scanning be included within a broadened definition of the practical meaning of "confocal."

A. DISK SCANNING MICROSCOPES: TSMs

The first successful type of rapid-scan confocal microscopy was originally called the tandem scanning microscope (TSM), because illumination and detection are scanned in tandem. (The definition includes all confocal microscopes.) Arrays of holes in opposite sides of a disk function to produce a line of illumination spots and a line of detection apertures as the disk rotates. Such two-sided disks are very efficient at removing the surplus unwanted light that strikes the opaque portions of the disk. The constraints for aligning such a two-sided TSM instrument (e.g., Noran Inc. TSM, Plzen TSM) are much tighter than for those that use only one set of holes in both illumination and detection (in one side of the disk, hence one-sided TSM; also properly called the autocollimation TSM, e.g., Newport Instruments VX100 confocal adaptor and Technical Instruments K2 Bios confocal attachment).

In the case of scanning aperture microscopes, it may be particularly important for the objective to have high magnification as well as high NA to be able to image any given aperture size at a smaller size in the specimen plane.

Larger holes in the disk will make it less "confocal"; i.e., it will have a greater depth of field. Exactly the same thing will be achieved by increasing the size of the detector pinhole in a slow-scan CSLM. Given that the function of the aperture disk is to block out light that is not used, then larger holes at a given spacing will produce a brighter image for a given illumination intensity. Small holes are in this sense less efficient, but the instrument is "more confocal." In the two-sided TSM, the constraints for aligning the instrument are decreased by making the holes larger. With small holes, one can use more holes and therefore have more scanned lines (more pixels) and an improved image.

In the limiting case, the amount of light passing the instrument may be reduced to the extent where no reasonable conventional light source would provide sufficient illumination intensity and an image intensifying camera will have to be used to capture the image (Tandem Scanning Corporation TSM).

The holes may be replaced with slits, which make for much greater transmissivity of the disks, so that the light is used more efficiently; this may be important in biological fluorescence applications. Scanning disk microscopes with slits and conventional sources such as mercury and xenon arc lamps give real-time colored fluorescence images that are confocal (high axial discrimination) and as bright as could be desired.

A considerable advantage of the one-sided TSM configuration is that the transmissivity of the disk, the size of the holes, the number of the holes, or the dimensions of slits can be changed at different radial zones in the disk. By moving the disk, while it is still scanning, it is possible to change the "confocality" in inverse proportion to the efficiency of the use of light. This is done in the Newport Instruments VX100 confocal adaptor and the Technical Instruments K2 Bios confocal attachment.

The disk scanning instruments use conventional sources: white light sources give real color in the image if the object is fluorescent or if it reflects light at different wavelengths with different intensities. The TSMs may be used with any conventional mode such as, for example, transmitted polarized light, phase contrast, or conventional epifluorescence at the same time that the confocal imaging mode is running.

For measurement of either motion or the third dimension, it is necessary to be able to record the image; therefore, the faster-than-video-rate image has to be converted to a photographic or a video image.

B. LASER-BASED RAPID-SCANNING CONFOCAL MICROSCOPE SYSTEMS

1. Acousto-optic Scanning Instruments

Scanning only one beam fast enough to generate at least a TV rate image can be achieved through acousto-optic deflection (AOD). An AOD device can be used to scan the frame axis, the line axis not actually being scanned, but originating from a beam broadened using a cylindrical lens. An array of detectors can simultaneously select light from all the conceptual points in the line (Lasertec Corporation 1LM21). Alternatively, the AOD device is used to scan on the line axis and a rapidly scanning galvanometer mirror mechanism is used to scan the frame axis (Odyssey, Noran Inc.).

The Lasertec instrument uses the 633-nm red line of a low-power helium/neon laser. The arrangement is so compact that it fits into a box no larger than many video cameras, adapting to the phototube port of a standard optical microscope. It can be used only in reflection mode. Reflections from within living tissues are too weak to be of practical use; however, the interference reflection mode image arising from focal planes extremely close to the contact of cells with an optically flat substrate, such as glass or plastic, has strong contrasts and can be used with live cells.

The Odyssey instrument usually uses an argon ion laser with the strongest line at 488 nm. It is even more suitable for use with live cells in reflection, as it can handle the lower intensity reflections found from intracellular organelles well away from strongly reflective backgrounds. It can also be used in conventional fluorescence work. An AOD can only be used to descan light of the same wavelength as the exciting light. The configuration can be perfectly confocal in reflection, but in fluorescence the light has to be directed to a detector before being descanned on the line axis by the AOD. The detector must therefore have a slit aperture, and the Odyssey is "slit confocal" in fluorescence. In practice, this really makes no important difference.

2. Galvanometer Slit Scanning for Fluorescence

In the direct view in fluorescence instruments represented by InSIGHT of Meridian Inc. and the DVC250 of Bio-Rad Laboratories Ltd., a line is scanned by a galvanometer system and the detector is essentially a slit. These systems have an advantage over TSMs if one can choose a laser line, with its inherent high intensity, to suit the excitation of a particular fluorophore. The real fluorescent image can be viewed, but as laser light is entering the instrument, the reflection image has to be viewed with a video camera.

C. MORE ABOUT CHOICES

Disk scanning microscopes using incoherent white light sources are generally better than the laser-illuminated instruments in reflection mode. Laser-illuminated instruments are generally better than white light-illuminated TSMs in fluorescence.

For laser instruments, the red He/Ne laser line at 633 nm is satisfactory for most reflection work and the improvement in resolution that could be achieved by using a shorter wavelength is not missed. Red lasers are considered to be very safe. For fluorescence work at a single wavelength, the blue-green 488-nm line of the argon ion laser is preferred in the majority of practical cases. It may be more important to separate output wavelengths than to excite them separately.

The temporal resolution of a unitary beam scanning confocal laser microscope is quite extraordinary. Information is only read into the image at the moment which the laser beam strikes the corresponding point in the focused on plane in the specimen. For a 512^2 image, the temporal resolution will be 512^2 times faster than in the conventional video camera case, where information is accumulated into every pixel during the entire frame capture period, with the exception of the moment when the particular pixel is read out. For neighboring pixels in the frame direction, the temporal interval is (in the European case) 1/25th sec. That it is not 1/50th sec is due to the use of the interlaced field mode for scanning.

To overcome the problem of noise in fast fluorescence scanning some small amount of frame averaging may be necessary, but averaging four or eight frames may make an important improvement. The time necessary to do this is still far less than it takes to obtain a single slow scan in a conventional CSLM.

The interference reflection mode gives particularly strong contrasts in confocal instruments. The resolution is a great improvement over the conventional phase-contrast and other interference methods used in the microscopy of living cells. These other methods can be used simultaneously.

D. GUESSTIMATES OF THE DOLLAR INVESTMENT

1. *Two-sided TSM:* Probable cost $20,000 to $50,000. A one-sided TSM conversion system for an existing microscope will cost $10,000 to $25,000.

2. *Video camera:* For use with same, or slow readout, integrating cooled-CCD camera for single frame capture, from $3000 to $30,000.

3. *Odyssey:* From $70,000 as a video-rate confocal camera to $200,000 as a complex including a "workstation."

4. *InSight or DVC250:* $60,000, again upward as far as you wish to expand the computing and image analysis side.

5. *Video tape recorder or digital disc recorder:* $500 to $200,000.

6. *Lasertec 2LM series:* $100,000; with SIS image analysis software for (cell) volume measurement, around $150,000.

7. *Image analysis station:* If purchased separately from the CSLM, $10,000 and up.

8. *Massive image storage potential on magnetic or magneto-optical or optical disks:* For example, $7000 for the drive unit and $400 each 650-MegaByte disk.

9. *60/1.4 oil immersion lens:* For example, Nikon, $3000.

10. *40/0.75 water immersion lens:* Zeiss, ca. $900; Lomo, ca. $50.

11. *20/0.75 dry objective for coverslip use:* For example, Nikon, $1200.

12. *Other oil immersion, glycerine immersion, and water immersion lenses.*

VI. Specimen Preparation

1. Live cells are seeded onto flat substrates such as coverslips in or the surface of the plastic in petri dishes. The dish must be large enough to accommodate a

WI lens and to permit translation to reach any desired region on the substrate. If no NCS-corrected lens is available, place a coverslip in the bottom of a dish in which cells are used.

2. Live small tissue slices and explants must be fixed to the bottom of a petri dish. This may be achieved by weighting them down with a glass coverslip, when a coverslip-corrected WI lens may be used. Stainless-steel washers may be used to restrain tissue slices for examination with NCS WI lenses.

3. Live cells on coverslips are best sealed into a "chamber" (of any standard form, including a well slide) such that the deep surface of the coverslip is viewed using a high-NA oil immersion objective. Focus only into the region next to the coverslip. Spherical aberration will wreck the image if you try to work at any distance into a watery sample using the wrong type of lens. This is another interpretation of "oil and water do not mix"; yet another concerns the need to use coverslips that are large enough to avoid contact between the oil of an oil immersion lens and the tissue culture medium at the edge of the coverslip (or any oil-soluble sealant used to fix the coverslip to the slide). High-NA immersion lenses tend to have broad front faces.

4. For interference reflection work to view the finest details of intracellular organelle motion and motility of the cell periphery, you will want to use the highest-NA lens (e.g., Nikon 60/1.4 OI with a laser beam instrument like the Odyssey, or Nikon 100/1.4 OI with a TSM). With Odyssey, zoom up the magnification (cut down the area of the scanned field) to concentrate attention on the subject of interest.

5. For live cell fluorescence work, you will require the range of dyes you wish to explore. These include those to (a) label the ambient medium, e.g., fluorescein and fluorescein–dextrans; (b) label mitochondria more than other organelles, e.g., DASPMI; (c) label DNA, e.g., propidium and ethidium and Hoechst dyes; and (d) study specific ionic concentrations. Here, the ratio dyes are unsuitable for real-time confocal work, and one would prefer, for example, fluo-3 for calcium waves in beating cardiac myocytes.

REFERENCES

Boyde, A., and Jones, S. J. (1992) Real time confocal microscopy. *Binary Computing Microbiol.* **4**, 119–123.

Vesely, P., Jones, S. J., and Boyde, A. (1992) Video-rate confocal reflection microscopy of neoplastic cells: Rate of intracellular movement characteristic of neoplastic cell-line (RSK4) with high degree of growth independence in vitro. *Scanning* **15**, 43–47.

SECTION **E**

Electron Microscopy

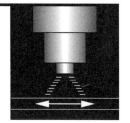

Fixation of Cells and Tissues for Transmission Electron Microscopy

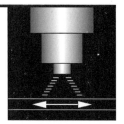

Arvid B. Maunsbach

I. Introduction

Chemical fixation is the first step in most procedures for the preparation of cells and tissues for transmission electron microscopy. It is a very critical step because the quality of fixation is of fundamental importance to the results of electron microscopical analysis. The main purposes of chemical fixation are to stop metabolic processes, to preserve cellular fine structure, and to stabilize the cells for subsequent steps in the preparatory procedure. In some studies care must also be taken to preserve enzyme activity, tissue antigenicity, or both. The choice of chemical fixation procedure requires careful consideration of three main factors:

1. Selection of the fixing agent itself, e.g., glutaraldehyde, formaldehyde, osmium tetroxide, or mixtures or sequences thereof

2. Selection of the proper vehicle for the fixative, e.g., choice of buffer, pH, added salts or other substances

3. Selection of the procedure for applying the fixative to the cells or tissues

No single standard fixation method is suitable for all types of cells and tissues. On the contrary, the above three factors usually have to be adjusted for each specific cell type, tissue, or experimental situation, and consequently, a very large number of fixation procedures have been described. The literature on chemical fixation for electron microscopy is voluminous (see, e.g., Glauert, 1975; Griffiths, 1993; Hayat, 1981; Maunsbach, 1966a; Robards and Wilson, 1993; Sabatini *et al.,* 1963; Sjöstrand, 1989). It is nevertheless possible to point at some general principles and procedures with wide applicability. This article describes such procedures that we have found useful for different applications in cell biology in our laboratory.

II. Materials and Instrumentation

Agar (Merck Art 1615)

Glutaraldehyde, 25% aqueous stock solution (EM grade, Merck Art 4239)

Sodium cacodylate ($C_2H_6AsNaO_2 \cdot 3H_2O$, Merck Art 820670)

Osmium(VIII) tetroxide (OsO_4, Johnson Matthey Materials Technology)

Paraformaldehyde powder (Merck Art 4005)

Operating table

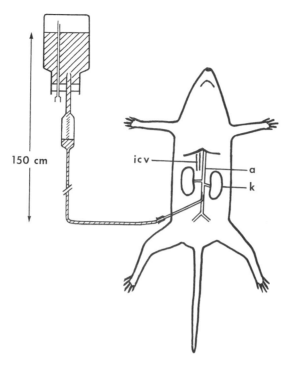

FIGURE 1 Schematic drawing of perfusion fixation of rat kidney through the abdominal aorta. The flask with the fixative and the drip chamber is placed about 150 cm above the animal. a, aorta; icv, inferior caval vein; k, kidney.

Anesthetic

Scissors, forceps, scalpels, and clamps for surgical procedures

Small forceps with fine claws

Gauze swabs

Plastic petri dishes

Thin razor blades

Vials (5–10 ml) with lids for specimens

Gloves

Short-beveled syringe needle for perfusion of aorta, length about 50 mm, outer diameter 1.3–1.5 mm

Blunt syringe needle for heart perfusion, length about 100 mm, outer diameter 2.0–2.4 mm

Perfusion set with drip chamber as used for intravenous blood infusions

Flask to which the perfusion set fits

Syringe needle (10–15 cm thick) to ventilate the flask

Stand to hold the fixative flask upside down about 150 cm above the operating table

Adequate ventilation

III. Procedures

For many purposes adequate fixation is obtained by simple immersion of small tissue pieces into the fixative solution. This is the only mode of fixation possible for many tissues and, e.g., for biopsies; however, a more rapid and uniform fixation is usually obtained if the fixative solution is perfused via the vascular system, either through the heart or through the abdominal aorta (Fig. 1) or in some cases through the venous system. Perfusion fixation (Fig. 2a) should be preferred over immersion fixation (Figs. 2b, 5) whenever possible. For most tissues 1% glutaraldehyde is sufficient for general ultrastructural studies (Fig. 3a). This concentration does not require a preceding rinse of the vascular system with a salt solution. For cytochemical or immunocytochemical studies, 4% formaldehyde plus 0.1% glutaraldehyde is preferable (Fig. 3b), but the glutaraldehyde should be omitted if the enzymes or antigens are inhibited by glutaraldehyde (Fig. 4a).

A. PERFUSION FIXATION THROUGH THE ABDOMINAL AORTA

The following procedure (Maunsbach, 1966a) results in efficient fixation of kidney, liver, pancreas, and small intestines. In the kidney, which is very sensitive to variations in the mode of application of the fixative, it preserves open tubules and normal relationships between tubule cells. The procedure is described for rats but can also be adapted for other animals.

Solutions

1. *0.2 M Sodium cacodylate buffer:* To make 1000 ml dissolve 42.8 g sodium cacodylate in 900 ml of distilled water. Adjust pH to 7.2 with 1 N HCl. Complete to 1000 ml with distilled water.

2. *0.1 M Sodium cacodylate buffer:* Dilute 0.2 M sodium cacodylate buffer with an equal amount of distilled water.

3. *1% Glutaraldehyde in 0.1 M sodium cacodylate buffer:* To make 500 ml of fixative solution mix 250 ml 0.2 M sodium cacodylate buffer and 20 ml 25% aqueous glutaraldehyde and add distilled water to 480 ml. Adjust pH to 7.2 with 0.1 N NaOH or 0.1 N HCl. Complete with distilled water to 500 ml.

4. *20% Stock solution of formaldehyde:* To make 100 ml solution mix 20 g of paraformaldehyde powder with 80 ml of distilled water in a glass flask. Heat to 60°C while gently agitating the milky solution. Add 1 N sodium hydroxide dropwise until the solution clears up. Complete to 100 ml with distilled water. This procedure should be carried out in a well-ventilated hood and with protection for the face. The solution can be stored for a few days in the refrigerator.

5. *4% Formaldehyde, 0.1% glutaraldehyde in 0.1 M sodium cacodylate buffer for immunocytochemistry:* To make 500 ml solution, mix 100 ml of 20% formaldehyde stock solution, 2 ml 25% glutaraldehyde, and 250 ml 0.2 M sodium cacodylate buffer. Add distilled water to 480 ml. Adjust pH to 7.2 with 0.1 N NaOH or 0.1 N HCl. Complete with distilled water to 500 ml. For sensitive antigens omit the glutaraldehyde.

6. *2% Osmium tetroxide stock solution:* One gram of crystalline osmium tetroxide is delivered preweighed in closed glass ampoules. Wash the ampoule carefully and score the vial around its perimeter with a diamond or a fine file. Break the vial cautiously and empty the crystals into 50 ml of distilled water in a glass vial with a tight lid. The crystals dissolve very slowly and the solution should be prepared at least the day before use. Shaking and ultrasonic treatment speed up the process. All steps should be carried out in a well-ventilated hood. Always wear gloves when handling osmium tetroxide solutions. The solution is stable if kept in the cold and protected from strong light.

7. *1% buffered osmium tetroxide:* To make 10 ml fixative solution, mix 5 ml of 0.2 M cacodylate buffer and 5 ml of 2% osmium tetroxide stock solution.

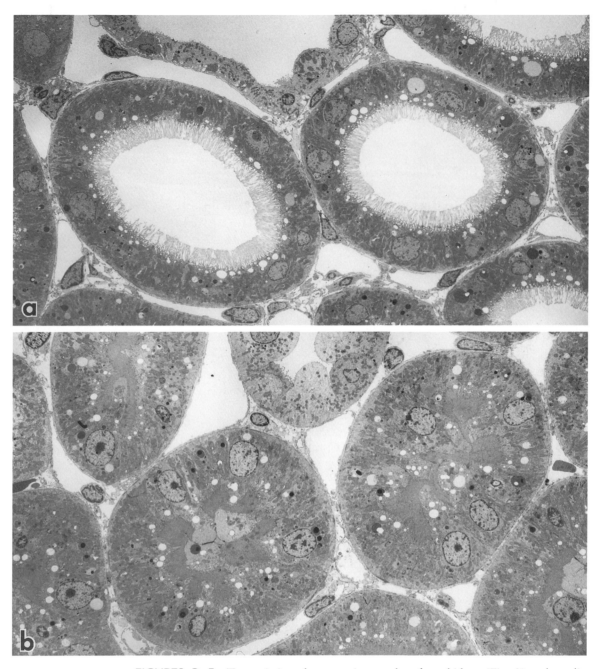

FIGURES 2–5 Transmission electron micrographs of rat kidney (Fig. 2) and rat liver (Figs. 3–5) fixed with different aldehyde fixatives and fixative application methods. Following aldehyde fixation and buffer rinse, all specimens were postfixed for 1 hr in 1% osmium tetroxide in 0.1 M cacodylate buffer, block-stained with 1% uranyl acetate in sodium maleate buffer at pH 5.5, dehydrated in ethanol, and embedded in Epon resin. All sections were double-stained with uranyl acetate and lead citrate.

FIGURE 2 (a) Rat kidney cortex perfusion-fixed through the abdominal aorta with 1% glutaraldehyde. Tubule lumens are open and brush borders of proximal tubules uniformly arranged. (b) Rat kidney cortex immersion-fixed with 1% glutaraldehyde. All proximal tubules are collapsed, with portions of cytoplasm occupying the tubule lumen, and nuclei have moved away from the basement membrane. 1200×.

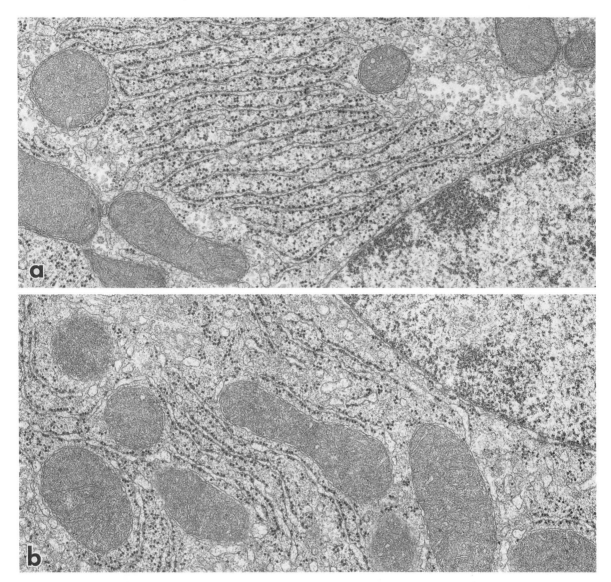

FIGURE 3   Parts of rat liver cells perfusion-fixed through the heart with 1% glutaraldehyde (a) and 4% formaldehyde plus 0.1% glutaraldehyde (b). Cell ultrastructure is similar but focal expansions of the endoplasmic reticulum occur in (b). 32,500×.

Steps

1. Place the closed flask containing the fixative upside down about 150 cm above the aortic level of the animal. The fixative has room temperature.

2. Connect the flask to the perfusion needle via the administration set for intravenous solutions and ventilate the flask.

3. The needle is 1.3–1.5 mm in outer diameter for a 300-g rat and proportionally smaller for lighter animals. The needle is bent at an angle of about 45° with the beveled side out (i.e., down during perfusion).

4. Connect the perfusion needle via the infusion set to the flask containing the fixative. Check that there are no air bubbles in the tubing of the infusion set.

5. Fix the anesthetized animal onto the operating table with its back down. No artificial respiration is used.

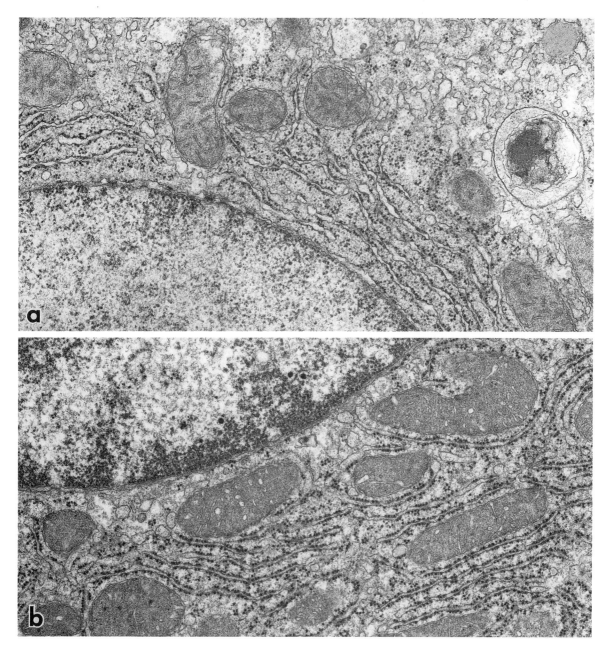

FIGURE 4   Rat liver cells perfusion-fixed with 4% formaldehyde (a) and 2.5% glutaraldehyde plus 2% formaldehyde (b). In (a) the endoplasmic reticulum shows irregular expansions, and some mitochondria appear distended with lightly stained matrix. In (b) mitochondrial matrix is densely stained and membranes of the endoplasmic reticulum parallel. 32,500×.

6. Open the abdominal cavity by a long midline incision with lateral extension, and move the intestines gently to the left side of the animal.

7. Carefully expose the aorta below the origin of the renal arteries and very gently free the aorta from overlaying adipose and connective tissues.

8. Hold the wall of the aorta firmly with the fine forceps with claws about 0.5–1.0 cm from its distal bifurcation. Insert the bent needle close to the forceps toward the heart into the lumen of the aorta (with the beveled side of the tip down).

9. In very rapid succession (a) cut a hole in the inferior caval vein with fine

scissors, (b) start the perfusion, and (c) clamp the aorta below the diaphragm, but above the origin of the renal arteries. When performing these manipulations accuracy and speed are essential and the fixation procedure is preferably carried out by two persons. It is particularly important to clamp the aorta rapidly after the perfusion has been started. This is most easily done by compressing the aorta toward the posterior wall of the peritoneal cavity with a finger (wear gloves) which is then replaced by a clamp. Finally, cut the aorta above the compression.

10. The kidney surface must blanch *immediately* and show a uniform, pale color. The flow rate should be at least 60–100 ml/min for an adult rat. Perfuse for 3 min. Stop the perfusion and excise and trim the tissues with a razor blade. Store the tissue in vials and immersion-fix in the same fixative for 2 hr.

11. Rinse the tissue 2× 30 min in 0.1 *M* sodium cacodylate buffer.

12. Postfix the tissue in 1% osmium tetroxide for 1 hr in the cold. Swirl the vial occasionally to secure uniform penetration of the fixative.

13. Rinse 2× 30 min in 0.1 *M* sodium cacodylate buffer. The tissue is now ready for dehydration and embedding.

B. PERFUSION FIXATION THROUGH THE HEART

The following procedure provides fixation of most rat organs with 1% glutaraldehyde. For some organs the glutaraldehyde concentration should be increased (e.g., to 5% for the brain) and the fixative preceded by a brief rinse with a balanced salt solution such as Tyrode's. For immunocytochemistry use the 4% paraformaldehyde plus 0.1% glutaraldehyde solution.

Solutions

1. *1% Glutaraldehyde in 0.1 M sodium cacodylate buffer:* See Section A.

2. *4% Formaldehyde plus 0.1% glutaraldehyde in 0.1 M sodium cacodylate buffer:* See Section A.

3. *0.1 M Sodium cacodylate buffer:* See Section A.

Steps

1. Place the closed flask containing the fixative upside down about 150 cm above the aortic level of the animal.

2. Connect the perfusion needle via the infusion set to the flask containing the fixative and ventilate the flask. Check that there are no air bubbles in the tubing of the infusion set.

3. Fix the anesthetized animal onto the operating table with its back down.

4. Open the thoracic cavity of the animal without giving artificial respiration.

5. Grasp the heart close to its apex with a forceps. Cut a small hole in the wall of the left ventricle close to the apex with fine scissors. Rapidly insert a blunt syringe needle (2.0–2.4 mm in outer diameter for a 300-g rat and proportionally smaller for lighter animals) and move it into the ascending aorta. Place a clamp on the aorta to hold the needle.

6. Cut a hole in the right atrium of the heart and start the perfusion immediately.

7. Check the flow rate in the drip chamber and flask. The flow rate should be at least 150 ml/min for an adult rat. Perfuse for 3 min. Stop the perfusion and remove pieces of tissue. Subdivide the tissue and fix it additionally for 2 hr in the same fixative.

8. Proceed as described above for perfusion fixation through the abdominal aorta, steps 11–13.

C. IMMERSION FIXATION

Immersion fixation of tissues for general ultrastructural studies is carried out with 1% glutaraldehyde for small tissue blocks (Fig. 5). If the tissue in one dimension is about 0.5 mm or more, the concentration should be increased to 3%, which is recommended, for example, for renal biopsies. For large specimens an alternative solution is the 2% formaldehyde plus 2.5% glutaraldehyde fixative (Fig. 4b). For immunocytochemical studies use the 4% formaldehyde plus 0.1% glutaraldehyde fixative. If the antigen is very sensitive to fixation omit the glutaraldehyde.

Solutions

1. *1% Glutaraldehyde in 0.1 M sodium cacodylate buffer:* See Section A.

2. *3% Glutaraldehyde in 0.1 M sodium cacodylate buffer:* To make 100 ml of fixative solution mix 50 ml 0.2 M sodium cacodylate buffer and 12 ml 25% aqueous glutaraldehyde and add distilled water to 90 ml. Adjust pH to 7.2 with 0.1 N NaOH or 0.1 N HCl. Complete with distilled water to 100 ml.

3. *4% Formaldehyde plus 0.1% glutaraldehyde in 0.1 M sodium cacodylate buffer:* See Section A.

4. *2% Formaldehyde plus 2.5% glutaraldehyde in 0.1 M sodium cacodylate buffer,* often referred to as half-strength "Karnovsky's fixative" (Karnovsky, 1965): To make 250 ml fixative solution, mix 25 ml 25% aqueous glutaraldehyde stock solution, 25 ml 20% formaldehyde stock solution, and 125 ml 0.2 M sodium cacodylate buffer. Add distilled water to about 240 ml and adjust pH to 7.2 with 0.1 N NaOH or 0.1 N HCl. Complete with distilled water to 250 ml.

5. *1% Osmium tetroxide in 0.1 M sodium cacodylate buffer:* See Section A.

6. *0.1 M Sodium cacodylate buffer:* See Section A.

Steps

1. Cut out a piece of tissue from the organ under study and place it in a precold, empty petri dish.

2. Hold the tissue gently with forceps and cut thin slices with a thin razor blade using sawing movements. The slices should not exceed 0.5 mm in thickness. Great care should be taken not to strain the tissue mechanically. Areas where the forceps have touched the tissue should be discarded.

3. Trim the slices to less than 0.5 × 5 × 5 mm and immerse them into the fixative solution.

4. Swirl the vial occassionally during fixation to secure uniform penetration of the fixative from all sides into the tissue. Fixation should last for at least 2 hr. In most cases the temperature of the fixative is not important. Initial fixation can be carried out at room temperature and followed by fixation in the cold.

5. Trim down the dimensions of the tissue slices while in the fixative solution to obtain small blocks suitable for embedding.

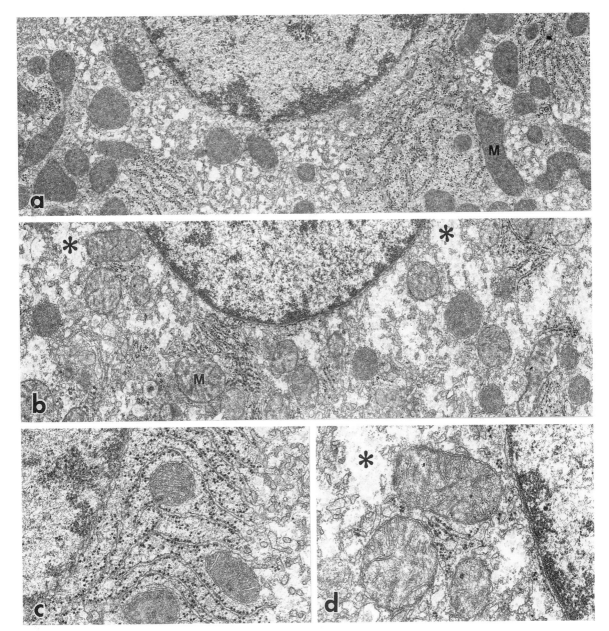

FIGURE 5 Liver cells fixed by immersion in 1% glutaraldehyde and observed in a section cut at a right angle to the liver surface. The cell in (a) is located at the very surface of the liver, whereas the cell in (b) is located about 200 μm from the surface and thus fixed with some delay. Part of the cytoplasm of the superficial cell is shown in (c) and part of the interior cell in (b) is shown at high magnification in (d). Cytoplasm of the interior cells shows evidence of cell swelling with almost empty regions (*). Mitochondria (M) are well preserved in (a) but dilated with partly empty matrix in (b). (a, b) 15,000×, (c, d) 32,500×.

6. Proceed as described above for perfusion fixation through the abdominal aorta, steps 11–13.

D. FIXATION OF TISSUE CULTURES

Solutions

1. *2% Glutaraldehyde in 0.1 M sodium cacodylate buffer:* To make 100 ml, mix 50 ml 0.2 M sodium cacodylate buffer, 8 ml 25% glutaraldehyde, and 30 ml

distilled water. Adjust pH to 7.2 with 0.1 N NaOH or 0.1 N HCl. Complete with distilled water to 100 ml.

    2. *0.1 M sodium cacodylate buffer:* See Section A.

Steps

1. Gently decant the tissue culture medium.
2. Immediately add 2% glutaraldehyde in 0.1 mM cacodylate buffer. Very gently swirl the fixative in the culture dish.
3. Fix for 2 hr.
4. Proceed as described above for perfusion fixation through the aorta, steps 11–13.

E. FIXATION OF CELL SUSPENSIONS

Solutions

1. *2% Glutaraldehyde in 0.1 M sodium caocdylate buffer:* See Section D.
2. *2% Agar in 0.1 M sodium cacodylate buffer:* Dissolve during stirring 2 g agar in 100 ml 0.1 M sodium cacodylate buffer. Heat to close to 100°C until dissolved.

Steps

    1. Mix the cell suspension rapidly with an equal volume of 2% glutaraldehyde in 0.1 M cacodylate buffer.

    2. Fix for 2 hr.

    3. Sediment the cells in a centrifuge tube by centrifugation at approximately 1000 g for 5 min. Decant the supernatant.

    4. Resuspend the cells in an excess of 0.1 M cacodylate buffer. Repeat step 3 after 15 min.

    5. Add 1% osmium tetroxide in 0.1 M cacodylate buffer and resuspend the cells. Fix for 30 min. Repeat step 3.

    6. Add 0.1 M sodium cacodylate buffer and resuspend the cells. Repeat step 3.

    7. To the pellet add an equal volume of 2% agar in 0.1 M sodium cacodylate buffer, which has been heated to about 40°C. Mix the agar and the pellet rapidly with a fine glass rod. Allow the pellet to cool. Thereafter treat the pellet as a tissue block during dehydration and further processing. Take care not to resuspend the cells.

IV. Comments

Chemicals used in fixation for electron microscopy, notably the aldehydes, osmium tetroxide, and cacodylate, are toxic and should be handled with adequate safety precautions, including gloves and good ventilation. Exposure to formaldehyde may lead to allergic reactions.

For immunocytochemistry the sensitivity of the antigen to aldehydes determines the compositions of the fixative. As a rule of thumb, insensitive antigens can be fixed with 1% glutaraldehyde, sensitive antigens with 4% formaldehyde plus 0.1%

glutaraldehyde, and very sensitive antigens with 4% formaldehyde only. In the last case the formaldehyde concentration may be increased to 8%.

Cells tend to swell if the osmolality of the fixative vehicle (buffer) is low; in contrast, they shrink if the fixative solution has a high solute concentration (Maunsbach, 1966b). For this reason the osmotic composition of the fixative vehicle has to be varied for some tissues. In the outer renal medulla, where the extracellular osmolality is high, the normal perfusion fixative (1% glutaraldehyde in 0.1 M cacodylate buffer) should be supplemented with 0.2 M sucrose, whereas for amphibian tissues the vehicle osmolality should be slightly decreased.

The pH of aldehyde fixatives is normally 7.0–7.5, and fine adjustments of pH are not crucial in most ultrastructural studies. The choice of buffer in the fixative may influence the appearance of the tissue but in most tissues only to a moderate degree. Phosphate buffers are often used instead of cacodylate (cheaper!) but give in some tissues a fine precipitate at concentrations around 0.1 M or greater.

In highly vascularized organs, such as the pancreas, perfusion fixation leads to distention of the extravascular space. Such swelling can be prevented by the addition of 2% dextran (molecular weight around 40,000) to the perfusion solution (Bohman and Maunsbach, 1970).

Storage of cells and tissues in glutaraldehyde fixatives has very little influence on the final appearance of the tissue in the transmission microscope. Except for immunocytochemical studies, the preparation procedure can be halted for days, sometimes even months, while the tissue is in the aldehyde fixative. Pieces of aldehyde-fixed tissue can therefore easily be transported in fixative between laboratories.

V. Pitfalls

1. If the fixative flow is compromised during perfusion fixation, sufficient concentration of fixative is not obtained throughout the tissue and cells may undergo various abnormal alterations before they are fixed. In a successful perfusion the surfaces of the organs blanch very rapidly, the kidney surface within less than a second, and the tissues harden quickly. There is usually a good correlation between the speed of tissue blanching, fixative flow as observed in the drip chamber, absence of blood in dissected tissues, and the final quality of tissue preservation as observed in the electron microscope.

2. It is very important that the tissues are not damaged mechanically when dissected and trimmed before immersion fixation or after fixation. Small pieces cut out with a razor blade should be transferred between vessels only with fine forceps holding onto corners of the tissue blocks or with a Pasteur pipette.

3. Following immersion fixation it is necessary to secure that the tissue analyzed in the electron microscope originates from the surface layers of the tissue block, as there is a gradient in the quality of fixation from the surface to the center of the block (Fig. 4). In the center of tissue slices, where the fixative has arrived with some delay, there is swelling of cytoplasm and organelles. Thus, it is practical first to examine thick sections (1–3 μm) of the same tissue block by light microscopy to select the optimal location of the tissue for electron microscope analysis.

REFERENCES

Bohman, S.-O., and Maunsbach, A. B. (1970) Effects on tissue fine structure of variations in colloid osmotic pressure of glutaraldehyde fixatives. *J. Ultrastruct. Res.* 30, 195–208.

Glauert, A. M. (1975) Fixation, dehydration and embedding of biological specimens. *In* "Practical Methods in Electron Microscopy" (A. M. Glauert, ed.), Vol. 3, Part 1. Elsevier, Amsterdam.

Griffiths, G. (1993) "Fine Structure Immunocytochemistry." Springer-Verlag, Berlin.

Hayat, M. A. (1981) "Fixation for Electron Microscopy." Academic Press, New York.

Karnovsky, M. J. (1965) A formaldehyde–glutaraldehyde fixative of high osmolality for use in electron microscopy. *J. Cell Biol.* **27,** 137A.

Larsson, L.-I. (1988) "Immunocytochemistry: Theory and Practice." CRC Press, Boca Raton, FL.

Maunsbach, A. B. (1966a) The influence of different fixatives and fixation methods on the ultrastructure of rat kidney proximal tubule cells. I. Comparison of different perfusion fixation methods and of glutaraldehyde, formaldehyde and osmium tetroxide fixatives. *J. Ultrastruct. Res.* **15,** 242–282.

Maunsbach, A. B. (1966b) The influence of different fixatives and fixation methods on the ultrastructure of rat kidney proximal tubule cells. II. Effects of varying osmolality, ionic strength, buffer systems and fixative concentration of glutaraldehyde solutions. *J. Ultrastruct. Res.* **15,** 283–309.

Robards, A. W., and Wilson, A. J. (eds.) (1993) "Procedures in Electron Microscopy." John Wiley & Sons, Chichester.

Sabatini, D. D., Bensch, K., and Barnett, R. J. (1963) Cytochemistry and electron microscopy. The preservation of cellular ultrastructure and enzymatic activity by aldehyde fixation. *J. Cell Biol.* **17,** 19–58.

Sjöstrand, F. S. (1989) Common sense in electron microscopy. About osmium fixation. *J. Ultrastruct. Mol. Struct. Res.* **102,** 1–8.

Embedding of Cells and Tissues for Ultrastructural and Immunocytochemical Analysis

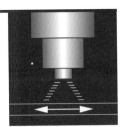

Arvid B. Maunsbach

I. Introduction

Tissues to be analyzed in the electron microscope are usually embedded in resin for ultramicrotomy. The embedding procedures vary with respect to chemical composition of resins, protocols for dehydration, procedures for infiltration with resins, as well as properties of the embedded tissue (e.g., sectioning quality, tissue shrinkage, and tissue contrast in the electron microscope).

Epoxy resins are the most commonly used embedding media in biological electron microscopy (Luft, 1961; Glauert, 1975). They combine good ultrastructural preservation of the tissues, ease of sectioning, reproducibility, and relative ease of handling. On the other hand, they preserve tissue antigenicity to only a very limited extent.

Acrylic resins, such as the Lowicryls (Carlemalm *et al.,* 1982, 1985), both provide good ultrastructural preservation and retain to a large extent tissue antigenicity. Embedding in acrylic resins is carried out at low temperature either by progressive lowering of the temperature during dehydration and resin infiltration or by cryofixation followed by freeze-substitution and UV polymerization at low temperature.

This article describes two embedding procedures that we use routinely in our laboratory for the analysis of a variety of chemically fixed tissues: ethanol dehydration followed by epoxy resin embedding for general ultrastructural studies, and freeze-substitution combined with low-temperature Lowicryl HM20 embedding for immunoelectron microscope analysis.

II. Materials and Instrumentation

A. DEHYDRATION AND EMBEDDING IN EPOXY RESIN

Epoxy resin kit (TO24, TAAB Laboratories Equipment Ltd.) containing epoxy resin (TAAB 812), dodecenyl succinic anhydride (DDSA), methyl nadic anhydride (MNA), and 2,4,6-tri(dimethylaminomethyl)phenol (DMP-30)

Ethanol

Maleic acid ($C_4H_4O_4$, Merck, Cat. No. 800380)

Uranyl acetate dihydrate (($CH_3COO)_2UO_2 \cdot 2H_2O$, Merck, Cat. No. 8473)

Propylene oxide (C_3H_6O, Merck, Cat. No. 12492)

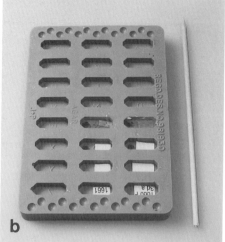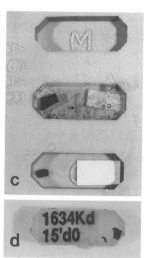

FIGURE 1 Embedding in epoxy resin. (a) Vials with specimens during ethanol dehydration (left) and infiltration in pure epoxy resin (right). At start of infiltration the tissue blocks are placed on top of the resin and allowed to sink to the bottom. (b) Flat embedding mold used for epoxy embedding. Specimens and labels are placed in the wells. The wooden stick (right) is used to orient blocks and labels in the resin. (c) Enlargement of central wells showing specimen and label without resin (below), specimen with label and epoxy (middle) and empty well (upper). (d) Polymerized epoxy block with label seen from back side.

Glass vials (5–10 ml) with lids (Fig. 1a)

Gloves

Disposable beaker for mixing resin

Disposable Pasteur pipettes

Flat embedding molds in resistant rubber (G3690, Agar Scientific Ltd., Fig. 1b)

Fine forceps

Wooden stick

B. FREEZE-SUBSTITUTION IN LOWICRYL HM20

Liquid nitrogen

Lowicryl HM20 kit (Agar Scientific Ltd) containing HM20 resin (monomer E), HM20 crosslinker (D), HM20 initiator (C)

Methanol (CH_3OH, Merck, Cat. No. 6007)

Sodium chloride (NaCl, Merck, Cat. No. 6404)

Sodium dihydrogen phosphate monohydrate ($NaH_2PO_4 \cdot H_2O$, Merck, Cat. No. 6346)

Disodium hydrogen phosphate dihydrate ($Na_2HPO_4 \cdot 2H_2O$, Merck, Cat. No. 6580)

Sucrose ($C_{12}H_{22}O_{11}$, BDH, Cat. No. 10274)

Paraformaldehyde (Merck, Cat. No. 4005)

Uranyl acetate dihydrate [$(CH_3COO)_2UO_2 \cdot 2H_2O$, Merck, Cat. No. 8473]

Fine forceps with cold-insulated shaft

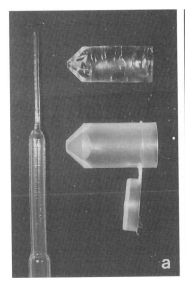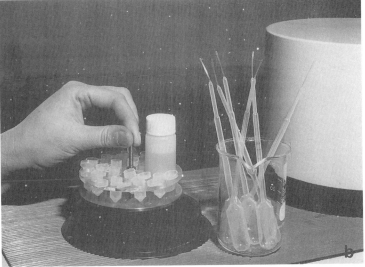

FIGURE 2 Freeze-substitution in HM20. (a) Polyethylene Pasteur pipette with elongated tip (left), polyethylene capsule with hinged lid (lower right), and polymerized Lowicryl block after removal of capsule (upper right). (b) Holder with polyethylene capsules and vial for substitution fluid before being lowered into Balzers FSU 010 freeze-substitution apparatus. To the right beaker with polyethylene Pasteur pipettes and to the far right part of UV polymerization unit.

Polyethylene capsules with pyramid shape and hinged lids for low-temperature embedding (BEEM G360-1, Agar Scientific Ltd., Fig. 2a)

Disposable beaker for mixing resin

Polyethylene Pasteur pipettes with extended fine tips (Fig. 2a)

Freeze-substitution apparatus with temperature regulation between −85 and 0°C: Balzers FSU 010 Freeze-Substitution Unit (Baltec), Reichert Freeze-Substitution Unit (Reichert Division der Leica AG) or equivalent (e.g., homemade) freeze-substitution apparatus

UV lamp for polymerization with 350-nm UV light (if not built into the freeze-substitution apparatus)

III. Procedures

A. DEHYDRATION AND EMBEDDING IN EPOXY RESIN

The following procedure results in embedded tissue blocks with good cutting properties from a variety of tissues (Fig. 3). It includes *en bloc* staining which improves contrast in subsequent section staining. If *en bloc* staining is not desired, steps 2–4 should be omitted and the tissue directly transferred to 70% ethanol.

Solutions

1. *70, 90, and 95% ethanol in water.*

2. *0.05 M maleate buffer:* To make 100 ml, dissolve 0.58 g maleic acid in about 80 ml water and adjust pH to 5.2 with 1 N NaOH. Fill up to 100 ml with water.

3. *0.5% uranyl acetate in 0.05 M sodium maleate buffer:* To make 100 ml,

---

Embedding for Ultrastructural and Immunocytochemical Analysis

dissolve 0.58 g maleic acid in 80 ml water and adjust pH to 6.0 with 1 *N* NaOH. Dissolve 0.5 g uranyl acetate dihydrate in this solution and adjust (if necessary) pH to 5.2 with NaOH. Fill up to 100 ml with water.

4. *Epoxy resin:* To make 100 g resin, mix 48 g TAAB 812, 19 g DDSA, and 33 g MNA. Stir continuously for 5 min. Add 2 g DMP-30 and stir continuously for another 5 min. The complete epoxy mixture should be used for initial infiltration within the next few hours as it will slowly start to polymerize also at room temperature. The freshly mixed complete resin can be stored in the freezer (e.g., −20°C) for months in closed vials. The vials must attain room temperature before being opened and used for embedding.

Steps

1. Rinse tissue fixed in aldehydes and/or osmium tetroxide for 2 × 30 min in buffer (e.g., same buffer as used for fixation). Keep the tissue at 0–4°C until step 6. If *en bloc* staining is not desired proceed to step 5.

2. For *en bloc* staining rinse for 2 × 15 min with sodium maleate buffer. As in all following steps up to step 10, remove fluid with a Pasteur pipette before adding new fluid. The tissue must never be allowed to dry.

3. Stain for 60 min in uranyl acetate in maleate buffer.

4. Rinse for 2 × 15 min in sodium maleate buffer.

5. Dehydrate for 2 × 15 min in 70% ethanol.

6. Dehydrate for 2 × 15 min in 90% ethanol. This and the following steps of dehydration and infiltration are carried out at room temperature.

7. Dehydrate for 2 × 15 min in 95% ethanol.

8. Dehydrate for 2 × 15 min in absolute ethanol.

9. Place the tissue for 2 × 15 min in propylene oxide. Take particular care that the tissue does not dry, as propylene oxide evaporates very rapidly. Because propylene oxide is toxic and very volatile, this and all subsequent steps should be carried out in a well-ventilated hood with gloves.

10. Infiltrate the tissue for 60 min in a mixture of 50% propylene oxide and 50% completely mixed epoxy resin.

11. Transfer the specimens to the surface of the epoxy resin in a clean vial containing 100% resin (see Fig. 1a). Use fine forceps or a wooden stick. Propylene oxide gradually diffuses out of the tissue blocks when they sink through the resin. Leave the specimens in the epoxy resin overnight at room temperature.

12. Fill the flat embedding mold with epoxy resin (see Fig. 1b). Place a small piece of paper with the identification number of the specimen in the resin next to the specimen. If necessary adjust the location of the tissue block and/or the paper with a wooden stick.

13. Polymerize the specimens at 60°C for 2 days.

B. FREEZE-SUBSTITUTION IN LOWICRYL HM20

For immunoelectron microscopy the tissue is usually fixed for short time with 4 or 8% paraformaldehyde or 4% paraformaldehyde plus 0.1% glutaraldehyde but is never postfixed in osmium tetroxide. The tissue blocks should not exceed 0.3 mm in any direction. Substitution in 0.5% uranyl acetate in methanol (Schwarz and

Humbel, 1989) results in good ultrastructural preservation combined with retained tissue antigenicity (Fig.4).

Solutions

1. *Lowicryl HM20:* To make about 20 g, gently mix 3.0 g crosslinker D and 17.0 g monomer E. Bubble dry nitrogen gas into the mixture for 5 min to exclude O_2 which inhibits Lowicryl polymerization. Add 0.1 g initiator C and mix gently until it is dissolved. Avoid making air bubbles.

2. *Methanol:* Lowicryl HM20 mixtures in proportions 2:1 and 1:1.

3. *2.3 M sucrose in PBS-buffered 2% paraformaldehyde:* To make 100 ml solution, weigh out 0.038 g sodium dihydrogen phosphate monohydrate, 0.128 g disodium hydrogen phosphate dihydrate, 0.877 g sodium chloride, and 78.7 g sucrose. Add water and 12.5 ml 16% paraformaldehyde to about 95 ml. Use a magnetic stirrer until the sucrose is dissolved, which usually requires several hours. Adjust pH if necessary to 7.2 and fill up with water to 100 ml.

4. *16% Stock solution of paraformaldehyde:* To make 100 ml solution, mix 16 g of paraformaldehyde powder with 80 ml of distilled water in a glass flask. Heat to 60°C while gently agitating the milky solution. Add 1 *N* sodium hydroxide dropwise until the solution clears up. Complete to 100 ml with distilled water. This procedure should be carried out in a well-ventilated hood and with protection for the face. The solution can be stored for a few days in the refrigerator.

5. *0.5% Uranyl acetate in methanol:* To make 100 ml, dissolve 0.5 g uranyl acetate dihydrate in methanol to a total of 100 ml.

Steps

1. Transfer the tissue directly from the aldehyde fixative to the buffered sucrose–paraformaldehyde solution. Place the specimens in the upper layer of the sucrose–paraformaldehyde and stir the solution. Infiltrate for 1 hr.

2. Cryofix the tissue in liquid nitrogen. Hold the specimen gently with the fine forceps provided with the cold-insulated handle. Dip the specimen quickly into the liquid nitrogen, where it is either left temporarily for immediate processing or placed in a tube for further storage in liquid nitrogen for weeks or months. Carefully follow the safety regulations when handling liquid nitrogen.

3. Transfer the frozen tissue very rapidly with precooled forceps from the liquid nitrogen to the 0.5% uranyl acetate/methanol solution, which is kept at −85 to 90°C in the capsules in the freeze-substitution unit. During this transfer great care must be taken not to warm the specimen. For this purpose the vessel with the liquid nitrogen must be placed immediately adjacent to the substitution unit.

4. Withdraw most of the substitution fluid from the capsules with a polyethylene Pasteur pipette. The diameter of the tip of the Pasteur pipette should be smaller than the size of the specimens as the specimens are difficult to observe at this step and may otherwise be removed. Fill the capsules with temperature-equilibrated substitution fluid of the same composition as before and increase the temperature to −80°C for 24 hr. Rinsing and infiltration periods in the following are adjusted to suit regular working hours.

5. Rinse the specimens for about 20 hr at −80°C with one change of methanol.

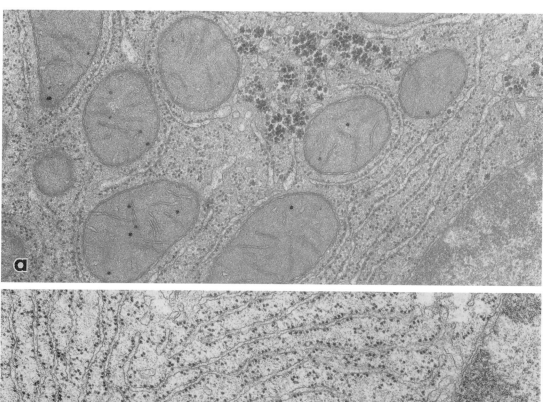

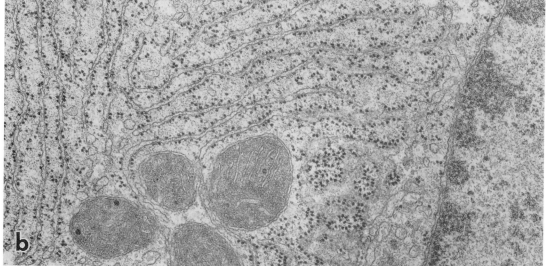

FIGURE 3   Electron micrographs of cells in liver perfusion, fixed with 1% glutaraldehyde, postfixed in osmium tetroxide, and embedded in epoxy resin. (a) Embedding without *en bloc* staining but section staining with lead citrate. This preparation gives a good overall image of subcellular architecture (× 40,000). (b) Same fixation and embedding except that the tissue was *en bloc* stained with uranyl acetate and the section double stained with uranyl acetate and lead citrate. The micrograph shows considerable contrast with emphasis on membranes, ribosomes, and nuclear components. (× 40,000.)

6. Rinse the specimens three times with methanol at −70°C over a period of 8 hr.

7. Rinse the specimens once with methanol at −45°C for 20 hr.

8. Infiltrate the specimens with a 2:1 mixture of methanol and Lowicryl HM20 for 6 hr.

9. Infiltrate the specimens with an 1:1 mixture of methanol and Lowicryl HM20 for about 14 hr.

10. Infiltrate the specimens with pure Lowicryl HM20 at −45°C for 8 hr with three changes.

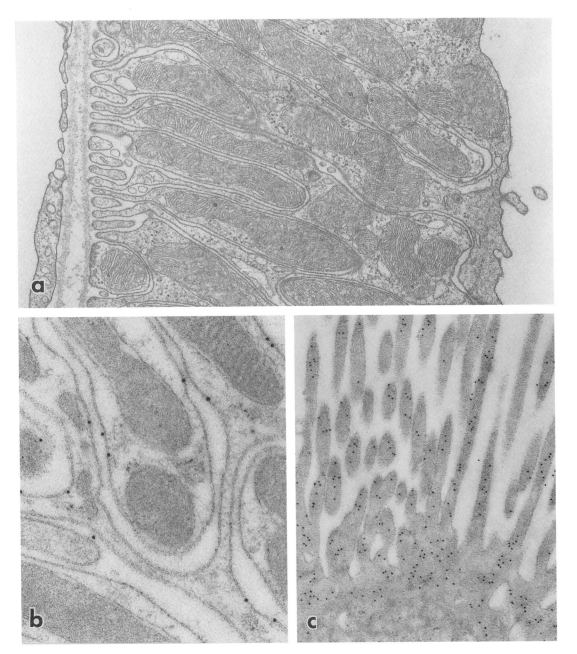

FIGURE 4 Electron micrographs of kidney cells following freeze-substitution and embedding in Lowicryl HM20. (a) Thick ascending limb of the renal distal tubule perfusion fixed with 4% paraformaldehyde containing 0.4% picric acid. Cell fine structure is well preserved and cellular membranes stand out in good contrast (× 30,000). (b) Immunolocalization of Na,K-ATPase to basolateral membranes of distal tubule in rat kidney cortex. Perfusion-fixation with 4% paraformaldehyde. The monoclonal antibody against the α-subunit of Na,K-ATPase was detected with goat anti-mouse IgG on 10 nm colloidal gold. Notice the precise association between basolateral membranes and gold particles (× 80,000). (From Maunsbach, 1992). (c) Apical part of proximal tubule cell in kidney perfusion fixed with 2% paraformaldehyde. Intracellular actin was immunolabeled with rabbit anti-actin antibody which was then detected with anti-rabbit IgG on 10 nm colloidal gold (× 40,000).

11. Infiltrate the specimens with pure Lowicryl HM20 at −45°C for 24 hr.

12. Fill up the capsules completely with fresh Lowicryl HM20 and close the lids. Polymerize with indirect UV light at −45°C for 48 hr.

13. Increase the temperature to 0°C and continue UV polymerization for 24 hr. The specimens are now ready for conventional ultramicrotomy at room temperature.

IV. Comments

Chemicals used during dehydration and embedding in epoxy or acrylic resins are toxic (mutagenic, allergenic, and, in some cases, perhaps carcinogenic) and should be handled with adequate safety precautions. Work in a well-ventilated hood and use gloves. Note that resins can penetrate most types of gloves within a short time.

The protocol for ethanol dehydration in connection with epoxy resin embedding can be varied considerably without great effects on the final result. In most cases short dehydration times seem preferable, but storage of the specimens overnight at 4°C is usually without problems.

Acetone is often used as an alternative to ethanol for dehydration but the results are in most cases essentially indistinguishable. Both ethanol and acetone dehydration lead to extraction of tissue lipids and shrinkage of tissue dimensions. These effects may be slightly different in different protocols but cannot be eliminated.

The chemical composition of epoxy resins from different manufacturers varies considerably (see Glauert and Hall, 1991; Mollenhauer, 1993; Robards and Wilson, 1993). Consequently also the properties of the different epoxy resins vary with respect to, e.g., viscosity and flow rate, hardness after polymerization, stainability, and stability in the electron beam. Despite some observable differences, however, ultrastructural observations using presently available epoxy resins are quite comparable and in many cases indistinguishable.

The hardness of the polymerized epoxy blocks can be modified by changing the ratio of DDSA/MNA. Thus, an increase in DDSA gives softer blocks, and an increase in MNA, harder blocks (Luft, 1961; Glauert, 1975).

V. Pitfalls

1. Difficulties in sectioning of tissue embedded in epoxy resin are often due to soft resin blocks. This condition may originate from one or more deviations from the dehydration/infiltration protocol: (a) wrong epoxy resin composition; (b) insufficient stirring of the components of the resin; (c) too short infiltration time in pure resin; (d) too large specimen (all dimensions exceeding 1 mm); (e) too short polymerization time; (f) incomplete dehydration; (g) incomplete removal of ethanol.

2. During freeze-substitution, to avoid recrystallization of the water, it is important that the temperature of the specimen does not increase in connection with fluid changes. New fluids must be properly temperature equilibrated in the freeze-substitution unit before being added to the samples.

3. The size of the specimen for freeze-substitution must be small to allow complete removal of water. Only small specimens will be properly dehydrated and infiltrated with Lowicryl HM20.

REFERENCES

Carlemalm, E., Garavito, R. M., and Villiger, W. (1982) Resin development for electron microscopy and an analysis of embedding at low temperature. *J. Microsc.* **126,** 123–143.
Carlemalm, E., Villiger, W., Hobot, J. A., Acetarin, J.-D., and Kellenberger, E. (1985) Low

temperature embedding with Lowicryl resins: Two new formulations and some applications. *J. Microsc.* **140**, 55–63.

Glauert, A. M. (1975) Fixation, dehydration and embedding of biological specimens. *In* "Practical Methods in Electron Microscopy" (A. M. Glauert, ed.), Vol. 3, Part 1. North-Holland, Amsterdam.

Glauert, A. M., and Hall, C. (1991) Epoxy resins: An update on their selection and use. *Eur. Microsc. Anal.*, September, 13–18.

Luft, J. H. (1961) Improvements in epoxy resin embedding methods. *J. Biophys. Biochem. Cytol.* **9**, 409–414.

Maunsbach, A. B. (1992) Trends in tissue preparation for electron microscopy. *In* "Electron Microscopy 92" (A. Ríos, J. M. Arias, L. Megías-Megías, and A. López-Galindo, eds.), Vol. 1, pp. 3–8. General University of Granada, Servicio de Publicaciones, Granada.

Mollenhauer, H. H. (1993) Artifacts caused by dehydration and epoxy embedding in transmission electron microscopy. *Microsc. Res. Technique* **26**, 496–512.

Ringo, D. L., Brennan, E. F., and Cota-Robles, E. H. (1982) Epoxy resins are mutagenic: Implications for electron microscopists. *J. Ultrastruct. Res.* **80**, 280–287.

Robards, A. W., and Wilson, A. J. (eds.) (1993) "Procedures in Electron Microscopy." Wiley, Chichester.

Schwarz, H., and Humbel, B. M. (1989) Influence of fixatives and embedding media on immunolabelling of freeze-substituted cells. *Scan. Microsc.*, Suppl. 3, 57–64.

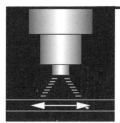

Negative Staining

Andreas Bremer and Ueli Aebi

I. Introduction

More than 30 years ago, Brenner and Horne (1959) introduced negative staining, a now widely used routine technique to prepare biological material for imaging in the transmission electron microscope (TEM) (for review, see Horne, 1991). Suitable specimens may either be in solution or in suspension and thus include the whole spectrum of structural organization of biomacromolecules, ranging from monomers, homooligomers, and heterooligomers such as RNA polymerase (Fig. 1a), to polymers as the helical strands of glutamine synthase (Fig. 1b), and eventually to complex protein machineries such as bacteriophages (Fig. 1c). Compared with, e.g., the preparation of frozen-hydrated specimens, negative staining requires only cheap instrumentation, is remarkably simple, and can provide reliable structural information down to resolutions of about 2.0 nm as quickly as 2 min after preparing the specimen (for review, see Bremer *et al.*, 1992).

As shown schematically in Fig. 2a, a negatively stained specimen is embedded in a microcrystalline heavy atom salt replica that portrays its molecular structure. As heavy metal atoms scatter electrons much more strongly than atoms common to biomacromolecules (i.e., C, H, O, P, N, S), the contrast of negatively stained preparations is much higher than that of unstained specimens (Fig. 2b) and reversed (hence "negative" staining). In addition, the stain replica provides good sustaining of the specimen and at least partially substitutes for the native aqueous environment of the biomacromolecule. The replica thus stabilizes the specimen against collapse and distortion due to the surface tension that acts at the air–liquid interface, and it also serves as a radiation protectant in the sense that it is more radiation resistant than biological matter.

II. Materials and Instrumentation

Negative staining requires only minor investment for instrumentation and supplies. For routine applications, the following items are needed:

1. *Specimen grids* (typically 200–400 mesh/inch, copper, 3.05 mm in diameter, 0.7 mm thick, e.g., from Bopp & Co.) coated with a specimen support film (mostly either a carbon–collodion composite film or a thin carbon film; Fig. 3a): The specimen grids should be stored dust-free, e.g., in a petri dish (Fig. 3b) that is kept at relatively low humidity.

2. *Dissecting forceps* (e.g., from Michel Terrier). It is advisable to bend the jaws of the forceps slightly inward (Fig. 3c) to prevent surface tension from

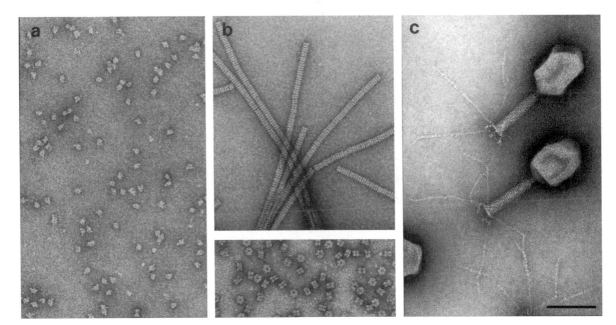

FIGURE 1 From molecules to replicating molecular machines—examples of negatively stained preparations. (a) Monomers of RNA polymerase holoenzyme. (b) Glutamine synthase from *Escherichia coli*. (Top) Helical filaments are formed in the presence of Co^{2+} ions. (Bottom) The molecule is composed of twelve identical 50-kDa subunits that associate with 622 symmetry; i.e., end-on views display a typical blossomlike appearance with sixfold symmetry, whereas side views reveal twofold symmetry. (c) *E. coli* T4 bacteriophages. The organization into a distinct elongated icosahedral head, a helical tail to which a base plate is attached at the bottom, and extended fibers is evident. RNA polymerase (a) and glutamine synthase (b) were stained with 0.75% uranyl formate, bacteriophage T4 (c) with 1% uranyl acetate. Bar = 100 nm.

trapping buffers and solutes between the jaws. A tightly fitting rubber band or piece of tubing allows the jaws to be fixed in the closed state.

3. *Glow-discharge unit* (Fig. 3d). It is used to render the support film of the specimen grids hydrophilic and can be built as detailed by Aebi and Pollard (1987). The specimen grid is glow-discharged on a small glass block coated with Parafilm (Fig. 3d, arrowhead).

4. A tray (e.g., metal or plastic) serves as the "workbench" (Fig. 3e). Drops of water and stain, typically 100 μl, can be placed on a piece of Parafilm (Fig. 3e, left). Filter or blotting paper (lower right) are required for removing excess liquid from the specimen grid.

5. Micropipettes: 5 μl and adjustable 20–200 μl or similar.

6. A stopwatch is required to control adsorption and staining times.

7. A Pasteur pipette drawn out into a capillary connected to a suction device such as a water jet pump serves to remove excess stain from the specimen grid.

III. Procedures

Solutions

Only a few solutions are needed for negative staining:

1. *Specimen solution/suspension.*

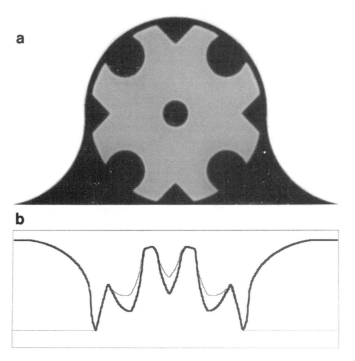

FIGURE 2 Negatively stained specimen. (a) The schematic view represents a cross section through a specimen (light gray) that is embedded in negative stain (dark gray). (b) The schematic view in (a) was projected down by adding the pixel values along the vertical axis. The projection of the schematic specimen embedded in the schematic "negative stain" is represented by a thick line, whereas the projection of the specimen without "stain" is depicted by a thin line (in this case, the projection was inverted, i.e., multiplied by −1).

2. *Double-distilled or deionized water:* Water is required for washing the specimen grid after specimen adsorption.

3. *Negative stain solution:* For instance, uranyl formate or sodium phosphotungstate.

A. PREPARATION OF NEGATIVE STAIN SOLUTION

Properties of various negative stains along with references describing their preparation are compiled in Bremer *et al.* (1992). The preparation of uranyl formate is described as an example:

Steps

1. Weigh out uranyl formate (obtained from BDH Chemicals Ltd., Cat. No. 30644), final concentration 0.75%, e.g., 37.5 mg/5 ml.

2. Boil an appropriate amount of water to remove CO_2 and to increase the solubility of the uranyl formate in the water.

3. Pour the boiling water onto the uranyl formate in a small beaker.

4. Stir slowly for 5–10 min in the dark (i.e., in a covered beaker).

5. Filter the solution through a 0.22-μm membrane filter (e.g., Skan AG, Basel, Switzerland).

6. Adjust pH to 4.25 by adding 10 N NaOH (about 10 μl per 5 ml solution);

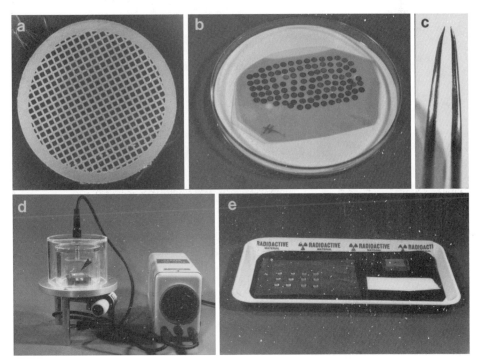

FIGURE 3 Materials and equipment required for negative staining. (a) Specimen grid (copper 200 mesh/inch, 3.05 mm in diameter, 0.7 mm thick) coated with a collodion–carbon composite film (the film is particularly evident at the edges. (b) The specimen grids are stored on filter paper in a covered petri dish (the cover is removed for clarity in this figure). (c) Forceps with the jaws slightly bent inward are used for all manipulations. (d) The specimen grids are rendered hydrophilic in a reduced atmosphere of air using a glow-discharge unit (see Aebi and Pollard, 1987). The specimen grids are glow-discharged on a small glass block that is covered with Parafilm (arrowhead). (e) A plastic or metal tray can serve as a workbench for staining. The water and stain drops are placed on a piece of Parafilm to the left, the glass block with a glow-discharged grid is seen to right at the back, and a piece of filter paper is seen in the front.

the solution should turn into a moderately intense yellow. (*Caution:* Increasing the pH toward neutral rapidly leads to precipitation of the uranyl fomate.)

7. Stir for another 5 min in the dark.

8. Filter a second time.

9. Readjust the volume to compensate for water loss due to evaporation, filtration, etc.

10. Store stain in the dark (e.g., in a tube wrapped into aluminum foil). The stain will be stable for 1 or 2 days.

B. STAINING

Our standard staining procedure for soluble proteins and their supramolecular assemblies is illustrated in Fig. 4; it is simple and straightforward.

Steps

1. Glow-discharge specimen grids in a unit as shown in Fig. 3d, e.g., for 15 sec (for details, see Aebi and Pollard, 1987).

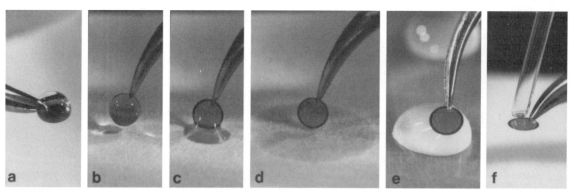

FIGURE 4 Negative staining. (a) The specimen solution/suspension is placed onto the specimen grid and allowed to adsorb for 30 sec. The specimen grid is held horizontally. (b) The specimen grid is then turned vertically and (c) allowed to gently touch the filter paper, which (d) removes excess liquid. (e) The adsorbed specimen is then washed by carefully placing it sideways onto a drop of water for 1 sec, blotting as shown in (b)–(d), and washing a second time. The actual staining is performed similarly by first washing the specimen grid on a drop of negative stain as described in (e), blotting, and repeating this step once more, this time leaving the specimen grid for 10 sec on the drop of the negative stain. (f) After blotting off excess stain, the residual stain is removed by gently moving a capillary (extended from a Pasteur pipette) around the edge of the grid. The capillary is connected to a device that produces a low vacuum, e.g., a water jet pump.

2. To the freshly glow-discharged specimen grid, apply a 5-μl drop of the specimen solution/suspension (Fig. 4a), adsorb for 30–60 sec, and then blot off as illustrated in Figs. 4b–d. Hold the specimen grid vertical (Fig. 4b); allow it to gently touch the filter paper (Fig. 4c), which will remove the drop by capillary forces (Fig. 4d).

3. Next, wash the specimen grid on a drop of deionized or double-distilled water by carefully lowering it sideways onto the surface of the drop (Fig. 4e). After 1 sec, carefully remove the specimen grid from the water, blot as in Figs. 4b–d, and repeat the washing step once more.

4. Finally, stain the specimen by lowering the specimen grid onto a drop of the negative stain as described for the washing step (see Fig. 4e), and blot the specimen grid as described in Figs. 4b–d. Repeat this step once; this time, however, hold the specimen grid for 10–15 sec onto the negative stain drop (as illustrated in Fig. 4e) before blotting.

5. After blotting (see Figs. 4b–d), remove residual stain prior to air-drying with a suction device such as a water jet pump that is connected to a Pasteur pipette with a drawn-out and slightly bent capillary. As shown in Fig. 4f, move the capillary around the edge of the specimen grid. The preparation is now ready for imaging in the EM.

V. Comments

The "quality" of a negatively stained preparation (i.e., the interpretable structural detail revealed by the micrograph or on the screen of an EM) depends primarily on the penetration properties (e.g., size, hydrophobicity) of the heavy metal salt used for negative staining and on the physicochemical properties of the specimen (e.g., charge, hydrophobicity). As some negative stains have a relatively acidic pH while others are neutral or moderately basic, and as they may be uncharged, anionic, or cationic (for review, see Bremer *et al.,* 1992), negative staining is quite versatile and

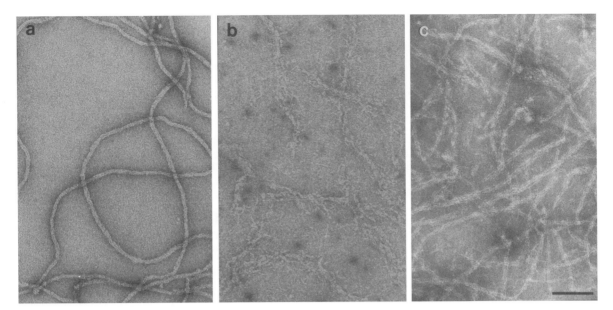

FIGURE 5 Negatively stained cultured human epidermal cell (HEC) keratin filaments. (a) HEC keratin filaments in 10 mM Tris, pH 7.5, negatively stained with 0.75% uranyl formate, pH 4.25, appear compact with more or less uniform width. (b) Dramatic unraveling is observed when the filaments are briefly washed with 10 mM sodium phosphate (NaP$_i$, pH 7.0) prior to staining with 0.75% uranyl formate, pH 4.25. (c) Negative staining with 2% sodium phosphotungstate, pH 7.0, also reveals local unraveling of such filaments. Bar = 100 nm.

can be tailored to specific needs. The optimal stain for the specimen under investigation has to be selected by trial and error. The two stains described here (uranyl formate and sodium phosphotungstate) are a good starting point and have been used successfully with a wide variety of proteins including cytoskeletal, membrane, and soluble cytosolic proteins and their supramolecular assemblies. We prefer uranyl formate over uranyl acetate because it is slightly more stable in the electron beam. The protocol for staining described above is suitable for most specimens and stains. With delicate proteins, an additional wash of the grid with water or specimen buffer prior to application of the specimen may be included to wet the specimen support film and to minimize surface denaturation of the specimen. An optimal specimen concentration displays evenly distributed and sufficiently spaced particles on the specimen grid and obviously has to be determined experimentally. It is governed by the adsorption properties of the proteins determining the fraction of molecules that bind to the support film. For larger molecules and polymers such as filaments, crystalline or paracrystalline specimens, a concentration higher than that for smaller molecules is required. As a rule of thumb, a few micrograms per milliliter for single particles (see Fig. 1a and inset in Fig. 1b) and a few hundred micrograms per milliliter for supramolecular assemblies such as filamentous (see Fig. 1b) and virus/phage particles (see Fig. 1c) yield a reasonable particle density with most specimens. The ionic conditions of the solution and the presence of, e.g., detergents are not critical if a sufficient number of washing steps (usually two to six for most compounds) are included in the procedure.

The stain may interact with the specimen. The resulting "preparation artifacts" can provide important information, often other than purely structural, as well. For instance, as is illustrated in Fig. 5a, cultured human epidermal cell (HEC) keratin filaments, when stained with uranyl formate (pH 4.25), have a very constant diameter and appear rather compact and featureless. By contrast, as is documented in Fig. 5c, preparations stained with sodium phosphotungstate (NaPT, pH 7.0) frequently

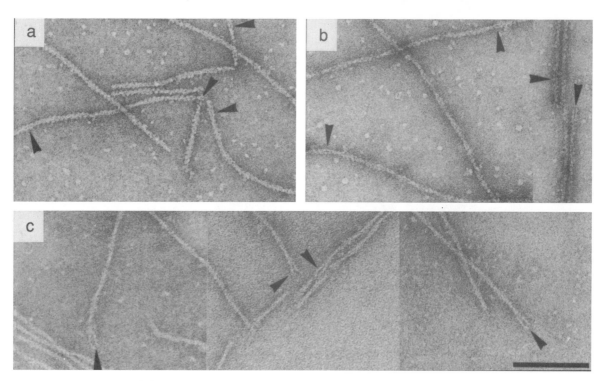

FIGURE 6 Negatively stained F-actin filaments. (a) F-actin filaments when negatively stained with 0.75% uranyl formate appear regular and compact. (b) After millimolar concentrations of inorganic phosphate, P_i (i.e., NaP_i, pH 7.0), are added to such preparations they appear less regular and also frequently show unraveling into their two constituent long-pitch helical strands. (c) These structural changes are even more pronounced when staining preparations as shown in (a) with 2% NaPT, instead of 0.75% uranyl formate. Bar = 100 nm.

reveal the protofilamentous substructure through local unraveling. As can be depicted in Fig. 5b, this local unraveling appears to be even more pronounced after briefly washing the filaments with 10 mM phosphate buffer (NaP_i, pH 7.0) prior to negatively staining them with uranyl formate. Accordingly, inorganic phosphate, P_i, may act as a modulator of the lateral interaction of protofilaments or protofibrils in the filament (Aebi *et al.*, 1983), and thus unraveling is most likely not just a preparation artifact. In fact, a similar response to different negative stains has been observed with F-actin filaments where inorganic phosphate appears to modulate the relative strength of the bonds *along* and *between* the two long-pitch helical strands defining the filament (reviewed in Bremer and Aebi, 1992). This phenomenon is demonstrated in Figs. 6a–c: F-actin filaments appear relatively compact when stained with uranyl formate (Fig. 6a). Adding millimolar concentrations of P_i to F-actin filaments renders them less compact and frequently locally unraveled into the two long-pitch helical strands (Fig. 6b, arrowhead). This is even more dramatic when staining with NaPT (Fig. 6c). Similar structural changes have also been observed with frozen-hydrated F-actin filaments (reviewed in Bremer *et al.*, 1992), eliminating the possibility that local unraveling of F-actin filaments is solely a specimen preparation artifact caused by negative staining or air-drying.

VI. Pitfalls

A. POOR SPECIMEN ADSORPTION

1. *Support film wrongly charged:* Highly negatively charged proteins or DNA do not adsorb very well to likewise negatively charged support films as they are

obtained by glow-discharge in a reduced atmosphere of air. By contrast, glow-discharging specimen grids in a reduced atmosphere of pentylamine produces a *net positive charge* on the support film (cf. Aebi and Pollard, 1987).

2. *Support film not properly glow-discharged:* Try longer glow-discharge, and glow-discharge only one grid at a time and use it immediately.

B. PATCHY, POOR, OR BAD STAINING

1. *Specimen concentration too high:* A high density of particles on the grid prevents quantitative removal of excess stain, resulting in inhomogeneities in the staining, even in particle-free areas. Try a lower specimen concentration.

2. *Stain not sufficiently removed:* Try removing stain more quantitatively by suction.

3. *Suboptimal stain for the specimen:* Try a different stain.

4. *Suboptimal wetting properties of the support film:* Try longer glow-discharge times.

5. *Incompatibilities between stain and buffers:* For instance, uranyl salts precipitate in the presence of inorganic phosphate. Try using different specimen buffers.

6. *Buffer contains high molar salt or detergent:* Try including more washing steps.

C. "BUBBLING" OF STAIN ON IRRADIATION

1. *Strong recrystallization, or excessive water content:* Try "prebaking" at a low magnification (e.g., $1000\times$) for 3–5 sec before using higher magnifications.

D. DISINTEGRATION OF SPECIMEN DURING PREPARATION

1. *Specimen unstable in water* (washing steps!): Wash and preequilibrate the specimen grid with specimen buffer instead of water. Mild crosslinking with, e.g., 0.05–0.2% glutaraldehyde for 2 min on ice (quench with 1% final concentration glycine, pH 7.0), also stabilizes many specimens.

E. SIGNIFICANT BACKGROUND OF MONOMERS AND/OR SMALL OLIGOMERS IN PREPARATION OF A SUPRAMOLECULAR ASSEMBLY

1. *Specimen in steady-state equilibrium with monomers/oligomers:* Pellet the specimen (e.g., in a table-top or air fuge at 100,000 g), discard the supernatant, resuspend the pellet, and immediately prepare the grid.

ACKNOWLEDGMENTS

We are most grateful to Ms. H. Frefel, L. Müller, M. Steiner, and M. Zoller for rapid and excellent photographic work. A. Hefti provided the scanning electron micrograph of a specimen grid. This work was supported by the M. E. Müller Foundation of Switzerland, by Grant No. 31-30129.90 from the Swiss National Science Foundation (to U.A.), and by a graduate student fellowship of the Studienstiftung des Deutschen Volkes and a postdoctoral long-term fellowship of the International Human Frontier Science Program Organization (both to A.B.).

REFERENCES

Aebi, U., Fowler, W. E., Rew, P., and Sun, T.-T. (1983) The fibrillar structure of keratin filaments unraveled. *J. Cell Biol.* **97,** 1131–1143.

Aebi, U., and Pollard, T. D. (1987) A glow discharge unit to render electron microscope grids and other surfaces hydrophilic. *J. Electron Microsc. Tech.* **7,** 29–33.

Bremer, A., and Aebi, U. (1992) The structure of the F-actin filament and the actin molecule. *Curr. Opin. Cell Biol.* **4,** 20–26.

Bremer, A., Henn, C., Engel, A., Baumeister, W., and Aebi, U. (1992) Has negative staining still a place in biomacromolecular electron microscopy? *Ultramicroscopy* **46,** 85–111.

Brenner, S., and Horne, R. W. (1959) A negative staining method for the high resolution electron microscopy of viruses. *Biochim. Biophys. Acta* **34,** 103–110.

Horne, R. W. (1991) Early developments in the negative staining technique for electron microscopy. *Micron Microsc. Acta* **22,** 321–326.

Whole-Mount Electron Microscopy of the Cytoskeleton: Negative Staining Methods

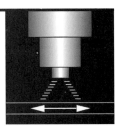

J. Victor Small and Monika Herzog

I. Introduction

Various techniques may be used for observing the cytoskeleton of whole cultured cells in the electron microscope. These include freeze-drying followed by metal coating (Heuser and Kirschner, 1980) and chemical fixation followed by either critical-point drying (Wolosewick and Porter, 1979; Schliwa *et al.*, 1982) or negative staining (Small and Celis, 1978; Small, 1988). Each of these techniques has its advantages and drawbacks (see, e.g., Small, 1988), and the choice between one or the other depends on the problem at hand. The negative staining method described here is the simplest and is well suited to studies of the thin, peripheral areas of cultured cells.

II. Materials and Instrumentation

The following items are obtainable from local electron microscopy and glassware suppliers:

1. Electron microscopy grids, silver, gold, or nickel, about 150 mesh.

2. Glass coverslips: 8 × 24 mm (optimal).

3. Forceps: Dumont No. 4 or 5 or equivalent.

4. For making thin films: glass slides, 100-ml glass measuring cylinder, glass trough 7 cm or deeper, tissue paper, lint-free paper, razor blade, Parafilm, foldback or spring clip attached to a piece of flexible wire (around 30 cm long).

5. Multiwell dish (24 wells, Nunc or Falcon).

6. Pasteur pipettes, petri dishes.

7. Stoppered volumetric flasks (50–100 ml) for staining and spreading solutions.

III. Procedures

A. PREPARATION OF FILMED GRIDS

Solution

1. *Formvar:* 0.3 g Formvar dissolved in 50 ml chloroform. Formvar needs about 2 hr to dissolve and should be used relatively fresh (up to 1 week). Store in a Coplin jar in aluminium foil, at room temperature.

Steps

We have used Collodion and Formvar films for whole-mount procedures. The method for making Formvar films is the simplest and is described here. In brief, the film is cast by dipping a glass slide into the Formvar solution, allowing it to dry, and then floating the film onto a water surface.

1. Rinse the 100-ml cylinder with chloroform in a fume cupboard, and then add about 40 ml of the Formvar/chloroform solution. Cover with a glass lid.

2. Clean a glass slide with tissue paper and then with lint-free paper so that no visible dust remains. Attach one end of slide to the clip with attached wire.

3. Dip the slide into the Formvar solution so that the clip is above the surface and then raise the whole slide above the solution, still keeping it in the measuring cylinder for a further 15 sec.

4. Remove slide, detach clip, and score around the edge of the slide with a razor blade.

5. Fill glass trough with distilled water, and sweep surface clean with one piece of lint-free paper.

6. Holding the nonfilmed end of the slide, dip it slowly into the water at an angle of 30°–45° to release film from the surface. If film separates poorly, breathe gently on the slide surface. Film should appear silver in reflected light.

7. Place grids gently onto film, taking care not to touch the film with forceps.

8. Cut a piece of Parafilm slightly larger than the slide and lay this gently on the grid-covered film. Remove immediately after the film has attached and place on a filter paper in a petri dish, grids upward, to dry.

For preparing "grid sets" (four or five grids on one 8 × 24-mm coverslip), score the dried film on the glass slide across the slide with a razor blade so that when the film is floated onto the water surface it separates into pieces about 8 × 24 mm in size. Place the grids down the center of the film, and pick up the grid–film combination using the coverslip. To do this, hold one end of the coverslip with forceps, and position the other end at one end of the film with the coverslip tilted upward. Then push the coverslip forward and downward into the water to force the film against the coverslip surface. Place coverslips on filter paper and allow them to dry. Sterilize with UV light in an open petri dish before plating the cells.

B. CELLS

Cells are plated onto the grids as for coverslips and the density chosen to give one to two cells per grid square after attachment and spreading. In general, cells spread more slowly on plastic films than on glass, and to encourage spreading the filmed grids may be incubated with a drop of serum overnight, prior to plating.

C. FIXATION

Solutions

1. *Cytoskeleton buffer (CB):* 10 mM MES (Sigma Cat. No. M-8250), 150 mM NaCl, 5 mM EGTA (Fluka Cat. No. 03780), 5 mM MgCl$_2$ 6H$_2$O (Merck Cat. No. 5833), 5 mM glucose (Merck Cat. No. 8337), pH 6.1 at room temperature. To make 1 liter, weigh 1.95 g MES, 8.76 g NaCl, 1.90 g EGTA, 1.02 g MgCl·6H$_2$O, and 0.90 g glucose. Dissolve in 900 ml H$_2$O, adjust pH to 6.1 with 1 N NaOH, and fill up to 1 liter. Store at 4°C. For extended storage, add 100 mg/liter streptomycin sulfate (Sigma S6501).

2. *Glutaraldehyde stock:* 2.5% solution of glutaraldehyde made up in CB and stored at 4°C. Dilute 25% EM-grade glutaraldehyde 1:9 with cytoskeleton buffer. Recheck that the pH is 6.1.

3. *Glutaraldehyde–Triton mixture:* The fixative consists of a mixture of glutaraldehyde and Triton X-100 made up by diluting appropriate volumes of the glutaraldehyde stock and Triton X-100 (stored as a 10% aqueous stock) into CB. We commonly use a mixture of 0.25% glutaraldehyde and 0.5% Triton in CB.

Steps

1. The washing and fixation solutions are all used at room temperature and the 24-well multiwell dish serves as a useful reservoir for holding the different solutions. Fill the wells of the dish as follows: 1 and 2, CB; 3, glutaraldehyde–Triton mixture; 4, CB; 5, 2.5% glutaraldehyde; 6 and 7, CB. Also prepare a small petri dish (3.5 or 5 cm in diameter) containing CB.

2. After removing the cells from the incubator, transfer the coverslips carrying the grids through the wells of the dish as follows: 1 and 2, 2 sec each; 3, 60 sec; 4, 2 sec; 5, 10 min; 6 and 7, 2 sec each. Store in petri dish in CB.

D. ACTIN STABILIZATION

Solution

1. *Phalloidin:* 10 μg/ml phalloidin (Sigma) in CB. Store the phalloidin as a 1 mg/ml stock in methanol at −20°C.

Steps

To stabilize actin so that filaments are better visualized after negative staining a treatment with phalloidin is advisable. At this stage the back side of the grids may also be dried, in preparation for negative staining.

1. Remove a grid from the coverslip with forceps, after scoring around the edge to break the surrounding film, and rinse twice briefly in water (conveniently placed in two 250-ml beakers). Then blot the back side of the grid on a piece of filter paper. At this stage it is best to briefly release the grid onto the filter paper, drain excess liquid from the forceps, retrieve the grid, and then invert it on a drop of phalloidin on a sheet of Parafilm. It is important that the cell side of the grid does not dry or come into contact with filter paper during these steps. If liquid drains rapidly through the grid onto the filter paper during blotting, the film is broken and the grid may quickly dry if appropriate care is not taken.

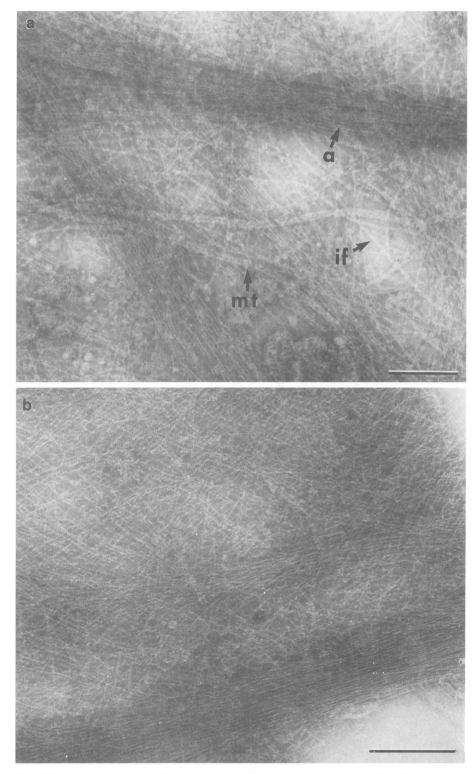

FIGURE 1 (a) Part of whole-mount cytoskeleton of chicken embryo fibroblast negatively stained with aqueous 2% sodium silicotungstate and showing microtubules (mt), actin filaments (a), and intermediate filaments (if). (b) Peripheral lamella region of human skin fibroblast negatively stained with 2% aqueous sodium silicotungstate, showing actin filament meshworks and a microspike bundle. Bars = 0.2 μm.

2. Leave the grid on phalloidin for 15–20 min or longer. For extra stabilization of microtubules, taxol can be used, if desired.

E. NEGATIVE STAINING

Solutions

1. *Negative staining solutions:* 1% aqueous uranyl acetate and 2% aqueous sodium silicotungstate, both stored at 4°C in stoppered flasks.

2. *Spreading solution:* 80 μg/ml bacitracin (Sigma) in H_2O with added 0.1% amyl alcohol, stored at 4°C in stoppered flask.

Steps

1. Clamp the grid in a pair of forceps using a large paper clip over the shaft to hold the tips together.

2. Keeping liquid away from the back side, rinse the cell side of the grid with several drops of bacitracin (for this step the grid can be tilted vertically and drops added from the side with a Pasteur pipette).

3. Place forceps on the lid of a petri dish so that the grid is held cell side up, and drain away excess liquid with the torn edge of a filter paper held where the forceps grip the grid.

4. Immediately add one drop of the negative stain solution, leave for a few seconds, and drain again with filter paper to leave a thin film.

5. Allow to air-dry and then observe in the microscope.

IV. Comments

Uranyl acetate produces higher contrast than sodium silicotungstate and better visualization of microtubules and intermediate filaments. With sodium silicotungstate (Fig. 1) actin filament order is better preserved. As is normal with negative staining, variability in stain intensity across the grid is not uncommon, so cells must be sought that exhibit the appropriate contrast. Experiment with different accelerating voltages if problems with stain contrast consistently arise.

REFERENCES

Heuser, J. E., and Kirschner, M. W. (1980) Filament organization revealed in platinum replicas of freeze-dried cytoskeletons. *J. Cell Biol.* **86,** 212–234.
Schliwa, M., van Blerkom, J., and Pryzwansky, K. B. (1982) Structural organization of cytoplasm. *Cold Spring Harbor Symp. Quant. Biol.* **46,** 51–67.
Small, J. V. (1988) The actin cytoskeleton. *Electron Microsc. Rev.* **1,** 155–174.
Small, J. V., and Celis, J. E. (1978) Filament arrangements in negatively stained cultured cells: The organization of actin. *Cytobiologie* **16,** 308–325.

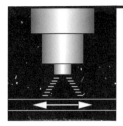

Glycerol Spraying/Low-Angle Rotary Metal Shadowing

Andreas Bremer, Markus Häner, and Ueli Aebi

I. Introduction

Heavy metal replication (Williams and Wyckoff, 1944) is one of the oldest and yet most effective methods to provide enhanced contrast when imaging biological specimens in the transmission electron microscope (TEM) (for review, see Fowler and Aebi, 1983). This technique requires that evenly distributed specimens (biomacromolecules, molecules or particles) adsorb to a support. The support should therefore have good adsorption properties for biomacromolecules. In addition, to minimize shadow-casting artifacts produced by corrugations of this support, it should be smooth at atomic dimensions. Mica fulfills both these requirements very well and thus emerges as an excellent support. The contrast-enhancing metal should produce a fine grain, separate easily from the support, and be stable in the electron beam. An example of a metal that meets these criteria is platinum.

The combination of mica and platinum was first proposed by Hall (1956) in his "mica replication" technique. Hall sprayed different solutions of molecules (i.e., an adenosine phosphate polymer, collagen, DNA, and fibrinogen) onto a piece of freshly cleaved mica. The mica was then dried in the vacuum and subsequently shadowed at a low angle (i.e., 5–15°) with platinum. The metal layer on the mica was stabilized by backing it with a layer each of SiO and Collodion. The resulting replica was then floated off the mica on distilled water, picked up on a specimen grid, and imaged in the TEM (Hall, 1956). Better spreading of the molecules on the mica surface and more reproducible and more even distribution of the specimens were achieved by adding glycerol to the solution to be sprayed (Fowler and Erickson, 1983; Tyler and Branton, 1980). Tyler and Branton coined the term *glycerol drying* for their modification of Hall's technique (i.e., they added glycerol and backed with carbon only). The more accurate and appropriate term used now is *glycerol spraying/low-angle rotary metal shadowing*.

For glycerol spraying, droplets of a glycerol-containing solution vaporized using air pressure are sprayed against a mica surface. The droplets spread on impact, and rapidly retract due to the high surface tension of the glycerol-containing solution. Molecules adsorbed to the mica substrate are left behind with little or no solvent surrounding them. Therefore, they instantaneously dry. The dried, retracted droplets produce the typical "droplet centers" (see Fig. 3a) that are seen with glycerol-sprayed preparations at low magnification. These droplet centers are a residue formed by the salts in the buffer and by unabsorbed protein and other debris that is swept off the mica by the advancing or retracting drop (Tyler and Branton, 1980).

Specimens that are suitable for glycerol-spraying/low-angle rotary metal shadowing range from single protein (e.g., myosin) and DNA molecules to relatively stable

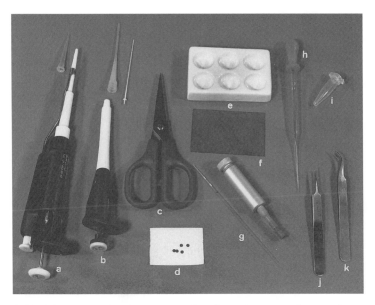

FIGURE 1 Standard equipment for glycerol spraying/low-angle rotary metal shadowing. (a,b) Two adjustable pipettes, Gilson Pipetman P20 (a) and Gilson Microman M25 (b), and the respective pipette tips; (c) pair of scissors; (d) copper specimen grids; (e) spot plate; (f) mica sheet; (g) 25-μl glass micropipettes with pipetter; (h) Pasteur pipettes; (i) Eppendorf tubes; (j,k) pair each of (j) fine, straight forceps and (k) fine, bent forceps.

noncovalent polymers such as intermediate filaments. The achievable resolution is a few nanometers and thus is sufficient to reveal the overall size and shape and/or the domain structure of many biomacromolecules.

II. Materials and Instrumentation

1. Gilson Pipetman adjustable pipette P20, with tips (Fig. 1a)
2. Gilson Microman adjustable pipette M25, with tips (Fig. 1b)
3. Pair of scissors (Fig. 1c)
4. Specimen grids (Fig. 1d), copper 400 mesh/inch, square, e.g., from Bopp & Company
5. Spot plate (Fig. 1e), e.g., from Balzers (Cat. No. B 8010 030 83)
6. Mica sheets (Fig. 1f); e.g., from Balzers (Cat. No. BU 006 027-T)
7. 25-μl glass micropipettes with pipetter (Fig. 1g)
8. Pasteur pipettes (Fig. 1h)
9. Eppendorf tubes (Fig. 1i)
10. Pair of fine, straight forceps (Fig. 1j), e.g., from Michel Terrier
11. Pair of fine, bent forceps (Fig. 1k), e.g., from Michel Terrier
12. Spray apparatus with air pressure controller (Figs. 2d and e)
13. Compressed air, 0.8 bar (80 psi)
14. Vortex apparatus
15. Glow-discharge apparatus, Balzers CTA 010 (Cat. No. BU 007 116-T, 220 V/50 Hz)

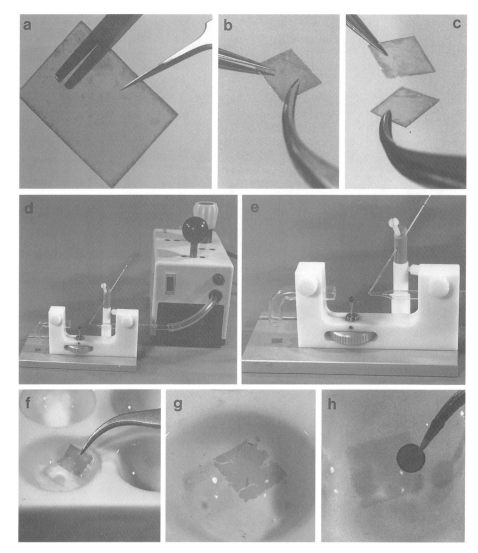

FIGURE 2 Selected steps of the glycerol spraying/low-angle rotary metal shadowing technique. (a) A piece of mica held with a pair of straight forceps is cut into square pieces with a pair of scissors. (b,c) Using forceps, the mica is next cleaved into two sheets. (d,e) The glycerol-containing solution is drawn into a 25-μl glass micropipette that is mounted on the spray apparatus so that it points to the center of the stream of pressurized air that is focused by a Pasteur pipette. (f) The Pt/C-shadowed and C-backed mica is slowly immersed into water, and (g) the mica sheet is removed when the Pt/C + C replica is floating on the water surface. (h) The replica is then placed on a specimen grid with a pair of forceps.

16. High-vacuum evaporation unit, Balzers BAE 080-T (Cat. No. BB P01 536 for 220 V/50 Hz); specifications:

   a. High-vacuum pumping unit with rotary vane pump

   b. Vacuum measuring device for rough and high vacuum

   c. Evaporation unit with controller and high current supply and cross-shaped vacuum chamber

17. Accessories for evaporation unit:

   a. Cold trap for BAE 080-T (Cat. No. BB 176 942-W)

   b. Quick-release flange WF 006, electron gun (Cat. No. BB 192 289-T)

c. Quick-release flange WF 011, rotary table (Cat. No. BB 192 241-T)

d. Quick-release flange WF 024, C-evaporator (Cat. No. BB 192 293-T)

e. Digital quartz crystal thickness meter QSG 060 (Cat. No. BG 804 250 for 220 V/50 Hz)

f. Electron beam evaporation device EVM 030, including electron beam gun EK-030 (Cat. No. BU 020 042-T)

18. Materials for evaporation unit:

a. Carbon rods for Pt/C evaporator (Balzers, Cat. No. BD 484 055)

b. Platinum inserts (Balzers, Cat. No. BD 481 505)

c. Carbon rods for C evaporator (Balzers, Cat. No. BD 484 060)

d. Tungsten cathodes (Balzers, Cat. No. BK 203 161)

19. Liquid nitrogen

20. Double-sided adhesive Scotch tape

III. Procedures

Solutions

1. *Glycerol, 100% anhydrous:* For example, from Fluka (Cat. No. 49770).

2. *Sodium hypochlorite solution 13–15%, technical grade:* For example, from Siegfried (Cat. No. 180550-01).

A. SPRAYING

Steps

1. Hold a piece of mica with a pair of straight forceps and cut it into square pieces (5 to 7 mm side length) with a pair of scissors (Fig. 2a).

2. Dilute the sample to a concentration of about 10–100 nM (0.1–1.0 mg/ml for most proteins) and pipette 20 μl into an Eppendorf tube.

3. Add 8.6 μl of 100% glycerol to the sample (i.e., 30% final glycerol concentration) using the Gilson Microman M25. Mix thoroughly with the pipette and vortex.

4. Draw 10 μl of the glycerol-containing solution into a 25-μl glass micropipette and mount it on the spray apparatus (Figs. 2d and e).

5. With two pairs of forceps, cleave the mica into two sheets (Figs. 2b and c).

6. With the freshly cleaved side up, place the mica below the bent glass tube of the spray apparatus. During spraying, the mica sheet should either be fixed with a piece of double-sided adhesive tape, as shown in Fig. 2e, or held in position with a pair of forceps.

7. Briefly (i.e., for about 1 sec) press the button of the air pressure control unit (depicted in Fig. 2d) to spray the sample suspension onto the freshly cleaved mica.

NOTE

The metal sphere placed in the spray path disperses the sample droplets evenly. The curved glass tube traps remaining large droplets, aggregates, and other heavy particles that will not follow the airflow when the spray path changes its direction by 90°.

8. Repeat spraying in the same way with another 10 μl of suspension onto the second piece of mica, etc.

B. METAL EVAPORATION

Steps

1. Switch on the thin-film quartz monitor.

2. Set up the electron gun for Pt/C evaporation and the carbon evaporation unit for C evaporation according to the instruction manual of the supplier.

3. The recommended working distance between the Pt/C tip in the electron gun and the middle of the table is 12 cm, and the tilt angle of the table relative to the evaporation axis should be 5°. For the C tips in the C evaporation unit, the recommended working distance is the same but the tilt angle should be 80° to 90°.

4. Mount the mica with double-sided adhesive tape onto the table. Make sure that the sprayed side of the mica is up!

5. Mount the table onto the rotating base in the vacuum chamber and start evacuating.

6. After 30 min, the vacuum meter should read better than 2×10^{-5} mbar.

7. Pour liquid nitrogen into the Meissner trap.

8. After an additional 5 min, the vacuum meter should read better than 6×10^{-6} mbar.

9. Degas Pt/C tip according to the instruction manual of the supplier.

10. Start the motor of the rotating base (set to about 120 rpm).

11. Set the thin-film quartz monitor to zero.

12. Start evaporating Pt/C according to the instruction manual. Open the manual shutter.

13. Read the frequency on the thin-film quartz monitor.

14. After the frequency has changed by 300 Hz, close the manual shutter and stop the evaporation.

15. Evaporate C according to the instruction manual of the supplier.

16. On a white reference the carbon layer should look deep brown (c.f., Figs. 2f and g).

FIGURE 3 Electron microscopy of glycerol sprayed/low-angle rotary metal shadowed preparations. (a) At low magnification, a very prominent feature of glycerol-sprayed/low-angle rotary metal shadowed preparations are the "droplet centers" formed by the salts in the buffer, unabsorbed protein, and debris that is swept off the mica by the advancing or retracting drop of the specimen/glycerol solution. (b) When moving from the center of such a droplet center outward, a transition from coarse and irregular to smooth and clean background is observed. Well-spread molecules are found in the zone that shows clean background (demarcated by dashed lines). The inset is a higher-magnification view that reveals the head-to-tail association of lamin dimers (see Heitlinger *et al.*, 1991).

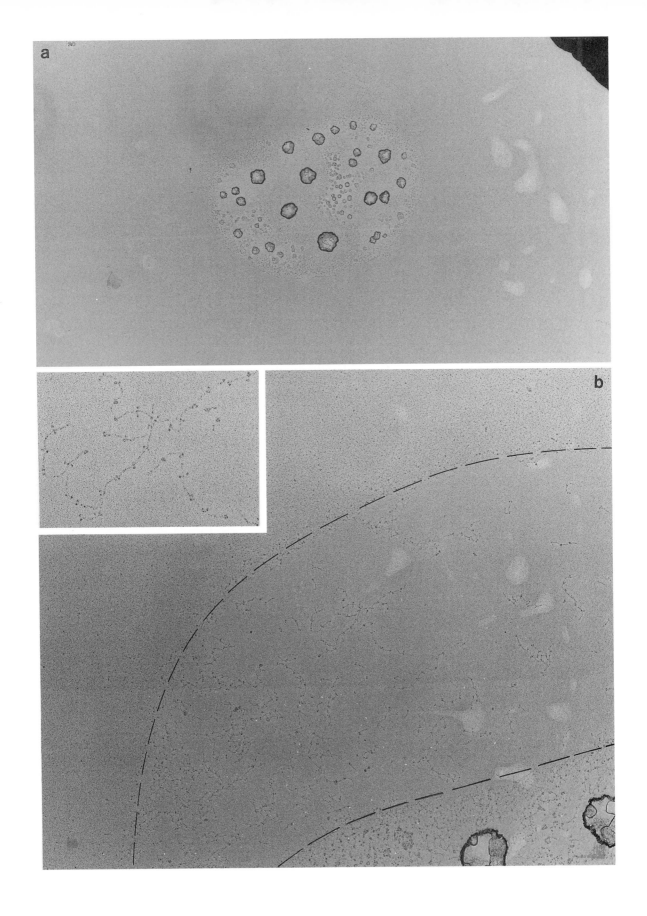

It is advisable to calibrate current and evaporation times of the power supply to be able to use standard settings.

17. Turn the rotating table off, break the vacuum, and remove the rotating table from the vacuum chamber.

C. FLOATING OFF THE Pt/C + C REPLICA

Steps

1. Fill the wells of the spot plate (Fig. 1e) with distilled water (Fig. 2f).

2. As illustrated in Fig. 2f, slowly immerse the mica at an angle of ~45°, holding it firmly with the forceps.

3. Submerge the mica completely and remove it when the Pt/C + C replica is floating on the water surface (Fig. 2g).

4. With a pair of forceps, submerge a freshly glow-discharged specimen grid, place it underneath the Pt/C + C replica, and use it as a sieve to collect it piece by piece.

5. Dry the specimen grids by layering them with the film side up onto a filter paper.

6. The specimen grids are now ready for inspection in the EM.

D. ELECTRON MICROSCOPY

Steps

1. Identify droplet centers as shown in Fig. 3a at a low magnification of, e.g., 5000×.

The droplet centers are easy to find if your sample is kept in nonvolatile buffers and/or contains salts. The droplet-center size varies from 5–50 μm. Choose droplet centers with a size of about 5–10 μm.

2. Increase the magnification to about 20,000–50,000×. Set coarse focusing, then slowly move from the center toward the edge of the droplet.

3. Dashed lines in Fig. 3b highlight the sharp transition from salt crystals to a clean background that is typically observed over increments of the droplet center distance by 0.5–2 μm. In this "clean belt" around the droplet center where well-spread and well-preserved protein particles are found (Fig. 3b, inset).

IV. Pitfalls

1. *Replica resists detaching from the mica.* Occasionally, the Pt/C + C replica sticks to the mica. The replica usually detaches more easily after the mica is incubated in a moist atmosphere at 37°C for 30 min. Alternatively, the replica may also be floated off on 6% sodium hypochlorite rather than water; however,

after this treatment, the replica has to be transferred with a platinum loop to distilled water and allowed to incubate for 10 min. One reason for frequent sticking of the Pt/C + C replica to the mica may be too good a vacuum during C evaporation. Breaking the vacuum after Pt/C evaporation, reevacuation to 7×10^{-5} mbar, and subsequent C evaporation may solve this problem.

2. *Preparation is not satisfactory.* (a) *Specimen-dependent:* The specimen may not be optimal for glycerol spraying. Some specimens including actin filaments are relatively sensitive to shearing forces and may thus break into small pieces on spraying. (b) *Buffer-dependent:* Many buffers and solutions can be used but detergents or high concentrations (i.e., $\geq 2\ M$) of urea or guanidine hydrochloride cause problems through eutectic effects. In this case, the buffer should be changed or diluted.

3. *Phases separate after addition of glycerol.* For good results, it is essential that the sample is a solution that contains glycerol. In the case of phase separation, different buffers should be tried. If volatile buffers are used, the evaporating unit should be evacuated for 2–3 hr rather than for 30 min before metal evaporation (see above).

ACKNOWLEDGMENTS

We are most grateful to Ms. H. Frefel, L. Müller, M. Steiner, and M. Zoller for rapid and excellent photographic work. This work was supported by the M. E. Müller Foundation of Switzerland, by Grant No. 31-30129.90 from the Swiss National Science Foundation (to U.A.), and by a graduate student fellowship of the Studienstiftung des Deutschen Volkes and a postdoctoral long-term fellowship of the International Human Frontier Science Program Organization (both to A.B.).

REFERENCES

Fowler, W. E., and Aebi, U. (1983) Preparation of Single Molecules and Supramolecular Complexes for High-Resolution Metal Shadowing. *J. Ultrastruct. Res.* **83**, 319–334

Fowler, W. E., and Erickson, H. P. (1983) Electron Microscopy of Fibrinogen, its Plasmic Fragments and Small Polymers. *Ann. N.Y. Acad. Sci. USA* **408**, 146–163.

Hall, C. E. (1956) Visualization of Individual Macromolecules with the Electron Microscope. *Proc. Natl. Acad. Sci. USA* **42**, 801–806.

Heitlinger, E., Peter, M., Häner, M., Lustig, A., Aebi, U., and Nigg, E. A. (1991) Expression of Chicken Lamin B2 in *Escherichia coli*: Characterization of its Structure, Assembly and Molecular Interactions. *J. Cell Biol.* **113**, 485–495.

Tyler, J. M., and Branton, D. (1980) Rotary Shadowing of Extended Molecules Dried from Glycerol. *J. Ultrastruct. Res.* **71**, 95–102.

Williams, R. C., and Wyckoff, R. G. W. (1944) The Thickness of Electron Microscopic Objects. *J. Appl. Phys.* **15**, 712–716.

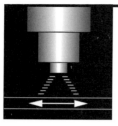

Rapid Freezing of Biological Specimens for Freeze-Fracture and Deep Etching

Nicholas J. Severs and David M. Shotton

I. Principles of Rapid Freezing

Stabilization of biological structure by the physical process of freezing (cryofixation) forms the starting point for freeze-fracture and deep etching (see article by David M. Shotton in this volume). To avoid ultrastructural damage to the specimen caused by the growth of large ice crystals, rapid freezing is essential. True vitrification (i.e., solidification without crystallization) can be achieved only by cooling rates greater than -2×10^5 °C/sec over the critical range 20 to -100°C, i.e., cooling over this range in a fraction of a millisecond. Rates of this magnitude can be attained in very thin (<3 μm) films of suspended liquid that are rapidly plunged into liquid nitrogen-cooled liquid propane or ethane, and particulate specimens (e.g., viruses) embedded in such frozen thin films may be directly observed in the vitrified state on the cold stage of a cryoelectron microscope. For freeze-fracture and deep etching, however, the requirement for a larger specimen size precludes true vitrification, because the maximal cooling rate possible for the deeper areas of the specimen is limited by the rate of heat conduction through the specimen itself. The techniques employed for the rapid freezing of such specimens may be divided into three groups: conventional rapid freezing techniques, with cooling rates of between -10^3 and -10^4 °C/sec; ultrarapid freezing techniques, with rates in excess of -10^4 °C/sec; and hyperbaric freezing in which, although a relatively slow cooling rate is employed, ice crystal nucleation and growth are retarded by high pressure. Comprehensive reviews of the field as a whole can be found in books by Robards and Sleytr (1985), Steinbrecht and Zierold (1987), Echlin (1992), and Severs and Shotton (1994).

A word of warning before putting what you read into practice. Working with cryogenic liquids is potentially hazardous. Novices to the field should ensure that they are fully conversant with appropriate safety precautions by consulting their Institutional Safety Advisor. For further guidance see Section IIIA and chapters on safety in the books by Robards and Sleytr (1985) and Steinbrecht and Zierold (1987).

II. Conventional Rapid Freezing for Freeze-Fracture

A. CHEMICAL FIXATION AND GLYCERINATION

Ice crystal damage can be avoided at relatively slow cooling rates if the specimen is first infiltrated with a buffered cryoprotectant. Glycerol, used at concentrations of 20 to 30%, is by far the most commonly used cryoprotectant. Prior fixation with aldehydes (usually glutaraldehyde) is routinely carried out with the aim of minimizing cryoprotectant-induced artifacts, although such aldehyde fixation may itself induce artifacts. A few specimens (e.g., cells of low water content, such as yeast and bacteria, or concentrated membrane preparations such as erythrocyte ghosts) can be directly frozen by conventional methods without chemical pretreatment.

B. MOUNTING OF SPECIMENS PRIOR TO FREEZING

To be processed through the various steps of freeze-fracture or deep etching, specimens are first mounted on specially designed supports. Standard specimen supports are made from metals of high thermal conductivity and are as small as is compatible with ease of handling. The precise design of support used will vary according to the nature of the specimen, the type of freeze-fracture apparatus, and the manner in which fracturing is executed. Careful mounting is critical and should always be done with the aid of a binocular microscope.

For conventional knife fracture of cell suspensions (see article by David M. Shotton), a droplet of concentrated cell suspension is placed on the central raised portion of a cleaned, flat-topped support. Avoid bubbles, which will explode when the specimen is evacuated, and avoid getting liquid on the rim of the holder, as this will prevent it from fitting the specimen table after freezing. Tissue blocks for knife fracture are conventionally mounted in similar supports that have a central well. The tissue is held securely in the well with a portion protruding for subsequent fracture. Flat-type holders without wells can also be used as mounts for tissue specimens; in this case polyvinyl alcohol (PVA) mounting medium is used to attach the sample firmly to the holder. PVA mounting medium has a multitude of uses in freeze-fracture preparation. It consists of 20–30% PVA in phosphate-buffered saline (PBS) containing 20–33% glycerol. A simple recipe is to dissolve PVA powder (mean molecular weight 10 kDa) to 45% in PBS by prolonged heating at below 100°C in a double boiler, and then dilute with half the volume of glycerol to give a solution containing 30% PVA and 33% glycerol. It may be conveniently applied from a syringe or using a sharpened applicator stick, and should be stored at 4°C or, for prolonged storage, at −20°C.

As an alternative to fracturing by knife, specimens may be fractured by being broken apart in a hinged double-replica device. This dictates an entirely different type of specimen mount involving a pair of holders between which the specimen is inserted. The double-mount principle was originally devised for making complementary replicas, but is often convenient for routine preparation.

A number of techniques have been developed for mounting cultured cells. The most versatile is that of Pauli et al. (1977). A piece of plastic coverslip, on which the cells have been grown, is inverted on a droplet of PVA on a standard flat-topped support. Leave a portion of the coverslip projecting horizontally by about 0.5 mm. Fracturing can then be done by raising the tip of the knife from below the coverslip; this flips the coverslip off the frozen PVA, directing the fracture plane into the cells.

C. FREEZING

Immersion of specimens directly into liquid nitrogen (boiling point −196°C) is of no use in freezing biological specimens for subsequent ultrastructural work, as only slow cooling rates can be achieved ($\sim 10^3$ °C/sec), leading to extensive specimen damage due to the growth of large ice crystals. This happens because the heat input from immersing a warm specimen in liquid nitrogen, which at atmospheric pressure is at its boiling point, generates an insulating layer of evaporated nitrogen gas which severely limits the rate of heat loss from the specimen (the *leidenfrost* effect). However, nitrogen slush, a mixture of solid and liquid nitrogen at its freezing point ($-208°C$), is an effective cryogen. The disadvantages of using nitrogen are that it cannot be kept near its freezing point using a secondary coolant, and that it has a very narrow freezing-to-boiling point temperature range ($16°C$). However, cooling rates obtainable with nitrogen slush, providing it is properly prepared and used, can be comparable to those achieved with other cryogens, and are certainly adequate for freezing cryoprotected specimens. The more widespread use of nitrogen slush should be encouraged in view of the deleterious effects of the commonly used halocarbon cryogens (see below) on the earth's ozone layer.

A simple way of making nitrogen slush is to fill a small, well-insulated styrofoam box with liquid nitrogen, place it in a plastic desiccator, and evacuate using a water pump or rotary pump until, through loss of latent heat of evaporation, the nitrogen ceases to bubble and solidifies. Wait 30 sec longer, then release the vacuum. Some of the solid nitrogen will melt, giving a slush at $-208°C$. Repeat this process several times to ensure that the entire volume of nitrogen is brought down to the same temperature before removing it for use. Slush can similarly be made using a standard vacuum evaporator or a commercially available slusher. Use the slush immediately for freezing specimens by immersion, as described below. Specimens should not cause bubbling as they enter the cryogen. After a few minutes (the exact time depending on the precise manner of preparation and the container used) the solid nitrogen will have melted and a new batch of slush must be prepared.

Rather than freezing in nitrogen slush, however, the standard method of freezing fixed and glycerinated specimens is to immerse the mounted specimen manually into a secondary cryogenic liquid, cooled to near its freezing point using liquid nitrogen as the primary cryogen. Such a secondary cryogenic liquid ideally combines the properties of high thermal conductivity, a high heat capacity, a freezing point close to the boiling point of liquid nitrogen, and a large temperature difference between its freezing and boiling points. The refrigerant gas Freon 22 (chlorodifluoromethane, $CHClF_2$, melting point $-160°C$, boiling point $-40°C$) is the standard secondary cryogen for the freezing of cryoprotected specimens, as its properties approach those of the ideal cryogen well enough, and it is clean, nonflammable, and nontoxic. Freon 12 (CCl_2F_2, melting point $-155°C$, boiling point $-30°C$) is also widely used. The standard equipment for freezing comprises a small receptacle at the top end of a solid metal cylinder which is supported within a dewar flask filled with liquid nitrogen. First liquefy the Freon gas by gently squirting it into the bottom of the cold receptacle. Wait for the Freon to solidify completely, then create a central pool in it by melting with a small metal rod. When the Freon crystals start to grow back toward the center of the liquid pool, this shows that the liquid has cooled to its freezing point and is ready to use for freezing. Freezing is accomplished by swiftly immersing the mounted specimen below the surface of the cryogen. After waiting 2 sec, transfer the specimen rapidly into liquid nitrogen in a second dewar flask, flicking off as much of the excess liquid Freon as possible during the transfer so that it does not solidify and interfere with subsequent specimen mounting. Always precool the tips of forceps under liquid nitrogen before further manipulation of the frozen specimens.

III. Ultrarapid Freezing

Ultrarapid freezing techniques have opened a new chapter in biological ultrastructure research, permitting the examination of specimens that have been frozen directly from the living state, without prior chemical treatment. Four principal methods exist for the ultrastructural preservation of biological specimens by extremely rapid freezing (cryofixation) in the absence of cryoprotectants: plunging, spraying, jetting,

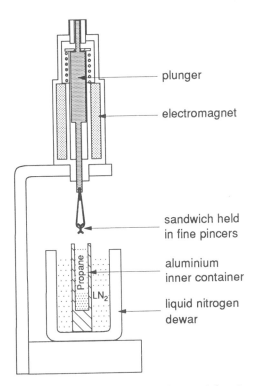

FIGURES 1–4 Apparatus for rapid freezing.

FIGURE 1 Example of a solenoid-operated plunge freezing apparatus. (Adapted, with permission, from Escaig, 1982).

and slamming (reviewed by Menco, 1986; Gilkey and Staehelin, 1986). With all these methods, good ultrastructural preservation is confined to a 10- to 20-μm surface layer. Further from the surface, the inherently low thermal conductivity of biological tissue limits the rate of heat loss and unavoidably leads to the growth of large ice crystals and consequent ultrastructural damage, similar to that observed if samples are frozen without chemical cryoprotection by standard immersion freezing.

A. PLUNGE FREEZING

By optimizing conditions for immersion of specimens in liquid cryogens, considerable improvements in cooling rates can be achieved, sufficient to permit observation of well-frozen structure in the absence of chemical cryoprotection. Numerous pneumatic, solenoid-operated, and spring-driven devices incorporating these features have been developed (Fig. 1). Key conditions for efficient cooling are that the specimen should be of maximal surface-to-volume ratio and mounted in thin supports of low mass, and that its entry velocity into the cryogen should be high (hence the term *plunge freezing*). The stirred cryogen should be in a deep container so that the specimen can complete cooling over the critical range while still in motion.

Liquid propane (C_3H_8, melting point −189°C, boiling point −42°C) and liquid ethane (C_2H_6, melting point −172°C, boiling point −89°C), cooled with liquid nitrogen toward their freezing points, are the most suitable cryogens for plunge freezing; they are, however, potentially hazardous and need special care in handling.[1]

[1]Extreme care must always be taken to eliminate any possibility of explosion hazard when working with liquified flammable gases, as ignition of even a small volume of liquid can have devastating conse-

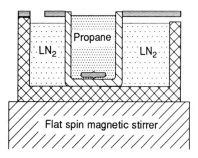

FIGURE 2 Vessel for holding liquid propane for manual plunge freezing under optimized conditions. The vessel is constructed from everyday laboratory materials; propane is held in an inner vessel (plastic beaker) of ~200 cm³, surrounded by liquid nitrogen in a styrofoam box. Stirring the propane reduces thermal gradients and ensures maximal contact with cryogen when specimens are rapidly inserted by hand. For further details, see Severs and Shotton (1994).

The usual mounting method is to sandwich the specimen between a pair of thin supports; not only can these mounts be readily adapted to fulfill the criteria above but, on their separation during fracturing in a double-replica device, the fracture plane tends conveniently to follow a superficial well-frozen layer of the specimen, adjacent to the support. If a mechanical plunge freezing machine is not available, simple manual plunge freezing of specimens into propane under optimized conditions is always worth trying, particularly for the freezing of sandwich-mounted suspensions or cells. A container suitable for manual propane plunge freezing can be built from common laboratory materials as shown in Fig. 2. The entry velocity attainable will not be as high or as reproducible as that achieved using a mechanical device, but the method is simple, has negligible cost, and, with practice, gives satisfactory results.

B. SPRAY FREEZING

Spray freezing is a version of immersion freezing in which, to lose heat rapidly, the specimen size is reduced to microscopic droplets, and as such is suitable only for suspensions of single cells, organelles, or membranes (Bachmann and Schmitt-Fumian, 1973). The low thermal mass of the individual droplets permits satisfactory freezing in the absence of cryoprotection. A summary of the procedure is shown in Fig. 3. The sample is forcefully sprayed, using an air brush, into liquid propane at $-180°C$. The ideal droplet size is ~10 μm, but cells of larger size (e.g., *Paramecium*) can be successfully frozen by pressure jetting a fine stream of the suspension through apertures of 20–100 μm. The sample is warmed to $-85°C$ on a cold stage, and the liquid propane evaporated using a vacuum pump. The powder of tiny frozen droplets is then mixed with butyl benzene (melting point $-88°C$) and transferred, using a cold metal wire, onto standard gold–nickel alloy supports held nearby on the cold stage. Immersion of the specimen supports into liquid nitrogen solidifies the butyl benzene, cementing the samples to the holders. Apart from specialized applications,

---

quences. Beware also that below $-183°C$, oxygen will condense from the air, forming a potentially explosive mixture. All work involving liquified flammable gases must be undertaken within the confines of an extraction fume cupboard suitable for flammable vapors, and naked flames and electrical switches that might generate sparks must be totally excluded from the work area. The liquified cryogens should not be stored, but should be safely discarded after each experiment either by evaporating them within the fume cupboard or, if direct access to outdoors is available, by carefully pouring the liquid onto the ground at a site distant from people, cars, buildings, and other manmade installations. Liquified gases should never be poured down a drain.

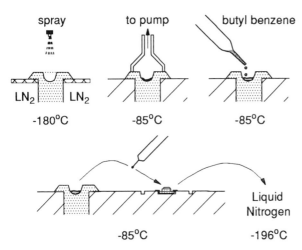

FIGURE 3 Spray freezing. Minute droplets of a cell suspension are sprayed into propane, held in a metal container supported in a dewar flask of liquid nitrogen. The metal container is transferred onto a cold stage and warmed to −85°C. The propane is removed using a vacuum pump, and butyl benzene is mixed with the frozen droplets. The resultant suspension is transferred, using a wire loop, to a standard flat-topped specimen support. Immersion of the specimen support under liquid nitrogen solidifies the butyl benzene, and the specimen can then be processed for knife fracture in the freeze-fracture machine.

spray freezing has been largely superseded by other more straightforward methods (e.g., plunge freezing a sandwich-mounted suspension into propane). It does, however, form an integral part of *quenched flow* devices designed to capture rapid dynamic cellular events, on a millisecond time scale, at defined intervals after rapid mixing of cells with a stimulating agent (Knoll, 1994).

C. JET FREEZING

In *jet freezing*, instead of moving the specimen rapidly through the cryogen, the reverse is done; propane is squirted at high velocity through single or double jets onto the stationary specimen (for review, see Gilkey and Staehelin, 1986). The commercially available apparatus (Balzers and RMC) are equipped with dual jets, which simultaneously squirt liquid propane at each side of a sample (e.g., a cell or membrane suspension) sandwich-mounted between a pair of thin copper supports. One-sided propane jet freezers are relatively easy to construct with the aid of workshop facilities, and have been used successfully in a number of laboratories.

D. SLAM FREEZING

In essence, the *slam freezing* (or *metal mirror freezing*) technique is very simple; the biological specimen is brought into rapid and firm contact with the highly polished surface of a pure copper block, cooled to a temperature of ∼18 K (−255°C) with liquid helium (boiling point 4 K, −269°C). Variations on this theme include the use of a silver block in place of copper, and cooling by means of liquid nitrogen instead of liquid helium. Various designs of slam freezing machine have been proposed (e.g., Heuser, 1981; Escaig, 1982) of which a number are commercially available. In the Heuser apparatus, the specimen is fixed beneath the lower end of a vertical falling plunger. As the specimen falls, a shutter, which protects the liquid helium-cooled copper block from condensation, is opened, the specimen strikes the

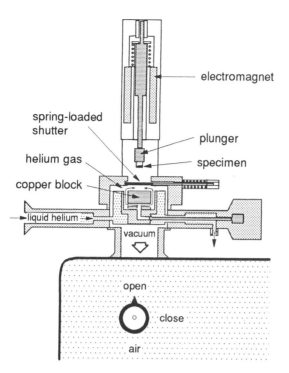

FIGURE 4 Example of an automated metal block slam freezing device, as developed by Escaig (1982). The specimen is mounted at the end of the plunger. The highly polished pure copper block is quickly cooled to liquid helium temperature in a closed compartment under vacuum. Helium gas is then admitted to the vacuum chamber. When atmospheric pressure is reached, the spring-loaded shutter opens to expose the copper block and activates a micro-switch controlling the solenoid, which propels the specimen onto the surface of the clean cold copper block.

copper block, and freezing is completed within 2 msec. The Escaig device uses an electromagnetic plunger to propel the specimen, and the helium-cooled block is protected under vacuum until the shutter opens just prior to specimen contact (Fig. 4). Both machines are designed to ensure that the specimen does not bounce on impact but remains applied firmly to the block until removed. Specimen mounting systems for slam freezing vary according to the apparatus employed, the requirements of the specimen, and its subsequent processing. Most incorporate features to cushion the specimen from the full force of the impact and to limit its flattening (e.g., by mounting it within a spacer ring on a piece of foam rubber or fixed lung).

If a sophisticated automated slam freezer is not available, it is well worth making a manual version based on the design of Dempsey and Bullivant (1976). A copper block, equipped with a handle, is cooled in liquid nitrogen, then raised, the upper surface wiped with absorbent tissue, and the specimen manually slammed onto it. Slam freezing using automated slammers reproducibly gives excellent cryofixation in the surface 10-μm layer of the sample, and satisfactory results can, with experience, also be obtained with simple manual freezers. Deeper regions of the specimen are badly damaged by large ice crystals and compression shock, and so, for freeze-fracture replication, the samples have to be fractured with precision by microtome through the well-frozen surface layer.

IV. High-Pressure Freezing

In high-pressure freezing, a sandwich-mounted specimen is frozen by double-sided jetting with liquid nitrogen while briefly being subjected to a pressure of 2100 bar

(Moor, 1987; Dahl and Staehelin, 1989). At high pressure, the critical cooling rate needed to limit ice crystals to a size below that causing ultrastructural damage is reduced from −10,000°C/sec to approximately −100 to −500°C/sec. This cryoprotective effect is achieved because high pressure lowers the freezing point and reduces the rate of ice nucleation and growth to a degree equivalent to using 20% glycerol for cryoprotection. The major advantage of high-pressure freezing is that structure is well preserved to a much greater depth (600 μm in planar samples, 1 mm for spherical samples) than is possible with the ultrarapid freezing techniques discussed above (Gilkey and Staehelin, 1986). High-pressure freezing is thus particularly useful for the direct freezing of solid tissue specimens.

V. Advantages of Ultrarapid and High-Pressure Freezing Methods

Ultrarapid and high-pressure freezing methods offer a multitude of advantages as preparation methods in cell biology. By avoiding the need for chemical fixation, these cryofixation techniques potentially permit the study of cell structure in a condition close to that existing in life. Because one particular instant in a biological process can be sampled, the accumulation of intermediate stages, which may occur during slow death in aldehyde fixatives, is avoided. Living specimens can thus be frozen for ultrastructural examination at known intervals after application of a biological stimulus. This has made it possible to use the electron microscope for studies of transient biological events which are completed within a few seconds or even, in certain favorable instances, within a few milliseconds. The ability to undertake such direct kinetic studies was a significant breakthrough in cell biology, as previously, sequences of such rapid events could only be guessed at indirectly from images of chemically fixed specimens. Slam freezing, spray freezing, plunge freezing, and jet freezing methods have all been adapted to permit time-resolved analysis of rapid events (Knoll, 1994).

Another important advantage is that ultrarapid-frozen specimens can be subjected to *deep etching* or freeze-drying, a technique in which water molecules are allowed to sublime from the frozen surface of a fractured (or in some cases, unfractured) specimen before replication (see article by David M. Shotton). Glycerol cannot be sublimed, but by directly freezing specimens in dilute aqueous solutions, the outer surfaces of membranes, extracellular matrix components, and intracellular cytoskeletal elements can be exposed by deep etching or freeze-drying. For deep-etch observations of the cytoskeleton and internal membrane surfaces of cells, a compromise has to be made to obtain clean views unobscured by cytoplasmic components. Typical procedures involve lysing cultured cells attached to a substrate with Triton X-100, or physically tearing them open by peeling off a strip of nitrocellulose membrane that has been allowed to adhere to their dorsal surfaces; this is followed by rinsing in dilute buffer to remove cytoplasmic components, light fixation with aldehydes, and then immersion in 10–15% methanol immediately prior to freezing. The methanol acts as a cryoprotectant, increasing the depth of good freezing, and also has the advantage of being volatile at −100°C (under standard vacuum conditions), thus facilitating the etching process. This application is thus quite distinct from studies aiming to preserve structure in the native state, but it is a very important one, as it provides access to structural information that cannot be obtained by other electron microscopical methods (Heuser, 1981). Deep etching has also been adapted to study macromolecules absorbed to microscopic mica flakes (Heuser, 1989).

In addition to freeze-fracture and deep etching, specimens stabilized by ultrarapid freezing may be examined in sections via freeze substitution or cryoultramicrotomy. Here the ability to preserve antigenicity by avoidance of fixation-induced alterations to epitopes is of prime importance for immunocytochemical studies. The complementary application of both freeze-substitution and freeze-fracture or deep etching after ultrarapid freezing is currently proving to be of wide application in cell biology. Details of freeze-fracture immunocytochemistry are given by Severs (1994).

REFERENCES

Bachmann, L., and Schmitt-Fumian, W. W. (1973) Spray-freezing and freeze-etching. *In "Freeze-Etching: Techniques and Applications"* (E. L. Benedetti and P. Favard, eds.), pp. 73–80. Société Française de Microscopie Électronique, Paris.

Dahl, R., and Staehelin, L. A. (1989) High-pressure freezing for the preservation of biological structure: Theory and practice. *J. Electron Microsc. Tech.* **13,** 161–174.

Dempsey, G. P., and Bullivant, S. (1976) A copper block method for freezing non-cryoprotected tissue to produce ice-crystal-free regions for electron microscopy. *J. Microsc.* **106,** 251–271.

Echlin, P. (1992) *"Low-Temperature Microscopy and Analysis."* Plenum Press, New York.

Escaig, J. (1982) New instruments which facilitate rapid freezing at 83K and 6K. *J. Microsc.* **126,** 221–230.

Gilkey, J. C., and Staehelin, L. A. (1986) Advances in ultrarapid freezing for the preservation of cellular ultrastructure. *J. Electron Microsc. Tech.* **3,** 177–210.

Heuser, J. (1989) Protocol for 3-D visualization of molecules on mica via the quick freeze, deep etch technique. *J. Electron Microsc. Tech.* **13,** 244–263.

Heuser, J. E. (1981) Preparing biological specimens for stereo microscopy by the quick-freeze, deep-etch, rotary-replication technique. *In "Methods in Cell Biology,"* Vol. 22, pp 97–122. Academic Press, New York.

Knoll, G. (1994) Time resolved analysis of rapid events. *In "Rapid Freezing, Freeze Fracture and Deep Etching"* (N. J. Severs and D. M. Shotton, eds.). Wiley–Liss, New York.

Menco, B. P. M. (1986) A survey of ultra-rapid cryofixation methods with particular emphasis on applications to freeze-fracturing, freeze-etching, and freeze-substitution. *J. Electron Microsc. Tech.* **4,** 177–240.

Moor, H. (1987) Theory and practice of high pressure freezing. *In "Cryotechniques in Biological Electron Microscopy"* (R. A. Steinbrecht and K. Zierold, eds.), pp. 175–191. Springer-Verlag, Berlin.

Pauli, B. U., Weinstein, R. S., Soble, L. W., and Alroy, J. (1977) Freeze-fracture of monolayer cultures. *J. Cell Biol.* **72,** 763–769.

Robards, A. W., and Sleytr, U. B. (1985) Low temperature methods in biological electron microscopy. *In "Practical Methods in Electron Microscopy"* (A. M. Glauert, ed.), Vol. 10. Elsevier, Amsterdam.

Severs, N. J. (1994) Freeze-fracture cytochemistry: An explanatory survey of methods. *In "Rapid Freezing, Freeze Fracture and Deep Etching"* (N. J. Severs and D. M. Shotton, eds.). Wiley–Liss, New York.

Severs, N. J., and Shotton, D. M. (eds.) (1994) *"Rapid Freezing, Freeze Fracture and Deep Etching."* Wiley–Liss, New York.

Steinbrecht, R. A., and Zierold, K. (1987) *"Cytotechniques in Biological Electron Microscopy."* Springer-Verlag, Berlin.

Freeze Fracture and Freeze Etching

David M. Shotton

I. Principles of the Freeze-Fracture Technique

The technique of freeze fracture is unique among electron microscopic (EM) methods in that it gives *en face* views of the internal organization of biological membranes, allowing the study of the in-plane distribution of integral proteins spanning the lipid bilayer and of other membrane features, as a function of developmental stage, experimental conditions, or onset of disease. Although freeze fracture can be undertaken using very simple equipment that can be constructed in any workshop, in conjunction with a standard vacuum coating unit (Bullivant and Ames, 1966; Bullivant *et al.*, 1979), or using a commercial attachment to such a coating unit, it is normally performed within a specialized high-vacuum freeze-fracture apparatus, with a temperature-controlled liquid nitrogen-cooled holder for specimens. The standard procedure for specimen preparation by freeze-fracture in such an apparatus is summarized in Fig. 1 and can be described briefly as follows.

A. FREEZING

Conventionally, a small block of biological tissue (approx $2 \times 2 \times 1$ mm) or a droplet of cell suspension on a copper or gold support (Fig. 1a), stabilized by glutaraldehyde fixation and cryoprotected by infiltration with 25–30% glycerol, is first rapidly frozen by manually plunging it, as described in the article by Nicholas J. Severs and David M. Shotton, into a liquified cryogen (e.g., Freon-22, chlorodifluoromethane), cooled to near its freezing point of −160°C by liquid nitrogen (Fig. 1b).

B. FRACTURING

After storage in liquid nitrogen, the frozen specimen is quickly transferred to the precooled temperature-controlled specimen table within the high-vacuum chamber of a freeze-fracture apparatus, either via an airlock, or more usually after venting the chamber, which is then reevacuated to better than 2×10^{-6} mbar (Fig. 1c). Freeze fracture is traditionally achieved by striking the specimen, maintained at −110°C, with a cold razor blade clamped within the jaws of the hollow microtome knife blade holder, which is itself filled and cooled to below −150°C with liquid nitrogen. As when a log of wood is cleaved by an axe, a plane of free fracture precedes the blade edge, following a line of least resistance through the frozen specimen (Fig. 1d). When this fracture plane encounters a cell, it frequently passes along the center of the lipid bilayer of the plasma membrane, as this is a line of

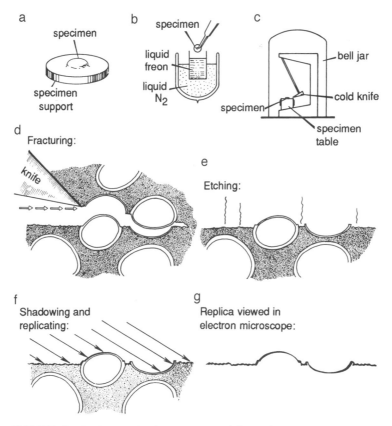

FIGURE 1 Basic steps in the conventional freeze-fracture procedure, described in the text. (Courtesy of Daniel Branton, first published by Shotton, D.M. (1982) *J. Neurol. Sci.* **57,** 161–190. Reproduced by permission.)

weakness at cryogenic temperatures, splitting the asymmetric membrane into an extracellular (E) half and a protoplasmic (P) half (nomenclature of Branton *et al.,* 1975). Integral proteins that span the membrane may partition with one or the other half of the membrane, from which they will protrude to form small freeze-fracture intramembrane particles (IMPs), leaving complementary pits in the other half-membrane from which they were wrenched. Internal cell membranes may be similarly fractured, if the fracture plane initially passes through the plasma membrane and into the cell interior.

Alternatively (not illustrated), the specimen may be sandwiched between two metal supports before freezing, and the frozen specimen sandwich placed in a special hinged specimen cold stage. When opened, this separates the two apposed specimen supports, propagating a tensile fracture through the frozen specimen. As both halves of the fractured specimen are retained, one on each specimen support, both may be replicated to give complementary replicas.

C. ETCHING

The specimen may then optionally be etched after fracturing (Fig. 1e). During etching, water molecules are allowed to sublime from the surface of the fractured specimen, which for this purpose is fractured at a slightly higher temperature at which the sublimation pressure of ice exceeds the partial pressure of the residual water molecules in the vacuum atmosphere by about tenfold (typically −100°C for a vacuum of 2×10^{-6} mbar), leading to an etching rate of about 2 nm per second.

The sublimed water molecules are condensed on a nearby cold trap, typically the underside of the cooled knife, which is positioned for this purpose above the fractured specimen. Etching lowers the specimen ice table and exposes the true surfaces of freeze-fractured membranes, thereby revealing membrane surface features of interest which were previously obscured by the overlying ice. Originally, such etching could only be applied effectively to specimens such as suspensions of individual cells (erythrocytes, yeast, bacteria, etc.) which can be frozen by standard immersion methods (see article by Severs and Shotton) without ultrastructural damage in the absence of glycerol, as this cryoprotectant is nonvolatile at cryogenic temperatures and thus obscures surfaces during etching. However, the introduction of ultrarapid freezing techniques using liquid helium or liquid propane (see article by Severs and Shotton) has made it possible to freeze a wide variety of living tissue sufficiently rapidly to achieve good cryofixation of the surface layer of cells in the absence of chemical fixation and glycerol cryoprotection, enabling their subsequent etching. More extensive etching (deep etching or freeze-drying) may be used to reveal more extensive cytoskeletal, extracellular, or membrane features (see article by Severs and Shotton; and Severs and Shotton, 1995).

D. REPLICATION

The frozen surface of a freeze-fractured or freeze-etched specimen is rich in topographical detail but is extremely labile. To convert this labile structural information into stable contrast information accessible in the electron microscope, the specimen is obliquely shadowed with a thin layer (typically with an average thickness of 1.5 to 2 nm) of atomic platinum (Fig. 1f), deposited from an evaporative source, usually an electron bombardment gun. The platinum atoms landing on the frozen surface of the replica do not form a homogeneous layer, even on smooth surfaces. Instead, after traveling short distances laterally on the membrane surface as they lose kinetic energy, the atoms coalesce to form small platinum grains, about 1 nm in diameter, leaving the immediately adjacent surface free from platinum. The deposited film contains 5% (w/w) carbon with the platinum, which limits the size of the grains to about 1.5 nm. These frequently form on existing surface particles, giving a "decoration" effect which may accentuate specimen detail in a useful way. The presence of these grains effectively limits the resolution of the replica to approximately 2.5 nm.

With conventional unidirectional shadowing, the platinum atoms accumulate on the near side of protrusions, leaving platinum-free "shadows" in their lee. Alternatively, the specimen may be rotated during replication, while maintaining a constant platinum deposition angle. Such rotary shadowing, which results in a uniform distribution of platinum grains around protrusions and an absence of shadows, is particularly useful for deep-etched specimens. This discontinuous and physically fragile platinum surface replica is then strengthened by a uniform backing (about 15 to 20 nm thick) of electron-translucent carbon (not shown in Fig. 1), deposited either unidirectionally from above or, for additional strength, from an angle of 75° while the specimen is rotating. This combined platinum–carbon replica is then removed from the vacuum chamber; is cleaned free of all the original biological material by digestion of the underlying thawed specimen with bleach or chromic acid, followed by washing with distilled water; and is viewed directly in the transmission electron microscope (Fig. 1g).

II. Technical Advice

Although precise details of the operation of the freeze-fracture apparatus, replication conditions, gun adjustments, etc., will vary between different models of freeze-fracture apparatus, and should be conducted according to the manufacturers' instructions, the following advice, based on experience with the Balzers BAF 300 machine, should be of general applicability.

A. BEFORE THE FREEZE-FRACTURE RUN

Check that there is enough liquid nitrogen. Prepare the electron bombardment guns for use according to the manufacturer's instructions. For Balzers electron beam guns, remove collimating covers, carefully clean away waste shadow material from the previous run using artists' brushes, renew or adjust the position of the anodes as necessary, taking care to avoid touching the tungsten cathode coils which become extremely brittle once used, and reassemble and replace the guns, reconnecting the high-tension cables. Check the incident shadowing angle of the platinum gun, changing it if necessary. The normal angle of incidence for unidirectional platinum shadowing of freeze-fracture replicas is 45°; from 6° to 16° is most useful for rotary shadowing of freeze-etch specimens, depending on the nature of the specimen; and 9° and 6° are used for unidirectional and rotary low-angle shadowing, respectively, of individual macromolecules absorbed onto mica sheets. For microtome fracture, fit an appropriate specimen stage and a reusable tungsten blade or a new single-edged carbon steel razor blade. Do not use stainless-steel razor blades, since their edges bend on contact with ice and thus do not fracture well. Using a binocular dissecting microscope, ensure that the blade is horizontal above the specimen positions. Alternatively, fit a double-replica opening device in place of the blade and an appropriate double-replica specimen stage. Good thermal contacts should be ensured by the use of small amounts of a thermal conductive paste or high-vacuum grease. If appropriate for your machine, prepare and fit a shadow paper (a piece of thin card with a central cutout, placed as a collar around the specimen stage where it will intercept some of the evaporated material). This will provide a permanent record of the replication run, to supplement a chart recorder trace of the stage temperature and quartz crystal replica thickness monitor output.

B. PRECOOLING OF THE STAGE AND SPECIMEN PREPARATION

Close and evacuate the chamber. Turn on the quartz crystal replica thickness monitor to warm up. At a vacuum of 10^{-4} mbar or better, turn on the chart recorder, start the stage cooling, and briefly test-fire both guns. Under liquid nitrogen, place the specimens in the appropriate specimen holder in preparation for transfer to the specimen stage of the apparatus.

C. LOADING OF THE SPECIMENS

After the stage has been allowed to equilibrate at its minimum temperature (below −170°C) for 5 min, turn off the high-vacuum gauge, vent the chamber with dry nitrogen gas (conveniently generated by running liquid nitrogen through a length of uninsulated copper tubing) to prevent the water vapor contamination, which will occur if venting with air, open the chamber door or specimen access port, quickly transfer the specimens from liquid nitrogen to the cold specimen table, close the chamber, and immediately reevacuate. Modern freeze-fracture machines are often equipped with an airlock, so that specimens may be loaded directly into the chamber without breaking the vacuum.

D. SPECIMEN TEMPERATURE ADJUSTMENT

At a vacuum of 10^{-4} mbar or better, start the knife cooling, and raise the specimen temperature to $-110°C$ (for freeze-fracture) or $-100°C$ (for freeze-etching). For the standard specimen stage, the indicated temperature and the actual stage temperature should correspond fairly exactly; however, the poor thermal contacts that may occur when using certain designs of double-replica specimen holders means that the specimens may in practice be 5° to 15° warmer than indicated, so that the indicated specimen stage temperature must be set low to compensate. One should determine these temperatures, etching rates, and contamination conditions using test specimens such as erythrocyte ghosts frozen in distilled water and/or a digital thermometer with the thermocouple clamped in place of one of the specimens for direct measurements. Note that the specimens may take 10 min to reach temperature equilibrium after a large change in the indicated temperature and 5 min to reach equilibrium after a small ($<10°C$) change.

E. THE FRACTURE PROCESS

When fracturing with a microtome blade, observe the specimens with the binocular microscope and use the microtome controls to lower the knife blade until it is just clear of the tops of the specimens. Then make a series of progressively lower passes of the blade over the specimens. If possible, it is preferable to make the actual cuts slowly by hand, thus feeling the blade passing through the ice of the specimens. Reduce the cutting depth to a minimum as soon as any appreciable area of specimen is being cut, and continue cutting until all specimens show large fractured areas. For elongated cells such as nerve and muscle fibers, extensive fracture planes are best obtained by orienting the specimens so that the fibers are parallel with the edge of the blade and by cutting fast by motor using only a few deep cuts.

When using a double-replica device, fracturing is a single event which should be done after temperature equilibration and preparation for shadowing.

Prior to the final cut (or to fracture in the double-replica device), check the specimen temperature, ensure that the vacuum is better than 2×10^{-6} mbar, and prepare for shadowing. (Modern freeze-fracture machines may achieve a vacuum of 2×10^{-7} mbar or better.) Then make the final cut, ensure that the specimen surfaces are clear of debris, and either shadow immediately or reverse the knife over the specimens to act as a cold trap while etching.

F. ETCHING

Normally, etching is conducted immediately after fracture at $-100°C$ for 60 sec in a vacuum of better than 2×10^{-6} mbar, with a cold trap (below $-160°C$) in close proximity to the specimen surfaces. This lowers the ice level approximately 120 nm. Deep etching, used, for example, to expose macromolecules adsorbed to the surfaces of mica flakes or to reveal the cytoskeleton of permeabilized cells, is performed either for a longer period or at a higher temperature ($-95°C$), or both. If taken to completion, this is equivalent to freeze-drying.

G. REPLICATION

A quartz crystal replica thickness (thin film) monitor is usually used to monitor replica deposition rates and amounts. Its output is the beat frequency between the inherent vibration frequency of the quartz crystal (which decreases as material is deposited onto its surface) and that of an electronic frequency generator whose frequency can be manually adjusted. If these two frequencies are matched (zero beats) before shadowing, any deposition on the quartz crystal will lead to an increase in the beats. Zero the monitor, and open the shutter (the automatic interlock which causes the high-tension supply unit to the guns to switch off when a preset monitor setting has been achieved). Turn on the high-tension supply unit, and select the platinum gun.

When using conventional freeze-fracture geometry of guns and monitor, it is usual for unidirectional shadowing to deposit a 1.5- to 2-nm thickness of a 95% Pt–5% C mixture from the platinum gun. The amount of platinum is critical, and should not be more than the minimum required to generate good contrast. It is best to deposit the platinum at as rapid a rate as possible, and it is convenient to start firing the platinum gun while the knife is still positioned over the specimens. Then, as soon as the gun is firing smoothly, the knife can be moved away to expose both the specimens and the thin-film monitor simultaneously. Alternatively, for freeze-fracture using a double-replica device, fire the platinum gun just before opening, thus immediately exposing the specimens to a stream of platinum vapor, reducing to a minimum the time during which contamination might occur.

Immediately after platinum shadowing, strengthen the replica with a 10- to 20-nm-thick layer of carbon from the carbon gun. Quite large differences in the amount of carbon deposited make little difference to the final appearance of the replica, but ideally the carbon thickness should be the minimum required to maintain the structural integrity of large replica fragments during the subsequent cleaning process.

Rotary shadowing is conducted as for unidirectional shadowing, except that a commutator unit is used to rotate the specimen during platinum and carbon deposition. A little over half the amount of platinum normally used for unidirectional shadowing is sufficient for rotary shadowed freeze-etch replicas, with the normal amount of carbon.

After carbon shadowing, return all gun controls to zero; switch off the high-tension supply, the monitor and recorder, the knife cooling, and the high-vacuum gauge; and prepare to remove the specimens. Stage cooling should be continued until the specimens have been removed.

H. SPECIMEN REMOVAL

Vent the chamber and remove the specimens, minimizing frosting on the specimens after venting by working fast.

For replicas of cell suspensions, hold the specimen above or just in contact with the surface of clean distilled water in a spotting tray or a small petri dish and wait for it to thaw and the frost on top of the replica to evaporate. Then slowly immerse the specimen support into the water at an approximate 30° angle. The hydrophobic replica of the fractured surface will float off intact onto the water surface, surrounded by junk from the surrounding nonfractured (and hence rough) surfaces of the specimen, from which it may easily be separated.

For tissue blocks, replicas usually will not detach in water, and subsequent swelling in bleach may disrupt the replica unless the tissue is first shrunken. One solution to this problem is to immediately submerge each specimen support with its attached specimen and replica in a petri dish of fresh methanol, which dehydrates and shrinks the tissue (see below).

I. APPARATUS SHUTDOWN

Turn off the stage cooling and reevacuate the chamber. If appropriate, turn on the stage and knife heating. When both are warm, revent the chamber, safely discard the disposable razor blade (if used), remove any water condensation droplets from the stage or microtome with paper tissues, and complete the drying process with a hot-air gun. Finally, close the chamber and reevacuate. If appropriate, raise the knife to its upper limit, ready for the next run. When the vacuum is better than 10^{-5} mbar, the pumping unit may be turned off, following the manufacturer's instructions. Complete the run record log sheet.

J. CLEANING OF REPLICAS

Replica cleaning is often the most difficult stage of the entire procedure, during which replica fragmentation is frequently experienced. All dishes, implements, and solutions must be scrupulously clean to avoid replica contamination.

Replicas of cell suspensions are easily cleaned. After floating the replica of the fractured surface onto distilled water, transfer it (without surrounding junk) onto the surface of a solution of 50% sodium hypochlorite (technical grade, 10–14% w/v available chlorine) containing 5 mM sodium hydroxide and leave covered at room temperature for at least 30 min (or overnight). (Commercial bleach should be used only if free from detergents, which tend to wet the replica and cause it to sink.) Then transfer the cleaned replicas onto two changes of distilled water. Replica fragmentation on transfer to and from cleaning solution is minimized if the replica is picked up on the upper surface of a round-ended glass rod or the bent sealed tip of a Pasteur pipette, as this transfers less liquid than the use of a platinum loop, and the violent mixing of cleaning solution and water occurs at the underside of the rod while the replica is still safe on the upper surface. More thorough replica cleaning may be achieved, if necessary, by acidifying the hypochlorite with concentrated hydrochloric acid to form a stronger oxidizing solution, by warming the hypochlorite to 60°C, or by using chromic acid. Concentrated sulfuric acid alone will digest the cellulose of plant specimens.

Bulk tissue can often be rapidly removed, with minimal disruption of the replica, by floating or partially submerging the replicated specimen in chromic acid. Alternatively, as mentioned above, replicas attached to tissue blocks may first be dehydrated by submersion, replica uppermost, in methanol, to prevent excessive tissue swelling and replica fragmentation during subsequent digestion in bleach. By exchanging the solution bathing the specimens, allowing 5 min equilibration time at each stage, transfer the specimen sequentially to fresh methanol, to 50% methanol, and then to distilled water. Now position the tissue block, replica side up, on a small circle of hard, smooth filter paper (Whatman No. 50) submerged under water at the bottom of a small petri dish. Carefully remove the water, leaving the tissue block sitting on the moist paper. The hydrophobic surface of the replica should dry. Finally, add sodium hypochlorite solution gently and slowly around the paper, using a drawn-out Pasteur pipette. The replica and attached specimen should now float off the paper. Avoid mechanical agitation which will cause the tissue to sink. Leave floating for 2–5 hr, during which time the tissue should be digested, until no residual tissue can be observed clinging to the floating replica. Transfer the replica to fresh sodium hypochlorite for 30 min, then wash twice on distilled water.

If a replica sinks during the cleaning process, complete the cleaning process with the replica submerged, and then gradually transfer it into distilled water. With patience and good fortune it can then usually be refloated by coaxing it flat onto a submerged EM grid or a glass rod and gently lifting it up through the meniscus. Once at the surface, its hydrophilic carbon surface will dry, and when lowered back onto the surface it will float again. A more extreme method for refloating is to drop the sunken replica, suspended in a droplet of methanol, onto the surface of distilled water. The surface tension differences between the ethanol and water will cause the replica to snap out flat on the water surface, but will also cause it to break apart.

K. MOUNTING OF REPLICAS

Floating replicas may be picked up on bare electron microscope grids from the meniscus either from above or from below. In the latter case, the EM grids should first be made hydrophilic by brief immersion in a 0.1 mg/ml bacitracin solution, or by washing in alcoholic sodium hydroxide (30 g NaOH dissolved in 30 ml distilled H_2O, added to 250 ml 98% EtOH) followed by vigorous agitation in two changes of distilled water. Replicas are then mounted by careful manipulation of the submerged grid below the replica fragment, followed by slow withdrawal of the grid through the water surface. If, during this withdrawal, the grid is rotated to be at 90° to the meniscus, with the replica fragment centrally located on it, little water will accompany the grid. This can be removed by gently blotting the back of the grid onto a circle of filter paper, and then drying between the tips of the forceps holding the grid with a pointed piece of the filter paper before placing the replica in grid box. If the replica is to be picked up from above, the EM grid should be brought down flat onto the replica, and then removed with a twist of the wrist to rotate it upside down at the meniscus, with partial submersion to ensure good adhesion of the replica with the grid. For certain investigations, it is important to know the orientation of the replica and, hence, the handedness of its projected image. For this one should adopt a convention of always mounting replicas in the same orientation on one of the surfaces of the EM grid (either the dull or the shiny surface) and of orienting this surface to the right in the grid storage box.

Bare 400-mesh EM grids are ideal for observing replicas of cell suspensions, but do not allow uninterrupted observation of extensive fracture faces of long myotubes or other large cells. For such replicas, Formvar-coated 150-mesh or slot EM grids may be used, which have been lightly coated with carbon on their reverse side (i.e., on the side of the grid bars not covered with Formvar, as opposed to the conventional method of depositing the carbon on top of the Formvar layer, out of contact with the grid itself). This has the advantage that the flat surface of the Formvar film remains hydrophilic and can be used to pick up floating replicas from below with ease.

III. Interpretation and Artifacts

The interpretation of freeze-fracture electron micrographs depends initially on knowledge of the direction from which the platinum was deposited. A normal positive print of a freeze-fracture micrograph should be viewed with the direction of platinum deposition from below, when an intramembrane particle or similar protrusion will generate a complex image having a black cap of accumulated platinum below, i.e., nearest the observer, and a short white shadow thrown upward (Fig. 2). Similarly, membranes with a convex curvature will appear dark at the bottom graduating to light at the top, while the reverse will obviously be true for pits and concavities. When presented with such an image of a particle "illuminated" with (black) platinum from below and casting a white shadow upward, the brain naively interprets it correctly as a particle, but does so by assuming that it is illuminated with (white) light from above, casting a black shadow downward, as this corresponds with everyday experience. This "error" does not generally lead to confusion in the interpretation of freeze-fracture electron micrographs, which are therefore usually presented as standard positive prints, a convention that is followed in Fig. 2. Ambiguity can be completely avoided, however, by the use of negative prints in which the platinum appears white, and this has proved particularly valuable for deep-etched specimens which have been rotary replicated rather than unidirectionally replicated with platinum, where many of the normal clues for three-dimensional interpretation (e.g., clear shadows) are absent.

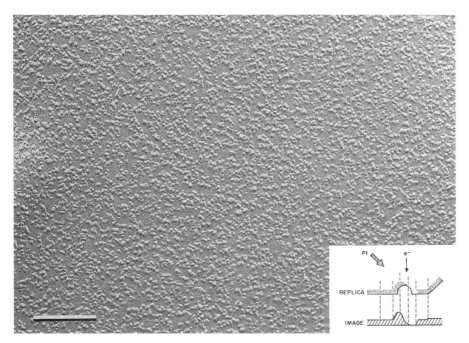

FIGURE 2 Protoplasmic fracture face (P face) of a normal erythrocyte ghost membrane. The platinum replication direction is from below, and individual intramembrane particles (IMPs) throw short white shadows upward. ×85,000; Bar = 200 nm. (From Shotton, D.M. (1982) *J. Neurol. Sci.* **57**, 161–190. Reproduced by permission.) *Inset:* Diagrammatic view of a single platinum-replicated IMP and of its projected electron scattering power, which determines the optical density of its photographic image when viewed with the electron beam normal to the replica. (From Steere and Rash (1979) Use of double-tilt device (goniometer) to obtain optimum contrast in freeze-fracture replicas. In Rash and Hudson (1979). Reproduced by permission.)

Biological membranes are usually curved rather than flat, and the freeze-fracture plane follows these curves to give a highly three-dimensional fractured surface. This fact cannot be fully appreciated when subsequently viewing electron micrographs of freeze-fracture replicas unless stereoscopic pairs of micrographs are employed, since an individual micrograph is a plane projection image of the original three-dimensional object. Even small variations in the angle between the plane of the membrane and the platinum deposition direction can enormously change the electron micrograph images obtained from otherwise identical areas, as also can variations in the thickness of platinum deposited. These factors may cause problems of interpretation, which become particularly acute when one is attempting to quantify the density of IMPs. Such quantitation is further complicated by the intrinsic size heterogeneity within the particle population, coupled with plastic distortion and the inherently limited resolution of the freeze-fracture replica discussed above, particularly when clustering or close packing of IMPs cause some to lie in the shadows of others and thus generate indistinct or unrecognizable images. In addition, the variations in the viewing angle (that between the plane of the counting area and the optical axis of the electron microscope) caused by the curved replica surface may lead, with nonstereoscopic electron micrographs, to unnoticed foreshortening of the replica image which may significantly increase the apparent particle densities.

As with any ultrastructural technique, freeze fracture has its own potential artifacts associated with each preparative stage. Those artifacts that most commonly cause problems are variations in replica quality, specimen contamination, and plastic distortion.

A. VARIATIONS IN REPLICA QUALITY

Variations in replica quality are caused largely by nonreproducibility of replication conditions from one specimen to the next, which were common when resistance heating guns were routinely used for platinum and carbon evaporation. The use of electron bombardment guns and quartz crystal replica thickness monitors in most modern freeze-etching plants has made the production of high-quality replicas routine and, thus, has largely overcome the problem.

B. SPECIMEN CONTAMINATION

Specimen contamination is caused by the condensation of water molecules present in the residual atmosphere of the vacuum chamber onto the cold surface of the frozen, fractured specimen before replication. It is the reverse of the etching process, and occurs either when the specimen temperature is too low or, more usually, when the vacuum is not good enough. In both cases the local partial pressure of water vapor above the specimen exceeds the sublimation pressure of water molecules leaving the ice surface, resulting in a net accumulation of water molecules on the fractured surface. These may obscure the protruding integral membrane proteins present on membrane fracture faces, thus reducing the number of intramembrane particles seen after replication, or alternatively may result in the formation of additional "pseudoparticles" of ice which, when replicated, are often almost indistinguishable from authentic integral membrane protein particles. Such contamination may be the result of improper positioning of the microtome knife blade after fracturing the specimen, as the chips of ice from the fractured specimen present on, but in poor thermal contact with, the blade will act as a rich source of water vapor molecules. Contamination can largely be avoided by ensuring that fracturing is done only after a satisfactory high vacuum is achieved, by correct positioning of the knife, by reducing the time between fracturing and replication, and (ideally) by closely surrounding the specimen with a liquid nitrogen-cooled shroud which will protect the fractured specimen surface from the arrival of water vapor molecules, including those outgassing from uncooled surfaces elsewhere in the vacuum chamber.

C. PLASTIC DISTORTION

Plastic distortion commonly affects integral membrane proteins during fracturing of the lipid bilayer, although it is most easily recognized in membranes with regularly ordered integral proteins. In those cases, the pits on the E face from which the integral proteins have been pulled remain in the orderly array previously adopted by the proteins in the intact membrane before fracture, but the intramembrane particles on the complementary P fracture face are distorted and no longer exhibit such precise crystallinity. There is now good evidence to suggest that fracturing at very low temperatures (10 K), which requires an ultrahigh vacuum system to prevent water vapor contamination, reduces the amount of plastic distortion experienced by some proteins during the fracture process.

A full discussion of these and other artifacts, and of specimen preparation methods and freeze-fracture techniques, will be found in Fisher and Branton (1974), Southworth *et al.* (1975), Sleytr and Robards (1977), Rash and Hudson (1979), Robards and Sleytr (1985) and Severs and Shotton (1995).

REFERENCES

Branton, D., Bullivant, S., Gilula, N. B., Karnovsky, M. J., Moor, H., Mühlethaler, K., Northcote, D. H., Packer, L., Satir, B., Satir, P., Speth, V., Staehlin, L. A., Steere, R. L., and Weinstein, R. S. (1975) Freeze-etch nomenclature. *Science* **190**, 54–56.

Bullivant, S., and Ames, A. (1966) A simple freeze-fracture replication method for electron microscopy. *J. Cell Biol.* **29**, 435–447.

Bullivant, S., Metcalfe, P., and Warne, K. P. (1979) Fine structure of yeast plasma membrane after freeze fracturing in a simple shielded device. *In "Freeze Fracture: Methods, Artifacts and Interpretations"* (J. E. Rash and C. S. Hudson, eds.), pp 141–147. Raven Press, New York.

Fisher, K., and Branton, D. (1974) Application of the freeze-fracture technique to natural membranes. *In "Methods in Enzymology"* (S. Fleischer and L. Packer, eds.), Vol. 32, pp. 35–44. Academic Press, San Diego.

Rash, J. E., and Hudson, C. S. (1979) *"Freeze Fracture: Methods, Artifacts and Interpretations."* Raven Press, New York.

Robards, A. W., and Sleytr, U. B. (1985) *In "Practical Methods in Electron Microscopy,"* Vol. **10**: *"Low Temperature Methods in Biological Electron Microscopy"* (A. M. Glauert, ed.). Elsevier, Amsterdam.

Severs, N. J., and Shotton, D. M. (1994) *"Rapid Freezing, Freeze Fracture and Deep Etching."* Wiley–Liss, New York.

Sleytr, U. B., and Robards, A. W. (1977) Freeze fracturing: A review of methods and results. *J. Microsc.* **111**, 77–100.

Southworth, D., Fisher, K., and Branton, D. (1975) Principles of freeze fracturing and etching. *In "Techniques of Biochemical and Biophysical Morphology"* (D. Glick and R. Rosenbaum, eds.), Vol. **2**, pp. 247–282. Wiley, New York.

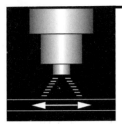

Use of Ultrathin Cryo- and Plastic Sections for Immunoelectron Microscopy

Norbert Roos and Gareth Griffiths

I. Introduction

Labeling of cell surface and intracellular components for light and electron microscopical observations is an important technique for studying their location and function in the cell. A wide range of cytochemical and immunocytochemical methods have therefore been developed. They can be divided into two classes, preembedding methods and postembedding methods.

Preembedding methods are those in which the cell, or isolated organelle, is labeled before embedding and sectioning. While the outside layer of the cell/organelle may be accessible to antibodies, the labeling of intracellular structures must be preceded by a solvent or detergent permeabilization step. Although this method is very useful for cytoskeletal elements (by definition, detergent/solvent insoluble) this approach cannot be recommended as a general method for all antigens and is not considered further here (for a review, see Griffiths, 1993).

The term *postembedding* refers to techniques in which the tissues, cells or organelles are labeled using sections. For this they either are first embedded in a resin that is polymerized or are simply cut in the frozen state and subsequently thawed. There is now general consensus that the labeling of sections is the best general approach for any immunocytochemical study (see Griffiths, 1993, for more theoretical background). The two most important advantages of postembedding over preembedding are (1) when the labeling is carried out on thin sections the whole surface of the section has equal access to the reagents, and (2) there is no need to use a permeabilization protocol, which destroys fine structure. In this review we discuss the practical aspects involved in the labeling of thin sections for electron microscopy.

II. Materials and Instrumentation

Essentially all the reagents mentioned below are widely available from all electron microscopy supply companies.

III. Procedures

A. CONVENTIONAL PREPARATION PROCEDURES

For conventional electron microscopy preparation procedures, the cells or tissues are chemically fixed using aldehydes (glutaraldehyde and/or formaldehyde) and then usually postfixed with osmium tetroxide, dehydrated in an organic solvent (ethanol or acetone), and subsequently embedded in a hydrophobic resin such as Epon or Spurr. The resin is polymerized at elevated temperatures (60–70°C), and the cured blocks are sectioned at room temperature. The ultrathin sections can then be stained using heavy metal salt solutions (uranyl acetate/lead citrate) and observed in the electron microscope. In general, this approach is not useful for immunolabeling; however, there are exceptions. The most striking involves an extensive and elegant series of studies by Ottersen and colleagues (1992) involved with immunolocalization of amino acid neurotransmitters in brain tissue.

During the 1980s a new class of methacrylate-based resins were developed for immunocytochemistry. The two key advantages of these resins over the Epoxy-based resins are that they are more hydrophilic and, in some cases, can be polymerized at low temperatures. There are two main "families" of these resins, namely, the Lowicryl resins and the London resins (LRs). In conjunction with the cryosectioning technique pioneered by Tokuyasu (1973, 1978) these resins have become widely and successfully applied for immunolabeling over the past 10–12 years. We now point out the key practical features involved in using these two approaches.

B. EMBEDDING IN THE NEW ACRYLIC RESINS

The London resins are perhaps the simplest to use, because in the case of LR White no low-temperature step is necessary. Both LR White and LR Gold are now widely used and the manufacturers give detailed instructions on their use. A protocol for LR Gold follows.

Solutions

1. *0.1 M PBS buffer, pH 7.4:* To make 1 liter, dissolve 2.25 g of $Na_2HPO_4 \cdot 2H_2O$, 0.257 g of $NaHPO_4 \cdot H_2O$, and 8.767 g NaCl in 1000 ml distilled water.

2. *0.5 M Ammonium chloride:* To make 1 liter, dissolve 26.75 g of NH_4Cl in 1 liter PBS.

Steps

1. Fix tissue pieces (less than 1 mm^3) with the fixative of your choice, e.g., 0.5% glutaraldehyde in phosphate buffer for 30 min to 2 hr [note that for all immunocytochemical techniques the fixation step is critical (see Griffiths, 1993, for discussion)].

2. Immerse in 0.5 *M* ammonium chloride in PBS (to quench free aldehyde groups) for 30 min.

3. Immerse in PBS for 15–60 min.

4. Immerse in 50% (v/v) methanol at 0°C for 10 min.

5. Immerse in 80% (v/v) methanol at −20 or at 4°C for 60 min.

6. Immerse in 90% (v/v) methanol at −20 or at 4°C for 60 min.

7. Immerse in methanol and LR Gold (1:1) at −20 or at 4°C overnight.

8. Immerse in methanol and LR Gold (1:2) at −20 or at 4°C for 4 hr.

9. Immerse in pure LR Gold resin at −20 or at 4°C for 2 hr.

10. Immerse in pure LR Gold resin + catalyst at −20 or 4°C for 2 hr.

11. Immerse in pure LR Gold resin + catalyst at −20 or at 4°C overnight.

12. Immerse in pure LR Gold resin + catalyst at −20 or at 4°C and polymerize for 24 hr.

LR White is similar but can be polymerized by heat (50°C), by a chemical accelerator at 4–20°C, or by ultraviolet light (see manufacturer's instructions).

C. PROGRESSIVE LOWERING OF TEMPERATURE IN LOWICRYL RESINS

The specimen is chemically fixed with aldehydes (postfixation with osmium tetroxide is omitted as it would interfere with the polymerization process) and dehydrated with increasing concentrations of alcohol. During dehydration the temperature is progressively lowered to finally reach −25 to −35°C. Infiltration of the specimens with resin and subsequent polymerization can be performed at low temperatures because the Lowicryl resins have been designed to have an extremely low viscosity at low temperatures and can be polymerized using ultraviolet light instead of heat. The blocks can be sectioned at room temperature using standard equipment. The progressive lowering of temperature (PLT) method preserves antigenicity much better than conventional preparation methods and has been extensively used recently. A PLT regime is summarized below.

Steps

1. Use any of the standard aldehyde fixation procedures.
2. Immerse in 30% (v/v) ethanol at 0°C for 30 min.
3. Immerse in 50% (v/v) ethanol at −20°C for 60 min.
4. Immerse in 70% (v/v) ethanol at −35°C (−50°C)* for 60 min.[1]
5. Immerse in 95% (v/v) ethanol at −35°C (−50 to −70°C)* for 60 min.
6. Immerse in 100% (v/v) ethanol at −35°C (−50 to −70°C)* for 60 min.
7. Immerse in 100% (v/v) ethanol at −35°C (−50 to −70°C)* for 60 min.
8. Immerse in ethanol and resin (1:1) at −35°C (−50 to −70°C)* for 60 min.
9. Immerse in ethanol and resin (1:2) at −35°C (−50 to −70°C)* for 60 min.
10. Immerse in pure resin at −35°C (−50 to −70°C)* for 60 min.
11. Immerse in pure resin at −35°C (−50 to −70°C)* overnight.
12. Polymerize for 2 days at low temperature (−50 and −70°C, respectively) with ultraviolet light.

The entire procedure can be done with homemade equipment or on one of two commercially available systems from Balzers or Leica.

D. CRYOPREPARATION METHODS

1. Rapid Freezing

In an attempt to reduce the artifacts related to chemical fixation of biological specimens a variety of cryotechniques have been developed over the last decade. The rationale behind these methods is that biological structures may be physically fixed by freezing the specimen rapidly. Rapid freezing is a prerequisite for obtaining

[1]Temperatures in parentheses followed by asterisks are for HM23 and K11M.

a frozen specimen that is not destroyed by ice crystals, which would inevitably grow at too low cooling rates. Typically, biological specimens would have to be cooled at a rate of 100,000 K/sec to obtain vitrification, i.e., a state of water/ice in the cell that is amorphous (lacks ice crystals). Different freezing techniques have been described and we refer the reader to Robards and Sleyter (1985) and Roos and Morgan (1990). To summarize, it is possible to freeze biological specimens rapidly with most freezing techniques provided the specimens are thin enough (virus suspensions, etc.). The only freezing method that allows fresh bulk specimens to be vitrified is the high-pressure freezing technique (see Studer *et al.*, 1989; Dahl and Staehlin, 1989).

2. Freeze-Substitution

For immunolabeling, vitrified specimens can be subjected to a dehydration regime called freeze-substitution. The vitrified ice is substituted by an organic solvent at low temperatures. The cold organic solvent is subsequently replaced by a suitable resin kept at temperatures between -40 and $-85°C$ and polymerized with ultraviolet light. The blocks can be sectioned and the sections labeled at room temperature; however, for most practical purposes when using bulk specimens such as cells and tissues and in the absence of a high-pressure freezing device, one has to resort to a method that allows vitrification of the specimen at lower cooling rates. This can be achieved by employing cryoprotectants. Cryoprotectants used at reasonably high concentrations will prevent the formation of ice crystals in the specimen even at very low cooling rates, such as those achieved by immersion into liquid nitrogen. To allow the cryoprotectant to infiltrate the entire specimen, chemical fixation must be used.

A freeze-substitution schedule for Lowicryl HM20 can be found in van Genderen *et al.* (1991):

Solution

1. *2.3 M Sucrose solution in PBS:* To make 500 ml disolve, 393.64 g of sucrose in PBS and adjust volume to 500 ml.

Steps

1. Fix cells (e.g., with 4% formaldehyde $\pm$ 0.1% glutaraldehyde in buffer) for 1 hr.
2. Infiltrate with cryoprotectant (e.g., 2.3 *M* sucrose) for 30–60 min.
3. Cut cells grown on filters or tissue blocks into small pieces (no more than 1 mm^3).
4. Mount specimens on specimen stubs and freeze in liquid nitrogen.
5. Transfer to methanol at $-90°C$ supplemented with 0.5% uranyl acetate for 36 h.
6. Raise temperature to $-45°C$ (at about 5°C/hr).
7. Rinse several times with fresh methanol at $-45°C$.
8. Infiltrate with Lowicryl HM20 in the following series of Lowicryl:methanol mixtures: 1:1 for 2 hr, 2:1 for 2 hr, pure Lowicryl for 2 hr and then overnight.
9. Polymerize for 2 days at $-45°C$ with ultraviolet light.
10. Section block at room temperature using a glass or preferably a diamond knife in an ultramicrotome.

11. Label with antibodies and gold (see below). All subsequent steps are done by floating the grids on drops as small as 5 μl.

12. Stain with 4% aqueous uranyl acetate for 10 min.

13. Rinse with distilled water.

14. Stain with lead citrate for 1–5 min.

15. Rinse in water, dry, and examine.

An alternative to freeze-substitution is to section the cryoprotected specimen at low temperatures (Tokuyasu technique).

3. The Cryosectioning Technique (Tokuyasu Technique)

The thawed frozen-section technique offers a number of advantages over most other methods for high-resolution immunolabeling. For more details see Griffiths (1993).

1. It is potentially the most sensitive technique for immunolabeling because the initial aldehyde fixation is the only denaturation step for the antigen (freezing and thawing of the specimen do not seem to affect the antigenicity).

2. As the sections are not embedded in resin they offer the highest access of the antigen to the antibody relative to other techniques. Consequently, this approach is the most sensitive one.

3. The possibilities for staining/contrasting are greater than for any other method.

4. The entire procedure including photographic documentation can be performed in one working day.

It is essential first to chemically fix the cells or tissues. Usually, 4–8% paraformaldehyde in phosphate, Hepes, or Pipes buffer is used. This is often supplemented with 0.1–0.5% glutaraldehyde, which is a stronger crosslinker. Cryoprotected, vitrified biological specimens can easily be sectioned at low temperatures provided the choice of cryoprotectant does not compromise the sectioning properties of the block. The most widely used cryoprotectant is sucrose. Employed at concentrations between 2.1 and 2.3 M the blocks are usually easy to section. High concentrations of sucrose give softer tissue blocks which have to be sectioned at lower temperatures. For more difficult specimens an alternative cryoprotectant mixture developed by Tokuyasu consisting of 1.8 M sucrose and 20% (w/v) polyvinylpyrrolidone (PVP, MW 10,000) is recommended.

Solutions

1. *Sucrose/PVP infusion mixture:* To make 100 ml, prepare paste consisting of 20 g of PVP, 4 ml of 1.1 M Na$_2$CO$_3$ in a buffer such as 0.1 M phosphate (Na$_2$HPO$_4$) (total volume 20 ml). Prepare 80 ml of 2.3 M sucrose in the same buffer. Mix thoroughly. Cover the mixture and leave at room temperature overnight so that minute air bubbles can escape. Adjust pH to neutrality using 1 M NaOH (use pH indicator paper).

Infusion of small tissue blocks with sucrose solutions usually takes 15–60 min, whereas with sucrose/PVP at least 2 hr is required. Infiltrated specimens are mounted on specimen stubs made of either aluminum or copper and frozen by simply plunging them into liquid nitrogen. The stub is inserted into its position in the specimen arm

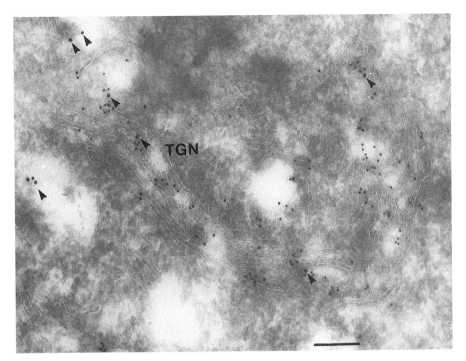

FIGURE 1 Example of double labeling using ultrathin cryosections (Tokuyasu method). Localization of invariant chain (Ii) and mannose 6-phosphate receptor (MPR) in the Golgi region of a human fibroblast cell line stably transfected with Ii. Ii is present throughout the Golgi stack, whereas MPR (large gold particles labeled with arrowheads) is only found in the trans side of the Golgi stack (TGN = trans Golgi network). Bar = 0.2 μm. (Courtesy Dr. E. Stang, Department of Molecular Cell Biology, Biology Institute, University of Oslo.)

of the microtome and the block sectioned at temperatures in the range of −60 to −80°C for semithin sections or −80 to −120°C for ultrathin sections.

Sections are picked up using a wire loop (any pliable metal with a diameter of 1–2 mm) containing a drop of 2.3 M sucrose in PBS. Ideally, the sucrose is still fluid at the moment it makes contact with the section(s). The surface tension of the fluid helps to stretch the compressed and wrinkly section(s). (*Note*: Stretching will not occur if the section is picked up with an already frozen droplet, even if it is subsequently warmed up to room temperature.) The sections picked up in this way have one face exposed to the sucrose and the other face to the air. The latter will avidly stick to the surface of, e.g., a Formvar/carbon-coated electron microscope grid or a glass slide.

The sections are usually stained after labeling (Fig. 1), then embedded and dried. Staining and embedding are achieved by exposing the sections to an inert organic polymer mixed with the stain, usually uranyl acetate. The polymer most often used for embedding is methyl cellulose (polyvinyl alcohol and even resins have also been used for this purpose) containing 0.2–0.3% uranyl acetate.

2. *0.2% Methyl Cellulose Solution:* Mix low-viscosity (25 centipoise) methyl cellulose powder with cold triple-distilled water to make a 2% solution. Leave refrigerated (methyl cellulose is more soluble at low temperatures) for 2–3 days. Centrifuge the mixture at 100,000 g at 4°C for 1 hr. Store the solution in the refrigerator, where it will be stable for up to 6 weeks. Mix 9 parts of the solution with 1 part of a 3% solution of uranyl acetate in water for contrasting/ embedding.

4. Labeling Procedure for Electron Microscopy

In all cases the grids are floated on drops (as little as 5 μl) on a strip of Parafilm. The upper (nonsection) side of the grids must be kept clean and dry.

Steps

1. Collect grids by floating them on 1–5% fetal calf serum (FCS)/PBS on ice; wash in PBS once before proceeding. Note that many other reagents, such as 1% fish skin gelatin and 2% gelatin, can be used to block nonspecific binding of antibodies.

2. If the cells have been fixed with glutaraldehyde, free aldehyde groups can be quenched in 0.02 M glycine in 5–10% FCS/PBS for 10 mins; rinse twice in PBS for a total of 5 min.

3. Centrifuge antibody solution (1 min at 13,000 g), dilute in 1–5% FCS/PBS; and incubate sections for 15–60 min. Use the highest concentration of antibody that does not give background labeling over structures that do not contain the antigen.

4. Wash six times in PBS for a total of 15 min.

5. Incubate grids in protein A–gold for 20–30 min. Dilute protein A–gold in 1–5% FCS/PBS. The concentration is critical. Too high a concentration gives nonspecific binding.

6. Wash six times in PBS for a total of 25 min.

7. Wash four times in distilled water for a total of 5 min.

8. Incubate three times with 2% methyl cellulose solution (25 CP) containing 0.1–0.4% uranyl acetate, for 10–20 min.

9. Pick the grid up with a 3-mm loop; remove the excess fluid with filter paper.

10. Air-dry the grid suspended in the loop.

11. The thickness of the methyl cellulose film determines the contrast and the extent of drying artifacts.

12. The grids can now be examined.

For the double labeling, after step 6, the grids are floated on 1% glutaraldehyde in PBS for 5 min followed by many rinses in PBS (Slot *et al.,* 1991). Steps 2 to 6 are then repeated using a different size of gold, followed by steps 7 to 12.

E. COLLOIDAL GOLD

This reagent is now the marker of choice for electron microscopy immunolabeling because it is very electron dense and clearly easily prepared in a range of sizes. The gold particles can be conjugated to IgG or protein A. We prefer the latter because we find it more stable and reproducible than IgG gold; however, a disadvantage of protein A is that it binds strongly only to certain species of IgG (rabbit, human, pig, and guinea pig always work; for a more detailed list see Griffiths, 1993). When using a species of antibody that binds poorly (such as most rat and mouse antibodies), use an intermediate antibody step, such as rabbit anti-mouse. These reagents are now widely available from many commercial sources. For more details on the preparation see Lucocq in Griffiths (1993).

IV. Comments

A positive signal in immunoelectron microscopy is significant only when independent proof is provided that the gold labeling observed is really due to the antigen of interest. Such proof of specificity should be obtained by two different approaches (see Griffiths, 1993, for more detail).

1. Immunochemical characterization, to show that the antibody recognizes the antigen in an independent method such as immunoblotting or immunoprecipitation.

2. Biological proof of specificity. The best control here is to be able to correlate the labeling pattern with structures that are known to contain or not contain the antigen. Any treatment that blocks or removes the antigen should eliminate the labeling.

V. Pitfalls

1. The antibody does not label. First try immunolabeling with a light microscopical approach (e.g., cryostat sections). If thick sections of lightly fixed specimens do not work (provided the secondary, visualizing antibodies are good), there is usually *no* point in continuing to the electron microscopical level. One exception is for small antigens that may be lost during the preparation for light microscopy; For these it is better to use an embedding approach, perhaps after freeze-substitution. Unless one can find some evidence that the antibody can recognize aldehyde-fixed antigen by any approach it is better to make new antibodies. Provided one has a strong positive, specific signal at the light microscopical level, a negative result at the electron microscopical level can be due to a number of reasons. In the case of plastic (e.g., Lowicryl) sections a common reason is that the antibody has no access to the fixed antigen on the surface of the section. Usually, this is less of a problem with thawed cryosections. In the latter approach the fixation conditions can be drastically reduced (e.g., 5 min in 2% formaldehyde). Although this will deleteriously affect the structure, it will help the investigator to decide if the problem is due to the fixation's preventing access to the antigen.

A second reason for a negative signal at the electron microscopical level, already alluded to, is that the antigen may have been washed away during the rinsing steps. This is a problem for small molecules, especially with the Tokuyasu approach. In this case one should crosslink the cells or tissues more severely (1–2% glutaraldehyde). For such antigens the resin approach is preferred.

The third reason for lack of labeling is the quantitative aspect; the concentration of the antigens may be too low to detect. Note that the surface of a thin section provides a very small amount of antigen for the antibody, when compared with, say, a whole cell at the immunofluorescent level. For more details see Griffiths (1993).

2. There is too much label/nonspecific binding. First, dilute both the antibody and the gold sufficiently. It is best to use a standardized gold reagent at its optimal concentration with a characterized primary antibody. If both are unknown measure the OD_{520} of the gold reagent (e.g., a 1:100 to 1:500 solution). The commonly used range of final concentration gives an absorbance of ≈ 0.1 at this wavelength (generally 1:10 to 1:100 final concentration). The optimal concentration is the highest that does not give background labeling in the absence of a primary antibody. When the gold concentration has been standardized combine this with a dilution series of the antibody and use the highest concentration that does not give background. The definition of background is, of course, at the discretion of the investigator and assumes some knowledge of the antigen; a membrane protein, for example, would not be expected in the nucleoplasm.

Background labeling is often due to impurities in the antiserum. The only possibility is to purify the antibody, either by preparing an IgG fraction (e.g., ammonium sulfate precipitation) or by performing affinity purification. It should be noted that the latter approach often results in a significant, or even total, loss of the highest-titer antibody molecules (they remain on the column during the elution procedure).

REFERENCES

Dahl, R., and Staehelin, L. A. (1989) High-pressure freezing for the preservation of biological structure: Theory and practice. *J. Electron Microsc. Tech.* **13**, 165–174.

Griffiths, G. (1993) "Fine Structure Immunocytochemistry," p. 459. Springer-Verlag, Heidelberg.

Ottersen, O. P., Zhang, N., and Walberg, F. (1992) Metabolic compartmentation of glutamate and glutamine: morphological evidence obtained by quantitative immunocytochemistry in rat cerebellum. *Neuroscience* **46**, 519–534.

Robards, A. W., and Sleytr, U. B. (1985) Low temperature methods in biological electron microscopy. *In* "Practical Methods in EM" (A. M. Glauert, ed.), Vol. 10, pp. 309–324. Elsevier, Amsterdam.

Roos, N., and Morgan, A. J. (1990) Cryopreparation of Thin Biological Specimens for Electron Microscopy: Methods and Applications. *In* "Microscopy Handbooks of Royal Society, 21." Oxford University Press, London.

Slot, J. W., Geuze, H. J., Gegengack, S., Leinhard, G. E., and James, D. E. (1991) Immunolocalization of the insulin regulatable glucose transporter in brown adipose tissue of the rat. *J. Cell Biol.* **113**, 123–135.

Studer, D., Michel, M., and Müller, M. (1989) High pressure freezing comes of age. *Scanning Microsc.* **3**, 253–269.

Tokuyasu, K. T. (1973) A technique for ultracrotomy of cell suspensions and tissues. *J. Cell Biol.* **57**, 551–565.

Tokuyasu, K. T. (1978) A study of positive staining of ultrathin frozen sections. *J. Ultrastruct. Res.* **63**, 287–307.

Van Genderen, I. L., van Meer, G. Slot, J. W., Geuze, H. J., and Voorhout, W. F. (1991) Subcellular localization of Forssman glycolipid in epithelial MDCK cells by immuno-electronmicroscopy after freeze-substitution. *J. Cell Biol.* **115**, 1009–1019.

Cryo-Transmission Electron Microscopy of Thin Vitrified Sections

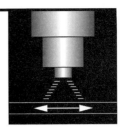

Nathalie Sartori and Laurée Salamin Michel

I. Introduction

Cryo-electron microscopy of vitrified sections allows the observation of specimens in there native hydrated environment without artifacts of chemical fixation or dehydration. In general, no stain is required (for a review, see Dubochet *et al.*, 1988; Roos and Morgan, 1990).

The major difficulty encountered in this method is in achieving vitrification of the sample within sufficient volume and without ice crystal formation. The most common vitrification method for biological sample is plunge freezing into liquid ethane. The vitrification depth attained rarely exceeds 20 μm (Ryan *et al.*, 1987; Costello, 1980; Handley, 1981; Bald, 1985; Sitte *et al.*, 1987). The introduction of high-pressure freezing was an important step forward, increasing the vitrification depth by a factor of 10 (Moor and Riele, 1968; Moor, 1987; Müller, 1984; Sartori *et al.*, 1993).

Another difficulty is obtaining and manipulating good, clean thin sections, without ice contamination.

Lastly specimen observation in the cryo-electron microscope must be performed under conditions minimizing contamination and beam damage.

We describe here how these difficulties are best overcome in practice.

II. Material and Instrumentation

A. VITRIFICATION

1. Plunge Freezing

1. Plunger with liquid nitrogen dewar (Freezer KF 80, Reichert–Jung from Leica).

2. Sharp aluminum pins (Fig. 1a, Nos. 1 and 2) (Leica).

3. Polishing stone, used for flattening the surface of the pins (Fig. 1b) (AS-12-hard, Arkansas, fine, Pelco International).

4. Bevel-edged yellow pipette tips (normally used for Eppendorf-type micropipette) used for carrying cell drops or pieces of tissue (Fig. 1d).

5. Bottle of pressurized ethan connected to the plunge-freezer.

6. Liquid nitrogen dewar connected to the plunge freezer (25 LD dewar, Taylor–Wharton).

7. Hair dryer for warming and drying the plunger after each use.

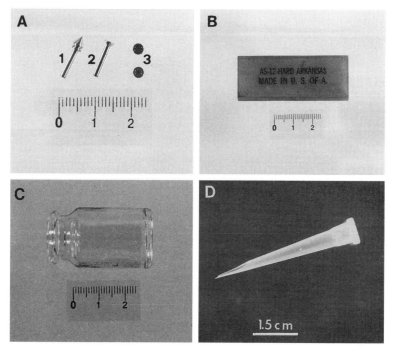

FIGURE 1 (A) Aluminum pins (1 and 2) and aluminum cupules (3). (B) Polishing stone. (C) Glass bottle. (D) Bevel-edged yellow pipette tips.

8. Forceps, medium strength, straight, 160 mm.

9. Glass bottles, 2 ml (Fig. 1c), for storage of the pins in liquid nitrogen.

2. High-Pressure Freezing

1. High-pressure freezing apparatus (HPM 010, Balzers, or PI 32-165, Engineering Office, M. Wohlwend).

2. Binocular lens.

3. Aluminum cupules (Fig. 1a, No. 3; see also Fig. 3), diameter 3 mm, inner diameter 1.6 mm, depth of the cavity 0.7 mm, wall thickness 0.15 mm (Balzers and own fabrication).

4. Two forceps for manipulating the cupules and then opening after freezing.

5. Liquid nitrogen (about 150 liters).

6. Glass bottles, 2 ml, for storing the specimens.

7. Liquid nitrogen dewar.

8. Aluminum block as support for aluminum pins (Fig. 2a), adapted for being set in the microtome at the place of the knife holder (own fabrication).

9. Aluminum pins with 0.65×0.65-mm^2 section (Fig. 1a, No. 2) (Leica).

10. Preparation needle for picking the specimen up, out of the cupule.

11. Tweezers, straight, 12 cm (No. 5 Dumont, Electron Microscopy Sciences).

B. PREPARATION OF THE SUPPORTING FILMS

1. Copper grids, 600-mesh (SPI).

2. Mica sheet, freshly cleaved.

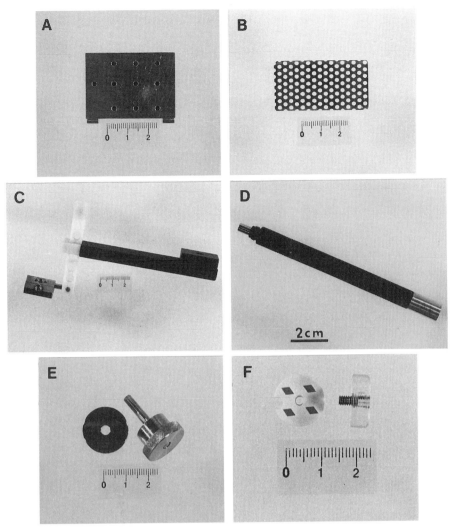

FIGURE 2 (A) Aluminum block as support for aluminum pins. (B) Metallic grid screen. (C) Cryoholder and its grid holder. (D,E) Polished metal surfaces. (F) Plastic grid box.

3. A recipient that can be drained from the bottom, used for laying the carbon film onto the grids.

4. Carbon filament.

5. Carbon evaporator (Med 010, Balzer).

6. Metallic grid screen with 2-mm holes for supporting grids (Fig. 2b).

C. CRYOSECTIONS

1. Cryoultramicrotome (Ultracut E, with the FC4 cryosystem, Leica).

2. 45° diamond knife and trimming diamond knife (Diatome AG Biel). A glass knife can also be used but with more difficulties.

3. Ionizer for controlling the electrostatic environment of the knife (Static Line, Haug).

4. Cold light, optic fibers for additional illumination of the cryochamber (Intralux 4000, Volpi, Schlieren).

5. Cryoholder and its grid holder (Fig. 2c), used for holding the grid in the microtome while collecting the cryosections (Leica).

6. Two polished metal surfaces (Figs. 2d and e), one of them can be a stamping tool (Fig. 2d), for pressing the sections on the grid (Leica).

7. Small glass bottle (Fig. 1c) containing nitrogen. It will be set in the microtome chamber for cooling the stamping tool.

8. Plastic grid box (Fig. 2f) for storing one grid with the frozen sections (Gatan) and a metallic support for the grid box.

9. A manipulator made of one eyelash for picking up the sections.

10. Two tweezers (Nos. 4 and 5, Dumont).

11. Dewar, 500 ml, for collecting the grid box.

12. Face mask, for avoiding breezing wet air in the microtome chamber.

D. CRYOELECTRON MICROSCOPE

1. Transmission electron microscope equipped for cryowork and low-dose operation (Philips CM 12).

2. Cold stage (Gatan 626 cryoholder).

3. Cryotransfer device (Gatan).

4. Sensitive, fine-grain electron film (Film Kodak SO-163, developed in Kodak D-19, full strength, 12 min).

III. Procedures

A. PREPARATION OF GRIDS

We recommend carbon instead of plastic film as a support because it can be thinner and is more stable.

Steps

1. Cleave mica and use it without delay to avoid contamination.

2. Evaporate a thin layer of carbon in a good vacuum ($<10^{-4}$ Pa).

3. Place the grids on the metallic screen in a recipient, filled with distilled water, that can be drained from the bottom.

4. Release the carbon from the mica by floating it onto the water surface.

5. Place the carbon film above the grids and maintain it there with the tweezers. Gently empty the recipient until the film lays onto the grids.

6. Dry on filter paper.

B. PREPARATION OF BIOLOGICAL MATERIAL

1. Tissues

Tissues from animals or plants have to be freshly prepared. For vitrification by plunge freezing, the sample must be as small as compatible with easy manipulation, as only the area close to the surface will be well frozen. The size should not exceed

0.5 mm. For high-pressure freezing, the sample can reach the size of the cupule cavity, but one should keep in mind that the cooling rate decreases rapidly with increasing size of specimen (Costello, 1980).

2. Cells

Solution

1. *Cryoprotectant:* Different sugar types like mannose (Merck), sucrose (Fluka), and dextran (Sigma) at various concentration (15–20%). Sugar solutions must be in the same buffer as the cells or the tissues.

Procedure

Centrifuge cell suspension in the appropriate buffer and resuspend for a few minutes in the cryoprotectant solution. Centrifuge cells into a dense pellet just before freezing.

Cryoprotectant is necessary in the extracellular compartment as dilute solution cannot be vitrified in the bulk. The enthalpy of ice crystal formation in this compartment will also prevent vitrification of the intracellular space. Sugar (mannose, sucrose) can be used as cryoprotectant, but polymers such as dextran produce less osmotic stress with comparable cryoprotectant effect.

With the plunge-freezing technique, the concentration of cryoprotectant in a usable volume must be at least 20% to avoid ice crystal formation. With the high-pressure technique, this concentration can be lowered to 15%.

C. VITRIFICATION

1. Plunge Freezing

Solution

1. *1% Osvan (benzalkonium chloride):* From Sigma, for coating of the aluminum pins.

Steps

1. Soak aluminum pins in 1% Osvan to make them hydrophobic. Polish the tip of the pins with the stone to flatten the surface, which becomes hydrophilic and hence allows good spreading of the drop of cells.

2. Put the ethane holder in the plunge freezer and cool it at −180°C. Rapidly add ethane at a pressure of 1 bar. Stop when the temperature rises above −140°C and let cool again. Repeat the process until the ethane recipient is full. Liquid ethane must be freshly prepared as it is rapidly contaminated with ice.

3. Adjust a pin on the guillotine and set it on the apparatus so that it can be seen with the binocular lens.

4. Using a yellow tip spatula, lay a small drop of cells or a piece of tissue on the pin. Plunge it rapidly in the liquid ethane and make sure that the specimen does not dry before cooling. After 30 sec in liquid ethane, remove the pin from the plunger and store it in a glass bottle in liquid nitrogen.

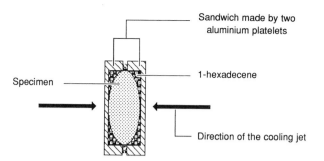

Sandwich made by two
aluminium platelets

Specimen

1-hexadecene

Direction of the cooling jet

FIGURE 3   Scheme of the sandwich formed by the two cupules shown in Fig. 1a (3).

2. High-Pressure Freezing

Solution

1. *1-Hexadecene:* From Sigma.

Steps

1. Follow the protocol of the manufacturer for preparation of the apparatus for cooling.

2. Immerse two cupules in hexadecene; avoid formation of air bubbles inside the cavity (Studer *et al.*, 1989). Set a drop of cells or a piece of tissue in the cupule cavity. Cover it with the other cupule to form a sandwich. Perform all these steps in hexadecene (Fig. 3).

3. Insert the sandwich in the specimen holder and freeze. After the freezing shot, rapidly plunge the extremity of the specimen holder in the liquid nitrogen dewar. Remove the sandwich from the specimen holder and open it with a sharp tool (the sandwich can also be opened in the cryomicrotome, but less easily).

All tools must be precooled before operating on the sandwich.

D. CRYOSECTIONS

Many factors are critical in obtaining good sections. In particular, the humidity of the ambient air, the exact temperature of the different parts of the microtome, and the quality of the diamond knife must be controlled carefully. The following conditions are those we found to be the best for vitreous sections.
One large practical problem is ice contamination. Humidity must be avoided in the microtome chamber. A face mask helps in avoiding breezing in the chamber.

Steps

1. Cool the cryomicrotome rapidly. Adjust the temperature of the chamber to −164°C and that of the specimen and of the knife to −160°C.

2. Introduce the diamond knife at a slight sideway tilt of 1–2° so that several ribbons can be obtained without readjusting the knife.

3. Introduce the polished metal surface with its protection and the metallic piece for holding the grids box as well as one tweezer for grid manipulation. Wait until the temperature stabilizes.

4. Orient the cold light optic fiber toward the knife edge. Good illumination is essential.

5. Fix the pin and cut sections at a very low speed (0.2–0.4 mm/sec) or manually. The cutting feed should be about 40 to 50 nm.

6. Adjust the ionization spray near the knife to prevent sections from sticking. Wait until the nitrogen gas flow is laminar again.

7. Prepare several ribbons of two to four sections, laying them side by side on the knife; more than two to four sections, cut in the same ribbon, tend to stick to the knife or fly away. Do not use more than one length of knife for one specimen. Plunge-frozen specimen are not vitrified deeply; after some 50 sections, the specimen is generally no more vitreous.

8. Fix a grid at the edge of the cryoholder and adjust it on the support. Let it cool in the cryochamber until the nitrogen gas flow is laminar again.

9. Pick up as many sections as possible on the grid with the help of the eyelash. Keep in mind that about half the sections will be broken during subsequent steps.

10. Cool the second polished metal surface in the small glass bottle containing liquid nitrogen in the microtome chamber.

11. Remove the protection of the first polished metal surface and gently lay the grid on it. Press the grid with the second metal surface. Store it in the plastic grid box in liquid nitrogen.

E. PREPARATION OF HIGH-PRESSURE FROZEN SPECIMENS FOR CRYOSECTIONING

Solution

1. *Ethanol:2-propanol* (1:3): From Merck.

Steps

1. Cool the microtome at −140°C.

2. Fix the aluminum block in the position of the knife in the microtome and put the flat pins into the holes. Wait until the temperature stabilizes at −140°C.

3. Put a drop of the ethanol:propanol solution on each pin. As described by Richter and Dubochet, (1989), the alcohol solution, which has the consistency of glue at −140°C, stiffens conveniently for sectioning at −160°C.

4. Remove the specimen from the cupule with a precooled needle. Select fragments that lie close to the cupule surface and mount them in the glue.

5. Cool the microtome as described in D. Start sectioning when the glue reaches sufficient hardness.

F. CRYO-ELECTRON MICROSCOPY

A transmission electron microscope adapted for cryo-observation must be used. A fork-type anticontaminator surrounding the specimen is important for keeping contamination at an acceptable level.

It is advisable to start working at relatively low magnification ($<20,000\times$) because the difficulties due to drift and beam damage increase rapidly with magnification.

Keeping a low fluence ($10^2 \ e \ nm^{-2} \ sec^{-1}$) and recording with a minimum dose are essential with vitrified specimens to minimize beam-induced drift and beam

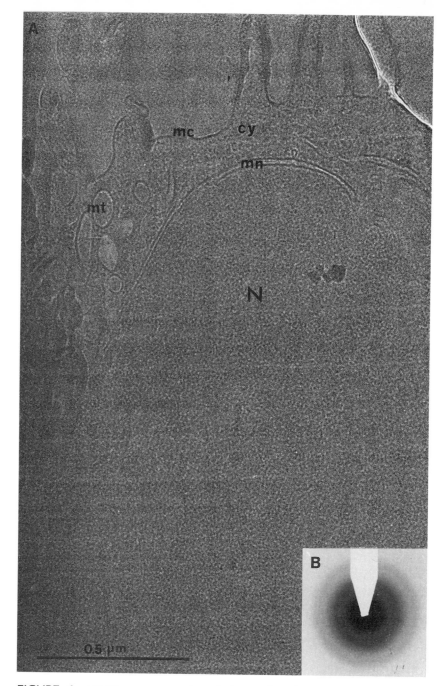

FIGURE 4 (A) Vitreous cryosection of a human lymphocyte obtained after plunge freezing in liquid ethane at −180°C. mc, Cellular membrane; mn, nuclear membrane; N, nucleus; cy, cytoplasm; mt, mitochondria. (B) Electron diffraction.

destruction (bubbling) of the specimen. Focusing must be done outside the area selected for recording.

The vitreous state of the specimen should be tested by electron diffraction (Fig. 4b).

Steps

1. Precool the microscope.
2. Put the cold stage in the microscope. Cool it.

3. Cool the cryotransfer device. Transfer the cool cold stage from the microscope to the transfer device, as quickly as possible. Be aware that the water in the air tends to condense on the cold parts of the cold stage.

4. Take care that all the tools are precooled. Mount the grid. Close the cold stage shutter.

5. Make sure that the pump on the airlock will operate without delay. Switch on the vacuum just before reintroducing the cold stage quickly in the microscope. Keep the protective lid close for a few minutes or when not observing.

6. Operate the microscope under low-beam conditions. Scan first the whole grid at very low magnification to find the best sections. Test whether the water is vitreous or crystalline by electron diffraction.

7. Adjust the tilt angle so that the grid is perpendicular to the electron beam. This point is essential because of the specimen displacement between the place of focusing and that where the micrograph is recorded.

8. At low magnification, select the area to be recorded and an adjacent one for focusing.

9. Record images at various underfocusing (typically 2–4 μm) and with various preirradiations (0–200 e nm^{-2}), as the contrast depends on these two parameters.

Micrographs of cryosections recorded at exact focus show very little contrast because the contribution of amplitude contrast is very small. Image formation therefore relies on phase contrast for any structure smaller than 10 to 20 nm. Such good conditions are generally obtained by underfocusing around 2–4 μm (Fig. 4a).

REFERENCES

Bald, W. B. (1985) The relative merits of various cooling methods. *J. Microsc.* **140**, 17–41.

Costello, M. J. (1980) Ultra-rapid freezing of thin biological samples. *Scanning Electron Microscopy* II, 361–370.

Dubochet, J., Adrian, M., Chang, J. J., Homo, J. C., Lepault, J., McDowall, A. W., and Schultz, P. (1988) Cryo-electron microscopy of vitrified specimens. *Q. Rev. Biophys.* **21**, 129–228.

Moor, H. (1987) Theory and practice of high pressure freezing. *In* "Cryotechniques in Biological Electron Microscopy" (R. A. Steinbrecht and K. Zierold, eds), pp. 175–192. Springer-Verlag, Berlin.

Moor, H., and Riele, U. (1968) Snap-freezing under high pressure: A new fixation technique for freeze-etching. *In* "Electron Microscopy 1968, *Proc. 4th Eur. Reg. Conf. Electron Microsc., Rome*" (S. D. Bocciarelli, ed.), Vol. 2, pp. 33–34.

Müller, M., and Moor, H. (1984) Cryofixation of thick specimens by high pressure freezing. *In* "Science of Biological Specimen Preparation" pp. 131–138. SEM Inc., AMF O'Hare, Chicago.

Richter, K., and Dubochet, J. (1989) Gluing of vitrified specimens for cryo-ultramicrotomy. *Experientia* **45**, A42.

Roos, N., and Morgan, A. J. (1990) Cryopreparation of thin biological specimens for electron microscopy: Methods and applications. *In* "Microscopy Handbooks of Royal Microscopical Society, 21." Oxford University Press, London.

Ryan, K., Purse, D. H., Robinson, S. G., and Wood, J. W. (1987) The relative efficiency of cryogens used for plunge-cooling biological specimens. *J. Microsc.* **145**, 89–96.

Sartori, N., Richter, K., and Dubochet, J. (1993) Vitrification depth can be increased more than 10 fold by high pressure freezing. *J. Microsc.*, in press.

Sitte, H., Edelmann, L., and Neumann, K. (1987) Cryofixation without pretreatment at ambient pressure. *In* "Cryotechniques in Biological Electron Microscopy." (R. A. Steinbrecht, and K. Zierold, eds.), pp. 87–114. Springer-Verlag, Berlin.

Studer, D., Michel, M., and Müller, M. (1989) High pressure freezing comes of age. *Scanning Electron Microsc. Suppl.* **3**, 253–269.

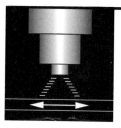

Preparation Methods for Quantitative X-Ray Microanalysis of Intracellular Elements in Ultrathin Sections for Transmission Electron Microscopy: The Freeze-Dry, Resin-Embed Route

Hugh Y. Elder and Stuart M. Wilson

I. Introduction

The protocol is appropriate for microanalytical measurement of relative changes in intracellular electrolyte elements of small tissue samples obtained under paired experimental protocols, e.g., comparing experimentally treated with control or pathological with normal (Elder et al., 1992). It is particularly suitable if there is a need for repeated sectioning to locate obscure target areas. It does not require cryoultramicrotomy or the availability of an electron microscope cold stage, but a low-temperature freeze-drier is necessary.

II. Cryofixation

Various methods for cryofixation have been extensively discussed in the literature (e.g., Robards and Sleytr, 1985; Echlin, 1992). The plunge freezing method described here is appropriate for small (≪1 mm) irregularly shaped pieces of experimental tissue.

The main performance criteria are (1) that the optimum quenchant fluid should be used, and (2) that it should be held at its coldest liquid temperature. Although ethane has been found to be marginally the most efficient quenchant, commercial propane is a good compromise as it can be obtained cheaply and the small percentage of impurities present are actually an advantage as they depress the freezing point. A small addition of another hydrocarbon, such as isopentane, will depress the freezing point below liquid nitrogen temperature of −196°C, thus avoiding the problem of quenchant freezing.

The depth of quenchant fluid should be sufficient for the specimen to be completely frozen by the time it stops plunging (see legend to Fig. 1). As ice crystals grow rapidly at temperatures warmer than about −60°C and more slowly thereafter as cooling continues, it is necessary to continue rapid cooling to below approximately −100°C. Rate of cooling also increases with plunge velocity (3) which should be as high as practicable and (4) the depth should be as large as feasible. (5) The quenchant container should be continuously and vigorously stirred to prevent formation of convective temperature gradients in the quenchant. To avoid "precooling," (6) there should be a negligible cold gas layer through which the plunging specimen passes before impact with the quenchant fluid.

III. Plunge Freezing

A simple apparatus and protocol incorporating these features that has been successfully used in the authors' laboratory over more than the last 10 years is described below and in Fig. 1.

Tissue specimens as small as possible, commensurate with the integrity of the target cell group, are mounted by lightly touching them onto the top of a small blob of an ~120% (w/v) aqueous solution of high-molecular-weight (400 kDa) polyvinyl pyrrolidone (PVP) on the end of a small metal stub (Fig. 1c) and immediately dropped from a height of about half a meter, specimen first, into stirred, isopentane–propane mixture at −196°C (Fig. 1d). The PVP is very viscous and attaches the tissue during the rapid freezing process. It provides a relatively poor conductor between the thermal mass of the metal stub and the specimen. A "blob" of the PVP, not just a smear, is therefore put on the tip of the stub. It is important that the tiny specimen be sitting on top of the PVP and *not* submerged in it or the cooling rate of the specimen becomes that of the larger volume of the PVP. This concentration of PVP is necessary not only to achieve viscosity but because it is approximately isotonic with vertebrate tissues (~300 mOsm).

Simplicity, ease, and rapidity of mounting the specimen are very important. One of the most critical steps in the preparative procedure is the time between removal of the sample from its stable state and plunging into the quenchant. Potentially larger physiological changes can occur in this period than are induced by subsequent cryofixation and other processing steps (Elder *et al.*, 1992). The elapsed time between removal of the specimen from its *in vivo* situation and the moment of cryoquenching can be about 4 sec using the above method.

Stubs are easily recovered from the quenchant fluid for storage in liquid nitrogen and are protected during *rapid* transfer from the cryogen through room air to liquid nitrogen by a film of propane. Specimens are conveniently stored still attached to the stub (Fig. 1f) and are easily handled in and out of labeled storage vials, which can be archived on numbered canes in liquid nitrogen refrigerators. Screw-cap vials should be perforated (Fig. 1f), e.g., by hot needle, prior to use to avoid potentially explosive buildup of vapor pressure. The specimen is separated from the stub, under liquid nitrogen, by splitting the frozen PVP with a sharp precooled blade (Fig. 1g) and transferred, using precooled forecps, with some PVP still attached.

Strict attention must be paid to safety precautions in handling cryoquenchant fluids, especially hydrocarbons (Robards and Sleytr, 1985; Steinbrecht and Zierold, 1987). If exposed to contact with air, the hydrocarbons can form explosive mixtures by oxygen condensation at temperatures below −180°C. This is avoided by the routine practice of keeping the surface of the cryogen container submerged deeply in cold nitrogen gas (Fig. 1e), except at the time of tissue plunging (Fig. 1d), and by promptly disposing of the quenchant fluid after use (burning it off in an appropriate hydrocarbon burner or, more simply, throwing it over open waste ground).

IV. Low-Temperature Freeze-Drying

All transfer steps are potentially dangerous for the specimen as the thermal inertia of the tiny specimen is very small. Comments below refer to low-temperature freeze-driers in which the specimen stage is cooled down to operating temperature, but the principles also apply to driers in which the specimen chamber is immersed in

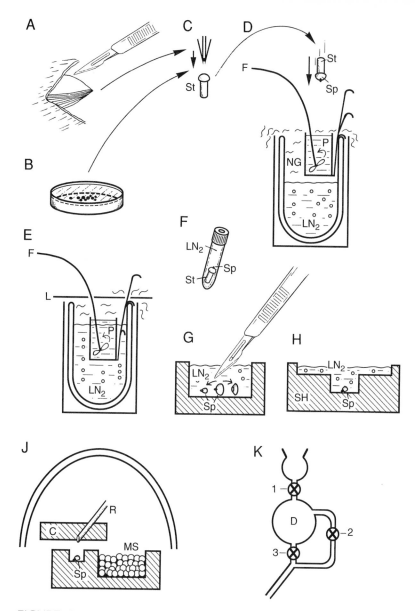

FIGURE 1 Tiny tissue samples (~0.5 mm) from either (A) *in vivo* or (B) *in vitro* experimental material are rapidly blotted (if necessary) and (C) touched onto the surface of a blob of isotonic PVP on a metal stub (1.5 g brass) which is then (D) dropped, specimen first, from a height of ≥0.5 m into a ≥50-mm deep container of rapidly stirred propane/isopentane mixture at liquid nitrogen temperature. The lip of the container stands just above (1–2 mm) the lip of the liquid nitrogen dewar. The specimen carrier of the freeze-drier, with specimen loaded under liquid nitrogen, is inserted through a port into the dry nitrogen gas-filled chamber of the freeze-drier and attached to the cold stage, precooled to liquid nitrogen (LN$_2$) temperature. Drying (J) is achieved by the three mechanisms of a good vacuum (~0.5 mPa), activated Molecular Sieve, and, for no longer than the first few hours, a liquid nitrogen-cooled cold finger. Drawings are not to scale. C, cold finger; D, glass resin expansion and degassing chamber; F, flexible stirrer drive cable; L, slotted lid for dewar; MS, Molecular Sieve; NG, cold nitrogen gas; P, propane/isopentane quenchant; R, resin outlet; SH, freeze-drier specimen holder; Sp, small specimen on PVP; St, stub with PVP blob; 1,2,3, high-vacuum taps.

liquid nitrogen and the stage is warmed up to operating temperature (Elder *et al.*, 1986). Freeze-drying is discussed by Robards and Sleytr (1985) and Echlin (1992).

Prior to transfer, the stage of the freeze-drier must be cooled to its coldest temperature, under vacuum. To prevent rapid frosting of the cold parts, the chamber is then let up to atmospheric pressure with dry gas. The specimens are now quickly transferred from liquid nitrogen storage with precooled foreceps to the liquid nitrogen-filled, precooled holder of the freeze-drier (Fig. 1h), which is then inserted into the vacuum chamber and clamped to the cold stage. Vacuum is reestablished as remaining liquid nitrogen rapidly boils off. Frosting of cold parts of the stage caused by admission of room air during transfer is highly detrimental, as the ice must be sublimed before specimen drying will begin. Following successful transfer, the stage can be warmed slowly to the temperature of the first phase of the selected freeze-drying protocol.

Freeze-drying should be carried out at temperatures around $-80°C$. At warmer temperatures the rate of ice crystal growth increases more rapidly than the specimen can be dried by sublimation. At temperatures colder than $-100°C$ the vapor pressure of crystalline ice becomes progressively so low that quite impracticable freeze-drying times are required.

At a temperature of about $-75°C$ ice vapor pressure is of the order of 10^{-3} Torr (133 mPa). If the vacuum of the freeze-drier is not better than this it is possible to have an atmosphere fully saturated with water vapor, when no further drying could occur. Water vapor is particularly difficult to pump as the molecules adsorb tenaciously to surfaces.

Even with a high-vacuum system further mechanisms of water vapor removal are strongly advocated. Inclusion in the vacuum chamber of strong desiccants such as phosphorus pentoxide (P_2O_5) or highly activated Molecular Sieve is one of the simplest to implement. The Molecular Sieve can be recycled repeatedly and the manufacturers supply guidance on the conditions required for activation to meet the given operating conditions.

As the vapour pressure of ice is of the order of 10^{-24} Torr ($\sim 10^{-22}$ Pa) at liquid nitrogen temperature, a cold trap is highly effective for water vapor removal. A danger is that the cold trap will operate most effectively if it is in direct "line of sight" of the specimen, but this configuration can cause radiative cooling, particularly of a partially dry specimen (Elder *et al.*, 1992), thus inhibiting further drying. The cold trap should therefore be used only during the first few hours of the protocol, when it is most needed, or configured not to be in direct line of sight of the specimen (Elder *et al.*, 1986). It is not redundancy to employ all of these mechanisms.

One millimeter of ice can sublime in 2 or 3 hr *in vacuo* at the temperature of $-80°C$ but about a week is required at $-100°C$. For several reasons (see Robards and Sleytr, 1985) the effective sublimation time for biological tissues may be two or three orders of magnitude slower, and for this reason it is prudent to allow about 72 hr drying time at $-80°C$ (depending on the size of the tissue pieces) as the first step in the drying protocol. Moreover, significant quantities of water remain "bound" by the tissue proteins even after this time, and the most successful freeze-drying protocols include a slow warmup phase (Elder *et al.*, 1992).

It has been found practical to begin the slow warmup early on the fourth day and to raise the temperature at an average rate of 1° per 6 min, i.e., 10° per hour, until $-30°C$ is reached, by which time the "bound" frozen water will have been sublimed. A more rapid warmup of about 1° per minute can then be adopted until the temperature has reached about 25°C, or just above ambient temperature, when vacuum resin embedding can commence. Temperature above ambient is chosen to avoid the danger of condensation onto the resin when the vacuum is finally cracked.

V. Vacuum Embedding in Resin

Of the nonpolar resins it seems that epoxies of the Araldite range may preserve the *in vivo* location of electrolytes better than others (see Elder *et al.*, 1992). All resins must first be degassed to avoid an almost explosive frothing and volume expansion when the vacuum valve draining the resin to the specimen chamber is opened. This can be achieved by having a second vacuum port opening to the resin chamber above the resin level (Fig. 1k). The resin chamber should be of significant size to contain the initial frothing of the resin as the pressure is reduced and the process must be performed gradually and carefully by vacuum port control (Fig. 1k, 2). When the resin has completely outgassed and returned to full vacuum, the drain port (Fig. 1k, 3) can be opened, allowing the resin to flow over the specimens. Under high vacuum, the resin very readily infiltrates the specimens and after a few minutes of total submersion the specimens may be recovered by gently cracking the vacuum to dry gas (nitrogen or air). Specimens are placed in fresh resin and blocks are cured by the normal protocol, under low humidity. Until required, blocks are conveniently stored under anhydrous conditions in clear plastic boxes containing silica gel, sealed with adhesive tape.

VI. Dry Sectioning

Sectioning must be done on a dry knife and under conditions of low humidity. Dry cutting is more difficult than sectioning onto a fluid and diamond knives prove best.

While sections can be cut at a setting of 50 nm, thicker sections (Fig. 2) in the setting range 100–150 nm on the microtome give good X-ray count rates and are more robust for subsequent handling. Even with some compression, which is inevitable in these dry-cut sections, the final section thickness is well within the criterion of "thin," as required by the Hall continuum normalization technique.

As in cryoultramicrotomy, ultrathin sections cut on a dry knife have a strong tendency to roll up. Rolling can be prevented by gently drawing out the leading edge of the emerging section during the cutting stroke, using a hair (e.g., eyelash or dalmatian dog hair) mounted on the tip of a cocktail stick with a droplet of clear glue. An ultramicrotome with a "pause" facility is most convenient as the cutting stroke can be temporarily interrupted when a section has been cut. The ability to section repeatedly in search of features of interest is one of the main advantages of the protocol. Periodic ~1-μm sections can be cut, stained (e.g., toluidine blue), and flattened for high-power light microscopical examination and location of target cells.

Using a pair of mounted hairs, ultrathin sections are carefully detached from the knife edge and transferred to grids with a suitable support film (Formvar, Collodion, nylon, etc.; carbon alone is too brittle). Sections must be in good contact with the support film and as flat and wrinkle-free as possible. If necessary, they can be "beaten" or teased flat, with practice, by the hairs. Grid-mounted sections should immediately be carbon coated, which helps to exclude water vapor and prevents charging under the beam during microanalysis. Sections must be stored again in a dry box for analysis at the earliest occasion.

VII. Microanalysis

Analysis can be done on a cold stage to minimize beam-induced mass loss, but it has been found that the dry, resin-embedded specimens are much more resistant to

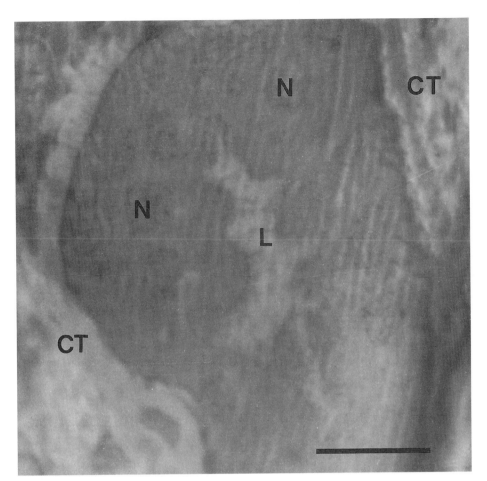

FIGURE 2 Cross section of a horse sweat gland secretory tubule prepared by this method. Resolution and contrast in this nonchemically fixed and unstained section (~150 nm) are much poorer than in conventional transmission electron microscopy images but enough detail can be seen to place the focused electron probe (~0.2 μm) within the cytoplasm of a cell. CT, connective tissue; L, gland lumen with microvilli; N, nucleus. Bar = 10 μm. (Reproduced, with permission of the Company of Biologists Ltd., from Wilson *et al.* (1988) *J. Exp. Biol.* **136**, 489–494.)

mass loss than freeze-dried cryosections and in practice analysis can be satisfactorily carried out at room temperature (Elder *et al.*, 1992).

VIII. Comments

While debate continues (cf. Zierold, 1992) regarding the absolute retention of diffusible elements by the resin-embed route, it is clear that for comparative studies on a relative basis, physiological changes in the diffusible electrolyte elements are reliably preserved and the method offers the advantages of room-temperature ultramicrotomy and the facility to section repeatedly and systematically to locate obscure target tissue components (Elder *et al.*, 1992).

REFERENCES

Echlin, P. (1992) "Low Temperature Microscopy and Analysis." Plenum Press, New York/ London.

Elder, H. Y., Biddlecombe, W. H., Tetley, L., Wilson, S. M., and Jenkinson, D. M. (1986) Construction of low temperature freeze driers. *EMSA Bull.* **16**, 111–113.

Elder, H. Y., Wilson, S. M., Nicholson, W. A. P., Pediani, J. D., McWilliams, S. A., Jenkinson, D. M., and Kenyon, C. J. (1992) Quantitative X-ray microanalysis of ultra-thin resin-embedded biological samples. *Microchim. Acta* **12** (Suppl.), 53–74.

Robards, A. W., and Sleytr, U. (1985) "Practical Methods in Electron Microscopy," Vol. 10: "Low Temperature Methods in Biological Electron Microscopy." (A. M. Glauert, Ser. Ed.). Elsevier, Amsterdam. 551pp.

Steinbrecht, R. A., and Zierold, K. (eds.) (1987) "Cryotechniques in Biological Electron Microscopy." Springer-Verlag, Berlin.

Zierold, K. (1992) Comparison of cryopreparation techniques for electron probe microanalysis of cells as exemplified by human erythrocytes. *Scanning Electron Microsc.* **6**, 1137–1145.

High-Resolution Scanning Electron Microscopy in Cell Biology

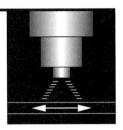

Terence D. Allen and Martin W. Goldberg

I. Introduction

Resolution in scanning electron microscopy (SEM) has been dramatically improved in recent years, so that for biological material, no significant differences exist in resolution between SEM and conventional transmission electron microscopy (TEM). High brightness sources (field emission) and novel final lens configurations have resulted in instrument resolutions of 0.5 to 1 nm, allowing direct, three-dimensional visualization of surface detail at molecular resolution.

Surface imaging allows bulk samples to be examined without limitation of specimen thickness. Visualization of intracellular surfaces requires some means of access, such as isolation of cell fractions or macromolecules, or *in situ* via fracture or sectioning techniques. Cell-free systems, e.g., *in vitro* nuclear formation, allow biological interfaces such as developing nuclear envelopes to be imaged directly (Goldberg *et al.,* 1992). True three-dimensional surface visualization can be achieved by tilting the specimen to make stereo pairs. The surfaces can be further characterized by standard immunogold labeling, which can be unequivocally localized by their strong backscatter signal. For specimens that are thin enough to allow electron penetration, a scanning TEM (STEM) image can also be readily obtained, and simultaneously displayed alongside the secondary electron image, circumventing the need for conventional TEM in some cases. The use of low accelerating voltages in high-resolution SEM (HRSEM) has also been shown to be of advantage with some specimens, reducing charging and penetration of the electron beam, but maintaining a high-resolution information content. Freeze-drying, freeze-substitution, and cryo-hydration methods may all be used for HRSEM (Muller and Hermann, 1990) but can be considered specialized and are not covered in this article, which deals with techniques that rely on chemical preservation, followed by dehydration, critical-point drying, and coating. Conventional SEM coating (up to 20 nm thickness) with sputtered gold completely obscures fine surface detail in HRSEM and must be replaced by high-resolution coating. Early reports cite ion beam-sputtered platinum as a suitable coating (Pawley and Erlandsen, 1989), but we routinely coat with a 1- to 2-nm film of chromium or tungsten, which has a grain size of 0.3 to 0.5 nm (Apkarian *et al.,* 1990).

II. Materials and Instrumentation

1. Glutaraldehyde (Cat. No. 49631, Fluka Gillingham)
2. Tannic acid (J. T. Baker UK)

3. TCH (Cat. No. T-2137, Sigma)

4. Osmium tetroxide (Johnson Matthey Ltd)

5. Uranyl acetate (Agar Scientific)

6. Diethylene glycol distearate (EM Corp.)

7. Molecular Sieve (Merck Ltd.)

8. Arklone (trichlorotrifluoroethane, ICI Chemicals and Polymers)

9. Hepes

10. Sorensen's phosphate buffer

11. Poly-L-lysine HBr, MW 150,000–300,000 (Cat. No. P-1399)

12. Glass coverslips, 5–7 mm

13. Silicon chips, 5×5 mm (Agar Scientific Ltd.)

14. Carbon-coated support grids

15. Fine forceps for handling

16. Microcentrifuge to spin suspended material onto coverslips

17. Microcentrifuge tubes, 1.5 ml, half-filled with polymerized EM resin, ideal to support coverslips, chips, and grids during specimen deposition by centrifugation

High-resolution scanning EM

Conventional "pinhole" final lens instruments with field emission sources will allow subcellular imaging, as will conventional transmission instruments with scanning attachments. To date, the highest resolution achieved has been in field emission instruments with the facility to position the specimen in, or very close to, the final lens. The microscope should also be equipped with a suitable high-resolution backscatter detector for immunogold labeling. The main suppliers for these instruments are Hitachi, Jeol, Topcon (formerly ISI), Philips and Zeiss.

Critical-point drier, with high-purity CO_2 (<5 ppm Water)

CO_2 should be passed through a filter to remove water (Tousimis Research Corp., filter 8782).

Coating units

Oxygen, hydrocarbons, and water vapor all adversely affect the grain size of chromium or tantalum deposited by sputter coating (Apkarian et al., 1990). We use an Edwards Auto 306 12-in. coating unit with cryopump, magnetron head, and suitable power source (Edwards High Vacuum International). Similar configurations using Denton HiVac and Balzers equipment with cold-trapped turbopumping have also been successful. Any system should use high-purity argon, have a shutter, and a specimen table which tilts and rotates. Film thickness monitoring of deposition is an advantage. Several "bench-top" systems have recently come on the market, many untested by the highest resolution. The Zenosput (Edwards XE 200) has been found satisfactory in our lab.

III. Procedures

A. EXPOSING SURFACES

1. Subcellular Fractionation

Organelles and macromolecules can be isolated by standard procedures, possibly requiring subsequent modifications in the light of HRSEM visualization, which are beyond the scope of this article. Basically, the specimen must be undamaged by osmotic shock, proteolysis, or unsuitable isolation buffers. They must also be clean. The surface of organelles should, for instance, be free of attached cytoskeletal remnants or cytoplasmic contamination. Where the specimens are available as purified macromolecules or viruses, they may be deposited on carbon coated TEM grids in the conventional manner, and viewed by HRSEM. In this situation, TEM negative staining will usually be replaced by fixation for SEM, and air-drying by critical-point drying followed by chromium coating. If a STEM detector is available, the virus/macromolecule can be recognized as a transmitted "reference image" after this protocol and directly compared with the secondary electron (SEM) image.

Adhering sample to support. Many cell components naturally adhere to glass coverslips, silicon chips, or carbon support film on grids. Glass coverslips may be a useful initial preparative substratum, as they can be checked in the phase-contrast microscope for the density and distribution of specimens. Once the isolation protocol is established, coverslips should be replaced with silicon chips, as silicon is a conductive substratum in contrast to glass, an insulator, that can generate problems with charging. Silicon chips are equivalently adhesive to glass for biologically isolated material. If samples are fixed in solution it may be necessary to coat the support with poly-L-lysine to facilitate adherence. Different samples may require slight modification, but the basic technique is as follows.

Solutions

1. *Poly-L-lysine:* Make a fresh 1 mg/ml solution of poly-L-lysine in sterile distilled water; use within 24 hr.

Steps

1. Mark surface of chip or coverslip with identification number using diamond marker.
2. Place a 50-μl drop of poly-L-lysine on coverslip or chip; allow to stand for at least 60 min in a moist chamber to avoid drying. Rinse in sterile distilled water.
3. Place a 50-μl drop of suspended material (fixed and rinsed) on coverslip/chip. Allow to settle at 0°C and unit gravity in a moist chamber (1 hr to overnight).
4. Allow bulk of drop to run off, put chip/cover slip back in fixative, and continue as for fresh tissue.

Unfixed samples may be distorted by poly-L-lysine. To spin down materials from suspension, use minicentrifuge tubes half-filled with polymerized EM resin to support the coverslip/silicon chip/grid.

2. "In Situ" Exposure of Intracellular Surfaces

Dry fracture. This is a crude but extremely effective way of exposing internal surfaces in both tissues and cells. After fixation, dehydration, and critical-point drying, merely touch the surface of the specimen to double-sided cellotape, pull away without shearing, coat as normal, and examine in the SEM. This technique may be enhanced by pretreatment with detergent (0.5% Triton X-100, 2–3 min for tissue culture cells), either alone or mixed with the primary fixative, (2.0% paraformaldehyde and 0.1% glutaraldehyde), and subsequently refixed as described below.

Resinless sections. These methods involve sectioning of embedded specimens followed by exposure of internal surfaces by removal of the supporting material. This may vary between epoxy resins, various waxes, and even ice. Resins requiring corrosive solvents will tend to be prone to surface etching. For HRSEM, the most promising removable resin to date appears to be DGD (Nickerson *et al.*, 1990), a technique that also allows immunostaining.

B. FIXATION

Solutions

All fixatives are ideally made up just before use or at least the same day; both glutaraldehyde and glutaraldehyde–tannic acid solutions should be filtered before use through a 0.22-μm filter. One percent aqueous uranyl acetate should be stored in a brown bottle. Osmium tetroxide is made by breaking the ampoules in which the crystals are delivered, having previously washed them free of label and adhesive under the tap, in a fume cupboard. The ampoules plus crystals are dissolved in the correct amount of buffer or distilled water to give the appropriate final concentration. Thiocarbohydrazide or tannic acid solutions should also be made just prior to use (Allen *et al.*, 1988).

Steps

Isolated proteins and nucleoproteins

1. Proteins and nucleoproteins on carbon support films on TEM grids may be floated on top of drops (25–50 μl) of the appropriate solutions spread on Parafilm.
2. Place in 1% glutaraldehyde in appropriate buffer for 10 min.
3. Wash in double-distilled water for 5 min.
4. Transfer to 1% uranyl acetate for 5 min.
5. Transfer to 100% ethanol 1–2 min.
6. Air-dry or critical-point dry (see below).

Small and easily preserved structures

1. Fix in 3% glutaraldehyde in Sorensen's phosphate buffer for 30 min.
2. Wash in Sorensen's for 5 min.
3. Postfix in 1% OsO_4 in Sorensen's 30 min.
4. Wash in double-distilled water for 5 min.
5. Dehydrate through ethanol series, 5 min each.
6. Place in Arklone for 5 min.
7. Critical-point dry (see below).

Large and/or fragile structures (e.g., whole cells, organelles, cytoskeletal preparations, isolated cell or nuclear membranes)

1. Whole cells, etc., attached to specimen supports such as silicon chips are usually handled by changing the solutions in 35-mm-diameter petri dishes.

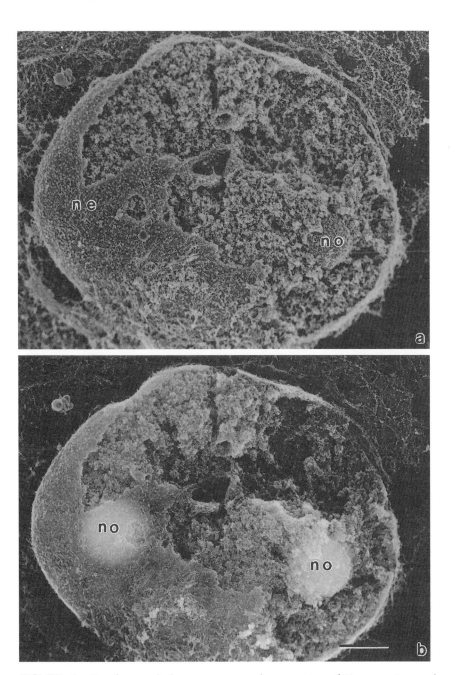

FIGURE 1 Dry-fractured, detergent-extracted preparation of *Xenopus* tissue culture cells viewed at (a) low (5 kV) and (b) high (25 kV) accelerating voltages. The nucleus contains two nucleoli: one exposed (no) by the fracture plane, and one underlying the intact area of nuclear envelope (ne). At high accelerating voltage (b), a subsurface signal generated by the dense nature of the nucleolus on the left of the nucleus produces a "bright patch," indicating its position (no). Bar = 2.0 μm.

2. Fix in 2% glutaraldehyde, 0.2% tannic acid, 0.1% Hepes, pH 7.4, for 10 min.

3. Wash in double-distilled water for 5 min.

4. Postfix in 0.1% OsO_4 in water for 10 min.

5. Wash in water for 5 min.

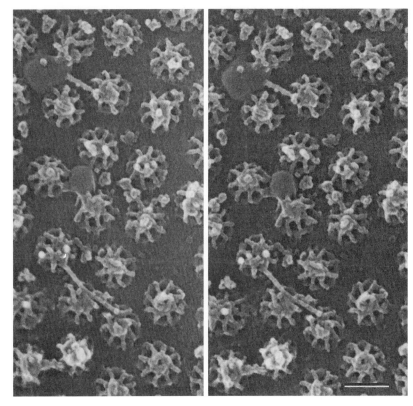

FIGURE 2 Stereo pair of isolated germinal vesicle nuclear envelope from *Xenopus*, viewed from the nuclear side, showing characteristic "basket" structure on the inner aspect of each nuclear pore complex. Bar = 100 nm.

6. Stain with 1% aqueous uranyl acetate for 10 min.

7. Dehydrate through ethanol series and Arklone and critical-point dry.

C. CRITICAL-POINT DRYING

All traces of water should be removed from ethanol, Arklone, and CO_2. Let 100% ethanol and Arklone stand with Molecular Sieve for more than 24 hr prior to use. High-purity CO_2 (<5 ppm water) should be used and passed through a water filter as a precaution.

Steps

1. Exchange Arklone for CO_2.

2. Flush six times.

3. Leave in CO_2 for 30 min.

4. Flush six times.

5. Raise temperature to 40°C.

6. Release gas slowly (over about 15–20 min).

7. Transfer to coating unit as soon as possible.

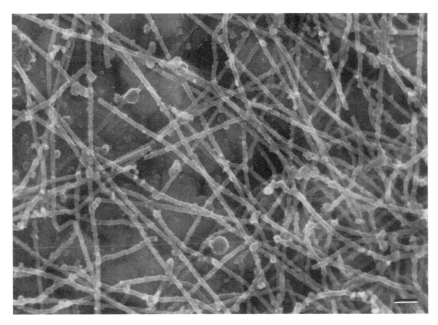

FIGURE 3 SEM of *in vitro* polymerized microtubules, from purified bovine brain tubulin in the presence of microtubule-associated proteins. Bar = 100 nm.

D. SPUTTER COATING

Steps

1. Pump specimen to at least 5×10^{-7} mbar.

2. Introduce high-purity argon to a pressure of 8×10^{-3} mbar.

3. Start specimen rotation.

4. Sputter at 50–100 mA current (voltage 450 V) and 60 rpm, specimen table tilted at 30° onto the shutter for 20–60 sec to remove chromium oxide layer from the target.

5. Open shutter and deposit ~2 nm chromium as indicated by a film thickness monitor.

6. Examine in microscope as soon as possible and at least within a day or two.

E. MICROSCOPY

Steps

1. A liquid nitrogen-cooled decontaminator (if present) should always be used.

2. Spot size and apertures should be as small as possible, consistent with enough signal to visualize high resolution.

3. An appropriate accelerating voltage must be selected. High-resolution scanning electron microscopes usually work in the range 1–30 kV. Instrument resolution decreases with kilovoltage; however, at high kilovoltage there may be problems with charging and specimen penetration, leading to nonspecific signal from below the specimen surface. At low kilovoltage, penetration and charging are reduced, but so are resolution and signal. Signal is generated almost completely from the surface (at 1.0 kV) so there is no problem of signal from underlying structures. In general, we use high kilovoltage for thin and conductive

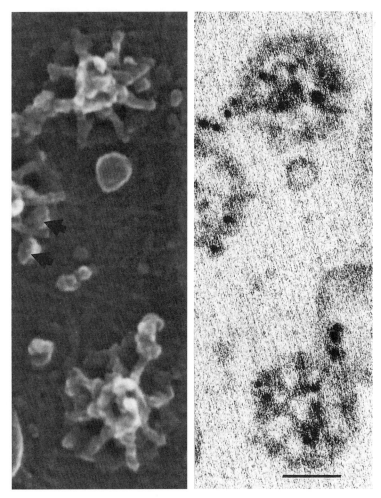

FIGURE 4 SEM visualization of lectin-binding sugar residues on the nucleoplasmic face of nuclear pore complexes. The bright signal from the 10-nm gold particles in the backscattered electron image has been contrast-reversed to appear as black dots and mixed with the secondary electron image. Bar = 50 nm.

specimens and low kilovoltage for bulky or less conductive specimens; however, a complete range of kilovoltages should be experimented with for each type of sample (Figs. 1–3).

F. IMMUNOGOLD LABELING

The basics of specimen preparation for immunogold labeling are beyond the length limits for this article and are adequately covered elsewhere. For immunogold labeling for HRSEM, the following points are important.

1. Size of Probe

The choice of probe size is a compromise between sensitivity and subsequent detection. Very small gold probes (around 1 nm) have minimal steric hindrance and consequently label with maximum sensitivity. One-nanometer gold has been visualized by backscatter imaging in HRSEM (Hermann *et al.,* 1991), but is best increased in diameter *in situ* by silver enhancement to a size at which it is more conveniently searched for (around 5–10 nm). We have used 5-nm gold directly as a good compromise between sensitivity and localization and 10-nm gold for strong antibody (or lectin) labeling (Fig. 4).

2. Coating

Using gold probes obviously prohibits gold coating for SEM. In the past, specimen charging has been inhibited by coating with carbon, but carbon produces a severely limited secondary electron signal, with little topographical information. A 1.5-nm chromium coating provides the ideal compromise, retaining the full secondary electron-generated surface information, without compromising detection of gold by backscattered electron detection (Allen and Goldberg, 1993).

IV. Comments

HRSEM is a relatively new technique and has great potential for many areas of cell biology. The procedures given here may need to be modified to optimize preservation of some structures. Probably the most difficult step is exposing recognizable and undamaged intracellular surfaces. Isolation offers the possibilities of further characterization by other methods, but gives no *in situ* information and may result in damage. Resinless sections and dry fracture give *in situ* information but only after some extraction of the cell. Freeze-fracture, followed by frozen hydrated coating and visualization, may alleviate these problems but is limited by the plane of fracture, as the structure of interest may not be exposed. It is also technically difficult and expensive. Osmium etching results in spectacular images of intracellular membranes but the uncertainty of what is removed makes interpretation difficult. Direct visualization of biological interfaces in cell-free systems (e.g., *in vitro* nuclear formation) is a particularly promising area (Goldberg *et al.,* 1992). Considerable fresh structural information has also been demonstrated for nuclear pore complexes and associated structures (Ris, 1991; Goldberg and Allen, 1992).

V. Pitfalls

1. Process samples as quickly as possible. Do not leave dried samples exposed to air longer than necessary. Chromium and tantalum coatings can deteriorate within days. Some samples are best examined immediately.

2. Beam damage/contamination can be a problem on samples without much thermal/electrical capacity (e.g., molecules on a carbon film). In HRSEM, the sample may not stand more than one or two scans of the electron beam; this is also the case with frozen material. In this case focus initially at low magnification, and do final focus adjustment on the line scan of the photographic exposure.

ACKNOWLEDGMENTS

T. D. Allen and M. W. Goldberg are supported by the Cancer Research Campaign (U.K.). The authors acknowledge the excellent technical assistance of G. R. Bennion, S. A. Rutherford, and A. J. Robson.

REFERENCES

Allen, T. D., and Goldberg, M. W. (1993) High resolution SEM in cell biology. *Trends Cell Biol* **3**, 203–208.
Allen, T. D., Jack, E. M., and Harrison, C. J. (1988) Three dimensional structure of human

metaphase chromosomes determined by scanning electron microscopy. *In* "Chromosomes and Chromatin" (K. W. Adolph, ed.), Vol II, pp. 52–70. CRC Press, Boca Raton, FL.

Apkarian, R. P., Gutekunst, M. D., and Joy, D. C. (1990) High resolution SEM study of enamel crystal morphology. *J. Electron Microsc. Tech.* **14**, 70–78.

Goldberg, M. W., and Allen, T. D. (1992) High resolution scanning electron microscopy of the nuclear envelope: Demonstration of a new, regular, fibrous lattice attached to the baskets of the nucleoplasmic face of the nuclear pores. *J. Cell Biol.* **119**, 1429–1440.

Goldberg, M. W., Blow, J. J., and Allen, T. D. (1992) The use of field emission in-lens scanning electron microscopy to study the steps of assembly of the nuclear envelope *in vitro*. *J. Struct. Biol.* **108**, 257–268.

Hermann, R., Schwartz, H., and Muller, M. (1991) High precision immunostaining electron microscopy using Fab fragments coupled to ultra-small colloidal gold. *J. Struct. Biol.* **107**, 38–47.

Muller, M., and Hermann, R. (1990) Towards high-resolution SEM of biological objects. *In* "Proceedings 12th International Congress on Electron Microscopy," Vol. 3 (L. D. Peachy and D. B. Williams, eds.), pp. 4–5. San Francisco Press, San Francisco.

Nickerson, J., Krockmalnic, G., He, D., and Penmar, S. (1990) Immunolocalisation in three dimensions: Immunogold staining of cytoskeletal and nuclear matrix proteins in resinless electron microscopy sections. *Proc. Natl. Acad. Sci. USA* **87**, 2259–2263.

Pawley, J. B., and Erlandsen, S. L. (1989) The case for low voltage high resolution scanning electron microscopy of biological samples. *In* "Scanning Microscopy" (R. M. Albrecht and R. L. Ornberg, eds.), Suppl. 3, pp. 163–179. Scanning Microscopy International, Chicago.

Ris, H. (1991) The three dimensional structure of the nuclear pore complex as seen by high voltage electron microscopy and high resolution low voltage scanning electron microscopy. *EMSA Bull.* **21**, 54–56.

PART **5**

MICRODISSECTION TECHNIQUES

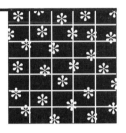

Microdissection-Based Techniques for the Determination of Cell Proliferation in Gastrointestinal Epithelium: Application to Animal and Human Studies

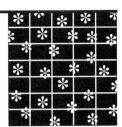

Robert A. Goodlad

I. Introduction

While several methods are available for the study of intestinal epithelial cell division, several of the more acceptable still have serious shortcomings (Maurer, 1981; Wright and Alison, 1984). Many of the problems associated with the *in vivo* uptake of tritiated thymidine can be avoided if the "all or nothing" nature of autoradiographs is exploited, however, the technique then becomes very labor intensive. An alternative is to score mitotic figures or arrested metaphases in microdissected crypts. This can give identical results but in far less time (Goodlad *et al.*, 1991). The great advantage of such techniques is that results are expressed on a per crypt basis, so that one does not need to count interphase cells. Furthermore, the many pitfalls associated with scoring crypt sections are avoided. Concomitant changes often occur in the denominator, so that proliferative indices gathered from sections may in fact only make sense if they are expressed in terms of a (reconstructed) crypt (Goodlad *et al.*, 1992). Although there are far fewer mitotic figures than DNA-synthesizing cells, microdissection enables all the figures in the entire crypt to be scored, and all the crypts in a sample can be quantified. Microdissection-based techniques are simple, fast, and robust. In animal investigations the "gold standard" method is the quantification of the rate of entry of cells into mitosis using a metaphase arrest agent, to determine the crypt cell production rate (CCPR), (Goodlad and Wright, 1982). If the number of animals is limited, valuable data can be obtained from the augmented mitotic index, obtained by sampling 2 hr after vincristine administration. This 2-hr metaphase collection index is a state not a rate measure, and as such is theoretically less robust, but it is more precise and facilitates complex, multivariate analysis.

Scoring native mitotic figures is a viable alternative if the use of metaphase arrest agents *in vivo* is not possible. This is particularly appropriate to human studies and the method is greatly preferable to the several *in vitro* methods available for the assessment of biopsies, which are laborintensive, require the immediate incubation of the tissue, and may not even be reliable. Furthermore, *in vitro* techniques are of limited value due to the trauma of biopsy and problems associated with limited diffusion (the birth rate at the edge of a cultured explant may be twice that seen at the center). Proliferative activity varies considerably with time after biopsy, but allowing the tissue to stabilize from the trauma of biopsy would then remove many of those systemic and local factors involved in the regulation of cell proliferation.

The use of antibodies to dividing cells also has its problems, as the results are highly dependent on the prior treatment of the tissue (Hall *et al.*, 1992). Furthermore, antigens can also be expressed anomalously (Hall *et al.*, 1992). Finally, all antibody techniques cannot escape from the difficulties inherent in standardizing immunohistochemical techniques and setting thresholds for scoring a cell as labeled and the problems associated with studying three-dimensional structures in two dimensions (Goodlad, 1992).

Biopsies for microdissection need little special treatment, apart from the use of Carnoy's fluid for fixation. They can then be stored almost indefinitely before being stained. The term *microdissection* is somewhat of a misnomer, as normally all that is involved is to gently tease the tissue apart and let pressure on the coverslip separate the crypts. A further advantage of the technique is that data on the location of dividing cells within the crypt can also be obtained (Matthew *et al.*, 1993).

II. Materials and Instrumentation

A stereo dissecting microscope is required, and this must have a good light source. Fiberoptic cold light sources are best.

Mounted needles should be sharpened first on a medium, then on a very fine oilstone. Old dental probes make excellent needles as they have good balance and, being made of surgical-grade steel, take a fine point. Twenty-seven-gauge injection needles can also be used, but need to be fitted to a weighted syringe or to a custom-built holder, which can be made by gluing male–male luer adapters (Portex) into a suitable handle, such as an old pen.

A good-quality laboratory microscope is required. It is best to have a low power to locate areas of interest (say 4×), a medium power (say 16×), and 25× and 40× objectives. The eyepiece should be fitted with a 10 × 10 grid (No. E11A, Graticules Ltd.).

A hand tally counter is useful, especially when metaphase arrest is used, but for serious counting electric counters are supreme. These can be made up as single counters or as multichannel counters, with or without an additional hand-held switch unit, which enables the operator's hands to be kept near the microscope controls. Counters can readily be constructed using suitable microswitches (RS Components) and a 12-V electro-magnetic reset counter (RS Components), or an all-electronic self-contained counter, such as the Omron H7EC (Farnnell Electronic Components) can be used. This only requires the connection of a microswitch and 0.1-μF (250-V) capacitor across the input signal terminals and a reset switch across the other terminals.

A drawing tube is required for the determination of crypt size and crypt area. These are available for most makes of microscope, and project an image of a pencil into the microscopist's field of view (Fig. 1). Quantification of these drawings can be performed using an image scanner and image analysis program on a PC or an Apple Macintosh. Image analysis is a memory hungry process. The NIH public domain program Image for the Apple Macintosh (with 8MB memory and a 256 color/shades of gray monitor) is a powerful and very cost effective option and can be downloaded via anonymous FTP from zippy.nimh.nih.gov [128.231.98.32]. Enter anonymous as user name and e-mail address as password. Image (and its documentation in word format) is in the /pub/image directory.

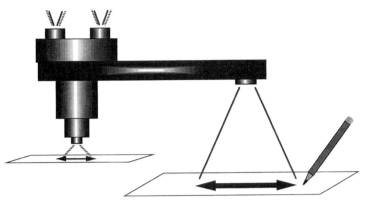

FIGURE 1 Drawing tube. The image of the pencil is projected into the microscopist's field of view, so that the outline of objects can be traced.

III. Procedures

Solutions

1. *Vincristine sulfate:* The product from Sigma is satisfactory, but it is best to use that formulated and packaged for human use. Hospital pharmacies are a good source, and supply the agent in septum vials such as those manufactured by David Bull Laboratories, which reduce the risks associated with handling powder. The dose is 1 mg/kg (the same dose is also used for intravenous injection). Vincristine is usually supplied as a 1 mg/ml solution, so dilute 1:9 for mice and inject 1/100th of body weight; i.e., a 25-g mouse gets 0.25 ml. For rats use neat (1 mg/ml), so a 250-g rat gets 0.25 ml. For other species a dose–response experiment may be required.

2. *Carnoy's fluid:* Mix 6 parts (v/v) ethanol (74% OP spirit or industrial methylated spirit is adequate), 1 part acetic acid, and 3 parts chloroform.

3. *Schiff's reagent:* Can be bought ready-made from Sigma or from BDH. To make 1 liter, bring 1 liter distilled water to the boil, *remove flame and leave for 30 sec,* add 5 g basic fuchsin (BDH). Cool to 50°C, and add 15 g sodium metabisulfite and 150 ml 1 *M* hydrochloric acid. Mix and cool to room temperature, then leave overnight in the dark. Add 5 g decolorizing charcoal, mix, leave for 2 min, and then filter. Store in dark at 4°C. Use within 3–4 months.

Tissue can be fixed and stored in a variety of tubes or vials, but the aggressive nature of Carnoy's fluid precludes polystyrene. It is also important that the tube lids make a very good seal (if one wishes to store the tissue for a long time). For large tissues, Zinsser scintillation vials are ideal; smaller tissues can be fixed and stored in scintillation vial inserts. Very small pieces of tissue, such as biopsies, can be stored in Nunc cryotubes or Sarstedt microtubes with rubber seal rings.

Steps

If only the native mitotic index (and morphometry) is to be determined, no pretreatment with vincristine is required.

Crypt cell production rate

1. Inject animals intraperitoneally with vincristine, using a 25-gauge needle.
2. Record time of injection (time zero) and kill animals at timed intervals after injection of vincristine, between 30 and 180 min after injection; record time of kill.

Two-hour metaphase collection

1. Inject animals as above, but kill all animals exactly 2 hr after vincristine injection. This will necessitate staggering the injections to allow time for the autopsy.

Autopsy

1. Dissect out the gastrointestinal tract.
2. Measure lengths of small bowel and colon.
3. Rinse, blot, and weigh stomach, small intestine, cecum, and colon.
4. Take samples defined by their percentage of segment length; 1-cm portions of rodent bowel are more than sufficient.

Fixation

1. Place fresh tissue in Carnoy's fluid for 1–3 hr.
2. Transfer to, and store, in 70% alcohol. If taken late in the day, samples can be stored in refrigerator and then transferred to alcohol next morning.

Staining

1. Cut out a small piece of tissue and place it in 50% alcohol for 5–15 min.
2. Transfer to 25% alcohol for 5–15 min.
3. Hydrolyze in 1 M hydrochloric acid for 10 min at 60°C (some tissues/species may require 12 min).
4. Place in Schiff's reagent for at least 45 min. The tissue should then be a deep magenta color.

Microdissection

1. Keep the tissue in Schiff's reagent until required.
2. Take a portion of the stained tissue and place it on a microscope slide.
3. Add a drop of 45% acetic acid.
4. Place the tissue under the dissection microscope; use one mounted needle to hold the tissue and use another needle to peel off the serosa and muscle layers.
5. Move a small portion of the prepared tissue to a fresh area of the slide.
6. Gently tease the tissue apart, so that several small clumps of crypts are present.
7. Add another drop of 45% acetic acid and place a coverslip on top.
8. Gently press down on the coverslip until the crypts separate. Microdissected crypts are illustrated in Fig. 2.

Quantification: Metaphase arrest

1. Count the number of metaphases per microdissected crypt. Arrested metaphases are readily identified by their intense color, lack of a nuclear envelope, and condensed chromatin. Mitoses migrate toward the crypt lumen, which also helps in their identification (see Fig. 2).

2. Score 10 small intestinal or 20 colon crypts (20 stomach glands) per animal using a 25× or 40× objective.

3. Plot the mean number of metaphases per crypt against time since injection.

4. Fit line by least-squares linear regression. The slope gives the rate of entry of cells into mitosis (CCPR) (Fig. 3).

For 2-hr metaphase collection score as above and take the mean.

Quantification: Native mitoses

Count the number of mitotic figures per crypt, using a 25× or 40× objective. Twenty glands or crypts are usually required.

The scorer must learn to distinguish interphase cells from the phases of mitosis shown in Fig. 4. Interphase cells have a distinct nuclear envelope and clear faintly stained nuclei with a few nucleoli. Chromatin begins to condense in prophase and the nuclear membrane disappears. In metaphase the condensed chromosomes have a jumbled appearance, and it feels that one could almost count the chromosomes. Anaphase has a characteristic "two bunches of bananas pulling apart" appearance, whereas in telophase distinctive pairs of new nuclei (two small sausages side by side) are seen (a pair of telophase nuclei counts as one figure). The identification of mitoses is facilitated by their luminal migration and their restriction to the proliferative zones of the gastrointestinal tract. Early prophases and late telophases can sometimes be clearly seen, but unless one can identify these on every occasion, it is better to exclude these. The stages of mitosis are shown in Fig. 4, and the investigator must adhere to a rigorous definition of the stages scored. One must also be able to identify wandering white blood cells and apoptotic figures, so that they can be excluded. This may be difficult if the tissue is highly inflamed.

Quantification: Positional data

Positional data can be gathered in one of three ways. The drawing tube can be used to record the location of mitoses, or an eyepiece graticule can be used to record grid positions. These data can then be used to produce either mitotic distribution curves or histograms showing the fraction of mitoses per crypt zone; five equal crypt zones are normally used. The third method uses a microscope with a zoom attachment (usually part of a microphotographic accessory) to fit the length of the crypt into the 10 × 10 grid; zonal scores can then be gathered directly (Fig. 5).

Quantification: Area measurements

1. Superimpose a line of known length on the drawing plane onto the scale of a calibrated microscope slide (Graticules Ltd) to set the magnification of the drawing tube.

2. Trace the outline of the crypts (or other units of interest) with a pen.

3. Quantify tracings using a flatbed scanner and image analysis system. Crypts are best traced using a low-power lens, such as a 6× objective. Neutral density filters and a desk lamp may be required to lower the microscope's light level and to boost the drawing tube image.

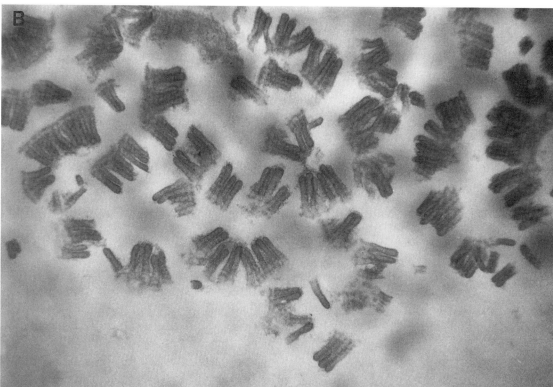

FIGURE 2 Microdissection (of vincristine injected rat tissue). (A) Teasing apart of the stained tissue under dissecting microscope. (B) Low-power view of a (colonic) squash under dissecting microscope. (C) Higher-power view of colonic crypts. (D) Higher-power view of a villus with attached crypts. (E, F) Higher-power view of small intestinal crypts, demonstrating the importance of focusing on different optical planes of the preparation.

C

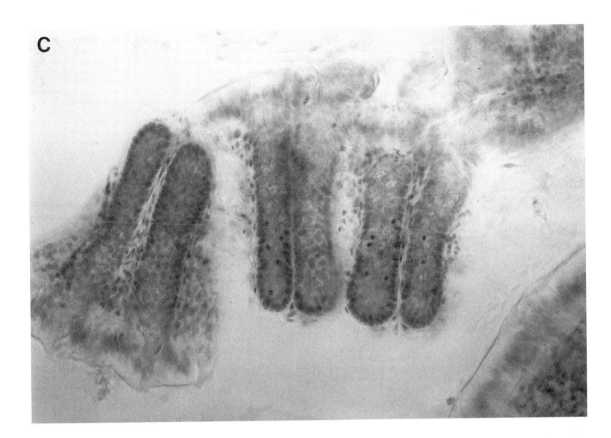

D

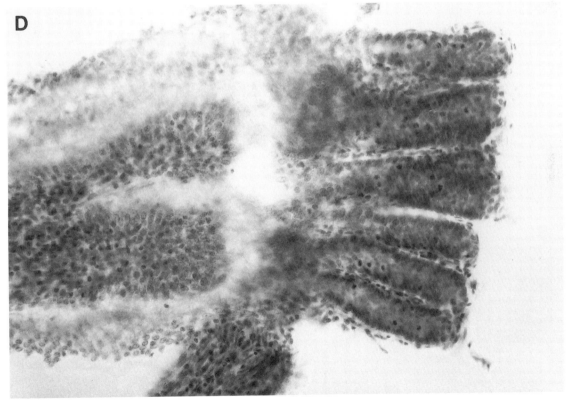

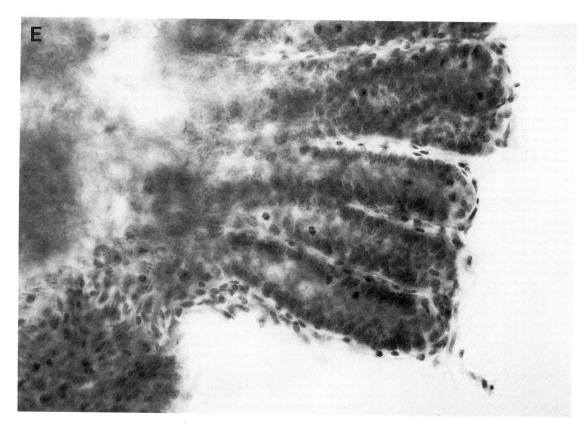

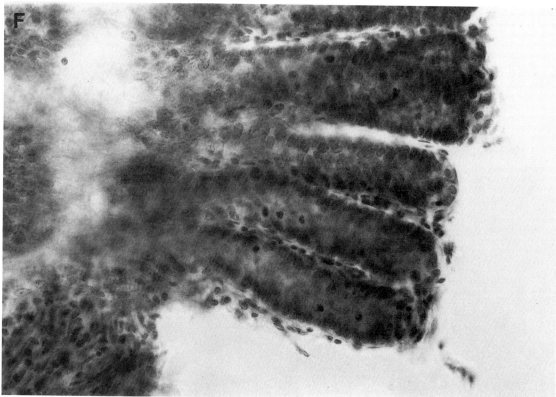

FIGURE 2 *continued*

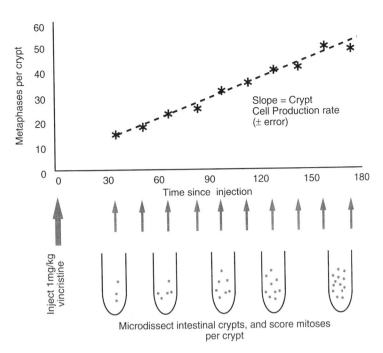

FIGURE 3 Crypt cell production rate method. The stathmokinetic agent vincristine is used to arrest cells as they enter metaphase. The number of arrested metaphases per crypt is scored and plotted against time. The slope of the line gives the rate of entry of cells into mitosis or crypt cell production rate (CCPR).

Quantification: Crypt villus ratio and density

1. Stain a larger piece of tissue, place on a slide, and remove the serosa and mucosa.

2. Add a few drops of 45% acetic acid and gently apply a coverslip.

3. Use a microscope with 10×10 eyepiece grid fitted. Turn up the illumination and focus on the crypt openings and count the number per grid; then focus on the villus bases and score these. Only score crypts or villi intersecting two of the lines of the grid (see Fig. 5). If you cannot use

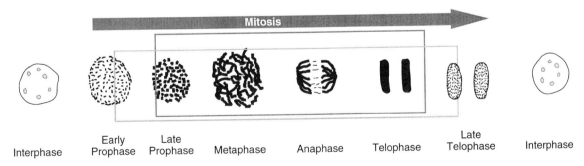

FIGURE 4 Stages of mitosis. Note the distinct nuclear envelope in interphase, and the nucleoli. Chromatin condenses in prophase and the nuclear membrane disappears. The condensed chromosomes appear jumbled in metaphase. Chromosomes pull apart in anaphase; distinctive pairs of new nuclei are seen in telophase. The investigator must adhere to a rigorous definition of the stages scored. It is recommended that only late prophases and early telophases are scored (smaller box).

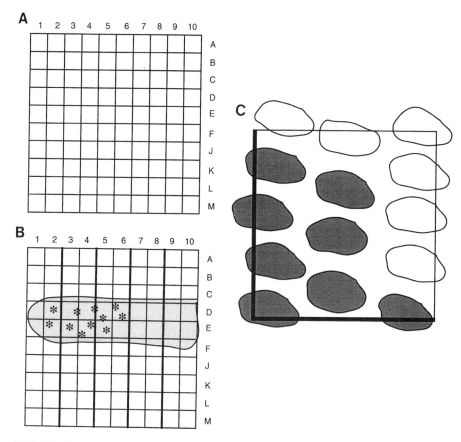

FIGURE 5 (A) The 10 × 10 eyepiece graticule can be used to guide the investigator, and by counting square by square, duplicate counting is avoided. (B) For all counting (crypt/villus ratio shown) only count structures on two sides (denoted by heavy lines) in each square. (C) A zoom attachment can be used to fit crypts into the grid, so that the mitotic distribution in each of five equal zones can be determined.

differential focus to select both crypts and villi, it may be necessary to turn the tissue over and count three grids per side.

4. Divide number of crypts by number of villi to derive crypt villus ratio. The number of crypts/number of villi per grid reflects the inverse of their area.

Quantification: Cell population counts

1. Carefully dissect out two or three individual crypts or villi at a time. Villi can be dissected out only in some species.

2. Separate the crypts or villi, and place a coverslip over these (length, width, and area can be measured, if desired)

3. Apply gentle pressure on the coverslip. The tissue should fly apart, giving a preparation of separate cells.

4. Mark the position of the groups of cells with a fine fiber-tip pen on the coverslip, transfer to a light microscope, and count all epithelial cells per unit; 10 crypts or villi should suffice.

IV. Comments

For animal experiments prepare an injection/kill plan as per Table I. For CCPR determinations it does not matter if one deviates from the plan, provided elapsed times

TABLE I Typical Injection/Kill Plan for CCPR Studies

Number	Code	Vincristine		Kill		Planned Time	Act Time
		Int	Act	Int	Act		
1		10.00		10.30		30	
2		10.05		10.45		40	
3		10.10		11.00		50	
4		10.15		11.15		60	
5		10.20		11.30		70	
6		10.25		11.45		80	
7		10.30		12.00		90	
8		10.35		12.15		100	
9		10.40		12.30		110	
10		10.45		12.45		120	
11		10.50		1.00		130	
12		10.55		1.15		140	
13		11.00		1.30		150	
14		11.05		1.45		160	
15		11.10		2.00		170	

Note. This plan involves 15 animals, which would be the optimum number for a mouse study. Ten rats would suffice. Int, intended time; Act, actual time. Other plans are best derived by working backward from the anticipated time taken for autopsy.

are known and the time does not exceed 3 hr. Vincristine constitutes a moderate hazard risk assessment, so adequate containment, protection, and disposal are required.

For human studies the native mitotic index is ideal as no pretreatment with vincristine is required. Several individuals per group give a precise estimate of mitotic activity. In animal studies the choice of technique may be determined by the number of animals per group. While CCPR estimations can be considered to be the "gold standard" method, as they cannot be confounded by concomitant changes, they are not very precise; thus, 10 animals per group are usually required. Two-hour metaphase collection gives a more precise (but less robust) measure and five animals should suffice.

An alternative one-step fixation/storage is to fix and store in acetic acid/ethanol (25/75), but the tissue should then be scored within 1 month, before it becomes very hard.

Aim to sample at a fixed time of day to avoid diurnal variation effects.

If the autopsy procedure takes a long time, stagger injection and kill times. It is usually best to plan the autopsy times and then calculate desired injection times.

Once stained, the tissue will be suitable for microdissection for several hours, but for optimum results it should be microdissected within 3 to 4 hr. If required the stained tissue can be microdissected the next day if the tissue (in Schiff's) is stored at 4°C.

The secret of the microdissection technique is not to have too much tissue on the slide, and to have just the right amount of fluid so that pushing on the coverslip does most of the separation. If too little tissue is present, one can generate a single-cell suspension (useful for cell population counts). If too much tissue is present the coverslip will crack.

If Carnoy's fixed material is not available it is possible to use frozen tissue which can then be postfixed in Carnoy's.

An image analysis system may also be used to trace the crypts, but this is usually slower than using the drawing tube, as one needs to move back and forth from the optical field of view to the monitor screen.

If desired, animals can also be injected with tritiated thymidine or bromodeoxyuridine for in-depth S-phase studies.

V. Pitfalls

1. The staining must be optimal for the subsequent microdissection and scoring; a good preparation should appear an intense magenta. If staining is suboptimal check the Schiff's reagent, and ensure that the tissue was immersed when hydrolyzed.

2. Crypts are three dimensional, thus one must continuously focus up and down; mitotic figures or metaphases will then jump into (and out of) focus. Most problems in scoring occur because operators fail to focus sufficiently and consequently underscore the tissue.

3. Proliferation is enhanced near lymphoid aggregates, and these should usually be avoided.

4. Some practice is required to differentiate between mitotic figures and the dense, but more ordered chromatin of white blood cell nuclei, and between the more homogenous blebs of chromatin seen in apoptotic fragments. On one occasion a student overestimated mitotic activity and was found to have been scoring inflammatory cells.

5. Care should be taken to inject vincristine carefully, and sometimes the intestine can be injected, if this happens metaphase arrest is not complete. If this occurs telophases are seen and the sample must be excluded from the analysis.

REFERENCES

Goodlad, R. A. (1992) The whole crypt and nothing but the crypt. *Eur. J. Gastroenterol. Hepatol.* **4**, 1035–1036.

Goodlad, R. A., Lee, C. Y., and Wright, N. A. (1992) Cell proliferation in the small intestine and colon of intravenously fed rats: Effect of urogastrone-epidermal growth factor. *Cell Proliferation* **25**, 393–404.

Goodlad, R. A., Levi, S., Lee, C. Y., Mandir, N., Hodgson, H., and Wright, N. A. (1991) Morphometry and cell proliferation in endoscopic biopsies: Evaluation of a technique. *Gastroenterology* **101**, 1235–1241.

Goodlad, R. A., and Wright, N. A. (1982) Quantitative studies on epithelial replacement in the gut. *In* "Techniques in the Life Sciences: Techniques in Digestive Physiology," (T. A. Titchen, ed.), Vol. P2, pp. 212/1–212/21. Elsevier, Amsterdam.

Hall, P. A., Levison, D. A., and Wright, N. A. (1992) Assessment of Cellular Proliferation in Histological Material. Springer-Verlag, Berlin.

Matthew, J. A., Pell, J. D., Prior, A., Kennedy, H., Gee, J. M., and Johnson, I. T. (1993) Detection of abnormal mucosal cell replication in humans: A new technique. *In* "Food & Cancer Prevention." Royal Society of Chemistry, London.

Maurer, H. R. (1981) Potential pitfalls of ³H-thymidine technique to measure cell proliferation. *Cell Tissue Kinet.* **14**, 111–120.

Wright, N. A., and Alison, M. R. (1984) "The Biology of Epithelial Cell Populations," Vol. 2. Oxford University Press, London.

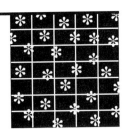

Micromanipulation of Chromosomes Using Laser Microsurgery (Optical Scissors) and Laser-Induced Optical Forces (Optical Tweezers)

Michael W. Berns, Hong Liang, Gregory J. Sonek, and Yagang Liu

I. Introduction

Individual chromosomes in living cells can be manipulated by optical scissors and optical tweezers. The first experiments (Berns *et al.*, 1969) demonstrated that a low-power pulsed argon laser focused onto chromosomes of living mitotic salamander cells resulted in the production of a 0.5-μm lesion in the irradiation region of the chromosome. In these studies the chromosomes were photosensitized with a low concentration of acridine orange. Subsequent studies on salamander and rat kangaroo (PTK$_2$) cells indicated that the laser microbeam could be used to selectively inactivate the nucleolar genes (Berns, 1978). By use of the 266-nm wavelength of a Nd:YAG laser, not only could the nucleolar genes be selectively deleted, causing a loss of nucleoli in the subsequent cell generation, but also a corresponding lack of one light-staining Giemsa band in the nucleolar organizers region of the chromosome could be demonstrated in cells proliferated from the single irradiated cell (Berns *et al.*, 1979). With the further development of cloning techniques specific for single irradiated cells, cellular sublines with deleted ribosomal genes resulting from laser microbeam irradiation of the rDNA on the mitotic chromosome were established (Liang and Berns, 1983).

In 1987, Ashkin and Dziedzic first used a tightly focused laser beam to generate optical trapping forces to move biological objects. The manipulation of chromosomes in living cells and in isolation buffer was reported by Berns *et al.* in 1989. In this study, later extended by Liang and Berns *et al.* (1991), an optical force applied to a late-moving metaphase chromosome caused it to accelerate toward the metaphase plate. In addition, anaphase chromosomes could be held motionless by optical trapping forces (Liang *et al.*, 1991). A recent study (Liang *et al.*, 1993) indicated that it was possible to combine the optical tweezers to grasp and pull, with the cutting and ablation capacity of the optical scissors. Cell biologists now have a complete set of optical tools to manipulate chromosomes for the study of chromosome movements, spindle function, and cell genetics.

II. Materials and Instrumentation

A. CELLS

1. Male rat kangaroo (*Potorous tridactylis*) kidney (PTK$_2$) cells.
2. Chinese hamster ovary (CHO) cells.

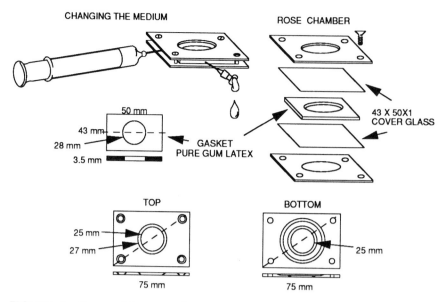

CHANGING THE MEDIUM

ROSE CHAMBER

50 mm
43 mm
28 mm
3.5 mm

GASKET
PURE GUM LATEX

43 X 50X1
COVER GLASS

TOP
25 mm
27 mm
75 mm

BOTTOM
25 mm
75 mm

FIGURE 1   Rose multipurpose chamber with its component parts.

B. MEDIA, CHEMICALS, AND SUPPLIES FOR CELL CULTURE AND ISOLATION OF CHROMOSOMES

Modified Eagle's medium (Cat. No. 410-1500 ED), penicillin-G (Cat. No. 600-5140AG) 100 units/ml (working concentration for experiment, same as follows), streptomycin sulfate (Cat. No. 600-5140AG) 100 μg/ml, trypsin (Cat. No. 610-5050AJ) 0.25%, L-glutamine (Cat. No. 320-5030AJ) 2 mM, pancreatin (Cat. No. 610-5720AG), phenol red (Cat. No. 15-100-019), PBS without Ca^{2+} and Mg^{2+} (Cat. No. 310-4200), colcemid (Cat. No. 120-5210AD), and fetal bovine serum (Cat. No. 230-6140AJ) are purchased from Gibco. EDTA (Cat. No. 34103) and Pipes (Cat. No. 528132) are purchased from Calbiochem. $CaCl_2$ (Cat. No. C-7902) is obtained from Sigma. Hexylene glycol (2-methyl-2,4-pentanediol, Cat. No. 1134329) is from Eastman Chemical. Culture flasks (T-25, Cat. No. 25106; T-150, Cat. No. 25126) are purchased from Corning. Centrifuge tube (15 ml, Cat. No. 2097; 50 ml, Cat. No. 2098) are from Falcon. Hemacytometer "Bright Line" (Cat. No. B3180-2) is from Baxter. Centrifuge Dynac II is provided by Clay Adams.

C. ROSE MULTIPURPOSE CHAMBER

Chamber tops and bottoms, screws, sterile gaskets, sterile needles, and sterile syringes are components of the Rose multipurpose chamber (Fig. 1).

D. LASER AND OBSERVATION INSTRUMENTATION

1. A pulsed laser for laser surgery, with wavelength λ < 550 nm and output energy E adjustable up to 10 mJ per pulse (e.g., Quantel YG481A Laser System, λ = 532 nm).

2. A CW laser for laser trapping, with wavelength λ > 650 nm and output power P adjustable up to 1 W (e.g., Quantronix 116 YAG Laser System, λ = 1.06 μm).

3. A circular variable attenuator A1 (Newport, 50G00AV.2). A high-power variable attenuator A2 (Newport, M-935-5-OPT).[1] A shutter system S1 (Newport, 845HP-01). A lens L1 with focal length $f = 150$ mm (Newport, KPX100AR.16).[1] Three to six pieces of aluminum-coated mirror (Newport, 10D20ER.1).[1]

4. A dichroic beam splitter BS1 (CVI, BSR-51-2025).[1] A chromatic beam splitter BS2 (CVI, HM-0803-45).[1]

5. A Zeiss Universal M microscope (inverted microscope is preferred). A motor stage control system with joystick (Zeiss, MSP65). A Ph3 Neofluar 100X, 1.3 NA oil immersion microscope objective lens (Zeiss, 440481).

6. A power/energy meter (Scientech, 362002), an infrared sensor card (Newport, F-IRC4), and an infrared viewer (FJW Optical Systems, Inc., 58100) for detecting and monitoring the laser.

7. A CCD camera (Panasonic, GP-MF 502), a VCR (Panasonic, AG-6030), and a TV monitor (Mitsubishi, CS-20EX1) for monitoring and recording the image from the microscope.

III. Procedures

A. PREPARATION OF PTK$_2$ DIVIDING CELLS IN ROSE CHAMBER

Solution

1. *0.125% Viokase solution:* To make 100 ml, dissolve 5 ml of pancreatin, 0.1 g of EDTA, and 0.25 ml of phenol red into 95 ml of PBS without Ca^{2+} and Mg^{2+}; adjust pH to 7.4.

Steps

1. Select a healthy, confluent or nearly confluent flask of cells.

2. Remove the old medium from the flask of cells using an unplugged sterile pipette attached to a vacuum flask.

3. Add 1.0 ml of viokase solution to the flask of cells.

4. Place the flask of cells with viokase in the 37°C incubator for 7–10 mins. When the cells begin to lift free from the flask, rap the flask sharply two or three times to dislodge the cells completely.

5. Add 5 ml MEM to inactive the viokase and wash any adhering cells free.

6. Transfer the medium, viokase, and cell mixture to a sterile centrifuge tube.

7. Centrifuge the cell suspension for 4–5 min at 800–1000 rpm.

8. After centrifugation, carefully remove the stopper from the tube and very carefully aspirate the supernatant from the tube.

9. Resuspend the cell pellet in the drop remaining in the tube bottom.

10. Add 5 ml of MEM to the resuspended pellet and take a sample to count on a hemacytometer. Count all four corners (i.e., four groups of 16 squares each), divide the result by 4 and multiply by 10^4. This gives the concentration of cells per milliliter of resuspended material.

---

[1] For the wavelength of continuous-wave (CW) trapping laser $\lambda = 1.06$ μm and pulsed surgery laser $\lambda = 0.532$ μm only. Lasers at other wavelengths can be used, but selection should been done in consultation with researchers in this field.

11. Adjust the cell concentration to give 2.5 to 3.5 × 10⁴ cells/ml and inject these into the Rose chambers using a sterile syringe and 23-gauge needle.

12. Incubate the chambers (cell side down) at 37°C in a 5–7.5% CO_2 incubator. After 36–60 hr, nonconfluent chambers with dividing cells are desirable for experimentation.

B. PREPARATION OF CHROMOSOME SUSPENSION

Solutions

1. *Colcemid solution:* To make 50 ml with a concentration of 0.06 μg/ml, solubilize 300 μl stock solution (concentration of 10 μg/ml) in 50 ml medium. Store at −20°C.

2. *Chromosome isolation buffer, 10X buffer stock:* Add 55.5 mg Cacl₂ and 34.2 mg Pipes to 95 ml distilled water, adjust pH to 6.5 with 1 N NaOH, and bring total volume to 100 ml. Store at 4°C.

3. *Chromosome isolation buffer, working solution (prepared the day of use):* To make 100 ml, take 10 ml of 10X stock and add to 80 ml distilled water. Add 11.82 g of hexylene glycol, stir to dissolve, and bring total volume to 100 ml. Check pH and adjust to 6.5 with 1 N NaOH. Keep at 4°C.

Steps

1. Culture CHO cells in five T-150 flasks up to 80% confluent.

2. Suck out medium, add 10 ml medium containing colcemid at a concentration of 0.06 μg/ml, and incubate in a 37°C incubator for 4 hr.

3. Remove medium containing colcemid, and add 10 ml fresh medium to each flask.

4. Detach the cells from the interior surface of the flask by gently rapping the flask.

5. Wash cells with fresh medium two times using 10 ml medium each time. Leave the cells on ice for 10–20 min.

6. Centrifuge for 2 min at 1000 rpm.

7. Resuspend cells in ice-cold chromosome isolation buffer. Add 2 ml chromosome isolation buffer to each test tube, and collect as a 10 ml sample.

8. Centrifuge for 3 min at 2000 rpm.

9. Resuspend cells in 2 ml ice-cold chromosome isolation buffer, and incubate cell suspension in 37°C water bath for 5–10 min.

10. Push cell suspension gently through 23-gauge needle to lyse the cells and free chromosomes and nuclei.

11. For further purification, filter the suspension through 8- or 5-μm filter to remove nuclei and unbroken cells. Centrifuge 5–10 min at 3000 rpm. Resuspend in chromosome isolation buffer to desired density.

12. Isolated chromosomes are morphologically stable for several months at 4°C. They may also be quick frozen, stored, and thawed with no apparent harm.

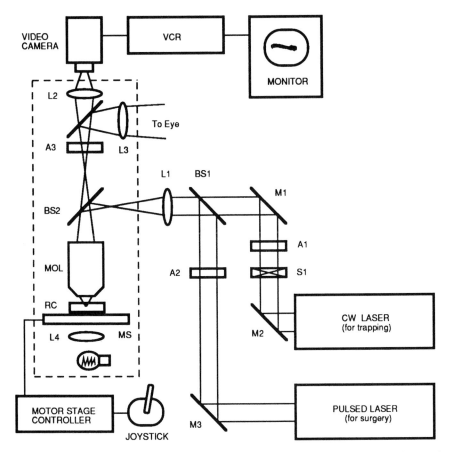

FIGURE 2 Schematic diagram for the combined use of optical scissors and optical tweezers. A1–A3: Attenuators; BS1, BS2: beam splitters; L1–L4; lenses; M1–M3: mirrors; MOL: microscope objective lens; MS: motor stage; RC: rose chamber; S1: shutter.

C. ALIGNMENT OF LASER MICROBEAM SYSTEM

Steps

1. Mount mirror M1 and beam splitter BS1 at the same height as beam splitter BS2 in the microscope (Fig. 2).

2. Turn on the CW trapping laser; adjust output power of the laser to between 10 and 50 mW.

3. Hold the infrared sensor card (IRC) in front of M1 (you can see a bright orange spot on the card where the laser beam is located), and adjust M2 until the spot is at the center of M1.

4. Guided by the IRC, adjust M1 until the beam is hitting the center of BS2.

5. Put the IRC under the microscope objective lens; finely adjust M1 until the beam shape shown on the IRC is symmetrically round.

6. Insert lens L1 in optical path, with the distance from the objective lens at 310 mm. Finely adjust the position of L1 until the spot on the IRC is brightest and still symmetrically round.

7. Close shutter S1 to block the laser beam; the system is now aligned.

8. Put the Rose chamber with test sample under the microscope and bring into focus.

9. Slightly defocus the laser beam toward the specimen slide; the bright spot of the laser beam will appear on the screen of the video monitor. Draw a cross with a marker pen at the bright spot on the screen. The trap is now coincident with the cross hair on the monitor screen.

The preceding steps complete the alignment of the trapping beam. The following steps are for alignment of the surgery beam.

10. Turn on the pulsed surgery laser and adjust its output energy to between 10 and 50 μJ per pulse, with a repetition rate greater than 20 Hz.

11. Using the infrared viewer (IRV) to see the spot of the trapping beam on the surface of BS1, adjust M3 until the surgery beam overlaps with the trapping beam on the surface of BS1.

12. Adjust BS1 to let the surgery beam hit the center of BS2.

13. Remove the test Rose chamber. Place a white paper card under the objective lens, and finely adjust BS1 until the beam is brightest and symmetrically round on the card.

14. Put the test Rose chamber under the microscope. Repeat the same steps as 7 and 8.

15. If the spots from the two lasers shown on the screen of video monitor are not superimposed, finely adjust BS1 until they exactly overlap. The surgery laser is now aligned.

D. MICROSURGERY OF CHROMOSOMES

Steps

1. After alignment of the laser microbeam, place a dried smear of red blood cells under the microscope objective. Fire a few pulses of the surgery laser beam on the red blood cells to produce a small hole (<1 μm) to verify that the cross hair on the TV screen is directly over the lesion. If the hole is too large, attenuate or reduce the laser output until a small threshold lesion is produced.

2. Remove the red blood cell slide, and place the experimental sample under the microscope.

3. Select dividing cells that appear healthy and flat (they should have very few vacuoles and the cytoplasm should be free of small dark granules).

4. The mitotic stage of dividing cells should be determined by the specific needs of the experiment.

5. Move the microscope stage so the specific target site of the selected chromosome is under the cross hair on the monitor screen.

6. Fire the laser on the selected chromosome site. Gradually increase the laser power until the desired lesion appears (Fig. 3).

7. Videotape the entire experiment or make photographs with a 35-mm camera. Record the image before and after irradiation.

In the case of genetic studies, the irradiated cell may be isolated and cloned into a viable population. Follow steps 8 to 12 (Fig. 4).

8. Under sterile conditions, remove unirradiated cells from near the target cell using a micromanipulator. Close the Rose chamber.

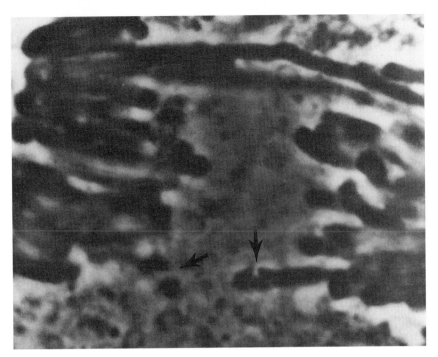

FIGURE 3 Model illustrating a 0.5-μm piece of a chromosome removed by optical scissors.

9. Check the chamber at 12 hr, and use the 532-nm laser beam to kill cells migrating into the area of the cell being followed.

10. Monitor the proliferation of the target cell using the VCR or simply by observation.

11. Collect descendent "clonal" cells by 0.125% viokase solution; then transfer into one well of a 12-well culture cluster containing normal medium.

12. Collect "clonal" cells with the 0.125% viokase solution until they are confluent and transfer them into T-25 culture flask.

13. When the proliferation of descendent "clonal" cells reaches a sufficient number they can be subjected to standard karyotypic and/or biochemical analysis.

E. OPTICAL TRAPPING OF CHROMOSOMES

Steps

1. Place a Rose chamber under the microscope that contains either dividing cells or chromosomes suspended in isolation buffer.

2. Select a specific chromosome under the microscope for experimentation.

3. In the case of the living cell, flat and large cells are especially good for micromanipulation. The selection of the mitotic stage depends on the specific goal of the experiment.

4. Locate the specific site of the selected chromosome at the cross hair on the monitor screen.

5. Open the shutter, allowing the trapping beam to enter the microscope. The trapping laser is focused at the prealigned site which is located in the image plane of microscope objective.

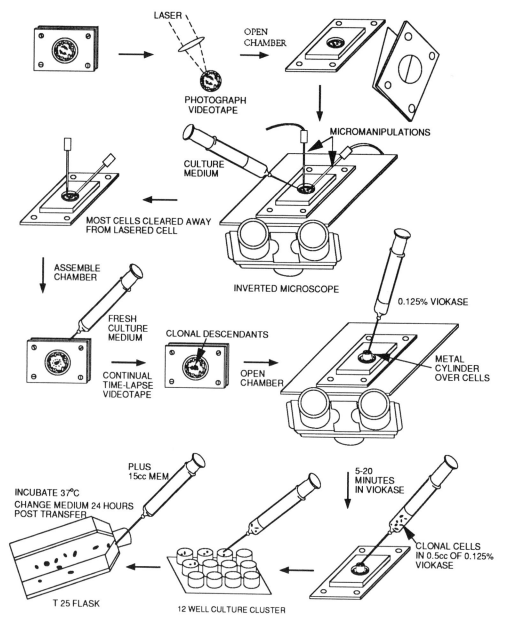

FIGURE 4 Diagrammatic representation of the procedure for cloning cells that have been irradiated at a specific chromosomal site.

6. The chromosome near the focal point of the trapping beam will be drawn into the focal point.

7. Move the specimen stage at a speed less than 25 μm/sec in the desired direction. The chromosome will be held at the trapping position. (Usually the sites on which the largest trapping force can be applied are at either ends of the chromosome.)

8. If the trapping force is not large enough to hold the chromosome, increase the power of the trapping beam by adjusting either the beam attenuator or the output of the laser. (The trapping force is linearly proportional to the incident power of trapping beam.)

9. Videotape the entire experiment and make photographs with a 35-mm

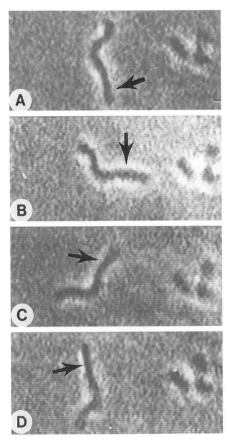

FIGURE 5 Model illustrating rotation of chromosomes with optical tweezers. The sequence A–D demonstrates the rotation of an isolated Chinese hamster ovary (CHO) cell chromosome with the 1.06-μm beam of a CW Nd:YAG laser operating at 50–200 mW. The arrows indicate the point on the chromosome where the trap was applied to cause the 180° rotation.

camera. Record the data before, during, and after the manipulation by the optical trapping force (Figs. 5 and 6).

IV. Comments

Newt lung cells are another desirable cell type that can be used for chromosome studies by optical scissors or tweezers. They are large and flat.

Laser light at wavelengths of 532, 355, and 266 nm are most often used in chromosome microsurgery.

If 266-nm ultraviolet laser light is to be used, either a quartz-ultrafluar objective or a reflective objective must be employed. Quartz Rose chamber windows must also be used.

V. Pitfalls

1. Variation in laser output power will cause inaccurate experimental results. Turn on the lasers $\frac{1}{2}$–1 hr before the experiment, and keep monitoring the output power of the trapping laser beam and output energy of the surgery laser beam using a power/energy detector.

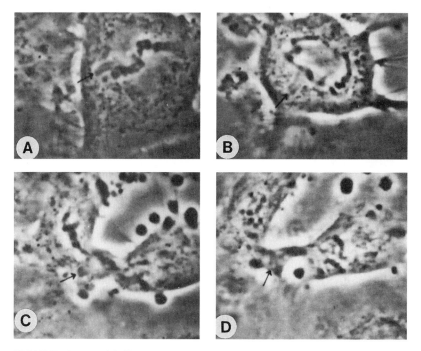

FIGURE 6   Model illustrating the holding of chromosomes with optical tweezers. (A) A live rat kangaroo cell (PTK$_2$) in metaphase of cell division is having a pair of large chromatids (arrow) held with the optical tweezers (wavelength is 1.06 μm and power 60 mW). (B) In anaphase the same two chromatids are still being held by the laser tweezers (arrow). (C) The cell is now in late telophase and undergoing cytokineses. The two chromatids (arrow) are trapped in the midbody between the two daughter nuclei. (D) The two chromatids are trapped in the interzone between the two daughter cells and eventually lost from both.

2. The living cells will be damaged if exposed to the laser beam either for a long period or at high intensities. A power $P < 100$ mW for the trapping beam and an energy $E < 10$ mJ per pulse for the surgery beam are recommended. Generally, only about one-third of the near-infrared trapping beam power and two-thirds of the visible surgery laser beam power are transmitted through the objective lens.

3. Photodamage to cells should also be considered. Choose a laser with the appropriate wavelength to avoid regions of strong photon absorption. The near-infrared wavelength (e.g., 1.06 μm from a Nd:YAG laser) is a relatively safe wavelength for most cells.

4. Microscope optics can be damaged if the laser beam is too intense. To prevent damage to the objective lens, do not adjust optical components (e.g., mirrors, beamsplitters) while being exposed to the intense laser beam.

5. Laser exposure may produce eye injury and physical burns. Never view a laser beam directly or by specular reflection. Use laser safety glasses whenever possible. Be sure that the laser microscope has appropriate filtration or beam blocks so that the laser beam does not directly go through the oculars into the eyes.

REFERENCES

Ashkin, A., and Dziedzic, J. M. (1987) Optical trapping and manipulation of viruses and bacteria. *Science* **235**, 1517–1519.

Berns, M. W. (1978) The laser microbeam as a probe for chromatin structure and function. *In* "Methods in Cell Biology" (G. Stein, J. Stein, and L. Kleinsmith, eds.), Vol. 18, pp. 277–294. *Academic Press,* New York.

Berns, M. W., Aist, J. R., Wright, W. H., and Liang, H. (1992) Optical trapping in animal and plant cells using a tunable near-infrared titanium–sapphire laser. *Exp. Cell Res.* **198,** 375–378.

Berns, M. W., Chong, L. K., Hammer-Wilson, M., Miller, K., and Siemens, A. (1979) Genetic microsurgery by laser: Establishment of a clonal population of rat kangaroo cells (PTK$_2$) with a directed deficiency in a chromosomal nucleolar organizer. *Chromosoma* **73,** 1–8.

Berns, M. W., Olson, R. S., and Rounds, D. E. (1969) *In vitro* production of chromosomal lesion using an argon laser microbeam. *Nature* **221,** 74–75.

Berns, M. W., Wright, W. H., Tromberg, B. J., Profeta, G. A., Andrews, J. J., and Walter, R. J. (1989) Use of a laser-induced optical force trap to study chromosome movement on the mitotic spindle. *Proc. Natl. Acad. Sci. USA* **86,** 4539–4543.

Berns, M. W., Wright, W. H., and Wiegand Steubing, R. (1991) Laser microbeam as a tool in cell biology. *Int. Rev. Cytol.* **129,** 1–44.

Liang, H., and Berns, M. W. (1983) Establishment of nucleolar deficient sublines of PTK$_2$ (*Potorous tridactylis*) by ultraviolet laser microirradiation. *Exp. Cell Res.* **144,** 234–240.

Liang, H., Wright, W. H., Cheng, S., He, W., and Berns, M. W. (1993) Micromanipulation of chromosomes in PTK$_2$ cells using laser microsurgery (optical scalpel) in combination with laser induced optical force (optical tweezers). *Exp. Cell Res.* **204,** 110–120.

Liang, H., Wright, W. H., He, W., and Berns, M. W. (1991) Micromanipulation of mitotic chromosomes in PTK$_2$ cells using laser induced optical forces ("optical tweezers"). *Exp. Cell Res.* **197,** 21–35.

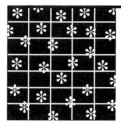

Microdissection of Chromosomes and Microcloning

Uwe Claussen and Bernhard Horsthemke

I. Introduction

Physical dissection of GTG-banded metaphase chromosomes and polymerase chain reaction (PCR)-mediated cloning constitute the fastest method of isolating DNA sequences from defined chromosome regions. Two strategies for PCR-mediated cloning of microdissected DNA have been developed. In the adapter ligation technique, DNA of known sequences is ligated to the microdissected DNA and used as primer annealing sites for PCR (Lüdecke *et al.*, 1989; Sounders *et al.*, 1989). Alternatively, the microdissected DNA is amplified directly with the help of random primers (Hadano *et al.*, 1991) or degenerated primers (Meltzer *et al.*, 1992). The region-specific DNA obtained by microdissection and amplification can be used for cloning and for chromosome painting (Lüdecke *et al.*, 1989; Trautmann *et al.*, 1991; Meltzer *et al.*, 1992). Translations of microclones into "sequence-tagged sites" (STSs) and PCR screening of YAC libraries appear to be the method of choice for large-scale DNA cloning (Green and Olson, 1990). One to two hundred randomly distributed microclones obtained from the excised region are sufficient to construct a YAC contig for a chromosome band containing 10 to 20 Mb.

In this article we describe the microdissection and microcloning system based on *Rsa*I digestion and ligation to pUC DNA (for further details see Lüdecke *et al.*, 1989, 1990; Senger *et al.*, 1990).

II. Materials and Instrumentation

For the pipette method, the small inverted microscope (ID 02 or ID 03) with a mechanically controlled micromanipulator, and for microdissection, the large inverted microscope (IM 10 or IM 35) with bright-field illumination and slipping desk needed for a complete rotation of the chromosomes are obtained from Zeiss. Focusing should be done with the microscope tube and not by moving the table. Four objectives are necessary: 2.5× (for manipulation of the microdrops), 6.3× (for the pipette method), 40× for transfer of the excised fragments into the collection drop (phase contrast), and 100× (oil immersion; for microdissection). The electronically controlled micromanipulator (MR Mot, Zeiss) is attached to the large inverted microscope. The horizontal pipette puller is from Bachhofer (similar pipette pullers can also be used). The Microgen T4, a pump needed for the pipette method, is from Orbis. The thermal cycler is from Perkin–Elmer and the micropipettes (long Pasteur pipettes, 230 mm) are from Brand. The microneedles are made of solid glass rods (diameter 2 mm) which are extended with the pipette puller. Petri dishes (150 mm) are obtained from Nunc. Coverslips (24 × 60 × 0.17 mm) are purchased from Bender & Hobein. Glass microdishes are made from the bottoms of small glass tubes (diameter 10 mm) which are cut off. Sephacryl S-300 spun columns are from Pharmacia, Qiagen columns are from Diagen and MAX efficiency competent DH5α cells are from BRL Life Technologies.

III. Procedures

A. PREPARATION OF INSTRUMENTS

All micropipettes, microneedles, and glass microdishes and some coverslips are siliconized with a solution of 1% dichlorodimethylsilane (Merck, Cat. No. 803452) in CCl_4 (Merck, Cat. No. 2222). After evaporation of the solution, the glassware is rinsed with 1 mM EDTA and heated at 100°C for 1 hr.

1. *Micropipettes:* These are extended with the horizontal pipette puller. The extended tips are mechanically broken to a length of about 15 mm. They should not have sharp edges and the diameter of the opening should be in the range 30 to 100 μm. About 20 siliconized pipettes are necessary for one experiment (discard after single use).

2. *Microneedles:* If the extended tips are too thin for dissection of chromosomes, they must be carefully broken. Avoid needles with a long extended tips, because such needles are not rigid enough. One needle can be used for several experiments, but it must be carefully cleaned with collection drop solution and sterilized under ultraviolet light.

3. *Petri dish:* Cut a rectangular hole in the middle of the bottom of the petri dish (5.5 × 5.5 cm) with the help of a hot scalpel.

4. *Coverslips:* Clean coverslips by incubation in 25% HCl at room temperature for several days. Then rinse them in water and store in 90% ethanol. Coverslips used for preparation of metaphase spreads are rinsed again with sterile, 4°C cold water prior to use. Coverslips prepared for the collection drop are dried and siliconized. In the middle of these coverslips, small silicone gaskets of a freeze tube (Nunc) are fixed with embedding material (Eukitt) and filled with paraffin oil (equilibrated with *Rsa*I buffer) prior to use.

5. *Glass microdish:* After each use, microdishes are cleaned in H_2O_2 overnight, rinsed with water, and siliconized.

B. PREPARATION OF METAPHASE SPREADS ON COVERSLIPS

Solutions

All solutions must be sterile and free of foreign DNA or nucleases and stored in aliquots.

1. *Trypsin solution:* Dissolve one vial of lyophilized bacto-trypsin (Difco) in sterile distilled water to make a 5% (w/v) trypsin stock solution. Store filter-sterilized at −20°C in aliquots of 100 μl. Dilute one 100-μl aliquot in 60 ml PBS buffer (final concentration 80 μg/ml) and incubate at 37°C.

2. *PBS buffer:* Room temperature.

3. *Giemsa solution for staining:* Add 6 ml Giemsa (filter-sterilized, Merck, Cat.

No. 9204) to 60 ml Sörensen's phosphate buffer, pH 6.88 (Merck, Cat. No. 7294, autoclaved).

4. *Sterile distilled water:* Room temperature.

5. *70% ethanol at −20°C.*

6. *Hypotonic solution:* 0.2% Na citrate, 0.2% KCl.

7. *Fixative:* Methanol/acetic acid 3/1, 4°C.

Steps

For chromosome harvesting using the pipette method (Claussen, 1980; Claussen *et al.*, 1986) normal amniotic fluid cell cultures or any other cell culture growing in a monolayer can be used after subcultivation in petri dishes. Colcemid is not necessary, because growing cultures contain a sufficient number of mitotic cells. Mitotic cells in the metaphase stage are clearly identifiable because they are circular.

Collection of mitotic cells

1. Draw up 20 to 30 circular mitotic cells into the extended tip of a siliconized micropipette at a magnification of 80× (inverted microscope) with the help of the Microgen T4.

2. Transfer these cells to a petri dish containing hypotonic solution. Collect again the swollen mitotic cells with the pipette after 14 min.

3. Immediately draw up fixative into the pipette (3 µl) and drop the fixed cells onto clean, wet coverslips. After evaporation of the fixative (a few seconds later), wash and store the coverslips in 70% ethanol, and place the coverslips between slides inside glass cuvettes at −20°C for no longer than 1 day.

GTG banding

1. Air-dried coverslips are GTG banded under sterile conditions. Prepare four sterile 100-ml staining glass cuvettes containing solutions 1 to 4 and transfer the coverslips from one cuvette to the other as follows:

	Solution No.			
	1	2	3	4
Temperature	37°C	Room temp.	Room temp.	Room temp.
Duration	10–30 sec	Short	3–5 min	Short

Coverslips have to be air-dried carefully under the hood to avoid moist chromosomes, which are soft and not useful for microdissection.

C. MICRODISSECTION

Solutions

All solutions must be sterile, free of foreign DNA or nucleases, and stored in small aliquots, and should be discarded after single use.

1. *Collection drop solution:* 10 mM Tris–HCl, pH 7.5, 10 mM NaCl, 0.1%

SDS. Add just prior to use: To 1 ml collection solution, add 5 µl proteinase K (100 mg/ml, Boehringer-Mannheim, Cat. No. 745723, final concentration 0.5 mg/ml). The proteinase K stock can be stored in aliquots at −20°C; repeated thawing and freezing should be avoided.

2. *Liquid paraffin:* (Merck, Cat. No. 7161, spectroscopic grade): Incubate at 100°C for 2 hr to inactivate nucleases and equilibrate with 1× *Rsa*I buffer. About 200 ml oil is necessary for one experiment.

3. *1× Rsa*I *buffer:* (for equilibration of paraffin oil). 10 mM Tris–HCl, pH 7.5, 10 mM $MgCl_2$.

Steps

Placement of the collection drop under oil

1. Place a coverslip with banded metaphase spreads in a petri dish with a rectangular hole in the bottom, the chromosomes facing upward (Fig. 1a). Place a second, siliconized coverslip carrying the silicone gasket (filled with paraffin oil) beside it or on an other petri dish with a rectangular hole in the bottom (Fig. 1b).

2. Pipette a 1-nl drop of collection solution with a micropipette, which is connected to the Microgen T4, under oil into the center of the silicone gasket on the siliconized coverslip and check the diameter of the drop with the help of an ocular with a graticule.

Dissection

1. For precise dissection place the chromosome of interest perpendicular to the needle and position the tip in front of the chromosome band to be excised.

2. Lower the tip of the needle carefully onto the coverslip. This leads to forward movement of the tip and excision of the chromosome material (Fig. 2).

3. To transfer the excised fragment to the collection drop touch it carefully with the tip of the needle. Normally, the excised piece sticks to the tip after a few trials.

4. Elevate the needle and move the petri dish to position the collection drop on the siliconized coverslip beside the center of the visual field (magnification 30×).

Transfer into the collection drop

1. Correct the position of the collection drop (beside the center) at a magnification of 400× until 1000× (40× objective, phase contrast, optovar 2.5×).

2. Lower the needle carefully until the tip with the excised chromosome fragment is visible beside the collection drop.

3. Wash the tip of the needle with the adhering chromosome fragment in the collection drop.

Transfer of collection drop

1. For subsequent microreactions take up the collection drop into a siliconized micropipette containing some oil and transfer it to a small siliconized glass microdish (diameter 1 cm) in a second petri dish (diameter 10 cm) filled with paraffin oil.

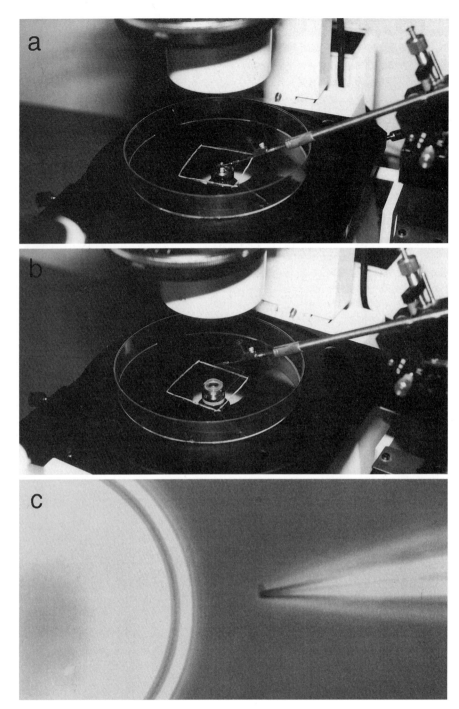

FIGURE 1 (a) Microdissection setup. The coverslip in the petri dish with a rectangular hole in the bottom is placed over the inverted microscope and carries the metaphase spreads. The objective is visible under the coverslip, and the tip of the extended glass needle is placed above it. (b) The siliconized coverslip in the petri dish with a rectangular hole in the bottom carries the collection drop overlain with paraffin oil inside the silicone gasket. The tip of the needle on which the excised chromosome fragment is hanging is placed above it. (c) View inside the silicone gasket (magnification 1000×; 40× objective, optovar 2.5×, phase contrast). The excised chromosome fragment sticks to the tip of the needle and is ready to be transferred into the collection drop (left).

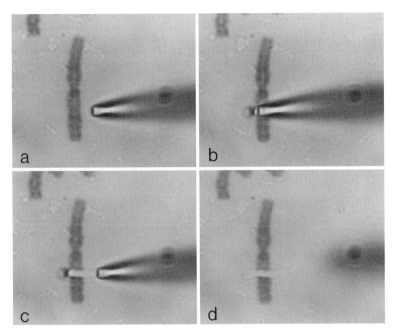

FIGURE 2 Excision of a defined chromosome region. (a) The tip of the needle is placed perpendicular to the chromosome (GTG-banded human chromosome 1). (b) The tip of the needle has been lowered, which leads to forward movement of the tip and to excision of the chromosome region. (c) The excised chromosome fragment lies beside the chromosome and the needle is moved back. (d) The excised chromosome fragment has been transferred to the collection drop.

D. MICROCLONING

This procedure is modified from that of Lüdecke *et al.* (1989, 1990).

Solutions

1. *Collection drop solution:* 10 mM Tris–HCl, pH 7.5, 10 mM NaCl, 0.1% SDS. Add just prior to use: To 1 ml collection solution, add 5 μl proteinase K (100 mg/ml, Boehringer-Mannheim, Cat. No. 745723, final concentration 0.5 mg/ml). The proteinase K stock can be stored in aliquots at $-20°$C; repeated thawing and freezing should be avoided.

2. *Phenol (Rathburn Chemicals, water saturated, glass-distilled grade) with 0.1% 8-hydroxyquinoline:* Equilibrate with 1× *Rsa*I buffer; store at 4°C for no longer than 2 months.

3. *Liquid paraffin (Merck, No. 7161, spectroscopic grade):* Incubate at 100°C for 2 hr to inactivate nucleases and equilibrate with 1× *Rsa*I buffer.

4. *1× Rsa*I *buffer* (for equilibration of phenol and paraffin oil): 10 mM Tris–HCl, pH 7.5, 10 mM MgCl$_2$.

5. *Polyethylene glycol:* 40% (w/v) polyethylene glycol 8000 (Sigma), 6% polyethylene glycol compound (Sigma).

6. *10× Ligase buffer:* 500 mM Tris–HCl, pH 7.8, 100 mM MgCl$_2$, 200 mM dithiothreitol, 10 mM ATP, 500 μg/ml bovine serum albumin. Store at $-20°$C.

7. *Tris–HCl buffer:* pH 7.6 containing 10 mM MgCl$_2$ and 1 mM dithiothreitol.

8. *Rsa*I *solution No. 1:* mix prior to use. To 2 μl 10× *Rsa*I buffer

(Boehringer-Mannheim, "L" buffer), add 6 µl H$_2$O and 2 µl RsaI (60 units/µl, Boehringer-Mannheim).

9. *RsaI solution No. 2:* Mix prior to use. To 1 µl 10× RsaI buffer, add 8 µl H$_2$O and 1 µl RsaI.

10. *Vector solution:* Mix prior to use. To 8 µl 10× ligase buffer, add 1 µl H$_2$O and 1 µl SmaI-cut pUC vector (17 ng/µl).

11. *T4 DNA ligase mix:* Mix prior to use. To 7 µl H$_2$O, add 1 µl 10× ligase buffer and 2 µl T4 DNA ligase (>5 units/µl).

Steps

DNA extraction

1. Fuse the collection drop with a second 1-nl drop of collection solution with proteinase K from a freshly thawed aliquot. Close the petri dish, place it into a larger petri dish containing wet filter paper (moist petri dish), and incubate at 37°C for 90 min.

Phenol extraction

1. Pipette phenol (room temperature, about 2 µl) plus approximately 0.5 µl of the aqueous phase into a second glass microdish next to the first one.

2. Pipette 6 to 8 nl of the phenol from this supply drop onto the 2-nl collection drop. Five minutes later, draw up the phenol phase away, and add a new aliquot of 6–8 nl phenol to the collection drop.

3. Remove the supply drop after a total of three phenol extractions.

4. Change the oil outside the microdish containing the collection drop.

5. Close the petri dish and place it into a moist petri dish. Residualy phenol in the collection drop is removed by diffusion into the oil overnight at 4°C.

6. Change the oil again the next day.

Restriction enzyme digestion

1. Fuse the drop with an equal volume (2 nl) of RsaI solution No. 1 and incubate at 37°C for 150 min in the moist petri dish (drop size now 4 nl). Add RsaI solution No. 2, and continue the digestion for another 150 min (drop size now 8 nl). Inactivate the restriction enzyme by three phenol extractions as described above.

Ligation

1. Fuse the drops successively with 8 nl vector solution (drop size thereafter 16 nl), 16 nl 40% PEG 8000 (drop size thereafter 32 nl), 32 nl 40% PEG 8000 (drop size thereafter 64 nl), and 64 nl T4 ligase mix (drop size thereafter 128 nl).

2. Perform ligation at 15°C overnight in a moist petri dish.

3. Add 2 µl of water to the 128-nl ligation mix. Draw up the mixture with a siliconized micropipette and transfer it to a 0.5-ml Eppendorf tube for amplification.

SmaI digestion

1. Recut nonrecombinant polylinker sequences with SmaI: Add 2 µl 2.5× SmaI

buffer to 2 μl microligation products, inactivate ligase at 65°C for 10 min, add 1 μl 2 units/μl SmaI, and incubate at 25°C for 1 hr.

DNA amplification

1. To 5 μl SmaI digest, add 40 μl H$_2$O, 10 μl 10× Taq polymerase buffer, 24 μl dNTP mix (1.25 mM each), 10 μl 50 ng/μl M13/pUC sequencing primer (17-mer + 10 μl 50 ng/μl M13/pUC), reverse sequencing primer (17-mer), and 1 μl 5 units/μl Taq polymerase, and overlay with mineral oil.

2. Use the following PCR conditions:

Cycle 1	2 min 94°C, 2 min 45°C, 3 min 72°C
Cycles 2–30	1 min 94°C, 2 min 45°C, 3 min 72°C
Time delay	7 min 72°C
Soak	4°C

3. Remove the oil and inactivate Taq polymerase by one phenol/chloroform and one chloroform extraction. Remove residual chloroform by incubating the uncapped tube at 65°C for 10 min.

EcoRI digestion

1. After DNA amplification, release the inserts by EcoRI digestion. To 50 μl amplification mix (freeze down the other half) add 39 μl H$_2$O, 9 μl 100 mM Tris–HCl, pH 8.0, 50 mM MgCl$_2$, 1000 mM NaCl, 10 mM 2-mercaptoethanol (buffer B, Boehringer-Mannheim), and 2 μl 10 units/μl EcoRI. Incubate at 37°C for 2 hr (heat-inactivate EcoRI at 65°C for 10 min).

Gel filtration

1. Gel filtration (Sephacryl S-300 spun columns) is used to remove unincorporated nucleotides; PCR primers; the primer binding sites containing DNA fragments, which have one EcoRI end and would interfere with the subsequent cloning step; as well as inserts below 50 bp and primer dimers produced by the DNA polymerase. The column eluate is used for ligating the insert fragments to a cloning vector. If necessary, the column eluate can be dialyzed against water and concentrated in a vacuum centrifuge.

2. Sephacryl S-300 spun columns are equilibrated with 66 mM Tris–HCl buffer, pH 7.6, containing 10 mM MgCl$_2$ and 1 mM dithiothreitol. Apply EcoRI digest to the column, spin, and collect eluate (see manufacturer's instructions for use of the columns).

Ligation and transformation

1. To 17 μl column eluate, add 1 μl 20 ng EcoRI-cut phosphatased pUC, 1 μl 20 mM ATP, and 1 μl T4 DNA ligase. Incubate at 16°C overnight. Inactivate ligase at 65°C for 10 min. Use 1 μl to transform MAX efficiency competent DH5α cells (BRL) and plate out on LB plates containing 100 μg/ml ampicillin and 50 μg/ml 5-bromo-4-chloro-3-indolyl-β-D-galactopyranoside (X-Gal).

Clone analysis

1. Prepare recombinant plasmids by standard procedures. It is absolutely necessary to obtain RNA-free plasmid DNA (e.g., by using Qiagen columns) or to remove RNA by treatment with RNase A and T1.

2. Release insert DNA by *Eco*RI digestion and isolate on 1.2% low-melting-point agarose gels. Alternatively, pUC primers and PCR can be used for amplifying the insert DNA.

3. Label DNA by random oligopriming using [^{32}P]dCTP, [^{32}P]dATP, or both nucleotides. Minigels and miniblots give the best hybridization results. The following cocktail for hybridizations at 65°C is recommended: 4× SSPE, 6% polyethylene glycol compound (Sigma Cat. No. P-2263), 0.5% SDS, 2× Denhardt's solution, and 100 μg/ml denatured sheared salmon DNA.

4. Optimize posthybridization washes for each clone. In general, a final wash at 65°C in 1× SSC and 0.1% SDS is optimal.

IV. Comments

As shown by others microdissection and microcloning can also be performed on metaphase spreads harvested using routine techniques. We used the pipette method for chromosome harvesting because it reduces time of fixation to a few seconds, which is important in avoiding depurination caused by the acetic acid. Furthermore, the coverslips contain metaphases only and are free of DNA from broken cells.

Microcloning as described here is more difficult to perform compared with PCR-mediated cloning using degenerated oligonucleotide primers. It is, however, less prone to contamination and the libraries appear to be more complex.

REFERENCES

Claussen, U. (1980) The pipette method: A new rapid technique for chromosome analysis in prenatal diagnosis. *Hum. Genet.* **54**, 277–278.

Claussen, U., Klein, R., and Schmidt, M. (1986) A pipette method for rapid karyotyping in prenatal diagnosis. *Prenat. Diagn.* **6**, 401–408.

Green, E. D., and Olson, M. V. (1990) Systematic screening of yeast artificial-chromosome libraries by use of the polymerase chain reaction. *Proc. Natl. Acad. Sci. USA* **87**, 1213–1217.

Hadano, S., Watanabe, M., Yokoi, H., Kogi, M., Kondo, I., Tsuchiya, H., Kanazawa, I., Wakasa, K., and Ikeda, J.-E. (1991) Laser microdissection and single unique primer PCR allow generation of regional chromosome DNA clones from a single human chromosome. *Genomics* **11**, 364–373.

Lüdecke, H.-J., Senger, G., Claussen, U., and Horsthemke, B. (1989) Cloning defined regions of the human genome by microdissection of banded chromosomes and enzymatic amplification. *Nature (London)* **338**, 348–350.

Lüdecke, H.-J., Senger, G., Claussen, U., and Horsthemke, B. (1990) Construction and characterisation of band-specific DNA libraries. *Hum. Genet.* **84**, 512–516.

Meltzer, P. S., Guan, X. Y., Burgess, A., and Trent, J. M. (1992) Rapid generation of region specific probes by chromosome microdissection and their application. *Nature Genet.* **1**, 24–28.

Senger, G., Lüdecke, H.-J., Horsthemke, B., and Claussen, U. (1990) Microdissection of banded human chromosomes. *Hum. Genet.* **84**, 507–511.

Sounders, R. D. C., Glover, D. M., Ashburner, M., Siden-Kiamos, I., Louis, C., Monastirioti, M., Savakis, C., and Kafatos, F. (1989) PCR amplification of DNA microdissected from a single polytene chromosome band. Comparison with conventional microcloning. *Nucleic Acids Res.* **17**, 9027–9037.

Trautmann, U., Leuteritz, G., Senger, G., Claussen, U., and Ballhausen, W. G. (1991) Deletion of APC region-specific signals by nonisotopic chromosomal *in situ* suppression (CISS)–hybridisation using a microdissection library as a probe. *Hum. Genet.* **87**, 495–497.

PART 6

HISTOCHEMISTRY

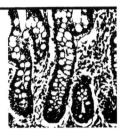

Mayer's Hematoxylin–Eosin: An Example of a Common Histological Staining Method

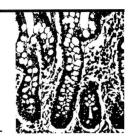

Hans Lyon

I. Introduction

The purpose of histological staining methods is to visualize and differentiate between tissue components, not to determine their chemical composition. On the other hand, histochemical methods show the occurrence and localization of chemical entities in the tissue. As all histological methods have a histochemical basis, this distinction between histological and histochemical methods is, however, no longer valid (Lyon and Barer, 1991).

I have selected to describe Mayer's hematoxylin–eosin as a representative histological method that emphasizes the morphological composition of cells and tissues. The precise histochemical basis of the method is still not quite clear in all details (Prentø and Schulte, 1991).

As sources for detailed descriptions of further histological and histochemical staining procedures, I recommend the following handbooks: Bancroft and Stevens (1990), Kiernan (1990), Lillie and Fullmer (1976), Pearse (1980, 1985), Stoward and Pearse (1991).

Standardization of a method for staining cytological or histological material requires consideration of all steps in the procedure. Because of space considerations, however, I have only given the detailed staining procedure for formaldehyde-fixed, paraffin-embedded, histological material. Concerning cytological material, cryostat sections, and material embedded in plastic, I have added notes where changes in the procedure are appropriate.

A flowchart (Fig. 1) shows the various kinds of specimens and the main steps before staining. For details of these procedures, see the above recommended handbooks. I suggest that for practical application, one should seek the assistance of a histology laboratory.

II. Materials and Instrumentation

A. GLASSWARE

Glass slides 76 × 26 mm (3 × 1 in.), thickness about 1 mm

Cover glasses or coverslips of various sizes, for example, 24 × 24 mm or 24 × 50 mm, thickness about 0.15 mm (We recommend the use of brands labeled "cleaned, ready for use." In our laboratory, we use glass slides from G. Menzel.)

Coplin staining jars (Fig. 2) manufactured by Glaswerk Wertheim GmbH

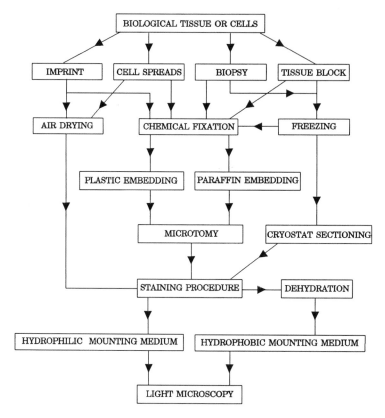

FIGURE 1

B. DYES

Hematoxylin (C.I. 75290, Natural Black)

Eosin (C.I. 45380, Acid Red 87) (We recommend the use of dyes certified by the Biological Stain Commission. For further details, see Section IV. We use hematoxylin (Cat. No. H-3136) and eosin Y (Cat. No. E-4382) purchased from Sigma Chemical Company.)

C. OTHER REAGENTS

The following reagents of analytical grade are purchased from E. Merck: potassium aluminum sulfate (Cat. No. 1047), sodium iodate (Cat. No. 6523), sodium bicarbonate (Cat. No. 6329), lithium carbonate (Cat. No. 5680), glacial acetic acid (Cat. No. 63), concentrated hydrochloric acid (Cat. No. 13386), ethanol 99% (v/v) (Cat. No. 986), ethanol 95% (v/v) (Cat. No. 971), ethanol 70% (v/v), and distilled water. Pertex mountant (Cat. No. 0080) is from Histolab Products AB.

III. Procedures

A. MAYER'S HEMATOXYLIN–EOSIN METHOD

Solutions

1. *Mayer's hematoxylin:* Hematoxylin, 1 g; potassium aluminum sulfate, 50 g; sodium iodate, 0.2 g; distilled water, 1000 ml. Dissolve hematoxylin, potassium

FIGURE 2

aluminum sulfate, and sodium iodate in the distilled water by allowing the mixture to stand at room temperature overnight. After filtration, the stain is ready for use. Storage time is up to 3 months.

2. *Eosin staining solution, 0.5% (w/v):* Eosin, 5 g; distilled water, 990 ml; glacial acetic acid, 10 ml.

3. *Acid ethanol:* Ethanol 95% (v/v), 99 ml; concentrated hydrochloric acid, 1 ml.

4. *Sodium bicarbonate solution, 5% (w/v):* Sodium bicarbonate, 5 g; distilled water, 100 ml.

5. *Lithium carbonate solution, 1% (w/v):* Lithium carbonate, 1 g; distilled water, 100 ml.

Steps

Figure 3 gives a summary of the method. Carry out all steps in the procedure under a fume hood.

1. Dewax paraffin sections (note 1). Place section(s) in staining vessels, for example, Coplin jars, according to the following schedule.

Xylene, three changes, 5 min in each

99% (v/v) Ethanol, two changes, 2 min in each

95% (v/v) Ethanol, two changes, 2 min in each

2. Hydrate sections by placing them in Coplin jars filled with distilled water for 1 min (note 2).

3. Stain in Mayer's hematoxylin solution for 5 min (note 3).

4. Wash in running tap water (*blue*) for 3 min (note 4).

5. Stain in eosin solution for 30 sec (note 5).

6. Rinse in running tap water (*differentiate*) for 30 sec.

7. Dehydrate in ethanol: 95% (v/v) for 2 min; 99% (v/v), two changes, 2 min in each.

8. Mount the wet section directly from the 99% (v/v) ethanol with a coverslip using Pertex. (Color Plate 15).

Notes

1. This step applies only to paraffin sections.

2. This step also applies to plastic sections, cryostat sections, and fixed imprints and cell spreads.

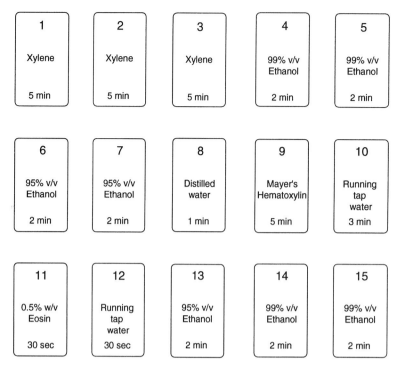

FIGURE 3

3. The staining time of 5 min applies to dewaxed paraffin sections less than 10 μm thick. Increase staining time to 8 min for paraffin sections thicker than 10 μm. For plastic sections the necessary staining time is about 20 min. Usually, for imprints and cell spreads and for cryostat sections a staining time of 2 min suffices.

4. In this step sections turn blue (*bluing*) due to the alkalinity of the tap water. If this should not happen, add 2 drops of a 1% (w/v) lithium carbonate solution to 500 ml tap water. Let sections stand in this alkaline water for 1 min. Rinse thoroughly in running tap water for 2 min.

5. The staining time of 30 sec applies to dewaxed paraffin sections, cryostat sections, imprints, and cell spreads. For plastic sections, increase staining time to 1 min.

IV. Comments

The detailed procedure given here usually works satisfactorily; however, several factors can cause erroneous results. For a discussion of some of these and their remedies, see immediately below and in Section V.

A common difficulty is to get pure dyes or even dyes with a consistent composition. This situation has improved in recent years but still presents a problem for achieving fully reproducible staining results. Consequently, we recommend the use of certified dyes (the dyestuff powder) and stains (solutions of dyes). These are dyes and stains tested for physicochemical and staining properties by the Biological Stain Commission in the United States (Lillie, 1977).

Eosin is available today in nearly pure form and rarely gives any problems. It is usually available as the sodium salt.

The compound hematoxylin is not a dye. After oxidation with sodium iodate, it becomes the dye hematein. This dye can react with certain metals (here aluminum) to form a metal complex dye. Often, samples of commercial hematoxylin exhibit considerable batch-to-batch variation in their composition. This is in part due to varying proportions of hematein and oxyhematein (a further oxidation product) in the hematoxylin samples. Furthermore, changes in composition continue to take place also in the final staining solution. For these reasons, Mayer's hematoxylin (aluminum–hematein) staining solution as given here is only "half-oxidized."

V. Pitfalls

1. *Nuclear overstaining:* The staining time is too long. This is usually due to freshly prepared solutions with a high hematein content.
Remedy: Differentiate the overstained slides after bluing (step 4) by agitating them for 5–10 sec in acid ethanol. Alternatively, take a new slide and, after staining in Mayer's hematoxylin solution (step 3) but before bluing, treat this with acid ethanol for 2 sec.

2. *Weak nuclear staining:* A low hematein content is caused by low hematoxylin content in the commercial batch used or overoxidation of an old solution. *Remedy:* Increase concentration of hematoxylin from 0.1 to 0.15% (w/v), or discard the staining solution and prepare fresh Mayer's hematoxylin solution.
Other reasons for weak nuclear staining are a very short staining time (old solutions require an increased staining time); overdifferentiation with removal of too much *aluminum–hematein* in the acid ethanol bath (see Pitfall 1); and pretreatment with acid either in acid fixatives or during decalcification with strong acids. *Remedy:* Sometimes, it is possible to restore some nuclear staining by immersing the slide in a 5% (w/v) aqueous solution of sodium bicarbonate for 6 hr before staining (between steps 2 and 3).

3. *Gross blue background staining:* The cause is overstaining with aluminum–hematein. *Remedy:* Differentiate in acid ethanol as described under Pitfall 1, nuclear overstaining.

4. *Red staining of cell nuclei:* The rinse in tap water was insufficient because either (a) the rinse in step 6 was too short, or (b) the pH of tap water in stain 4 was too low. *Remedies:* (a) Increase the length of the bluing (step 4) to 10 min. (b) Make tap water in step 4 alkaline by adding lithium carbonate (see note 4 in Section III).

5. *Gross cytoplasmic overstaining with eosin:* (a) The staining time in eosin (step 5) was too long. *Remedy:* Shorten staining time to 15 sec. (b) The concentration of eosin was too high. *Remedy:* Reduce the concentration of eosin in the staining solution to 0.25% (w/v). (c) Differentiation of eosin in step 6 was insufficient. *Remedy:* Increase length of differentiation (step 6) to 45 sec.

6. *Weak cytoplasmic counterstaining with eosin:* (a) The concentration of eosin was too low. This can be due to low dye content in the commercial dye batch. *Remedy:* Try increasing concentration of dye to 1% (w/v). (b) The staining time in step 5 was too short. *Remedy:* Increase staining time in step 5 to 1 min.

REFERENCES

Bancroft, J. D., and Stevens, A. (1990) "Theory and Practice of Histological Techniques," 3rd ed. Churchill–Livingstone, Edinburgh.
Kiernan, J. A. (1990) "Histological & Histochemical Methods: Theory and Practice," 2nd ed. Pergamon Press, Oxford.

Lillie, R. D. (1977) "H. J. Conn's Biological Stains," 9th ed. pp. 14–18, 566–570, 591–592, 609–610. Williams & Wilkins, Baltimore.

Lillie, R. D., and Fullmer, H. M. (1976) "Histopathologic Technic and Practical Histochemistry," 4th ed. McGraw-Hill, New York.

Lyon, H., and Barer, M. R. (1991) The scope of histochemistry. *In* "Theory and Strategy in Histochemistry" (H. Lyon, ed.), pp. 3–6. Springer-Verlag, Berlin.

Pearse, A. G. E. (1980) "Histochemistry, Theoretical and Applied," 4th ed., Vol. I. "Preparative and Optical Technology." Churchill–Livingstone, Edinburgh.

Pearse, A. G. E. (1985) "Histochemistry, Theoretical and Applied," 4th ed., Vol. II: "Analytical Technology." Churchill–Livingstone, Edinburgh.

Prentø, P., and Schulte, E. (1991) Staining involving metal complex dyes. *In* "Theory and Strategy in Histochemistry" (H. Lyon, ed.), pp. 109–114. Springer-Verlag, Berlin.

Stoward, P. J., and Pearse, A. G. E. (1991) "Histochemistry, Theoretical and Applied," 4th ed., Vol. III: "Enzyme Histochemistry." Churchill–Livingstone, Edinburgh.

Selected Enzyme Staining in Histochemistry

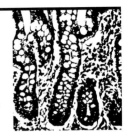

Joseph Chayen and Lucille Bitensky

I. Introduction

Conventional biochemistry normally requires samples of 10^6 identical cells for each assay. When results obtained by quantitative histochemical methods (20 cells/sample) have been compared with those obtained by conventional biochemical procedures the results have been quantitatively similar (e.g., Olsen *et al.*, 1981). One of the advantages of quantitative histochemistry is that it measures activity in individual defined cells lying within a complex histology, so that the measurements are not confused by the activities, or lack of activity, in other cells (Fig. 1). For example, the activity of a particular enzyme in the renal distal convoluted tubules can be measured separately from that activity in the closely associated proximal tubules. It literally relates biochemical activity to histology (Chayen, 1978).

Another major advantage of quantitative histochemistry involves the preparation of the sample. In many instances, conventional biochemistry requires that the tissue be homogenized and the enzyme isolated into a foreign medium. This can alter the activity considerably, so that changes induced in life by, for example, a toxic substance, are obliterated by the greater changes caused by the homogenization (as discussed by Chayen and Bitensky, 1968). Quantitative histochemistry does not suffer from this defect.

It therefore follows that any biochemical cellular changes that may be induced by a drug, a disease process, or a toxic agent should be studied by quantitative histochemistry. The procedures have been discussed fully by Chayen (1980) and Chayen and Bitensky (1991).

II. Materials and Instrumentation

For chilling the tissue, the coolant is *n*-hexane (British Drug Houses, low in aromatic hydrocarbons grade, boiling range 67–70°C). The sectioning is done with a cryostat (Bright Instrument Company). For reactions that require a colloid stabilizer, either Polypep 5115 (Sigma) or polyvinyl alcohol (grade G04/140, Wacker Chemical Co.) is used. Colored reaction products are measured with a Vickers M85A scanning and integrating microdensitometer (Bio-Rad Micromeasurements Ltd.).

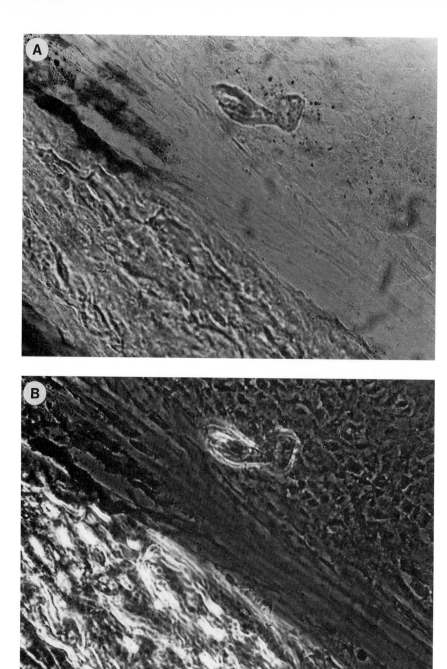

FIGURE 1 Longitudinal cryostat section through the midshaft of an unfixed, undemineralized rat metatarsal 5 days after fracture, reacted for alkaline phosphatase activity. (A) Visible light photograph showing the alkaline phosphatase activity in the periosteum remote from the fracture site, which is just out of view, but no activity close to the fracture. ×250. (B) The same field viewed under phase-contrast illumination. The bone is very refractile (bright) in the lower left-hand part of the field; developing callus is in the upper right-hand part of the field. ×250. This inhibition of alkaline phosphatase activity close to the fracture site, in the presence of high glucose-6-phosphate dehydrogenase activity (in serial sections), was related to a change in the glutathione redox couple.

III. Procedures

A. CHILLING

Steps

1. Place the coolant, *n*-hexane, in a small beaker.
2. Place the beaker in a bath of a constant-freezing mixture of solid carbon dioxide and ethanol.
3. Check that the temperature of the coolant has reached $-70°C$.
4. Project the block of tissue (not larger than $5 \times 5 \times 3$ mm) into the cold hexane and leave for 1–2 min.
5. With cold forceps transfer the tissue to a cold glass tube, surrounded by CO_2–ice containing a small strip of filter paper to mop up any hexane that may be transferred with the block of tissue.
6. Recork the tube and store at $-70°C$.
7. Cut the sections within 1–2 weeks.

B. SECTIONING

Steps

1. Cool the haft of the heavy microtome knife with solid carbon dioxide.
2. Set the thickness gauge of the microtome to the required thickness, usually 10 μm.
3. Set the temperature of the cabinet of the cryostat to $-25°C$.
4. Cut sections of constant thickness by means of the automatic drive.
5. Pick each section off the knife by apposing a warm glass slide (e.g., at about 20°C) to the section. The section should jump from the knife when the gap between the knife and the slide is about 2 mm.
6. Store the sections, on the slides, over a desiccant in a desiccator.
7. Do the reaction as soon as possible and certainly within a few hours.

C. MEASUREMENT

Steps

1. Measure the amount of reaction product with a scanning and integrating microdensitometer. Basically this instrument is a spectrophotometer built around a microscope.

2. Place the section on the stage of the microdensitometer and choose the objective and size of the optical mask appropriate to the cells to be measured.

3. Select a wavelength appropriate to the reaction product.

4. For very precise measurement select a scanning spot that, in combination with a $\times 100$ objective, will scan the selected cell with a narrow beam of 0.2-μm diameter, namely, the limit of resolution with visible light. This ensures that the image measured at each point is optically homogeneous (Chayen and Bitensky, 1991).

5. Record the integrated value, as reported on the density scale, of an area of clear field (value *a*).

6. Using the same optical conditions record the values for appropriate areas of the specimen (value *b*).

7. Subtract *a* from *b* to give the relative absorption due to the cells. Such values are sufficient for most purposes.

8. If required, convert the relative absorption values into units of absolute extinction (or absorptivity) by suitable calibration (Chayen and Bitensky, 1991).

D. ALKALINE PHOSPHATASE: A CELL SURFACE MARKER

Solutions

1. *Main solution:* Combine 10 ml of a 2% solution of sodium 5,5-diethylbarbiturate (barbital), 10 ml of a 3% solution of sodium β-glycerophosphate, 20 ml of a 2.7% solution of calcium chloride ($CaCl_2 \cdot 2H_2O$), 1 ml of a 5% solution of magnesium sulfate ($MgSO_4 \cdot 7H_2O$), and 5 ml of distilled water. Adjust the pH of this solution to pH 9.4 if necessary.

2. *Control solution:* Replace the sodium β-glycerophosphate solution with 10 ml of distilled water. Except for the intestinal enzyme, it is better to add 0.4 mM L-p-bromotetramisole (Aldrich) to the full reaction medium.

Steps

Unfixed cryostat sections should be used.

1. React the sections in this medium at 37°C. This initial reaction does not produce a colored product. It is therefore necessary to do the full reaction on some trial sections for, e.g., 15, 30, and 60 min, to decide the best reaction time.

2. Wash in several changes of alkaline water for 5 min. An acidic pH will render the calcium phosphate precipitate soluble, giving rise to a false localization of the final reaction product.

3. Transfer the sections to a 2% solution of cobalt nitrate for 5 min. Ensure that this solution is alkaline.

4. Rinse in distilled water.

5. Transfer to a 0.5% solution of ammonium polysulfide. Leave for 1 min.

6. Rinse in distilled water.

7. Mount the sections in an aqueous mountant such as Farrants' medium or Aquamount (BDH).

8. Activity is shown by a black precipitate of cobalt sulfide.

E. ACID PHOSPHATASE: A MARKER OF LYSOSOMAL ACTIVITY

Typically, acid phosphatase is a lysosomal enzyme. Short incubation times should be used; with long exposure to the acidic medium the lysosomal membranes are damaged, and the enzyme and the reaction product diffuse to other sites, notably the nucleus.

Solutions

1. *Acidic solution of sodium β-glycerophosphate:* Add 0.53 g of lead nitrate to 400 ml of a 0.05 M acetate buffer at pH 5.0. Add 40 ml of a 3% solution of sodium β-glycerophosphate. Leave for 24 hr at 37°C. Cool to room temperature. Filter, and use immediately.

2. *Control solution:* The full reaction medium (as above) to which you add 0.01 M sodium fluoride. This should abolish any true reaction.

3. *Hydrogen sulfide:* In a fume hood bubble hydrogen sulfide through a wash bottle containing 0.1 M hydrochloric acid to wash the gas before exposure to the sections.

Steps

Unfixed cryostat sections or air-dried smears or cytocentrifuge preparations (unfixed) should be used.

1. React in the main solution (above) for various times (see Section D, step 1). To give some indication of the time that may be required: cryostat sections of rat liver may require between 5 and 20 min; for sections of human endometrium, 20 min was the correct time for samples taken at midcycle, 40 min for tissue at the proliferative stage, but 5 min was more than sufficient for tissue taken at the secretory phase. This test of the time required to produce discernible coloration of the lysosomes is the basis of the Bitensky fragility test (Bitensky and Chayen, 1977).

2. Wash well in distilled water to remove adsorbed lead. Do not use acid for this purpose because it will remove the specific precipitate of lead phosphate as well.

3. Saturate distilled water with hydrogen sulfide gas and leave the sections in this solution for up to 1 min.

4. Wash thoroughly with distilled water.

5. Mount in an aqueous mountant such as Farrants' medium or Aquamount.

6. In normal tissue, activity should be shown by small black dots corresponding to lysosomes.

F. DEHYDROGENASE ENZYMES

Glyceraldehyde 3-phosphate dehydrogenase is used as a marker of the activity of the Embden–Meyerhof pathway, together with the activity of lactate dehydrogenase. Glucose-6-phosphate dehydrogenase is taken to indicate activity of the pentose phosphate shunt, which is a major source of NADPH (for biosynthetic activity); succinate dehydrogenase activity is a marker of mitochondrial activity; and hydroxyacyl dehydrogenase activity indicates the utilization of fatty acids. The procedures are given in Table I.

G. SODIUM–POTASSIUM ATPase

This marker of cell membrane activity is an example of the new "hidden capture" reactions. The lead is "hidden" from the tissue as the lead ammonium citrate/acetate complex (LACA, Sigma) until it is precipitated by released phosphate (Chayen *et al.,* 1981).

TABLE I Methods for Selected Dehydrogenase Enzymatic Activities

Dehydrogenase enzyme	Substrate		Coenzyme		Buffer	pH	Extras
	Name	Concn	Name	Concn			
Succinate[a]	Sodium succinate	0.05 M	—	—	Phosphate (0.1 M)	7.8	+ PMS + NBT (0.1%)[b]
Lactate[c]	Sodium lactate	0.05 M	NAD	3.6 mM	Glycylglycine[d]	8.0	+ PMS + NBT (3 mM)
Glyceraldehyde 3-phosphate[c]	Fructose 1,6-diphosphate + aldolase (25 units/ml)	3 mg/ml	NAD	2.5 mg/ml	Glycylglycine[d]	8.5	+ PMS + NBT (3 mM) + KH_2PO_4 (0.5 mg/ml)
Glucose 6-phosphate[e]	Glucose 6-phosphate disodium salt	5 mM	NADP	3 mM	Glycylglycine[d]	8.0	+ PMS + NBT (3 mM)
Hydroxyacyl-CoA[f]	β-Hydroxybutyryl cysteamine	50 mM	NAD	1 mM	Glycylglycine[g]	8.0	Sodium nitroprusside (4 mM) Menadione (1 mM) Neotetrazolium chloride (1%)

[a] Mitochondrial.
[b] PMS, Phenazine methosulfate, 0.7 mM; NBT, nitroblue tetrazolium.
[c] Glycolytic.
[d] 50 mM in 30% PVA or 40% Polypep 5115.
[e] Pentose phosphate shunt.
[f] Fatty acid metabolism.
[g] 50 mM in 30% PVA.

Solutions

1. *Solution 1:* Combine 1 mM sodium acetate, 40 g Polypep 5115 (Sigma), and 100 ml 0.2 M Tris buffer, pH 7.4. Once this has been dissolved, add the following, sequentially: 410 mM sodium chloride, 20 mM magnesium chloride, 37.5 mM potassium chloride, 16.5 mM disodium adenosine 5′-triphosphate, 32 mg/ml LACA. The final pH should be pH 7.5. Dissolve the LACA with constant shaking in the smallest possible volume of dilute ammonia (5 drops of 0.88 ammonia/ml) before adding it to the reaction medium.

2. *Solution 2:* Prepare as for solution 1, but add 0.4 mM ouabain octahydrate (Sigma).

3. *Mountant (Z5):* Combine 12 g polyvinyl alcohol, 20 ml glycerine, 20 ml lactic acid, and 0.4 M acetate buffer up to 100 ml. The pH should be pH 6.5.

4. *Control solution:* Where alkaline phosphatase is also likely to occur, add 0.4 mM L-*p*-bromotetramisole (Aldrich) to both solutions to inhibit this activity.

Steps

The sectioning and reaction should be done on the same day that the tissue is chilled, or the next day, but not later because the enzyme is very unstable.

1. To remove free phosphate, immerse the section (5 min) in a 40% solution of Polypep 5115 in Tris buffer, pH 7.5, containing 0.1 M potassium acetate.

2. Remove the solution (of potassium acetate in Polypep 5115). To facilitate this removal because the reagents are expensive, the whole reaction should be

done by encircling the section with a glass or Perspex ring (depth 3 mm) and the solutions pipetted into the ring.

3. React some sections in solution 1, others in solution 2, at 37°C.

4. Wash in a Coplin jar with several changes of 0.2 M Tris buffer, pH 7.4, at 37°C.

5. Immerse in a saturated solution of hydrogen sulfide for 1–2 min.

6. Rinse in distilled water.

7. Mount in the aqueous mountant Z5.

8. The amount of Na^+–K^+-ATPase activity is derived by subtracting the activity given to solution 2 from that given to solution 1.

IV. Comments

These methods have been selected to test markers of the main metabolic systems of cells. When reactions are done under acidic or basic conditions, the pH may be sufficient to stabilize the section and its contents; however, at pH values of 6 to 8.5, unfixed sections lose much of their material into the medium. To stabilize sections at these pH values it is essential to include a colloid stabilizer in the reaction medium. For most reactions 30% (w/v) polyvinyl alcohol is used. Polypep 5115 at 40% (w/v) or even 50% is used for some reactions; it can be used as a substitute for polyvinyl alcohol.

V. Pitfalls

1. All solutions should be prepared fresh, just before they are to be used.

2. Histochemical reactions involve the formation of a colored precipitate. Because their measurement is of a solid precipitate, and not a chromophore in solution, certain restrictions operate. Consequently to avoid inhomogeneity error, it is essential to use a suitable scanning and integrating microdensitometer and to use it correctly, for example, to use sufficient magnification.

3. Histochemical enzyme reactions are so designed that a colored product of the reaction is precipitated as close as possible to the site at which the reaction took place. This is not true for many so-called "histochemical reactions." As regards one such reaction, it has been shown that the reaction product diffused more than 1000 μm from the site at which it was generated (McCabe and Chayen, 1965). This can be especially serious with immunohistochemistry: the localization of the antibody–antigen reaction may be precise but the localization of the histochemical reaction to detect the enzyme label may be remarkably imprecise.

REFERENCES

Bitensky, L., and Chayen, J. (1977) Histochemical methods for the study of lysosomes. In "Lysosomes, a Laboratory Handbook" (J. T. Dingle, ed.), 2nd ed., pp. 209–243. North-Holland, Amsterdam.
Chayen, J. (1978) The cytochemical approach to hormone assay. Int. Rev. Cytol. 53, 333–396.
Chayen, J. (1980) "The Cytochemical Bioassay of Polypeptide Hormones. Monographs on Endocrinology." Springer, Berlin/Heidelberg/New York.

Chayen, J., and Bitensky, L. (1968) Multiphase chemistry of cell injury. *In* "The Biological Basis of Medicine" (E. E. Bittar and N. Bittar, eds.), Vol. 1, pp. 337–368. Academic Press, New York.

Chayen, J., and Bitensky, L. (1991) "Practical Histochemistry," 2nd ed. Wiley, New York/London.

Chayen, J., Frost, G. T. B., Dodds, R. A., Bitensky, L., Pitchfork, J., Baylis, P. H., and Barrnett, R. J. (1981) The use of a hidden metal-capture reagent for the measurement of Na^+–K^+-ATPase activity: A new concept in cytochemistry. *Histochemistry* **71**, 533–541.

McCabe, M., and Chayen, J. (1965) The demonstration of latent particulate aminopeptidase activity. *J. R. Microsc. Soc.* **84**, 361–371.

Olsen, I., Dean, M. F., Harris, G., and Muir, H. (1981) Direct transfer of a lysosomal enzyme from lymphoid cells to deficient fibroblasts. *Nature* **291**, 244–247.

PART **7**

ANTIBODIES

SECTION **A**

Production of Antibodies

Production of Polyclonal Antibodies in Rabbits

Christian Huet

I. Introduction

The major problem encountered in the production of antibodies is the amount of antigen available. This amount determines the method of injection. Subcutaneous injection along the spine can be used when 1 mg of antigen is available. Usually, however, the amount of purified antigen is as small as 100 μg. In this case the best location for injection is the popliteal lymph nodes in the hind legs. Even a smaller amount of antigens can be efficient in raising antibodies but probably with lower serum titers.

On the basis of 200 μg of antigen, the method of immunization to be described here implies injections in both lymph nodes and subcutaneously along the spine. Usually the lymph nodes are buried in fat and are rather difficult to isolate; that is why young animals should be used. To aid in their location, we inject Evans blue into the two hind paws of the rabbit 2 hr before injecting the antigen. The dye is carried via the lymphatic vessels to the popliteal lymph nodes, making them more clearly visible.

About a third of the rabbits have endogenous antikeratin antibodies, which can give a false reaction in immunocytochemistry. It has been suggested that the false reaction is due to chicken feathers (composed largely of keratin) used as a filler in commercial rabbit chow. This emphasizes the importance of taking preimmune serum from a rabbit that will be used to prepare antibodies against a particular antigen.

II. Materials and Instrumentation

Rabbits

Animals weighing approximately 2–3 kg should be chosen. White rabbits are preferable because the node, after injection of the blue dye, is easier to detect through the leg skin.

Syringes

1-ml (Cat. No. BS-01T), 2-ml (Cat. No. BS-H2S), 10-ml (Cat. No. BS-10ES), and 50-ml (Cat. No. BS50ES) plastic syringes from Terumo Europe NV

2 × 3-ml Multifit syringes with luer-lok from Becton Dickinson (Cat. No. SMBDL 1020F)

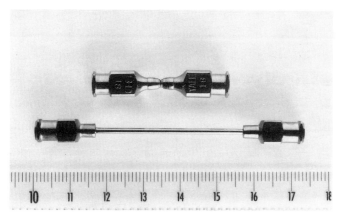

FIGURE 1   Two two-headed 18-gauge needles.

0.45 × 12-mm (Cat. No. NN-2613R), 0.6 × 25-mm (Cat. No. NN-2325R), and 1.2 × 40-mm (Cat. No. NN-1838R) non-reusable needles are from Terumo Europe NV

Two-headed 18-gauge needles (adjusted as shown in Fig. 1 and used to bridge two glass syringes when preparing the antigen–adjuvant emulsion) usually obtained from the local machine shop or from Aubry

Tools

1 pair of scissors with straight heavy and blunt blades

1 pair of microscissors with sharp delicate blades

1 pair of dissection forceps, straight

1 pair of dissection forceps, curved

Clamp "mosquito"

1 MikRon Autoclip Applier (9 mm) and MikRon wound clips (Cat. No. 7631, distributed by Clay Adams–Becton Dickinson)

Chemicals

Complete Freund's adjuvant (Cat. No. 0638-60-7) and incomplete Freund's adjuvant (Cat. No. 0639-60-6) from Difco Laboratories

Instamed phosphate-buffered saline (Cat. No. L 182-10) prepared by Seromed

Evans blue (Cat. No. E-2129), sodium azide (Cat. No. S-2002), sodium chloride (Cat. No. S-9625), and lysine (Cat. No. L 6001) from Sigma

Glutaraldehyde EM grade (Cat. No. G003) from TAAB

Hemocyanin (Cat. No. 37 48 05) from Calbiochem

Fentanyl (which is a regulated substance) from Janssen

Sephadex G-10 and G-50 from Pharmacia

Miscellaneous Items

50-ml Falcon plastic tubes (Cat. No. 2098) from Becton Dickinson

Dialysis tubing

70% alcohol in a squeeze bottle and in a beaker large enough to submerge instruments

0.22-μm (Cat. No. SLGV 025 BS) and 0.45-μm (Cat. No. SL HV 025 LS) filters from Millipore

Mortar (Cat. No. 01 447 341) from Prolabo

Rabbit restraining box, razor blades, lab coat and kitchen towel, animal grooming shears, gauze, liquid nitrogen, ice bucket

III. Procedures

Rabbits should be kept in the animal house for at least a week before surgery to ensure that healthy rabbits have been obtained and that they are adjusting properly to their new conditions of living.

Tools can be either autoclaved (dry) or soaked in 70% alcohol to sterilize.

A. INJECTION OF DYE TO DISPLAY POPLITEAL LYMPH NODE

Solutions

1. *Sterile 0.15 M NaCl solution:* To make 100 ml, dissolve 0.9 g of NaCl in distilled water and adjust to a total volume of 100 ml in a cylinder. Filter on a 0.22-μm Millipore filter adjusted on a 50-ml syringe and store in a sterile 50-ml Falcon tube.

2. *2.5% Evans blue solution:* Add 1.25 g Evans blue powder to 50 ml of saline solution and filter on 0.45-μm Millipore filter. Store at 4°C.

Materials

1. Needles, 0.6 × 2 mm
2. Syringe, 2 ml
3. Lab coat

Steps

1. Spread out a lab coat (with a knotted sleeve) on a bench or table. Bring the rabbit from its cage, and place it on the lab coat. Put its head in the knotted sleeve of the lab coat to immobilized it as much as possible. One person should hold the two hind legs while another injects the dye.

2. Spread the two middle toes apart, and squirt the area with 70% alcohol from a squeeze bottle. This has the advantage of cleaning the area and also clumps the hairs together, rendering the injection easier.

3. Insert the needle into the skin between the two toes, pass it subcutaneously for about a centimeter, and inject 0.2–0.5 ml of the dye solution. Repeat for the other hind paw. Hold the rabbit very firmly when doing these two painful injections because the animals usually react very nervously.

Dye should be injected at least 2 hr before injection of antigen into the lymph node (the antigen solution can be prepared in the meantime). The staining remains visible for a couple of days. One should not be surprised to find, later, a blue bunny exhibiting pale blue ears in the cage (however, we never found him in a hurry shaking its pocketwatch).

B. PREPARATION OF THE ANTIGEN SOLUTION

The antigen should be in solution in a sterile and nonimmunogenic solvent such as saline or PBS (100–500 μg/ml). About 1 ml of antigen solution will be made into an emulsion with an equal amount of complete Freund's adjuvant. Then, 2 ml of emulsion will be injected into the rabbit, about 1 ml into the two popliteal lymph nodes and the rest subcutaneously along the spine.

1. Solution of a Proteic Antigen

Solutions

1. *0.15 M NaCl or PBS:* 0.15 M NaCl in 10 mM NaPO$_4$ in sterile water. Prepare saline as directed in Section A.

2. *PBS 10× stock solution:* Dissolve one flask of Seromed PBS powder in 1 liter distilled water.

Step

Prepare about 1 ml of purified antigen in a saline solution or in PBS
(100–500 μg/ml final).

2. Antigen in Bands on Nitrocellulose Blots

Very often the pure antigen is not isolated but visualized on nitrocellulose blots in which the protein bands are stained with Ponceau S. The frozen isolated band is pulverized with a mortar and pestle cooled down with liquid nitrogen.

Solution

0.15 M NaCl or PBS: 0.15 M NaCl in 10 mM NaPO$_4$ in sterile water. See
Section B1.

Materials

1. Mortar and pestle.
2. Liquid nitrogen
3. Spatula or scalpel
4. Glass syringe, 3 ml
5. Needle: 1.2 × 40 mm

Steps

1. Pour liquid nitrogen into the mortar (with the pestle in it) and let it cool.

2. Cut the nitrocellulose band into small pieces with scissors, and let the pieces fall into the liquid nitrogen in the mortar.

3. When the nitrogen is essentially gone, though the surfaces are still near liquid nitrogen temperature, grind vigorously with the pestle to pulverize the nitrocellulose.

4. If there were several bands of sample antigen, then the powder can be scraped from the surfaces of the mortar (using a scalpel or a spatula) and transferred into a 5-ml glass vial (plastic snap cap). After adding 1 ml of saline solution (see above), vigorously mix with a Vortex mixer. Take up 1 ml antigen solution from the vial into a 3-ml glass syringe with a 1.2 × 40-mm needle.

5. If the antigen band is sparse, then warm the mortar above 0°C, and add 1 ml of saline solution into the mortar. Take up 1 ml of antigen suspension directly into a 3-ml glass syringe, fitted with a 1.2 × 40-mm needle.

3. Synthetic Peptides Coupled to KLH as Antigens

Synthetic peptides may be a good source of antigens. A good size is a sequence of 10–15 amino acids. These amino antigens must be coupled to a carrier. Keyhold limpet hemocyanin (KLH) is most commonly used. The peptide is covalently cross-linked to KLH by adding glutaraldehyde.

Solutions

1. *PBS:* See Section B1.
2. *5% glutaraldehyde:* Dilute the 25% glutaraldehyde stock to 5% in water.
3. *1 M lysine:* Dissolve 1 g of lysine in 10 ml water.

Materials

1. Sephadex G-10 column
2. Sephadex G-50 column or dialysis tubing

Steps

1. Desalt peptide over a Sephadex G-10 column (column volume should be about 9 × the sample volume) in PBS buffer.

2. Desalt KLH either by dialyzing or by running through a Sephadex G-50 column in PBS buffer. Adjust concentration to 5–10 mg/ml (OD$_{280}$ = 1).

3. A 20–40 molar excess of peptide is added to the KLH solution. (The molecular weight of KLH is considered to be 100 kDa.)

4. At 30-min intervals, add five aliquots of 5% glutaraldehyde solution (MW = 100). Final concentration is 10 mM. Leave the reaction to complete overnight with agitation in the cold.

5. Block the potential free unreacted aldehyde groups by adding 1 M lysine to a final concentration of 25 mM.

6. To immunize, use the complete mixture, including occasional aggregates.

C. PRODUCING THE EMULSION

Solutions

Use one of the antigen solutions as prepared in Section B.

Tools

1. Two 3-ml glass syringes
2. Two-headed needle
3. Needles, 1.2 × 40, 0.6 × 25, and 0.45 × 12 mm

Steps

1. Take up 1 ml of complete Freund's adjuvant in a 3-ml glass syringe with a 1.2 × 40-mm needle.

2. Remove the needle and replace it with a two-headed needle. Push the syringe plunger until adjuvant appears at the open end of the needle.

3. Attach the syringe containing the antigen solution (100 μg in 1 ml) on that end. Make sure that no air is trapped and that both ends are tightly fitted. Hold one syringe in each hand and run the solutions back and forth between the two syringes with your thumbs. Continue until the emulsion becomes rather firm, then push two or three more times and stop (if you continue the emulsion may become too stiff).

4. When a stable emulsion is achieved, push the emulsion into one of the two glass syringes and remove the other one. Place a 0.45 × 12-mm needle on the syringe. Use a 0.6 × 25-mm needle to avoid clogging if the antigen is on powdered nitrocellulose. Remove any bubbles by tapping the syringe on the edge of a bench until the bubbles rise, then expel them.

5. Push the plunger until the emulsion begins to emerge at the tip of the needle, then put the plastic cover on the needle and put the syringe in an ice bucket, oriented vertically with the covered needle and emulsion in the ice. Keeping the syringe on ice should prevent phase separation of the emulsion.

D. ANESTHETIZING AND SHAVING THE RABBIT:

Solution

Fentanyl citrate (50 μg/ml) stock solution.

Tools

1. Plastic syringe, 10 ml
2. Needle, 0.6 × 25 mm
3. Animal grooming shear
4. Lab coat and towel

Steps

1. Weigh the rabbit.

2. Place the rabbit on a towel on a table and inject the anesthetic intramuscularly into the leg muscle. (Do not let rabbits stand on a slippery surface; they hate it. Put a piece of cloth under their paws.) It is not necessary to cover the rabbit's head. With a 10-ml syringe and a 0.6 × 25-mm needle, inject about 5 ml/3 kg body weight of the anesthetic: First inject into each leg three-fourths of the total amount and then the remainder about 10–15 min later.

3. Wait about 20 min to see the effect. The rabbit is somewhat calmed by the anesthesia (but not necessarily unconscious).

4. Shave (against the grain of the fur) a strip along the back (roughly 5 cm wide). Gather the shavings and throw them in a wastepaper basket (do not wait until the end of the procedure).

5. Shave the backs of both legs, extending from midthigh to the heel, and passing roughly 3 cm forward on the outside of the leg.

E. POPLITEAL LYMPH NODE ISOLATION

Solution

70% alcohol

Tools

1. Surgical tools (autoclaved or imersed in alcohol)
2. Clean kitchen towel
3. Gauze

Steps

1. The rabbit should be unconscious from the anesthesia, although there may still be some reflex movements.

2. Lay it on the clean kitchen towel (the lab coat used before is presumably dirty and full of fur hair).

3. To find the node on the left leg, grasp the knee with the left hand and feel with the thumb the area where the node would be expected. (The node is at the back (posterior) of the bend of the knee, somewhat to the outward (lateral) side.) You will feel a mass about 1 cm in diameter; it may appear bluish through the skin and moves as you manipulate it with your thumb.

4. Apply 70% alcohol (from a squeeze bottle) to the general area.

5. Use small surgical scissors to make an incision in the skin approximately 2 cm long over the node and arranged roughly parallel to the axis of the leg. Carefully make the incision deeper until the node (appearing blue because of the previous dye injection) bulges out, under pressure from the side by your thumb (Fig. 2).

6. Isolate the lymph node using the bent forceps to dilacerate the connective tissue. (This is safer than using sharp tools because of the proximity of the artery.) In some cases the node is just below the artery, which makes access to the node difficult. The node often appears smaller than might be expected.

F. INJECTING THE ANTIGEN:

Solution

Antigen emulsion: Prepare as described in Section B and keep in the glass syringe.

Materials

Autoclip Applier and wound clips (immersed in 70% alcohol)

The immunization schedule is given in Table I.

Steps

1. Remove the syringe containing the emulsion from the ice bucket, and take the plastic cover off the needle.

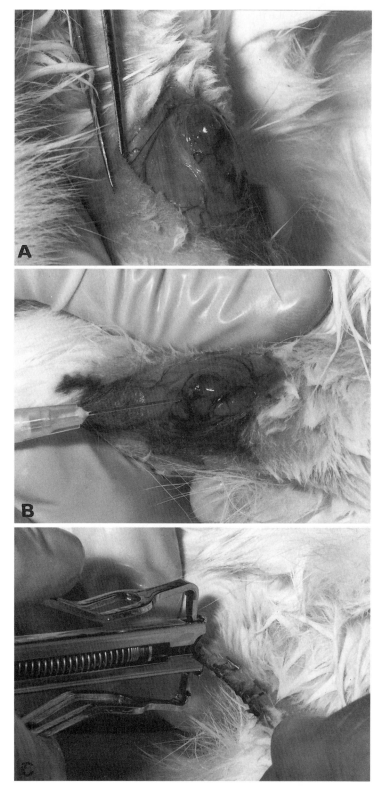

FIGURE 2 (A) Exposing the lymph node. (B) Injecting into the lymph node. (C) Stapling the wound.

TABLE I   Immunization and Bleeding Schedule

Immunization

Day	Injection mode	Amount
−10	*Rabbit in the animal house*	
0	Lymph node	20–100 μg + complete Freund's adjuvant
21	Subscapular	40–100 μg + incomplete Freund's adjuvant
28	Intramuscular	50–100 μg in PBS
29	Intravenous	20–50 μg in PBS

Bleedings

	Day	Bleeding
	36	Fasting
	37	First bleeding
	41	Fasting
	42	Second bleeding
	48	Fasting
	49	Third bleeding
	55	Fasting
	56	Fourth bleeding

2 weeks rest

Boosters

Day	Injection mode	Amount
0	Subscapular	20–50 μg in PBS
8–10	Intramuscular	20 μg in PBS
9–11	Intravenous	20 μg in PBS

Bleedings

Same schedule as above

2. Insert the needle into the node, reaching approximately the middle. Carefully expel the emulsion until the node seems full. You will see white spots here and there as the node fills, and some may leak out (especially if the needle goes too far or is otherwise ill-placed). Each node can take approximately 0.3–0.5 ml.

3. Close the wound with the surgical clip applier and spray 70% alcohol in the surrounding area. Repeat for the popliteal node in the other leg.

4. Apply 70% alcohol to the shaved portion of the back, using a squeeze bottle.

5. Inject the remaining emulsion (approximately 1 ml) subcutaneously into numerous small depots arranged along the spine. To do so, insert the needle through the skin and pass it horizontally under the skin for a short distance. Then expel the emulsion to make a small bump roughly 0.5 cm in diameter.

6. The rabbit can now be returned to its cage.

G. BOOSTERS

Solutions

1. *Incomplete Freund adjuvant*
2. *Stock antigen solution in saline or PBS*

Materials

1. Needles, 0.45 × 12 and 0.6 × 25 mm
2. Plastic syringes, 1 ml

Steps

1. *Three weeks later,* detect the subscapular cavity by palpation between the spine and the scapulae. Inject approximately 100 μg of protein mixed with an equal volume of incomplete Freund's adjuvant (1–2 ml can be injected). Use a 0.45 × 12-mm needle on the syringe.

2. *Seven to ten days later,* inject protein (approximately 50 μg) in 1 ml saline solution (*no adjuvant*) into the gluteus maximus (leg muscle). Use a 0.45 × 12-mm needle.

3. *One day later,* inject intravenously (into the lateral ear vein) approximately 50 μg (0.5 to 1 ml) of protein (*no adjuvant*). Use a 0.6 × 25-mm needle

H. BLEEDINGS

Ten days after the last booster, obtain 40–50 ml from the central artery of the dorsal face of the ear. To clear the blood of lipids, it is advisable to fast the rabbit overnight before the procedure. The bleeding schedule is summarized in Table I.

Materials

1. Restraining box
2. Razor blades
3. Needles, 1.2 × 40 mm
4. Falcon tubes, 50 ml
5. Clamp "mosquito"
6. Gauze

Steps

1. Place the rabbit in the restraining box on the bench.

2. With a razor blade shave about 1 cm of ear skin above the central artery of the ear. Rub the skin on that area to obtain clearly visible vasodilation (do not use solvent for this purpose as it severely damages the skin and renders further bleedings difficult).

3. Insert a large (1.2 × 40-mm) needle about 0.5 cm into the skin and parallel to the artery. To insert the needle into the blood vessel, push it to the right or to the left with your thumb, depending on the ear and the place of insertion you have chosen. This method, though a little more difficult than direct insertion into the artery, has the advantage of maintaining the needle by the skin during the bleeding and of preventing its rejection due to struggling by the rabbit.

4. Keep rubbing the ear base with one finger during the bleeding to keep the artery fully dilated while holding the needle and the plastic tube with the other hand. Collect the blood (one can obtain 40–45 ml) into a 50-ml plastic tube.

5. Remove the needle and stop blood by firmly holding gauze on the wound (use a mosquito clamp). Make absolutely sure that bleeding completely stops before returning the rabbit to its cage.

6. Repeat the bleeding three times at 1-week intervals.

I. SERUM STORAGE

Solution

1% NaN₃ stock: Dissolve 0.5 g sodium azide in 50 ml distilled water. Store at 4°C.

Materials

1. Wooden sticks or glass rods
2. Falcon tubes, 50 ml
3. Plastic blood containers, 25 ml

Steps

1. The blood is collected at room temperature and left on the bench for about 60 min.

2. Carefully detach the clot from the sides of the plastic tube with a wooden stick or a glass rod. The clot is fully detached from the walls when it turns freely in the tube.

3. Let it stand overnight at 4°C to allow complete contraction of the clot.

4. Pour the serum out of the tube into another Falcon tube and spin it for 10 min at 3000 rpm.

5. Store the serum in 25-ml plastic containers in the fridge at 4°C (never in a freezer). Add sodium azide (0.1% final) to prevent contaminant growth.

6. When used, the serum container is kept continuously on an ice bucket and never warmed up to prevent growth of contaminants. From time to time sodium azide may be added.

IV. Pitfalls

1. The nitrocellulose powder must be very fine. If not fine enough it will clot the injection needle. The size of the particles is also important for proper uptake by the macrophages and for proper processing and presentation of the antigen to the lymphocytes. If the powder is not fine enough, the solution can be poured back into the mortar, frozen with liquid nitrogen, and ground again with the pestle. After thawing, it can be taken back into the syringe.

2. Unsuccessful coupling is generally due to the presence of amino groups in the solutions. Normally it comes from ammonium sulfate used to precipitate the proteins or peptide or from the use of Tris buffer. Desalt or dialyze very carefully. Also make sure that no amino groups are present in the water used.

3. If the emulsion is unstable, it will separate within a few minutes into aqueous and lipid phases (e.g., if the antigen solution contains a little detergent). In that case you can leave the freshly prepared emulsion for about 5 min in a −20°C freezer. Mix again by pushing the pestle back and forth before injecting.

4. Tetanization of the rabbit may occur; do not panic. The animal can easily recover with strong and prolonged cardiac massage. Inject the anesthetic in several aliquots (normally two sets of injections at 10 to 15-min intervals are sufficient). If tetanization occurs during the surgery or while you are injecting your most precious and rare antigen, simply place the tools on the bench and start to activate the cardiac reflexes by pressing on the thorax. During the massage you will be able to feel the heart beats and monitor the rabbit's recovery.

5. Very often, insertion of a needle into the ear artery produces severe vasoconstriction and the artery turns white. Proceed by rubbing the ear base of the rabbit until blood flow resumes.

SUGGESTED READING

Avrameas, S., and Terninck, T. (1969) The cross linking of proteins with glutaraldehyde and its use for the preparation of immunoadsorbents. *Immunocytochemistry* 6, 53–66.

Goudie, R. B., Horne, C. H. W., and Wilkison, P. A. (1966) A simple method for producing antibodies specific to a single selected diffusible antigen. *Lancet* 2, 1224.

Kreis, T. E. (1986) Microinjected antibodies against the cytoplasmic domain of vesicular stomatitis virus glycoprotein block its transport to the cell surface. *EMBO J.* 5, 931–941.

Louvard, D. (1987) Production of polyclonal antibodies. *In* "EMBO Practical Course: Antibodies in Cell Biology." EMBO, Heidelberg.

Production of Mouse Monoclonal Antibodies

Ariana Celis, Kurt Dejgaard, and Julio E. Celis

I. Introduction

The aim of this article is to illustrate the various steps involved in the production of mouse monoclonal antibodies (Köhler and Milstein, 1975; Galfre *et al.*, 1977; Goding, 1987; Milstein, 1986; Harlow and Lane, 1988; Liddel and Cryer, 1991). First, the mouse is immunized with an appropriate antigen and then cell lines are created *in vitro* by fusing spleen lymphocytes with a myeloma cell line (e.g., P3-X63-Ag8, HGPRT−, immortal) that confer immortality to the somatic cell hybrid (hybridoma). Spleen and myeloma cells are fused and plated in a special medium containing hypoxanthine, aminopterin and thymidine (HAT) that allows the growth of some of the hybrids but not of the parent cells. Selected hybridomas which are capable of endless reproduction produce only one kind of antibody that is specific for one kind of antigen.

II. Materials and Instrumentation

Freund's complete and incomplete adjuvants were obtained from the Statens Serum Institute. Polyethylene glycol (M_r 6000) was from Koch–Light, and the $50\times$ stock HAT (hypoxanthine, aminopterin, thymidine) solution (Cat. No. 03-080-1B) from Biological Industries. The fluid plaster was obtained from Aerosols.

The 96-well plates (Cat. No. 655180) were from Greiner and the 1-ml sterile plastic syringes (Cat. No. 308400) from Becton Dickinson, Dublin. The gauze (Medical gauze EUR.PH, 100% cotton, 28 threads/cm^2) was obtained from Smith & Nephew, the Gilson tips (C20, Cat. No. G 23800) from Gilson, and the 20G1 sterile needles (Cat. No. 304827450) from Becton Dickinson Fabersanitas.

All other reagents, materials, and equipment were as described in the article by Ariana Celis and Julio E. Celis in Volume 1.

III. Procedures

A. IMMUNIZATION

Solutions

1. *Hanks' buffered saline solution (HBSS) without Ca^{2+} and Mg^{2+}, $10\times$ stock solution*: To make 1 liter, weigh 4 g of KCl, 0.6 g of KH_2PO_4, 80 g of NaCl, and 0.621 g of $Na_2HPO_4 \cdot 2H_2O$. Complete to 1 liter with distilled water.

2. *1× HBSS without Ca²⁺ and Mg²⁺:* To make 1 liter of 1× solution take 100 ml of the 10× stock and complete to 1 liter with distilled water. Autoclave and keep at 4°C.

3. *Freund's complete adjuvant:* Sterile. Keep at 4°C.

4. *Freund's incomplete adjuvant:* Sterile. Keep at 4°C.

5. *Fluid plaster.*

6. *70% ethanol.*

Steps

1. Suspend the antigen in 0.25 ml of HBSS and mix with an equal volume of complete Freund's adjuvant. Make an emulsion by aspirating the solution up and down with the aid of a 1-ml syringe connected to a 20G1 needle. If you have enough antigen, emulsify the solution as described in the article by Christian Huet in this volume. The Freund's complete adjuvant should be handled with care as it contains killed *Mycobacterium tuberculosis* bacteria. For soluble proteins we routinely use 20–50 μg of protein for injection. See also the article by Christian Huet in this volume concerning antigens contained in acrylamide gels or nitrocellulose blots.

2. Select an adult Balb/C mouse, squirt the area with 70% ethanol, and inject 0.5 ml of the emulsion intraperitoneally and subcutaneously.

3. Four weeks after the first injection inject 0.5 ml of the antigen suspended in HBSS and mixed with an equal volume of Freund's incomplete adjuvant. Emulsify before injection. On week 5, cut a little piece of the mouse tail with a sterile blade and collect 30–50 μl of blood in a Gilson tip closed at the pointed end by flaming. Massage the tail to increase the blood flow. Stop the bleeding by pressing the tail firmly for a few seconds with a tissue paper. Spray with a liquid plaster.

4. Leave the blood to coagulate and test the plasma (diluted 1:40 in HBSS).

5. Repeat injections every 2 weeks until the result of the immunization is satisfactory.

6. Usually the spleen is removed for fusion 4 to 5 days after the boost injection. To boost, inject the soluble protein (in the absence of the adjuvant) into the tail vein of the mouse.

B. PREPARATION OF MOUSE MYELOMA CELLS (P3-X63-Ag8)

Solutions

1. *Complete Dulbecco's modified Eagle's medium (DMEM):* DMEM medium supplemented with antibiotics (penicillin, 100 U/ml; streptomycin, 100 μg/ml), glutamine (2 mM) and 10% fetal calf serum (FCS). To make 500 ml mix 440 ml of DMEM medium, 5 ml of a 100× stock solution of glutamine, 5 ml of a 100× stock solution of penicillin–streptomycin, and 50 ml of FCS.

Steps

1. Grow P3-X63-Ag8 cells in several 75-cm² flasks until they reach a density of 5×10^5 cells/ml (see also article by Ariana Celis and Julio E. Celis in Volume 1).

2. The night before the fusion remove the culture supernatant by aspiration and add fresh DMEM medium.

3. The day of the fusion centrifuge the cells at 300–400 g in a bench centrifuge for 3 min and wash two times with DMEM without FCS. Resuspend at a final concentration of 2×10^6 cells/ml in DMEM without FCS and keep in the CO_2 incubator until use. You need a total of 5 ml (1×10^7 cells).

C. PREPARATION OF MOUSE MACROPHAGES

Solutions

1. *DMEM without FCS:* As in Section B but add 50 ml of sterile water instead of FCS.

Steps

1. Sacrifice an adult Balb/C mouse by cervical dislocation.

2. Disinfect the abdominal region with 70% ethanol and inject intraperitoneally 5 ml of DMEM without FCS using a 5-ml syringe connected to a 20G1 needle. Carry out the operation in the sterile hood.

3. Rock the mouse (massage the abdomen) and slowly aspirate the injected medium (Fig. 1A). Observe under a microscope and check for the presence of blood and feces. The medium should look clear.

4. Centrifuge the suspension in a bench centrifuge at 300–400 g and resuspend in 10 ml of DMEM without FCS. Count the cells in a hemocytometer (see article by Ariana Celis and Julio E. Celis in Volume 1). A total of about 1×10^7 macrophages are needed. Keep cells in a 37°C humidified 8% CO_2 incubator.

D. PREPARATION OF SPLEEN CELLS FROM THE IMMUNIZED MOUSE

Solutions

1. *DMEM without FCS:* As in Section B but add 50 ml of sterile water instead of FCS.

2. *DMEM with 20% FCS:* Prepare as described in Section B but containing 20% FCS.

3. *50× stock HAT (hypoxanthine, aminopterin, thymidine) solution:* Aliquot and keep at −20°C.

4. *DMEM-HAT:* To 500 ml of DMEM containing 20% FCS, add 10 ml of a 50× stock HAT solution.

Steps

1. Clean the left side of the immunized mice with 70% ethanol and make a lateral incision (left side, Fig. 1B).

2. Cut first the skin and then the muscle layer. The spleen is easy to localize due to its elongated shape and dark red color (Fig. 1C).

3. Remove the spleen aseptically and place it in a 60-mm tissue culture dish containing 7 ml of DMEM without serum. Trim off the adherens and wash two times with DMEM without serum.

4. Place the spleen inside a pocket of sterile gauze (6 × 6 cm) placed in a 60-mm tissue culture dish (Fig. 1D) containing 4 ml of DMEM without serum. The

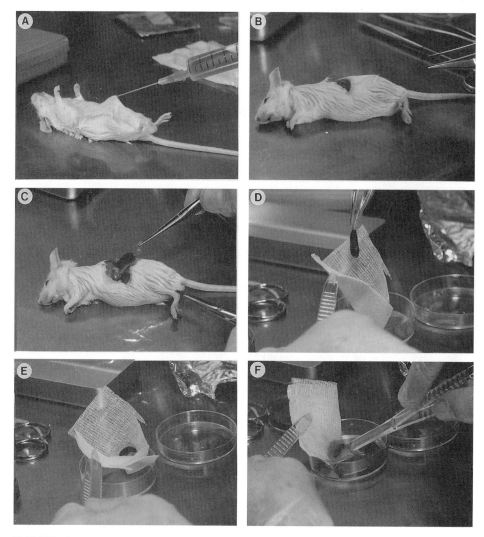

FIGURE 1 (A) Intraperitoneal injection of medium to obtain macrophages. (B, C) Surgical steps to recover the spleen. (D–F) Disaggregation of the spleen.

gauze, folded in four, is placed in aluminum foil and sterilized for 30 min in an oven at 160°C.

5. Disaggregate the tissue with the aid of the flat handle of a disposable sterile plastic forceps (Fig. 1F). Scrape gently against the tissue. Wash the gauze with 6 ml of DMEM without serum and collect the cells in a 10-ml conical centrifuge tube.

6. Wash the splenocytes once in DMEM without serum. Centrifuge the suspension for 3 min at 300–400 g and resuspend the cells at a final concentration of 2×10^7/ml in DMEM without serum. You need 5 ml (1×10^8) for the fusion. Keep the cells in the 37°C humidified 8% CO_2 incubator until use.

E. CELL FUSION

Solutions

1. *50% Polyethylene glycol (PEG):* To make 5 ml, weigh 5 g of PEG 6000 and add 5 ml of 2× HBSS. Warm carefully in a microwave oven until it melts.

The temperature should not exceed 56°C. Rock it carefully until all the particles dissolve. Allow the solution to cool and filter-sterilize. The solution should be made fresh. Keep at 37°C.

2. *2× HBSS without Ca²⁺ and Mg²⁺*: To make 100 ml, take 20 ml of 10× HBSS and complete to 100 ml. Filter-sterilize and keep at 4°C.

Steps

1. Remove the flask containing the P3-X63-Ag8 cells (5 ml, total of 1×10^7 cells) from the CO_2 incubator. Have a stopwatch ready.

2. Mix 5 ml of the spleen cell suspension (10^8 cells) with 5 ml of the P3-X-63-Ag8 cells (10^7 cells).

3. Centrifuge the suspension at 300–400 g for 2 min in a bench centrifuge.

4. Discard the supernatant by aspiration.

5. Disperse the pellet by gently tapping the tube (important), and rotate the tube to achieve a fine dispersion of the cells.

6. Add 0.6 ml of 50% PEG kept at 37°C. Rotate the tube and rock for $1\frac{1}{2}$ min at room temperature.

7. Slowly add 8 ml of DMEM–HAT (kept 37°C) and resuspend by gently pipetting up and down. Centrifuge at 300–400 g for 2 min. Aspirate the supernatant and tap the pellet gently (important).

8. Repeat step 7 twice.

9. Resuspend the pellet in 30 ml of DMEM–HAT and place in a 25-cm² tissue culture flask.

10. Centrifuge the macrophages and resuspend in 20 ml of DMEM–HAT.

11. Add the macrophages to the fused cells. Mix.

12. Transfer to a 175-cm² tissue culture flask containing 500–600 ml of DMEM-HAT.

13. Plate 0.25 ml of the cell suspension in microtiter plates (96 wells). Wrap the plates with Saran Wrap to avoid evaporation (Fig. 2A) and place in a 37°C humidified 8% CO_2 incubator.

14. It is optimal to have single colonies growing after 8–10 days (Fig. 2B). Screen the plates for the production of specific antibody using ELISA (see

 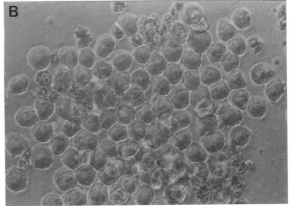

FIGURE 2 (A) Plating the fused cells in microtiter wells and mitrotiter plates wrapped in Saran Wrap. (B) Hybridoma colony.

article by Hedvig Perlmann and Peter Perlmann in this volume) or immunofluorescence (see other relevant articles in this volume).

F. CLONING BY LIMITING DILUTION

Steps

1. Count and dilute cells in DMEM–HAT to a concentration of about 300 cells per 100 ml. Shake the cell suspension to ensure homogeneous dispersion.
2. Plate 0.3 ml in 96-well microtiter plates.
3. Wrap the plates with Saran wrap and place in the 37°C humidified 8% CO_2 incubator.
4. Select wells having a single colony (Fig. 2B). Repeat cloning. Screen once again for the production of specific antibodies.
5. Expand and freeze (see article by Ariana Celis and Julio E. Celis in Volume 1).

G. DETERMINATION OF THE IMMUNOGLOBULIN SUBTYPE

Several kit-based procedures (Serotec, Amersham International, Behring Diagnostics, and others) are available commercially.

H. PRODUCTION OF ANTIBODY IN ASCITIC FLUID

Steps

1. Centrifuge exponentially growing hybridomas and resuspend in 0.5 ml of DMEM lacking serum at a concentration of 10^7 cells/ml.
2. Inject intraperitoneally 0.5 ml of the cell suspension per mouse. Observe the animals regularly.
3. Following abdominal swelling kill the animal by cervical dislocation. Disinfect the abdomen with 70% ethanol and aspirate the fluid with a syringe connected to a 20G1 needle. Work in the sterile hood.
4. Centrifuge the ascites at 300–400 g for 5 min. Store the supernatant at −80°C. Freeze the cells as described in the article by Ariana Celis and Julio E. Celis in Volume 1.
5. If the cells do not produce ascites, inject the mouse intraperitoneally with pristane (0.5 ml) 2-weeks prior to injection of the cells.

IV. Pitfalls

1. Following addition of PEG and onward, the cells are very sensitive and should be handled with care.
2. Clone hybridomas as soon as possible as they may be overgrown by nonproducing cells.
3. If the hybrids do not grow well, try another batch of fetal calf serum.

4. When cloning by limiting dilution, it is advisable to add macrophages or spleen cells to help growth.

REFERENCES

Galfre, G., Howe, S. C., Milstein, C., Butcher, G. W., and Howard, J. C. (1977) Antibodies to major histocompatibility antigens produced by hybrid cell lines. *Nature* **266,** 550–552.

Goding, J. W. (1987) "Monoclonal Antibodies: Principles and Practice," 2nd ed. Academic Press, London.

Harlow, E., and Lane, D. (1988) "Antibodies: A Laboratory Manual." Cold Spring Harbor Laboratory Press, Cold Spring Harbor, NY.

Köhler, G., and Milstein, C. (1975) Continuous cultures of fused cells secreting antibody of predefined specificity. *Nature* **256,** 495–497.

Liddel, E., and Cryer, A. (eds.) (1991) "A Practical Guide to Monoclonal Antibodies." John Wiley & Sons, Chichester.

Milstein, C. (1986) From antibody structure to immunological diversification of the immune response. *Science* **231,** 1261–1269.

Production of Human Monoclonal Antibodies via Fusion of Epstein–Barr Virus-Transformed Lymphocytes with Heteromyeloma

Miroslaw K. Gorny

I. Introduction

The generation of human monoclonal antibodies (mAbs) is a much more complex procedure than the production of mouse mAbs. Reasons for this include the scarcity of antibody (Ab)-producing cells in peripheral blood, the difficulty of obtaining blood from individuals immunized with the antigens of interest, and the instability of antibody production by fused cells or Epstein–Barr virus (EBV)-transformed cells. The present technique is based on two main methods: (1) fusion of Ab-producing cells with myeloma cells according to Kohler and Milstein (1975), and (2) transformation of human B lymphocytes by EBV (Steinitz et al., 1977). The combination of EBV transformation followed by fusion with human lymphoblastoid cells proved to be advantageous over either method alone (Kozbor et al., 1982). In our laboratory, EBV-transformed cells are fused with heteromyeloma cell lines to produce human mAbs directed against different antigens of human immunodeficiency virus type 1 (HIV-1) and parvovirus B19. Numerous mAbs have been produced that neutralize different strains of HIV-1 and B19 (Karwowska et al., 1992; Gorny et al., 1993; Arakelov et al., 1993).

II. Materials

RPMI-1640 (Cat. No. 12-167B), L-glutamine (Cat. No. 17-605A), and penicillin–streptomycin mixture (17-603A) are purchased from Bio-Whittaker. Fetal bovine serum (FBS, Cat. No. A-1111-L) is from Hyclone. HAT medium supplement (50×, hypoxanthine, aminopterin, thymidine), (Cat. No. H-0262), HT medium supplement (50×, hypoxanthine, thymidine, Cat. No. H-0137), ouabain (Cat. No. 0-5754), Histopaque 1077 (Cat. No. 1077-1), and PEG/DMSO solution (Cat. No. P-7306) are obtained from Sigma. Cyclosporin A (CsA) is on request from Sandoz. Iscove's modified Dulbecco's medium (Cat. No. 380-2440AJ) is from Gibco-BRL. Cell lines B95-8 (EBV-transformed marmoset leukocytes, Cat. No. CRL-1612) and SHM-D33 (heteromyeloma, Cat. No. CRL-1668) are purchased from the American Type Culture Collection.

Tissue culture plates [96-well flat-bottom (Cat. No. 3596), 24-well flat-bottom

(Cat. No. 3592)], 25-cm² cell culture flasks (Cat. No. 3055), and 75-cm² cell culture flasks (Cat. No. 3375) are from Costar. Nalgene disposable filters (0.45 μm, Cat. No. 245-0045) are from Nalge Company.

III. Procedures

A. SCREENING HUMAN SERA FOR ANTIBODY OF INTEREST

The serum titer is a critical factor for the generation of monoclonal antibodies from peripheral blood mononuclear cells (PBMCs). A higher titer of the antibody of interest is indicative of a greater chance for the production of mAbs. The screening system is dependent on the relevant antigen to be used. In the case of a soluble antigen, the most useful screening assay is the enzyme-linked immunosorbent assay (ELISA) system. (see also article by Hedrig Perlmann and Peter Perlmann in this volume).

B. PURIFICATION OF PBMCs FROM WHOLE BLOOD

Solutions

1. *Whole blood:* From a patient or immunized individual drawn in heparin.
2. *RPMI-1640:* Used for washing cells.
3. *Histopaque 1077:* Used for gradient centrifugation.

Steps

The procedure is based on the method of Boyum (1968).

1. Bring RPMI-1640 and Histopaque to room temperature.
2. Dilute blood in an equal volume of RPMI-1640 in a 50-ml conical tube.
3. Underlayer the diluted blood with 10 ml of Histopaque.
4. Centrifuge at 900 g for 30 min at room temperature. Do not use the break on the centrifuge at the end of the spin.
5. Aspirate the mononuclear cells, which are located at the interface between the plasma and the Histopaque solution, using a 10-ml pipette.
6. Wash the cells three times with RPMI-1640 by centrifugation at 400 g for 10 min, and resuspend the PBMCs in the medium designated for EBV transformation.

C. TRANSFORMATION OF PBMCs BY EBV

Solutions

1. *B95-8 culture supernatant:* B95-8 marmoset cell lines, established by Miller *et al.* (1972), release virus into the culture supernatant which is then used as the source of EBV. Grow the B95-8 cells in tissue culture flasks at 1×10^5 cells/ml at 37°C. After 10 days, centrifuge the culture supernatant at 400 g for 15 min to spin out the cells. Filter the supernatant through a 0.45-μm pore filter. Aliquot this EBV stock in tubes at a volume of 5 ml and store at −80°C. Use each virus stock only once, as repeated freezing and thawing inactivate EBV.

2. *Cyclosporin A:* CsA is used to suppress EBV-specific cytotoxic T cells which may eliminate EBV-transformed cells in culture *in vitro.* Prepare a stock solution by dissolving CsA powder in grade alcohol at 1 mg/ml.

3. *Complete medium:* Supplement RPMI-1640 with 2 mM L-glutamine, 100 IU/ml penicillin, 100 μg/ml streptomycin, and 15% fetal bovine serum.

Steps

1. Suspend the PBMCs to a concentration of 2×10^6 cells/ml in B95-8 culture supernatant that has been diluted 1:2 with complete medium.

2. Culture the PBMCs with the B95-8 overnight at 37°C.

3. Centrifuge the PBMCs the next day and resuspend the cell pellets in complete medium supplemented with CsA at 0.5 μg/ml.

4. Plate the PBMCs in 96-well flat-bottom plates at 8×10^4 cells per well.

5. Culture the cells for 3 weeks. Feed the cultures once per week by replacing half of the supernatant in each well with fresh complete medium. Note that CsA is added at the beginning of culture.

6. Proliferating transformed colonies of B lymphocytes can be seen in the wells after 1 week using an inverted microscope. After 2 weeks large clumps of cells are macroscopically visible.

Screening Plates

7. After 3 weeks of culture, screen the supernatants from each well by ELISA (see also article by Hedvig Perlmann and Peter Perlmann in this volume) for the presence of desired IgG antibodies.

8. Transfer B lymphoblastoid cells (LCLs) producing IgG Abs from the 96-well plates to 24-well flat-bottom tissue culture plates and resuspend in 1 ml of complete medium; transfer each well separately.

9. Culture the cells for 1 week; screen the wells by ELISA for antibody activity against specific antigens as well as bovine serum albumin (BSA). Activity against BSA indicates nonspecific binding.

10. Pool together from the different wells cells that are producing IgG antibodies against a specific antigen but not against BSA. To prepare these cells for fusion, culture them for 2 days at a concentration of 1×10^6 cells/ml in T-25 tissue culture flasks. If the total number of LCLs is not sufficient for fusion ($<1 \times 10^6$ cells) then expand the cells for 1–2 weeks further. Measure the antibody activity of these cells once again before fusing.

D. FUSION OF LCLs WITH THE HETEROMYELOMA SHM-D33

Solutions

1. *PEG/DMSO solution for cell fusion.*

2. *Ouabain:* Prepare a 10^{-3} M stock solution by dissolving 0.0584 g ouabain in 100 ml RPMI-1640 and store in 1-ml aliquots at −20°C.

3. *Selection medium:* To make 100 ml, add to complete medium 4 ml of HAT and 200 μl of ouabain stock solution. HAT kills unfused SHM-D33 cells, whereas ouabain kills unfused lymphoblastoid cells.

Cells

1. Use mouse peritoneal washed cells (PWCs) as a feeder layer for the fused cells. Inject 4 ml of RPMI-1640 intraperitoneally into a euthanized BALB/c mouse. Aspirate the peritoneal fluid (approximately 3 ml), transfer to a tube, and spin down the PWCs by centrifugation at 200 g for 10 min. Resuspend the pellet in selection medium at 1×10^5 cells/ml and plate in a 96-well microplate at a final concentration of 1×10^4 PWCs per well.

2. SHM-D33 is a mouse $\times$ human heteromyeloma cell line established by Teng *et al.* (1983). These cells grow as a monolayer in Iscove's modified Dulbecco's medium supplemented as complete medium.

Steps

1. Twenty-four hours prior to fusion, split the SHM-D33 cells to obtain logarithmic growth.

2. Wash the LCLs and SHM-D33 cells three times in RPMI-1640 without serum by centrifugation at 200 g for 10 min.

3. Mix the LCLs and SHM-D33 cells at a ratio of 1:3 and centrifuge to a pellet.

4. Disrupt the cell pellet by gently shaking the tube. Add 1 ml of the warm 37°C PEG/DMSO solution dropwise for 1 min. Continue stirring the cells 1 min longer.

5. Dilute the cells slowly by adding 9 ml of prewarmed RPMI-1640. Centrifuge the cells at 200 g for 10 min.

6. Resuspend the cells in complete medium at 8×10^5 cells/ml. Plate the cells in 96-well flat-bottom culture plates in 100 μl at 8×10^4 cells per well.

7. The next day, add 100 μl of selection medium containing 1×10^4 PWCs to each well.

8. Feed the cells twice per week with selection medium supplemented with HAT but without ouabain.

9. Screen the plates after 2–3 weeks by ELISA for the production of the antibody of interest. Expand the hybrids that are producing reactive IgG Abs in complete medium, supplemented with HT, to 24-well plates; expand each well separately.

10. After 1–2 weeks, screen the expanded hybrids once again for the production of specific Abs (activity to relevant antigen versus BSA). Quantitate the human IgG in the culture supernatant from these "positive" wells.

E. CLONING OF HYBRIDS

Cloning allows the selection of stable hybrid cells producing specific antibody and establishes a monoclonal cell line by growing cells from wells that had been seeded with one hybrid cell.

Cells

1. GK5 cells, human myeloma cells (Satoh *et al.*, 1983) kindly provided by Dr. M. V. Haspel, were used as feeder cells during cloning. These cells grow in suspension in complete medium. For cloning purposes, irradiate the cells with 5000 rads just prior to use. *Note:* Besides GK-5, other various cells can be used

as a feeder layer. One of these alternatives is irradiated PBMCs from healthy donors.

Steps

1. Plate 100 μl of irradiated GK5 cells in a 96-well microtiter plate at 2×10^4 cells per well.

2. The next day, add 100 μl of hybrid cells suspended in complete medium to the GK5 feeder layer. Plate the hybrid cells at concentrations of 100 cells/well (1×10^3 cells/ml) and 10 cells/well (1×10^2 cells/ml).

3. Culture the plates for 2–3 weeks. At this point, the wells should be half-confluent with growing hybrids. Feed the cells once per week with complete medium.

4. Screen the cells for the production of specific antibodies and expand the cells "positive" for specific antibody to 24-well plates; expand each well separately.

5. After 1 week of expansion screen the supernatants from the 24-well plates for antibody activity. Determine the IgG concentration in the cultures highly positive for antibody activity. Clone the best antibody-producing hybrids at 10 and 1 cell per well.

6. Repeat the screening and expanding process once again. Clone the best culture in terms of Ab production and IgG concentration at 1 cell/well.

7. Expand into flasks the cells with the highest antibody activity and IgG level that came from one well after successive cloning at 1 cell/well. Store 10 vials of cells in liquid nitrogen.

8. Characterize the mAbs by IgG subclass, light chain type, affinity, and epitope.

IV. Pitfalls

1. Weak EBV transformation (very small or no LCL clumps after 3 weeks of culture) may occur because of an inactive source of EBV (B95-8 supernatant), from incorrect storage or a low immortalization titer of EBV, or because of mycoplasma contamination of the B95-8 cell line.

2. There may be only a small number of wells containing IgG Abs because the titer of serum Abs to the required antigen is low or because the patient received cytotoxic or immunosuppressive drugs.

3. Unstable secretion of Abs is a common problem characteristic of LCLs. "Positive" results after the first screening could be due to the polyclonal activation of nontransformed B lymphocytes.

4. Failure of hybrid growth after HAT selection may be the result of mycoplasma contamination of the heteromyeloma cell line.

5. Failure of cell growth during cloning may be caused by delayed cloning of the primary culture, resulting in overgrowth of nonproducing cells.

REFERENCES

Arakelov, S., Gorny, M. K., Williams, C., Riggin, C. H., Brady, F., Collett, M. S., and Zolla-Pazner, S. (1993) Generation of human monoclonal antibodies derived from HIV-infected patients that neutralize human B19 parvovirus. *J. Infect. Dis.* **168,** 580.

Boyum, A. (1968) Isolation of mononuclear cells and granulocytes from human blood. *Scand. J. Clin. Lab. Invest.* **21,** 77.

Gorny, M. K., Xu, J., Karwowska, S., Buchbinder, A., and Zolla-Pazner, S. (1993) Repertoire of neutralizing human monoclonal antibodies specific for the V3 domain of HIV-1 gp120. *J. Immunol.* **150,** 635.

Karwowska, S., Gorny, M. K., Buchbinder, A., Gianakakos, V., Williams, C., Fuerst, T., and Zolla-Pazner, S. (1992) Production of human monoclonal antibodies specific for conformational and linear non-V3 epitopes of gp120. *AIDS Res. Hum. Retrovir.* **8,** 1099.

Kohler, G., and Milstein, C. (1975) Continuous culture of fused cells secreting antibodies of defined specificity. *Nature* **256,** 495.

Kozbor, D., Lagarde, A., and Roder, J. (1982) Human hybridomas constructed with antigen-specific, EBV-transformed cell lines. *Proc. Natl. Acad. Sci. USA* **79,** 6651.

Miller, G., Shope, T., Lisro, H., Stitt, D., and Lipman, M. (1972) Epstein–Barr virus: Transformation, cytopathic changes and viral antigens in squirrel, monkey and marmoset leukocytes. *Proc. Natl. Acad. Sci. USA* **69,** 383.

Satoh, J., Prabhakar, B. S., Haspel, M. V., Ginzberg-Fellner, F., and Notkins, A. L. (1983) Human monoclonal autoantibodies that react with multiple endocrine organs. *N. Engl. J. Med.* **309,** 217.

Steinitz, M., Klein, G., Koskimies, S., and Makel, O. (1977) EB virus induced B lymphocyte cells lines producing specific antibody. *Nature* **269,** 420.

Teng, N. N., Lam, K. S., Riera, F. C., and Kaplan, H. S. (1983) Construction and testing of mouse–human heteromyelomas for human monoclonal antibody production. *Proc. Natl. Acad. Sci. USA* **80,** 7308.

Rapid Production of Antibodies in Chicken and Isolation from Eggs

Harri Kokko, Ilpo Kuronen, and Sirpa Kärenlampi

I. Introduction

Rabbits were preferred as producers of polyclonal antibodies; however, by 1962 it was found that immunoglobulin concentration in the yolk is equal to or greater than that found in hen serum (Patterson *et al.*, 1962). Today, hens are recognized as convenient and inexpensive sources of antibodies. According to an increasing number of publications, the antibodies produced in hens are useful in many applications, including immunotherapy and immunodiagnostics (Schade *et al.*, 1991; Akita and Nakai, 1992). The increasing preference of hens as antibody producers is partly based on the development of efficient methods for the purification of antibodies from egg yolk (Jensenius *et al.*, 1981; Akita and Nakai, 1992, 1993). In some cases, hens as more distant relatives of mammals, offer a good alternative to rabbits in producing antibodies against mammalian antigens (Stuart *et al.*, 1988).

We have produced in hens antibodies against several different types of antigens, e.g., proteins, synthetic peptides (Kokko and Kärenlampi, 1992; Kuronen *et al.*, 1993), plant viruses, and fungal and bacterial cell walls. According to our experience, hens are very effective producers of specific antibodies. With the protocol described in this article, antibodies can be recovered from egg yolks of an immunized hen in amounts corresponding to 300 ml of high-titer rabbit antiserum per month. Specific antibodies can be isolated from egg yolks 2 weeks after the first immunization. Antibody production continues for at least 100 days.

II. Materials and Instrumentation

Freund's complete (Cat. No. F-4258) and incomplete (Cat. No. F-5506) adjuvants, Trizma base (Cat. No. T-1503), and *p*-nitrophenyl phosphate, sodium salt, Sigma104 (Cat. No. 104-0) are from Sigma. Alkaline phosphatase-labeled anti-chicken IgG (AP-anti-chicken IgG, Cat. No. 61-3122) is from Zymed Laboratories. Dextran sulfate, sodium salt (MW ≈ 500,000, Cat. No. 17-0340-01) is from Pharmacia. Anhydrous Na_2SO_4 (Cat. No. 6649), $CaCl_2 \cdot 2H_2O$ (Cat. No. 2382), NaCl (Cat. No. 6604), $MgCl_2 \cdot 6H_2O$ (Cat. No. 5833), $Na_2HPO_4 \cdot 2H_2O$ (Cat. No. 6580), KH_2PO_4 (Cat. No. 4873), and 25% glutaraldehyde solution (Cat. No. 4239) are from Merck (Darmstadt, Germany). Fat-free milk powder (food grade) is from the local grocery store.

Water is purified by a Milli-Q apparatus. Dialysis tubing with 12-kDa molecular weight cutoff (Spectra/Por 4, Cat. No. 3787-D22) is provided by Spectrum. The 96-well vinyl assay plates (ELISA plates, Cat. No. 2596) are purchased from Costar. The ELISA reader is from SLT Labinstruments (Grödig, Austria).

III. Procedures

A. IMMUNIZATION OF HENS

Steps

1. House the hens in individual cages to avoid mixing of the eggs.

2. You may want to use an assistant in the handling of the hen (Fig. 1). Grab the hen with your left hand from the back by locking the wings. With the right hand, grab the feet. Put the hen on the table and move your left hand over its head. In this position, the hen is calm and easy to immunize. Let your assistant do the immunization. You can also immunize the hen by yourself. Lift the hen from the back with your right hand. Grab the feet with the left hand. Push the hen's head under your left arm. Immunize with your right hand.

3. For the primary immunization, dilute the antigen (maximal concentration of

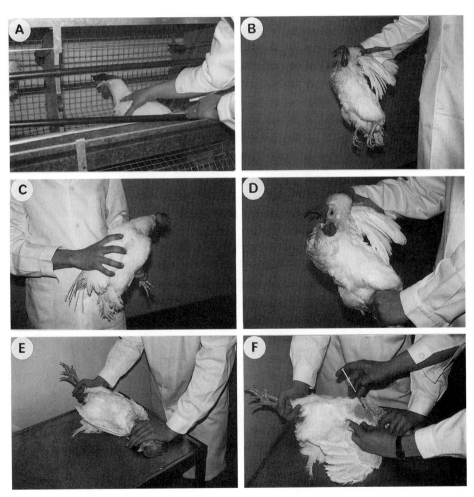

FIGURE 1   Immunization of chicken.

the adjuvant is 50% v/v) in Freund's complete adjuvant and emulsify in an Eppendorf tube using a syringe with an 18- to 21-G needle.

4. Give one to two injections of the antigen emulsion into the pectoralis muscles of the hen (see Fig. 1). The maximal volume to one muscle is about 500 μl. The injected amount (10–1000 μg) depends on the type of the antigen.

5. Repeat the immunization every 2 to 4 weeks by the same procedure but using Freund's incomplete adjuvant as an emulsifier.

6. Collect the eggs daily. Label the eggs with an identification number and date using a waterproof pen and store the eggs refrigerated at +4°C until the isolation of the immunoglobulins. Yolk antibodies are stable *in situ* in the refrigerator for at least 1 year.

B. ISOLATION OF EGG IMMUNOGLOBULINS

Several different methods have been published for the isolation of immunoglobulins from eggs. Two alternative methods are provided here. The dextran sulfate method (Section B1), modified from Jensenius *et al.* (1981), is classical and works well. The water dilution method (Section B2), adapted from Akita and Nakai (1993), is simpler and less expensive. In the few cases where it has been applied so far, it has given good results.

1. Dextran Sulfate Method

This method is modified from that of Jensenius *et al.* (1981).

Solutions

1. *10× TBS (Tris-buffered saline) stock solution:* To make 1 liter of 1.4 M NaCl–100 mM Tris–HCl solution, add 81.82 g of NaCl and 12.11 g of Trizma base to approximately 900 ml of purified water, adjust pH to 7.4 with 6 M HCl, and bring to a total volume of 1 liter with purified water. Store at room temperature. Dilute 1:10 with purified water before use.

2. *10% (w/v) Dextran sulfate solution:* To make 100 ml, solubilize 10 g of dextran sulfate in purified water and adjust to a total volume of 100 ml. Store at room temperature. Discard the solution if it is cloudy after prolonged storage.

3. *1 M Calcium chloride solution:* To make 100 ml, solubilize 14.7 g of $CaCl_2 \cdot 2H_2O$ in purified water and adjust to a total volume of 100 ml. Store at room temperature.

4. *36% (w/v) Sodium sulfate solution:* To make 100 ml, solubilize 36 g of anhydrous Na_2SO_4 in purified water and adjust to a total volume of 100 ml. Store at room temperature. If precipitates appear, make a fresh solution.

5. *10× PBS (phosphate-buffered saline) stock solution:* To make 2 liters, dissolve 136 g of NaCl, 37.6 g $Na_2HPO_4 \cdot 2H_2O$, and 4 g of KH_2PO_4 to purified water and bring to a total volume of 2 liters. Store at room temperature. Dilute 1:10 with purified water before use.

FIGURE 2   Separation of egg yolk from the white.

Steps

Carry out the entire procedure at room temperature.

1. Separate the egg yolk from the white (Fig. 2).

2. Add 1× TBS on the yolk to bring the volume to 50 ml and mix. (From this mixture you can take a small sample, dilute it 1:100 with 2% MP–TBS, and titer the antibody in ELISA or Western blot.)

3. Centrifuge the diluted yolk for 10 min at 2000 g. Discard the pellet and save the supernatant.

4. Mix the supernatant with 3 ml of 10% dextran sulfate solution and 7.5 ml of 1 M calcium chloride solution and incubate for 30 min. Centrifuge as before. If the resulting supernatant is cloudy, add an additional 1 to 3 ml of dextran sulfate solution and recentrifuge. Save the clear supernatant.

5. Slowly add solid sodium sulfate (a total of 20 g/100 ml) to the supernatant and incubate for 20 min. Centrifuge as before. Save the pellet.

6. Dissolve the pellet in 10 ml of 1× TBS. Separate the dissolved immunoglobulins from nondissolved material by centrifugation for 10 min at 2000 g. Save the clear supernatant.

7. Add 6.2 ml of 36% sodium sulfate solution to the supernatant. Centrifuge as before and save the pellet.

8. Dissolve the immunoglobulin pellet in 5 ml of 1× TBS or 1× PBS.

9. Dialyze the immunoglobulin solution at +4°C overnight with constant stirring against 1 liter of 1× TBS or 1× PBS in Spectra/Por 4 dialysis tubing.

10. Repeat step 9 once.

11. Divide the dialyzed immunoglobulin solution into small aliquots and store at −20°C. Immunoglobulins can also be stored at +4°C for short periods. Lyophilized preparations can be stored at +4°C for several years.

2. Water Dilution Method

This method is adapted from Akita and Nakai (1993).

Solutions

1. *10× TBS:* See Section B1.

2. *10× PBS:* See Section B1.

Steps

1. Separate the egg yolk from the white carefully to avoid breaking the yolk and rinse it once with purified water (see Fig. 2).

2. Dilute the yolk by adding 9 vol of purified water (i.e., one yolk to about 100 ml). Adjust the pH to 5.0–5.2 with 1 M HCl (about 1 ml) and incubate for 6 hr at +4°C without shaking.

3. Centrifuge for 25 min at 10,000 g at +4°C. Save the supernatant.

4. Add solid sodium sulfate (a total of 20 g/100 ml) to the supernatant which has been prewarmed to room temperature. Incubate for 20 min at room temperature. Centrifuge for 20 min at 2000 g. Save the pellet.

5. Dissolve the pellet in 5 to 10 ml of 1× TBS or 1× PBS, depending on the intended use of your antibody.

6. You may further purify the immunoglobulins by ultrafiltration, alcohol precipitation, ion-exchange chromatography, gel chromatography, affinity chromatography, etc.

C. TITERING OF THE ANTIBODY

Solutions

1. *10× Tris–NaCl buffer stock solution, pH 9.5:* To make 100 ml of 1 M Tris–1 M NaCl, dissolve 12.11 g of Trizma base and 5.84 g of NaCl to 90 ml of purified water. Adjust the pH to 9.5 with 6 M HCl and bring to a total volume of 100 ml. Store at room temperature.

2. *200× MgCl$_2$ stock solution:* To make 100 ml of 1 M MgCl$_2$, add 20.33 g of MgCl$_2$·6H$_2$O to 100 ml of purified water. Store at room temperature.

3. *Alkaline phosphatase substrate solution (1 mg of p-nitrophenyl phosphate/ml of 100 mM Tris, 100 mM NaCl, 5 mM MgCl$_2$, pH 9.5):* Weigh 10 mg of p-nitrophenyl phosphate; add 1 ml of 10× Tris–NaCl buffer stock solution and 50 μl of 200× MgCl$_2$ stock solution and bring to a total volume of 10 ml with purified water. Prepare just before use.

4. *0.5% (v/v) Glutaraldehyde solution:* To make 10 ml, dilute 200 μl of 25% glutaraldehyde solution to 10 ml with purified water. Prepare just before use.

5. *10× TBS:* See Section B1.

6. *2% Fat-free milk powder (MP–TBS):* To make 50 ml, dissolve 1 g of fat-free milk powder into 50 ml of 1× TBS. This solution is stable for 1 day.

Steps

Carry out the entire procedure at room temperature. You may use a plate shaker for the incubations.

1. Treat the ELISA plate by adding 50 μl of 0.5% (v/v) glutaraldehyde in each well for 0.5 hr to improve the binding of a peptide antigen. For other antigens, you may need other methods (follow the instructions of ELISA plate manufacturers; see also article by Hedvig Perlman and Peter P. Perlman in this volume); (Harlow and Lane, 1988). Wash the wells with 200 μl of 1× TBS. Shake the solution off the plate. Dry the plate by pressing against a paper towel.

2. For binding of the antigen, add the antigen in a volume of 50 μl (in case of

peptide antigen, 1 μg of peptide/50 μl of 1× TBS) in each well and incubate for at least 1 hr (you may incubate the plate overnight). Remove the solution.

3. For blocking, add 250 μl of 2% MP–TBS and incubate for 0.5 hr. Wash with 250 μl of 1× TBS.

4. Add the immunoglobulin solution (yolk preparation from Section B1, step 2, diluted 1:100 with 2% MP–TBS) in a volume of 50 μl, incubate for 2 hr, and wash thoroughly (five times) with 1× TBS.

5. Add 50 μl of the second antibody (AP-anti-chicken IgG, 1:1000 dilution in 2% MP–TBS) and incubate for 1 to 2 hr. Wash the wells five times with 1× TBS.

6. For developing, add 150 μl of alkaline phosphatase substrate solution and incubate for 10 to 20 min. Stop the reaction by adding 50 μl of 0.1 M NaOH and measure the absorbance at 405 nm with an ELISA reader.

IV. Comments

All antigens are unique and elicit different responses. Peptides and haptens require binding to a carrier protein (BSA, ovalbumin) to become sufficiently antigenic. The response may also depend on the animal species or individual that is immunized. Therefore, only general instructions can be given as to the amount of antigen that should be used in the immunization (see further details from Harlow and Lane, 1988).

When producing antibodies against synthetic peptides representing a known protein, it is useful to screen first the protein for hydrophilicity and antigenicity indexes by a suitable computer program (commercially available sequence analysis software can be obtained from, e.g., GCG, PROSIS, and Intelligenetics).

Hens produce useful antibodies 2 weeks after the first immunization. The response does not necessarily rise dramatically after the second or third immunization, as happens in rabbits. This suggests that in chicken the booster immunizations mainly maintain the IgY production elicited by the primary immunization.

The antigen response can be tested by several methods. Different types of antigens (proteins, peptides, haptens, bacterial and viral particles, etc.) require their own method of binding to the immobilizing surface (ELISA plate, dot blot, Western blot). For details, see Harlow and Lane (1988). The binding of peptide antigens to an ELISA plate can be improved by glutaraldehyde.

The immunoglobulin concentration can be determined using an approximate A_{280} value of 1.4 as equal to 1 mg immunoglobulin/ml. By following the technique in Section B1, approximately 100 to 190 mg of immunoglobulin per egg can be recovered.

V. Pitfalls

1. Glycoproteins are good immunogens and often give rise to antibodies with nonspecific cross-reactivity.

2. Every egg should be regarded as an individual. There is a great day-to-day variation and successive eggs may contain very different amounts of the specific antibody. Therefore, it is important to screen (titer) all the eggs before pooling the antibody preparations.

3. All lipids (cloudiness) should be removed carefully by dextran sulfate (see Section B1, step 4). The immunoglobulin yield will otherwise decrease dramatically.

4. No specific binding proteins are available for chicken immunoglobulins (protein A and protein G do not bind IgY).

5. If you want to label your antibody via amino groups, remove all other reactive substances like Tris (TBS) or sodium azide (preservative). You may dissolve the final precipitate (see Section B1, step 8) in PBS instead of TBS.

REFERENCES

Akita, E. M., and Nakai, S. (1992) Immunoglobulins from egg yolk: Isolation and purification. *J. Food Sci.* **57**, 629–634.

Akita, E. M., and Nakai, S. (1993) Comparison of four purification methods for the production of immunoglobulins from eggs laid by hens immunized with an enterotoxigenic *E. coli* strain. *J. Immunol. Methods* **160**, 207–214.

Harlow, E., and Lane, D. (1988) "Antibodies, A Laboratory Manual." Cold Spring Harbor Laboratory Press, Cold Spring Harbor, NY.

Jensenius, J. C., Andersen, I., Hau, J., Crone, M., and Koch, K. (1981) Eggs: Conveniently packaged antibodies. Methods for purification of yolk IgG. *J. Immunol. Methods* **46**, 63–68.

Kokko, H., and Kärenlampi, S. O. (1992) Antibody from hen's eggs against a conserved sequence of the gametophytic self-incompatibility proteins of plants. *Anal. Biochem.* **201**, 311–318.

Kuronen, I., Kokko, H., and Parviainen, M. (1993) Production of monoclonal and polyclonal antibodies against human osteocalcin sequences and development of a two-site ELISA for intact human osteocalcin. *J. Immunol. Methods* **163**, 233–240.

Patterson, R., Youngner, J. S., Weigle, W. O., and Dixon, F. J. (1962) Antibody production and transfer to egg yolk in chickens. *J. Immunol.* **89**, 272–278.

Schade, R., Pfister, C., Halatsch, R., and Henklein, P. (1991) Polyclonal IgY antibodies from chicken egg yolk—An alternative to the production of mammalian IgG type antibodies in rabbits. *ATLA Alternatives Lab. Anim.* **19**, 403–419.

Stuart, C. A., Pietrzyk, R. A., Furlanetto, R. W., and Green, A. (1988) High affinity antibody from hen's eggs directed against the human insulin receptor and the human IGF-I receptor. *Anal. Biochem.* **173**, 142–150.

SECTION B

Purification and Labeling of Immunoglobulins

Purification of Immunoglobulins

Christian Huet

I. Introduction

Purification of immunoglobulins is recommended when one wants to achieve good quality in immunocytochemistry and is necessary when one wants to prepare antibodies labeled with either fluorochromes, enzymes, or electron-dense reagents. The purification of antibodies may be performed at two levels. Either one needs to obtain the bulk fraction of immunoglobulins or highly purified monospecific antibodies have to be obtained by affinity purification.

The immunoglobulin fraction is obtained by salt precipitation or on an ion-exchange resin. The affinity purification presented here may be used to purify either the antigen (using purified immunoglobulins) or the antibody (if the purified antigen is available).

II. Materials and Instrumentation

Glycerol (Cat. No. 4095) from Merck

Plastic syringes, 1 ml (Cat. No. BS-01T) and 2 ml (Cat. No. BS-H2S) from Terumo Europe NV

DE-52 preswollen anion exchanger from Whatmann

Ultrogel AcA 22 and ACT-Ultrogel AcA 22 (Cat. Nos. 230 121 and 249 203) from Sepracor

Sephadex G-50 (Cat. No. 17 0045 01) and CNBr–Sepharose 4B (Cat. No. 17 04 30 01) from Pharmacia

Ammonium chloride (Cat. No. A-4915), sodium azide (Cat. No. S-2002), sodium bicarbonate (Cat. No. S-6014), sodium chloride (Cat. No. S-9625), lysine (Cat. No. L-6001), $K_2HPO_4 \cdot 3H_2O$ (Cat. No. P-5504), and KH_2PO_4 (Cat. No. P-5379) from Sigma

Glutaraldehyde EM grade (Cat. No. G 003) from TAAB

Instamed phosphate-buffered saline (Cat. No. L 182-10) prepared by Seromed

III. Procedures

A. PRECIPITATION OF IMMUNOGLOBULINS WITH AMMONIUM SULFATE

Solutions

1. *Antiserum.*
2. *$(NH_4)_2 SO_4$-saturated solution:* 53.1 g $(NH_4)_2 SO_4$/100 ml saturated solution at 20°C.

---

3. *1 M K₂HPO₄·3H₂O:* 228.2 g/liter H₂O.

4. *1 M KH₂PO₄:* 136.1 g/liter H₂O.

5. *1 M KH₂PO₄/K₂HPO₄, pH 7.8:* Mix 8.5 vol of 1 M KH₂PO₄ with 91.5 vol of 1 M K₂HPO₄. Check the pH before use.

6. *1 M KH₂PO₄/K₂HPO₄, pH 7.4:* Mix 19 vol of 1 M KH₂PO₄ with 81 vol of 1 M K₂HPO₄. Check the pH before use.

Steps

1. Spin the antiserum at 10,000 rpm for 10 min to clear the serum.

2. Cool the serum on an ice bucket.

3. Keep the serum at 4°C under constant agitation with a magnetic stirrer.

4. Slowly add dropwise the saturated solution of ammonium sulfate to a final concentration of 40% saturation. This should be done in about 30 min (volume of ammonium sulfate added = 0.66 × volume of serum).

5. Let solution sit for 1 hr on ice.

6. Spin at 10,000 rpm for 10 min at 4°C and save the pellet.

7. Dissolve the precipitate in about half of the initial volume of the serum.

8. Dialyze against 2 liters PBS for 2 days (four changes) or against 10 mM phosphate buffer (pH 7.8) if the purification is to be continued on a DE-52 column.

9. Measure the absorbance at 280 nm. The absorbance of a 1% (w/v) IgG solution is 14.0. Usually a 1:20 dilution in PBS is convenient.

$$\text{total mg protein} = \frac{A_{280} \times \text{dilution} \times \text{volume}}{1.4}$$

10. Continue purification or store at −20°C in 50% glycerol.

B. PURIFICATION ON DEAE COLUMN

Solutions

1. *1 M KH₂PO₄/K₂HPO₄, pH 7.8.*

2. *1 mM KH₂PO₄/K₂HPO₄, pH 7.8.*

3. *PBS 10× stock solution:* Dissolve one flask of Seromed PBS powder in 1 liter distilled water.

4. *1% NaN₃:* Dissolve 0.5 g NaN₃ in 50 ml distilled water. Store at 4°C.

5. *DE-52 preswollen anion exchanger.*

6. *1 M NaCl:* Dissolve 5.8 g in 100 ml distilled water.

Steps

1. Stir the resin with 1 M KP$_i$, pH 7.8, for about 15 min. About 15–30 ml of buffer is used for every dry gram of cellulose or about 6 ml per gram of wet anion-exchange exchanger.

2. Adjust the pH to 7.8 while stirring with 1 M K₂HPO₄.

3. Allow the slurry to settle and decant the supernatant containing the fines. The stock resin can be stored at 4°C in the presence of 0.01% azide.

4. Pack the resin in a plastic syringe (nothing fancy): 1 ml packed volume of DEAE can adsorb 10–20 mg of immunoglobulins, or 2.5 ml DEAE can retain immunoglobulins from 1 ml of serum. Column volume = mg protein/15.

5. Wash the column with 10 vol of 10 mM KP$_i$, pH 7.8.

6. Allow the serum or ammonium sulfate-precipitated IgG to run through the resin column.

7. Elute the column with 10 mM KP$_i$. Discard the dead volume (V_0 = one-third of the column volume) and collect 1.5 the volume of the column.

8. Read the OD of the fractions and pool all fractions having an OD higher than 0.2.

9. Elute with salt. For mouse or guinea pig serum, use 70 mM NaCl in 10 mM KP$_i$, and for rabbit serum, 40 mM NaCl in 10 mM KP$_i$.

10. Read the OD of the fractions and pool all fractions having an OD higher than 0.2.

11. Dialyze against PBS. If necessary concentrate the pooled fraction by dialyzing against PBS–50% glycerol. Store at 4°C in 0.01% sodium azide or at −20°C in 50% glycerol.

C. IMMUNOADSORBENT PREPARATION AND AFFINITY PURIFICATION

Solutions

Gel Activation with Glutaraldehyde

1. *1 M KP$_i$, pH 7.4.*

2. *25% Glutaraldehyde stock solution.*

3. *1% NaN$_3$:* Dissolve 0.5 g NaN$_3$ in 50 ml distilled water. Store at 4°C.

Coupling the Protein to the Gel (Glutaraldehyde as Crosslinker)

1. *0.1 M KP$_i$, pH 7.4.*

2. *Protein solution:* 2–5 mg/ml in phosphate buffer.

Coupling the Protein to Sepharose 4B (Cyanogen as Crosslinker)

1. *1 M NaCO$_3$:* Dissolve 8.4 g in 100 distilled water.

2. *1 M Lysine:* Dissolve 1 g of lysine in 10 ml water.

3. *1 mM HCl.*

4. *1 M NaCl:* Dissolve 5.8 g in 100 ml distilled water.

5. *1 M CH$_3$ COONa/HCl, pH 4:* 1 M CH$_3$COONa is made by dissolving 27.22 g in 200 ml water. To 50 ml of 1 M CH$_3$COONa, add 40 ml of 1 N HCl solution, made up to 250 ml.

Affinity Purification

1. *PBS.*

2. *1 M K$_2$PO$_4$.*

3. *1 N HCl/2 M lysine buffer:* To make 2 M lysine, dissolve 2 g of lysine in 20 ml of water. Add the lysine slowly to the HCl, measuring the pH until it reaches 2.2.

Steps

Gel Activation with Glutaraldehyde

We present this step here although activated gels are commercially available. If you obtained such an activated gel go to step 1 under Coupling the Protein to Act Ultrogel AcA 22.

1. Wash AcA 22 Ultrogel on a Buchner funnel, porosity C, with double-distilled water (10–20 vol).

2. Wash the gel with 0.1 M KP$_i$ buffer, pH 7.4.

3. Activate the gel by mixing 20 parts gel, 10 parts 0.1 M KP$_i$, pH 7.4, 20 parts 25% glutaraldehyde, and 50 parts H$_2$O in a flask. Keep rotating the flask at 37°C for 18 hr or at 4°C for 48 hr.

4. Remove the flask from agitator, let it sit for a while, then remove the fines generated during incubation. Add 2 vol double-distilled H$_2$O to the gel, mix, and remove the fines (repeat three times).

5. Wash the gel with double-distilled H$_2$O thoroughly (i.e., until you do not smell the glutaraldehyde at all).

6. Add NaN$_3$ (to 0.01%) to the washed activated gel and store in a 50-ml tube in the cold. If you want to store for a long period (over a month) add 0.1% glutaraldehyde to the beads.

Coupling the Protein to Act Ultrogel AcA 22 (Glutaraldehyde as Crosslinker)

1. The concentration of dialyzed protein in 0.1 M KP$_i$ must be 2–4 mg/ml.

2. Wash the gel with 0.1 M KP$_i$ buffer thoroughly (i.e., you do not smell glutaraldehyde at all).

3. Mix equal volumes of protein and gel, incubate at 37°C for 18 hr (or at 4°C for 48 hr) and keep rotating.

4. Spin the beads 100 g for 2 min. Remove and save supernatant for step 5.

5. Wash the uncoupled protein from the gel with 10 vol PBS at room temperature. Combine the supernantants and calculate coupling efficiency.

6. Add equal volume of 0.1 M lysine in PBS, pH 7.4, to the protein-coupled gel and incubate at 37°C (keep rotating) for at least 2 hr.

7. Wash the gel with PBS at room temperature.

Coupling the Protein to CNBr-Activated Sepharose 4B (Cyanogen Bromide as Crosslinker)

You can use Sepharose 4B that has been activated with cyanogen bromide, a ready-to-use stabilized derivative.

1. Weigh out the required amount of CNBr-activated Sepharose 4B (1 g gives about a 3.5-ml packed column).

2. Wash and reswell on a Büchner funnel (porosity 6) with 200 ml of 1 mM HCl per gram of Sepharose powder.

3. Dissolve protein or peptide to be coupled in 0.2 M NaHCO$_3$, 0.5 M NaCl, pH 8.5.

4. Wash with the coupling buffer.

5. Mix protein solution (use 1–10 mg of antigen/ml of gel) with gel suspension and incubate for 2 hr at room temperature and then overnight under agitation (rotate, do not stir).

6. Spin out beads (100 g for 2 min) and remove supernatant.

7. Wash uncoupled protein from beads with 10 vol of coupling buffer.

8. Combine supernatants and read the OD$_{280}$. Calculate coupling efficency.

9. Block free unreacted crosslinker groups by incubating with 0.1 M lysine in coupling buffer for 2 hr.

10. Wash excess lysine and nonconvalently bound protein by cycles of coupling buffer followed by acetate buffer 0.5 M NaCl, 0.1 M CH$_3$ COONa/ HCl, pH 4.

11. Resuspend beads, add 0.01% sodium azide, and store at 4°C.

Affinity Purification

1. Incubate the gel (keep rotating with serum or antiserum for 2 hr at 37°C or for 18 hr at 4°C or pass the serum through a packed column). If the volume of serum is larger than the void volume of the column, recycle the serum.

2. The volume of antiserum to be used depends on the titer of antiserum. Usually, the maximum capacity of the column is equal to 70% of the equivalent point; 10 mg IgG retains between 30 and 50 mg anti-IgG.

3. Wash the gel with PBS until the OD$_{280}$ is less than 0.02.

4. Pack the column.

5. Prepare fraction tubes, adding 0.3 ml of 0.1 M K$_2$PO$_4$ to each of them.

6. Elute the column in the cold with 0.2 M HCl/2 M lysine, pH 2.2.

7. Collect 30 drops per tube.

8. Read the OD$_{280}$ of each tube. (Mix well before reading the OD.)

9. Pool the fractions in which the OD is greater than 0.1. Adjust pH to 7–7.4.

10. When the OD of the fraction is lower than 0.08, neutralize the column by eluting with 1 M K$_2$PO$_4$ immediately.

11. Rinse the column immediately with PBS, add NaN$_3$ to 0.01%, and store in the cold. (The column may be reused several times if carefully stored.)

12. Eluted protein is dialyzed in the cold against 100 vol of 0.01% NaN$_3$, PBS for 48 hr (three or four changes).

13. Protein is concentrated up to 3–5 mg/ml and store in 50% glycerol–PBS at −20°C.

D. PURIFICATION OF PROTEIN A–SEPHAROSE COLUMNS

Protein A is a 42,000 MW protein extracted from *Staphylococcus aureus* and has the ability to bind two immunoglobulin molecules. It has a strong affinity for the Fc region of the immunoglobulins.

Protein A–Sepharose CL-4N resins are commercially obtained from Pharmacia

Biotechnology. One milliliter of resin has bound some 2 mg of protein A and this can bind about 20 mg of IgG.

Binding and eluting conditions are available from the suppliers for the different subclasses of antibodies and for different animal species.

IV. Pitfalls

1. Polyclonal affinity-purified rabbit antibodies are very difficult to concentrate higher than 2–3 mg/ml. Furthermore, they precipitate slowly when stored at 4°C. Storage in 50% glycerol PBS at −20°C is recommended. Purified monoclonal antibodies stay well in solution at concentrations as high as 10 mg/ml.

2. Never use a magnetic stirrer to agitate gel; it will break the beads. Any other method of smoothly agitating will do (rotating, rocking).

3. Unsuccessful coupling is generally due to the presence of amino groups in the solutions. Normally it comes from the ammonium sulfate used to precipitate the proteins or peptides or from the use of Tris buffer. Desalt or dialyze very carefully, with volumes of buffer large enough. Also ensure that no amino groups are present in the water used (storage in plastic containers may be a source of contamination).

4. Other eluants may be used to desorb the affinity-bound immunoglobulins: raising or lowering pH of the initial solvent, addition of polarity-reducing agents (i.e., ethylene glycol, dioxane), denaturing agents (i.e., urea, guanidine), chaotropic agents (i.e., thiocyanate, trifluoroacetate).

5. As denatured immunoglobulins may be obtained from the affinity column, it is critical to elute at low pH and to elute quickly and at a carefully maintained low temperature.

SUGGESTED READING

Ey, P., Prowse, S., and Jenkin, C. (1978) Isolation of pure IgG1, IgG2a and IgG2b immuno-globulins from mouse serum using protein A–Sepharose. *Biochemistry* **15**, 429–436.
Harlow, E., and Lane, D. (1988) "Antibodies. A Laboratory Manual." Cold Spring Harbor Laboratory Press, Cold Spring Harbor, NY.
Kreis, T. (1987) Purification of antibodies. *In* "EMBO Practical Course: Antibodies in Cell Biology." EMBL, Heidelberg.
Mäkelä, O., and Seppälä, I. (1986) Haptens and carriers. *In* "Hanbook of Experimental Immunology" (D. M. Weir, ed.) Vol. 1. Blackwell Scientific, London.
Terninck, T., and Avrameas, S. (1987) "Techniques immunoenzymatiques." Editions IN-SERM, Paris.
Terninck, T., and Avrameas, S. (1976) Polymerization and immunobilization of proteins using ethylchloroformate and glutaraldehyde. *Scand. J. Immunol.* **3**, 29.

Conjugation of Fluorescent Dyes to Antibodies

Benjamin Geiger and Tova Volberg

I. Introduction

For more than four decades, fluorescence microscopy has been the leading method for the sensitive and specific localization of a large variety of molecules in cells and tissues. Such molecular mapping has over the years provided much information, not only on the distribution of the molecules of interest but also on their functional properties. The first and most commonly used flurophore-conjugated probes are antibodies, which enable direct or indirect localization of antigenic molecules. The list of specific probes that have been used for fluorescence microscopic analysis has expanded and presently includes such molecules as lectins, toxins, hormones, and growth factors. It is beyond the scope of this article to discuss extensively the various aspects of fluorescence microscopy and the chemistry of fluorophore conjugation. It should nevertheless be pointed out that the quality and fidelity of immunofluorescence localization depend on multiple factors, all of which should be optimized for each experimental system. These include:

1. Proper processing of the specimen (i.e., fixation and permeabilization when necessary)
2. High affinity and specificity of the probes (i.e., antibodies, lectins)
3. Optimal choice of fluorophore and conjugation procedures
4. Appropriate labeling procedure
5. Availability of a microscopic system suitable for examination of the labeled specimens

Although each of these variables may significantly affect the quality of labeling, we focus, in this article, on only one of these factors, namely, the conjugation of various fluorophores to antibodies. The very high demand for immunofluorescent regents has resulted in the introduction of many different fluorescent dyes suitable for conjugation to proteins. The new fluorophores offer a broader excitation–emission range than previously attainable, allow for multiple labeling of specimens, and are often less susceptible to photobleaching. Moreover, in addition to the "classical" amine-reactive fluorophores (such as the isothiocyanate derivatives), there are now batteries of fluorescent reagents, suitable for coupling to thiols, hydroxyls, carboxylates, etc. The procedures to be described here are, however, restricted to fluorophores bearing amine-reactive groups, including sulfonyl chloride, isothiocyanate, and dichlorotriazinyl. For most immunocytochemical purposes these fluorophores and conjugation procedures appear to be satisfactory. There are, however, some general considerations affecting the choice of suitable fluorophase that are broadly applicable and that we would like to point out:

1. The choice of fluorophores should take into account factors such as photobleaching, autofluorescence of the specimen, and the filter sets available in the microscope. Usually rhodamine-based dyes are preferable to fluorescein-based dyes due to their lower susceptibility to photobleaching during microscopic examination.

2. For most conjugation procedures it is advisable not to use highly diluted IgG solutions. Optimal conjugation is obtained using 0.5–5 mg/ml IgG solutions.

3. It is important to monitor carefully the extent of conjugation. Usually, conjugates containing two to five fluorophores per antibody molecule are optimal. A lower level of modification results in a weak signal, whereas overmodification may lead to high nonspecific background labeling.

4. The solution of fluorescent antibodies should be protected from intense light and from frequent changes in temperature. Storage of labeled antibodies at 4°C or frozen in liquid nitrogen in small aliquots is recommended.

Another practical consideration of many researchers is whether they should carry out the conjugation themselves or, alternatively, purchase conjugated antibodies from commercial sources. There are no general rules that apply to all preconjugated antibodies, yet they are usually quite expensive, are often of variable quality, and are commonly available only as secondary ("anti-IgG") reagents for indirect ("sandwich") labeling.

II. Materials and Instrumentation

Lissamine–rhodamine B (sulforhodamine B, Polysciences Inc., Cat. No. 0643)

Dichlorotriazinyl Amino Fluorescein (DTAF 2096D-1, Research Organics, Inc., or Sigma or Molecular Probes)

Fluorescein isothiocyanate (FITC, Calbiochem or Sigma)

Phosphorus pentachloride (PCl_5, BDH)

Sephadex G-50 (Cat. No. A-0043-01, Pharmacia)

DEAE-cellulose (DE-52, Whatman)

carbonate buffer, phosphate buffer, sodium chloride, acetone, ethanol, glycine

Pestle and mortar, small funnels, Whatman No. 1 filter paper, ice bucket, 15-ml glass tubes, microfuge tubes (Eppendorf 3810), small stirring bar, magnetic stirrer, Vortex, centrifuge, spectrophotometer

III. Procedures

A. CONJUGATION OF RHODAMINE B 200 SULFONYL CHLORIDE (RB200SC) TO ANTIBODIES

1. Preparation of RB200SC

This procedure follows that of P. Brandtzaeg, (1973) *Scand. J. Immunol. Suppl.* **2**, 273.

Caution: The entire procedure should be performed in a fume hood! Avoid direct contact with PCl₅ or activated rhodamine.

Steps

1. Weigh in fume hood 1 g of lissamine–rhodamine B and 2 g PCl$_5$.

2. Mix the two powders thoroughly with pestle and mortar for 5 min at room temperature.

3. Add 10 ml acetone (or dioxane) to the activated rhodamine and mix occasionally for 5 min to maximally dissolve the activated fluorophore.

4. Filter the solution through Whatman No. 1 filter paper, into a tube kept on ice.

5. Distribute 100- to 200-μl aliquots into small stoppered bottles or microfuge tubes, and store at $-70°C$.

6. Determine the concentration of RB200SC by diluting it 1:10 in acetone and further 1:100 in PBS. Measure the absorbance of the solution at 565 nm and calculate the concentration of RB200SC using an extinction coefficient $E_{565\,nm}^{1\%}$ of 1265.

Do not refreeze a fluorophore solution once it has been thawed and opened.

2. Conjugation of RB200SC to Antibodies and Fractionation of the Conjugate

Solutions

1. *1.0 M carbonate buffer pH 9.0:* Mix 1.0 *M* sodium carbonate and 1.0 *M* sodium bicarbonate until the pH is 9.0.

2. *1 M glycine (7.5 g in 100 ml distilled water).*

3. *0.1 M phosphate buffer pH 8.0:* Mix 0.1 *M* sodium phosphate with sodium hydrogen phosphate until the pH is 8.0.

4. *0.25 M NaCl (1:20 dilution of 5 M NaCl stock) in 10 mM phosphate buffer pH 8.0 (1:10 dilution of 0.1 M stock solution).*

Steps

1. Working at room temperature, mix 1 vol of 1.0 *M* carbonate buffer, pH 9.0, with 4 vol of the antibody solution.

2. While stirring the antibody solution, add 20–30 μg RB200SC/mg of antibody in 3 to 4 aliquots over a period of 30 min. Stir the solution for an additional 20 min and stop the reaction by adding 0.1 vol of 1 *M* glycine.

3. Load the reaction mixture on a Sephadex G-50 column (5–6 bed vol per sample volume), preequilibrated with 10 m*M* phosphate buffer, pH 8.0. Collect the first colored peak.

4. Load the fluorescent protein solution on a DEAE–cellulose column (1-ml bed volume/mg of antibody), preequilibrated with 10 m*M* phosphate buffer, pH 8.0.

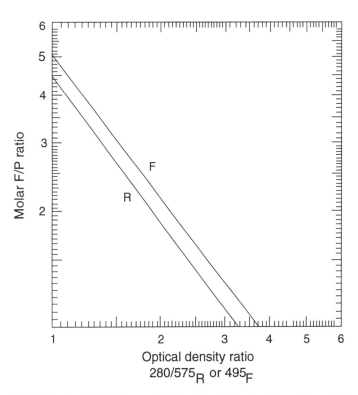

FIGURE 1 Calculation of *F/P* ratio of rhodamine- (R) and fluorescein (F)-conjugated antibodies.

5. Wash the column with the same buffer and elute the labeled protein with 0.25 *M* NaCl in 10 m*M* phosphate buffer, pH 8.0.

6. Read the absorbance at 280 and 575 nm and calculate the protein concentration and the fluorophore/protein ratio (*F/P*), according to the following equation and Fig. 1:

$$\text{Rhodamine-labeled antibodies (mg/ml)} = \frac{\text{OD}_{280} - (0.32 \times \text{OD}_{575})}{1.4} \quad (1)$$

7. Store the labeled antibodies at 4°C or freeze small aliquots in liquid nitrogen.

B. LABELING OF IgG WITH DICHLOROTRIAZINYL AMINO FLUORESCEIN

Solutions

1. *DTAF 5 mg/ml in ethanol.*
2. *1 M carbonate buffer.*
3. *10 mM phosphate buffer.*
4. *0.25 mM NaCl in 10 mM phosphate buffer.*
5. *1 M glycine in water.*

Steps

1. Prepare a fresh stock solution of DTAF 5 mg/ml in ethanol (heat the solution slightly to completely dissolve the powder).

2. Mix the antibody solution with $\frac{1}{4}$ vol of 1 M carbonate buffer, pH 9.0.

3. Add 40 μg DTAF (8 μl) per milligram of IgG and mix well.

4. Incubate the mixture on ice for 30 min with gentle stirring, then add 0.1 vol of the glycine.

5. Separate the IgG-bound DTAF from the unbound dye on Sephadex G-50 and save the first colored peak.

6. Load the fluorescent protein solution on a DEAE–cellulose column (1 ml bed volume/mg antibody), preequilibrated with the 10 mM phosphate buffer, pH 8.0.

7. Wash the column with the same buffer and elute the labeled protein with 0.25 M NaCl in 10 mM phosphate buffer, pH 8.0.

8. Read the absorbance at 280 and 495 nm and calculate the protein concentration and the fluorophore/protein ratio (*F/P*), according to the following equation and Fig. 1:

$$\text{Fluorescein-labeled antibodies (mg/ml)} = \frac{OD_{280} - (0.35 \times OD_{495})}{1.4} \qquad (2)$$

9. Store the labeled antibodies at 4°C or freeze small aliquots in liquid nitrogen.

C. COUPLING OF FLUORESCEIN ISOTHIOCYANATE TO ANTIBODIES

Solutions

1. *1 M carbonate buffer.*

2. *10 mM phosphate buffer.*

3. *0.25 mM NaCl in 10 mM phosphate buffer.*

Steps

1. Mix the IgG solution with $\frac{1}{4}$ vol of 1 M carbonate buffer, pH 9, at room temperature in a 15-ml glass centrifuge tube.

2. Weigh out Celite–FITC (0.5 mg powder/mg of IgG).

3. Add the Celite–FITC to the IgG solution and immediately mix by Vortex or centrifuge briefly.

4. Add the stir bar and mix continuously to suspend the Celite–FITC. Stir for 20 min at room temperature.

5. Separate the labeled IgG from the Celite by a brief centrifugation.

6. Separate the IgG-bound FITC from the unbound dye on Sephadex G-50 and save the first colored peak.

7. Load the fluorescent protein solution on a DEAE–cellulose column (1 ml bed volume/mg antibody), preequilibrated with 10 mM phosphate buffer, pH 8.0.

8. Wash the column with the same buffer and elute the labeled protein with 0.25 M NaCl in 10 mM phosphate buffer, pH 8.0.

9. Read the absorbance at 280 and 495 nm and calculate the protein concentration and the fluorophore/protein ratio (*F/P*), according to Eq. 2 and Fig. 1.

10. Store the labeled antibodies at 4°C or freeze small aliquots in liquid nitrogen.

SECTION C

Antibody Specificity

Determination of Antibody Specificity by Western Blotting and Immunoprecipitation

Julio E. Celis, Jette B. Lauridsen, and Bodil Basse

I. Introduction

Immunoblotting (Towbin *et al.*, 1979; Symington, 1984; Harlow and Lane, 1988; Otto and Lee, 1993; see also article by Amandio Vieira, Robert J. Elkin, and Karl Kuchler in this volume) and immunoprecipitation (Harlow and Lane, 1988; Otto, 1993) are among the most common techniques used to determine the specificity of an antibody. As some antibodies work well in immunoblotting but not in immunoprecipitation and vice versa, it is important to set up both techniques in the laboratory.

II. Materials and Instrumentation

Trizma base (Cat. No. T-1503), glycine (Cat. No. G-7126), bovine hemoglobin (Cat. No. H-2625), and bovine serum albumin (Cat. No. A-4503) were obtained from Sigma. EDTA (Cat. No. 8418), 30% hydrogen peroxide (Cat. No. 7209), sodium deoxycholate (Cat. No. 6504), and trichloroacetic acid (Cat. No. 810) were from Merck. Protein A–Sepharose CL-4B (Cat. No. 17-0780-01) was from Pharmacia Biotech and Nonidet P-40 (NP-40, Cat. No. 56009) from BDH. Peroxidase-conjugated rabbit anti-mouse immunoglobulins (Cat. No. P260), rabbit immunoglobulins to mouse immunoglobulins (Cat. No. Z259), and the mouse monoclonal antibody against PCNA (Cat. No. M879) were from Dako. Dehydrated bacto skim milk (Cat. No. 0032-01) was from Difco Laboratories, and modified Eagle's medium lacking methionine (MEM, Cat. No. 041-01900H) from Gibco-BRL. HRP color development reagent (Cat. No. 170-6534) was obtained from Bio-Rad. Tissue culture media and supplements were as described in the article by Ariana Celis and Julio E. Celis.

Nitrocellulose Hybond-C (Cat. No. RPN 203C) and [^{35}S]methionine (Cat. No. SJ 204) were purchased from Amersham and Filter-Count (Cat. No. 6013149) from Packard. Plates (96-well, Cat. No. 655180) were from Greiner. Other sterile plasticware were as described in the article by Ariana Celis and Julio E. Celis. Rectangular (24 × 19 cm) pie dishes were obtained from Corning (Cat. No. PX 385687) and X-ray films (X-Omat DS; 18 × 24 cm, Cat. No. 508 7838) from Kodak. The Trans-Blot electrophoretic transfer cell was from Bio-Rad (Cat. No. 170-3910) and the orbital shaker (Red Rotor PR75) from Hoefer. The power supplies (EPS 500/400) were from Pharmacia Biotech.

III. Procedures

A. TWO-DIMENSIONAL GEL IMMUNOBLOTTING

The procedure is illustrated using Simian virus 40 (SV40)-transformed human keratinocyte (K14) proteins (whole extracts) separated by IEF 2-D gel electrophoresis, blotted to a nitrocellulose membrane (Towbin *et al.*, 1979) and reacted with a monoclonal antibody (mAb 30A5) that reacts specifically with the glucose-regulated protein 75 (grp 75).

1. Labeling of K14 Cells with [^{35}S]Methionine

Solutions

1. *Labeling medium:* Combine MEM lacking methionine and supplemented with antibiotics (100 U/ml penicillin, 100 μg/ml streptomycin) and 10% dialyzed (against 0.9% NaCl) fetal calf serum (FCS). Keep at −80°C.

2. [^{35}S]*Methionine:* Aliquot in 100-μCi portions in sterile 1-ml cryotubes. Keep at −20°C. Freeze-dry just before use.

Steps

1. Plate SV40-transformed human keratinocytes (K14; Taylor-Papadimitriou *et al.*, 1982) in a microtiter plate (96 wells) and leave in the 37°C humidified 5% CO_2 incubator until they reach the desired cell density.

2. Freeze-dry the [^{35}S]methionine and resuspend in labeling medium at a concentration of 1 mCi/ml. For one well, one needs 100 μCi of [^{35}S]methionine in 0.1 ml of labeling medium.

3. Remove the medium from the well with the aid of a sterile, drawn-out (under a flame) Pasteur pipette. Wash once with labeling medium. Add the labeling medium containing the radioactivity.

4. Wrap the well plate in Saran wrap (see also Fig. 2A of the article by Ariana Celis, Kurt Dejgaard, and Julio E. Celis in this volume) and place in the 37°C humidified 5% CO_2 incubator for 16 hr or shorter period if necessary.

5. At the end of the labeling period, remove the medium with the aid of a drawn-out Pasteur pipette. Place the 96-well plate at an angle to facilitate removal of the liquid. Dispose the radioactive medium according to the regulations enforced in your laboratory.

6. Resuspend the cells in 0.1 ml of O'Farrell's lysis solution (O'Farrell, 1975; see article by Julio E. Celis, Gitte Ratz, Bodil Basse, Jette B. Lauridsen, and Ariana Celis). Pipette up and down (avoid foaming). Keep at −20°C until use.

2. Determination of Hot Trichloroacetic Acid-Precipitable Radioactivity in Samples

Solutions

1. *Stock trichloroacetic acid (TCA):* Dissolve the entire contents of the bottle (1 kg) in distilled water and bring to 1 liter.

2. *10% TCA:* Take 100 ml of stock TCA and complete to 1 liter with distilled water.

3. *Bovine serum albumin (BSA) (1 mg/ml):* Weigh 10 mg and resuspend in 10 ml of distilled water.

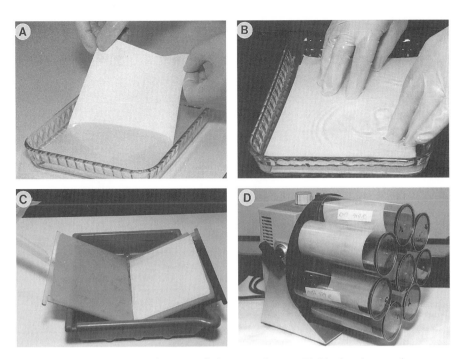

FIGURE 1 (A) Wetting the nitrocellulose membrane. (B) Placing the membrane on top of the gel. (C) Holder with fiber gel pads. (D) Rotating roller system (Navigator).

Steps

1. Take 5 μl of the sample in lysis solution and mix with 10 μl of BSA (1 mg/ml) in a conical tube. Add 5 ml of 10% TCA, mix, and heat in a boiling water bath for 10 min. Work in a hood.

2. Cool in ice and filter through a millipore filter (0.45 μm).

3. Wash several times with 10% TCA and dry under an infrared lamp.

4. Place the filter in a scintillation vial, add 4 ml of Filter-Count, leave for at least 15 min, and count for 5 min in a scintillation counter.

3. Blotting

Solution

TGM (Tris, glycine, methanol): 25 mM Tris, 192 mM glycine and 20% (v/v) methanol. To make 5 liters, weigh 15.14 g of Tris and 72.07 g of glycine. Add 1 liter of methanol and complete to 5 liters with distilled water.

Steps

1. Run two-dimensional (2D) gels as described in the article by Julio E. Celis, Gitte Ratz, Bodil Basse, Jette B. Lauridsen, and Ariana Celis. In this particular case we have run an isoelectric focusing (IEF) 2D gel of human K14 keratinocyte proteins. Unlabeled K14 cells grown in monolayer (nearly confluency; 75-cm^2 flask) were washed twice with Hanks' buffered saline and resuspended directly in 1 ml of O'Farrell lysis solution. To 40 μl of this sample we added 5 μl of [^{35}S]-methionine-labeled K14 proteins (about 500,000 cpm; see Sections A1 and A2) to facilitate the immunodetection of the antigen(s). For 1D blots, resuspend the samples in Laemmli's buffer (Laemmli, 1970).

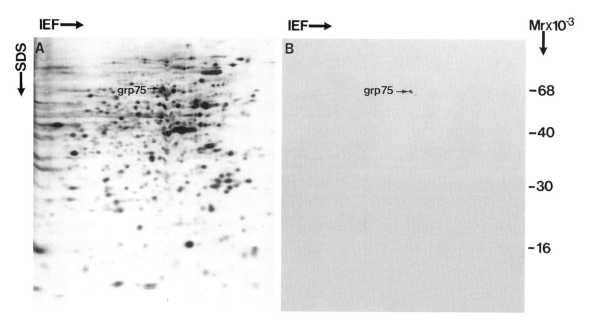

FIGURE 2 Two-dimensional gel immunoblot of human K14 protein extracts (mixed with a small amount of [^{35}S]methionine labeled sample) blotted to a nitrocellulose membrane (A) and reacted with monoclonal antibody 30A5 which recognizes the glucose-regulated protein 75, grp 75 (B). SDS, sodium dodecyl sulfate; IEF, isoelectric focusing.

2. Place a piece of 3MM Whatmann paper (a bit larger than the size of the gel) in a rectangular glass pie dish (24 × 19 cm) containing about 100 ml of TGM. Place the gel on top of the paper (Fig. 1A).

3. Equilibrate for 5 min at room temperature.

4. Wet the fiber gel pads in TGM.

5. Open the gel holder (Fig. 1C) and place one fiber gel pad in each side.

6. Wet the nitrocellulose membrane (14 × 16 cm) in TGM by capillary action as shown in Fig. 1A. Use gloves to handle the membranes.

7. Place the wet nitrocellulose membrane on top of the gel (Fig. 1B). The operation should be done under the buffer. Rub the membrane from one end to the other to eliminate bubbles.

8. Place another wet 3MM Whatmann paper on top of the nitrocellulose membrane. Rub the paper carefully to avoid bubbles. Lift the "sandwich" (same side up) and place it on top of the fiber gel pad located on the black holder (Fig. 1C).

9. Close the gel holder and place it in the Trans-Blot tank containing about 750 ml of TGM. The black side of the holder should face the cathode side (indicated with black in the tank). Up to three gel holders can be inserted in the tank. If only one cassette is used, insert it in the middle track.

10. Fill the tank with TGM, connect the electrodes, and run for 24 hr at 130 mA.

11. Following protein transfer, dry the membrane, mark the corners with radioactive ink, and expose to an X-ray film to assess the quality of the transfer (Fig. 2A). Dry sheets can be kept for extended periods without significant changes in the reactivity of the proteins. Blots that do not contain radioactivity can be stained with Ponceau S (see article by Amandio Vieira, Robert G. Elkin, and Karl

Kuchler in this volume) or amido black (see article by Hans Jürgen Hoffmann and Julio E. Celis).

4. Immunodetection

(see also article by Amandio Vieira *et al.* in this volume).

Solutions

1. *Hanks' buffered saline solution (HBSS) without Ca^{2+} and Mg^{2+}:* 10× stock solution. To make 1 liter, weigh 4 g of KCl, 0.6 g of KH$_2$PO$_4$, 80 g of NaCl, and 0.621 g of Na$_2$HPO$_4$·2H$_2$O. Complete to 1 liter with distilled water.

2. *1× HBSS without Ca^{2+} and Mg^{2+}:* To make 1 liter of HBSS, use 100 ml of the 10× stock solution and complete to 1 liter with distilled water.

3. *2× TBS stock:* 40 mM Tris, 1 M NaCl, pH 7.5. To make 1 liter, add 4.84 g of Tris and 58.44 g of NaCl. Adjust to pH 7.5 with HCl and complete to 1 liter with distilled water. Store at 4°C.

4. *Hemoglobin:* To make 100 ml, weigh 1.5 g of hemoglobin and add 100 ml of HBSS.

5. *mAB 30A5 (culture supernatant).*

6. *Peroxidase-conjugated rabbit anti-mouse immunoglobulins:* To make 10 ml of a 1:200 dilution, add 50 μl of peroxidase-conjugated anti-mouse immunoglobulins to 10 ml of HBSS.

7. *HRP color development solution:* To make 60 ml, dissolve 30 mg of HRP color development reagent in 10 ml of methanol (protect from light). Mix 30 ml of 2× TBS and 20 ml of distilled water. Just before use add 30 μl of ice-cold 30% H$_2$O$_2$ to the TBS and mix the two solutions.

Steps

1. Cut the appropriate area of the blot with a scalpel using the x-ray film as reference and wet by capillarity in the hemoglobin solution. Incubate with shaking for 16 hr at room temperature in the same solution. Alternatively, use dehydrated bacto skim milk (50 mg/ml in HBSS). If the blots are for enhanced chemiluminiscence (ECL) detection, use the skim milk blocking solution (see also article by Amandio Vieira *et al.* in this volume). Incubation can be done in a rectangular plastic dish (15 × 10.5 cm; need a minimum volume of 40 ml per dish) or a rotating roller system (Navigator Model 128, BIOCOMP, Fig. 1D). In the latter case, the volume needed is considerably less (8 ml). For 1D gel strips we use the chamber shown in Fig. 3 (Pierce). The procedure is illustrated below using a rectangular plastic dish.

2. Add 8 ml of mAB 30A5 (culture supernatant) to the hemoglobin solution. Shake for 2 hr at room temperature.

3. Wash three times for 10 min each with HBSS.

4. Add 40 ml of a 1:200 dilution of peroxidase-conjugated rabbit anti-mouse immunoglobulins in HBSS. Shake for 2 hr at room temperature.

5. Wash three times for 10 min each in HBSS.

6. Prepare the HRP color development solution just before use.

7. Aspirate the HBSS and add 30 ml of the HRP solution. Shake at room temperature until the staining appears (Fig. 2B). Discard the HRP color developer according to the safety regulations enforced in your laboratory.

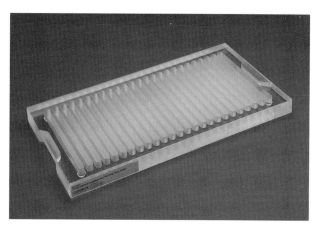

FIGURE 3   Chamber for incubating 1D gel strips with antibodies.

8. Rinse well in demineralized or tap water and dry. Superimpose the dry blot and the x-ray film with the aid of the radioactive marks.

5. Comments

Figure 2 shows immunoblots of human K14 proteins extracts (mixed with a small amount of [^{35}S]methionine-labeled sample) blotted to nitrocellulose (autoradiography, Fig. 2A) and reacted with mAB 30A5 (specific for grp75) (Fig. 2B). Ideally, 2D gel protein blots [IEF and nonequilibrium pH gradient electrophoresis (NEPHGE)] should be used to determine the specificity of the antibody. The procedure described here has been used in no less than 1000 blots using hundreds of polyclonal and monoclonal antibodies (Celis *et al.*, 1991).

6. Pitfalls

1. It is a good idea to remove excess of vaseline floating in the buffer (see Section A3, step 2) with a tissue.

2. Avoid air bubbles when making the "sandwich" and lifting it to the fiber gel pad (see Section A3, step 8).

3. For 2D blotting it is important to run a range of concentrations of the protein mixture. Choose a protein concentration that does not give streaking (see Fig. 2A). Never run more protein than is necessary.

4. Membrane proteins may streak and it may be necessary to use detergents such as Triton X-114.

5. H_2O_2 is unstable. Check the expiration date on the bottle.

6. In case of no signal (low abundance of the antigen), use higher concentrations of the antibody or try the more sensitive detection procedures described in the article by Amandio Vieira *et al.* in this volume. Alternatively, try immunoprecipitation (see Section C).

B. DOT BLOTTING

Solutions

See the immunodetection protocol (Section A3).

Steps

1. Pipette increasing amounts of the antigen solution directly onto the nitrocellulose membranes (Glenney *et al.*, 1982).

2. Proceed as described in the immunodetection protocol (Section A4) starting with step 1 (see also article by Amandio Vieira *et al.* in this volume).

C. IMMUNOPRECIPITATION

The procedure is illustrated using a [^{35}S]methionine-labeled extract from transformed human amnion (AMA) cells and a mouse monoclonal antibody directed against the proliferating cell nuclear antigen (PCNA). See also Harlow and Lane (1988).

Solutions

1. *1 M Tris·HCl, pH 7.4 (stock solution):* To make 100 ml, dissolve 12.11 g of Tris in distilled water. Adjust the pH to 7.4 with HCl and complete to 100 ml with distilled water.

2. *1 M NaCl (stock solution):* To make 500 ml, weigh 29.22 g of NaCl and complete to 500 ml with distilled water.

3. *0.5 M EDTA (stock solution):* To make 50 ml, take 9.31 g of EDTA and add about 40 ml of distilled water. Stir and slowly add dropwise 10 N NaOH until the EDTA goes into solution. Complete with distilled water.

4. *NP-40 (stock solution) 10% w/v:* To make 100 ml, weigh 10 g of NP-40 and complete to 100 ml with distilled water.

5. *Sodium deoxycholate (stock solution) 2.5%:* To make 500 ml, weigh 12.5 g sodium deoxycholate and complete to 500 ml with distilled water.

6. *10% Sodium dodecyl sulfate (stock solution):* To make 50 ml, weigh 5 g of sodium dodecyl sulfate (SDS) and complete to 50 ml with distilled water.

7. *Buffer C:* 50 mM Tris·HCl, pH 7.4, 150 mM NaCl, 5 mM EDTA, 0.5% NP-40, 0.5% sodium deoxycholate, and 0.1% SDS. To make 1 liter, add 50 ml of 1 M Tris, pH 7.4, 150 ml of 1 M NaCl, 10 ml of 0.5 M EDTA, 200 ml of 2.5% sodium deoxycholate, 10 ml of 10% SDS, and 50 ml of 10% NP-40. Adjust pH to 7.28 and complete to 1 liter with distilled water. Keep at 4°C.

8. *Buffer C with bovine serum albumin (BSA):* To make 100 ml, weigh 200 mg of BSA and add 100 ml of buffer C.

9. *Protein A–Sepharose:* To make 1 ml, weigh 100 mg of protein A–Sepharose and add 1 ml of buffer C containing BSA.

10. *Mouse monoclonal antibody against PCNA:* Tissue culture supernatant, protein concentration = 15.1 g/liter.

11. *Rabbit anti-mouse immunoglobulins.*

Steps

1. Label AMA cells with [^{35}S]methionine as described in Section A1. Use a 35-mm tissue culture dish instead of a microtiter well. One needs about 0.6 ml of labeling medium to cover the monolayer. Use [^{35}S]methionine at a concentration of 500 μCi/ml. Cover the tissue culture dish with Saran wrap and place in the 37°C humidified 5% CO_2 incubator.

2. Aspirate the radioactive medium and wash the cells twice with HBSS.

3. Add 1.5 ml of buffer C containing BSA and rock the culture dish at room temperature. If the antigen is known to be proteolyzed easily, add protease

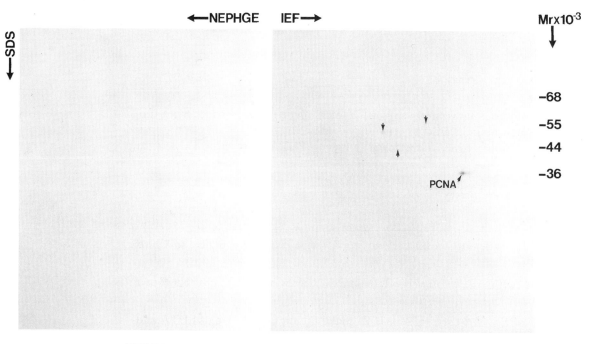

FIGURE 4   Autoradiograms of IEF and NEPHGE 2D gels of [^{35}S]-methionine labeled proteins immunoprecipitated with PCNA antibodies.

inhibitors (phenylmethylsulfonyl fluoride, aprotinin, leupeptin, and pepstatin A) to buffer C.

4. Bend the end of a Pasteur pipette under the flame and use it to remove the cells.

5. Place the cell suspension in a plastic conical tube and centrifuge at 6,000 g in the SS-34 rotor of the Sorvall centrifuge (4°C).

6. Take 0.1 ml of the supernatant and add it to a 1.5-ml Eppendorf micro test tube. Add 10 μl of the anti-PCNA monoclonal antibody.

7. Incubate with rotation for 1 hr at 4°C (cold room).

8. Add 5 μl of rabbit anti-mouse immunoglobulins. Incubate with rotation for 1 hr at 4°C (cold room). This step is not necessary for polyclonal antibodies.

9. Add 100 μl of the protein A solution and incubate with rotation at 4°C for 1 hr (cold room).

10. Centrifuge in an Eppendorf centrifuge for 30 sec at 10,000 g and wash the pellet four times with buffer C.

11. After the last centrifugation, remove all the liquid and resuspend in 50 μl of O'Farrell lysis solution (O'Farrell, 1975; see also article by Julio E. Celis, Gitte Ratz, Bodil Basse, Jette B. Lauridsen, and Ariana Celis). Leave for 60 min at room temperature.

12. Centrifuge in an Eppendorf centrifuge and run a fraction of the supernatant in IEF and NEPHGE gels as described in the article by Julio E. Celis, Gitte Ratz, Bodil Basse, Jette B. Lauridsen, and Ariana Celis (Fig. 4).

IV. Comments

Figure 4 shows IEF and NEPHGE gels of PCNA immunoprecipitates. In addition to PCNA, one can also detect keratins and vimentin (arrowheads). The latter are also detected in control immunoprecipitates (results not shown). Ideally, the immunoprecipitates should be analyzed by 2D gel electrophoresis (IEF and NEPHGE).

V. Pitfalls

1. Variable levels of keratins and vimentin are usually observed in the immunoprecipitates (short arrows in Fig. 4). Make sure you run a proper control.

2. The amount of antibody needed for immunoprecipitation varies from antibody to antibody. It is advisable to try a range of concentrations. Recommended initial volumes are 10–20 μl for culture supernatant and 5 μl for sera.

3. Label the cells with as much radioactive isotope as possible to enrich low-abundancy proteins.

4. In case of no signal, use other buffers to solubilize the sample (see Harlow and Lane, 1988; Otto and Lee, 1993). Try a different amino acid for labeling. If still no signal, try immunoblotting.

REFERENCES

Celis, *et al.* (1991) The master two-dimensional gel database of human AMA cells proteins: Towards linking protein and genome sequence and mapping information (Update 1991). *Electrophoresis* **12**, 765–801.

Glenney, J. R., Jr., Glenney, P., and Weber, K. (1982) Erythroid spectrin, brain fodrin, and intestinal brush border proteins (TW-260/240) are related molecules containing a common calmodulin-binding subunit bound to a variant cell type-specific subunit. *Proc. Natl. Acad. Sci. USA* **79**, 4002–4005.

Harlow, E., and Lane, D. (1988) "Antibodies: A Laboratory Manual." Cold Spring Harbor Laboratory Press, Cold Spring Harbor, NY.

Laemmli, U. K. (1970) Cleavage of structural proteins during the assembly of the head of bacteriophage T4. *Nature (London)* **227**, 680–685.

O'Farrell, P. H. (1975) High resolution two-dimensional electrophoresis of proteins. *J. Biol. Chem.* **250**, 4007–4021.

O'Farrell, P. Z., Goodman, H. M., and O'Farrell, P. H. (1977) High resolution two-dimensional electrophoresis of basic as well as acidic proteins. *Cell* **12**, 1133–1142.

Otto, J. J. (1993) Immunoblotting. *In* "Antibodies in Cell Biology" (D. J. Asai, ed.), pp. 105–117. Academic Press, San Diego.

Otto, J. J., and Lee, S. (1993) Immunoprecipitation methods. *In* "Antibodies in Cell Biology" (D. J. Asai, ed.), pp. 119–127. Academic Press, San Diego.

Symington, J. (1984) *In* "Two-Dimensional Gel Electrophoresis of Proteins: Methods and Applications" (J. E. Celis and R. Bravo, eds.), pp. 126–168. Academic Press, New York.

Taylor-Papadimitriou, J., Purkis, P., Lane, E. B., McKay, I. A., and Chang, S. E. (1982) Effect of SV40 transformation on the cytoskeleton and behavioural properties of human keratinocytes. *Cell. Diff.* **11**, 169–180.

Towbin, H., Staehelin, T., and Gordon, J. (1979) Electrophoretic transfer of proteins from polyacrylamide gels to nitrocellulose sheets: Procedure and some application. *Proc. Natl. Acad. Sci. USA* **76**, 4350–4354.

Western Blotting and Ligand Blotting Using Enhanced Chemiluminescence and Radioiodine Detection

Amandio Vieira, Robert G. Elkin, and Karl Kuchler

I. Introduction

Enhanced chemiluminescence (ECL) and radioiodine-based techniques represent two of the most commonly used methods to visualize proteins immobilized on nitrocellulose membranes after electrophoretic transfer from sodium dodecyl sulfate (SDS)–polyacrylamide gels (see also article by Julio E. Celis, Jette B. Lauridsen, and Bodil Basse in this volume). ECL is a nonradioactive method based on enzyme-catalyzed production of light and subsequent amplification of the light by chemical enhancers (Fig. 1). In terms of sensitivity, safety, speed, and convenience of handling, ECL is the current method of choice for the immunodetection of proteins. The extraordinary sensitivity of ECL permits protein detection down to the subpicogram level, surpassing the sensitivity of other detection methods by more than an order of magnitude. In many cases, ECL detection can even be used to visualize immuno-precipitated proteins obtained from total cell extracts, which eliminates the need for metabolic labeling of cells. ECL detection can also be employed to study receptor–ligand interactions using unlabeled ligands. Thus, it can eliminate potential ligand blot artifacts caused by the labeling of a given ligand.

In contrast to ECL, radioiodine detection is more tedious, hazardous, and time consuming to perform; however, it is still widely used in Western blotting (also known as immunoblotting) and ligand blotting procedures because it provides reasonable sensitivity while allowing for the quantitation of labeled proteins. In this article, we describe the essential methodology to perform both ECL- and ^{125}I-based detections in Western blotting and ligand blotting experiments.

II. Materials and Instrumentation

For performing SDS–polyacrylamide gel electrophoresis (SDS–PAGE) and electrophoretic transfers, we use the Bio-Rad Protean IIxi or Mini-Protean II vertical electrophoresis systems together with the respective Trans-Blot apparatus as manufactured by Bio-Rad. Broad-range SDS-PAGE molecular weight markers (Cat. No. 161-0317) and prestained markers (Cat. No. 161-0395) were also obtained from Bio-Rad. The following materials were purchased from Amersham: ECL-Western blotting detection kit (Cat. No. RPN 2106), ECL-Hyperfilm (Cat. No. RPN 2103), horseradish peroxidase–secondary antibodies (Cat. No. NA 934), HRP–streptavi-

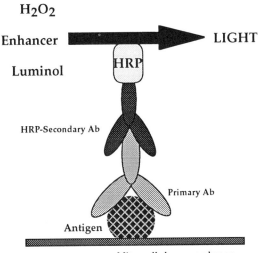

H₂O₂

Enhancer ➡ LIGHT

Luminol

HRP

HRP-Secondary Ab

Primary Ab

Antigen

Nitrocellulose membrane

FIGURE 1 The principle of ECL detection. Simplified depiction of the reactions involved in ECL detection. Ab, antibody; HRP, horseradish peroxidase.

din (Cat. No. RPN 1051), ^{125}I-protein A (Cat. No. IM 144), Na^{125}I (Cat. No. IMS 300). We purchased the following from Sigma: Ponceau S (Cat. No. P-3504), HRP–protein A (Cat. No. P-8651), bovine serum albumin (fraction V, Cat. No. A-3425), D-biotin-N-hydroxysuccinimide ester (BNHS, Cat. No. H-1759), and exposure cassettes (Cat. No. E-9385). Nitrocellulose membranes were obtained either from Schleicher & Schuell (PH79, pore size 0.1 μm, Cat. No. 402 093) or from Hoefer Scientific Instruments (pore size 0.45 μm, Cat. No. TM-NC4). An eight-lane incubation tray for nitrocellulose strips is available from Schleicher & Schuell (Cat. No. 448 000). Iodo-Gen was obtained from Pierce (Cat. No. 28600), and prepacked PD-10 Sephadex G-25M columns (Cat. No. 17-0851-01) were purchased from Pharmacia. Spectra/Por dialysis membranes with a molecular weight cutoff of 6000–8000 were from Spectrum (Cat. No. 132 677). All other chemicals and reagents were of the highest purity commercially available.

III. Procedures

A. LABELING OF PROTEINS AND LIGANDS

1. Radioiodination of Proteins

Radioiodination of proteins can be carried out according to the following method, which was adapted from a previously published procedure (Fraker and Speck, 1978). This method yields ^{125}I-proteins of high specific activity (greater than 5–50 mCi/mg) with only minor radioinactivation. Protein solutions for iodinations should be free of interfering substances such as azide, detergents, bromide, and urea. The molar ratio of Na^{125}I to protein in the labeling reaction should be at least 1:1. To separate the radiolabeled ^{125}I-protein from free Na^{125}I, a gel filtration column (e.g., Sephadex G-25M, bed volume 10 ml) equilibrated with TBS may be used instead of, or in addition to, the dialysis step described below (step 5).

Solutions

1. *Tris-Buffered Saline (TBS):* To make 1 liter of a 10× TBS stock, dissolve 80 g NaCl, 2 g KCl, 11.5 g Na$_2$HPO$_4$, and 2 g KH$_2$PO$_4$ in water. Sterilize 20 min at

121°C and store at room temperature. Dilute tenfold using sterile H_2O to give a 1× working solution.

2. *Iodo-Gen (Pierce):* Dissolve 1 mg of Iodo-Gen in 1 ml of chloroform.

3. *Protein:* Dissolve 1 mg protein to be radiolabeled in 5 ml TBS, aliquot, and store frozen at −70°C.

Steps

1. Add 100 μl of Iodo-Gen solution into a screw-cap Eppendorf tube and evaporate with a stream of nitrogen. Add another 100 μl of chloroform and evaporate as before.

2. Add 150 μl of protein solution in TBS (30 μg) into the test tube and place the tube inside a lead container in the fume hood.

3. In the fume hood, withdraw 10 μl of the Na[125]I solution (1 mCi) with a Hamilton syringe by piercing the rubber septum in the lid of the vial.

4. Carefully transfer the Na[125]I into the tube containing the protein to be labeled and tightly close it. Label for 15 min with gentle agitation on a rotary shaker, or gently vortex the tube a few times over a 15-min period.

5. Cover the Eppendorf tube with a piece of dialysis membrane of desired molecular weight cutoff (e.g., 6000–8000) and close it tightly using the screw cap. *Before* screwing the cap onto the tube containing the labeling mixture, punch a few holes in it using a hot needle. Stick the test tube *inverted* into a piece of styrofoam and dialyze labeling mixture in a glass beaker filled with 1 liter TBS for 1–2 hr. Change buffer and repeat dialysis until the radioactivity in the dialysis solution is lower than 3000 cpm/ml.

6. Centrifuge the test tube for 2 sec at full speed in a microfuge to collect ^{125}I-protein solution at the bottom of the tube and place in a lead container. Store at 4°C or, alternatively, at −70°C in aliquots placed inside a lead container. Calculate the specific activity of radiolabeled protein.

2. Biotinylation of Proteins

This general procedure can be readily adapted for the labeling of a given protein. Best results are obtained using a molar ratio of protein to biotin greater than 5:1 (Roach and Noël, 1987).

Solution

1. *Biotinylation reagent:* Dissolve 2 mg of BNHS in 100 μl of dimethylformamide. Prepare fresh before use.

Step

1. Add biotinylation reagent to protein dissolved in a non-Tris (nonamino group)-containing buffer, *gently* vortex, cover vial with aluminum foil, and incubate at room temperature for 1 hr. Dialyze overnight at 4°C against the labeling buffer. On the following morning, change dialysis solution and continue dialysis for at least 8 hr. Store biotinylated proteins protected from light.

B. WESTERN BLOTTING

1. Western Blotting Using ECL Detection

Solutions

We find that the following solutions give the most consistent and reproducible results. A complete list of alternate buffers and recipes is described elsewhere (Harlow and Lane, 1988).

1. *Ponceau stain:* Prepare a 10× stock solution by dissolving 30 g of trichloroacetic acid and 30 g of sulfosalicylic acid in 100 ml distilled H_2O. Then add 2 g of Ponceau S and dissolve. A 1× working dilution in distilled H_2O can be reused many times and stored at ambient temperature.

2. *TBS-Triton X-100 (TBS-T):* To make TBS-T, add 5 ml of a 20% (w/v) Triton X-100 detergent solution per liter of 1× TBS, and store TBS-T at room temperature.

3. *Blocking buffer (Blotto):* Dissolve 50 g of nonfat dry milk (any brand) in 880 ml of sterile H_2O and stir for a few hours to dissolve milk completely. Add 100 ml of 10× TBS, 5 ml of a 20% (w/v) Triton X-100 detergent solution, and 10 ml of a stock of 1 *M* sodium azide (a 100× stock is 65 g in 100 ml distilled H_2O). Blotto-containing azide may be stored at 4°C for more than 2 months. (*Caution: Sodium azide is highly toxic.*)

4. *HRP–protein A:* Dissolve 1 mg of HRP–protein A in 2 ml sterile TBS and store frozen in 50- to 100-μl aliquots at −20°C. Avoid repeated freeze–thaw cycles. Use at 1/5000 to 1/20,000 dilutions prepared in TBS-T **without** azide.

Steps

1. After SDS–PAGE, electroblot proteins onto nitrocellulose membranes (see article by Julio E. Celis, Jette B. Lauridsen, and Bodil Basse this volume). Immerse the nitrocellulose membrane in Ponceau stain for 2–10 min with gentle agitation, rinse briefly with distilled H_2O, and mark the position of the molecular weight standards with a pencil or ballpoint pen. If necessary, wrap wet nitrocellulose membrane in Saran wrap and cut into strips using a scalpel blade.

2. Wash membrane briefly with small volume of Blotto to remove Ponceau stain. Add fresh Blotto and block the membrane by shaking for at least 2 hr at room temperature or overnight at 4°C.

3. Remove Blotto by aspiration and add primary antibody diluted in fresh Blotto (dilution may vary between 1:100 to 1:100,000 depending on antibody affinity). Incubate either for 1–2 hr at room temperature or overnight at 4°C with gentle agitation. Remove antibody solution and store at 4°C. Many antibody dilutions may be reused several times.

4. Wash membrane three or four times for 10–15 min in a large volume of TBS-T *without* azide. Membranes should float freely in wash buffer.

5. Add appropriate amount of HRP-conjugated secondary antibody or HRP–protein A (diluted 1:5000–1:20,000) in TBS-T and incubate for 30–60 min with gentle agitation. Discard secondary antibody solution, rinse once in TBS-T, and wash three times for 5–10 min in a large volume of TBS-T (10–20 ml/25 cm^2).

6. Place membrane briefly on Whatman 3MM to remove excess liquid and put in a plastic vessel. Add ECL solution I (approximately 1 ml volume/20 cm^2 of membrane) and completely wet membrane. Add equal volume of ECL solution II and incubate for 60 sec. Flip membrane a few times using flat tweezers.

7. Quickly remove the membrane and place briefly between two Whatman 3MM sheets to soak excess solution, but do not dry completely. Cover the membrane on both sides with Saran wrap and put into an exposure cassette with the protein side facing up.

8. In the darkroom, press a piece of film for 10–20 sec onto the plastic-wrapped membrane and develop. Examine the developed film to decide if additional exposures are needed. Exposure times between 20 sec and 2 min are optimal. The ECL signal output is greatest 1–5 min after detection with a decay half-life of about 1 hr. After complete decay, blots may be redetected as before or stored at −20°C.

9. ECL blots can be stripped and reprobed with different antibodies several times by placing the membrane in *stripping buffer* (60 mM Tris–HCl, pH 6.7, 2% SDS w/v, 100 mM β-mercaptoethanol) and shaking for 30 min at 50°C. Membranes are then ready for reblocking and redetection as described.

2. Western Blotting Using ^{125}I-Protein A Detection

Solution

^{125}I-*Protein A:* For radioiodination of proteins, see the method described in Section A1. ^{125}I-Protein A can also be purchased from various vendors. Specific activity should be greater than 30 mCi/mg protein.

Steps

1–4. Essentially as described in Section B1, steps 1–4.

5. Add 2 µCi of ^{125}I-protein A (specific activity > 30 mCi/mg) in 5–10 ml of TBS-T and incubate at room temperature for 30 min with gentle shaking. Rinse membrane once in TBS-T and wash three or four times for 10–15 min with each 20–30 ml TBS-T.

6. Remove membrane from final wash solution and dry briefly on Whatman 3 MM paper. Then wrap in Saran wrap and expose to Kodak XAR-5 film in an exposure cassette. Exposure times usually range from 5 to 48 hr at −70°C using two intensifying screens (Swanstrom and Shank, 1978).

3. Quantitative Analysis of Western Blots

Results obtained from quantitative analysis of immunoblots have to be interpreted with caution due to the differences in efficiency of electrophoretic transfer of polypeptides of various molecular weights. If, however, proteins of the *same* mobility are to be quantified relative to each other, densitometric scanning of autoradiographs obtained by either ECL or ^{125}I detection is a legitimate way to quantify immunoblots. A major drawback of quantitative analysis is the nonlinearity of film response to low levels of light (or radioactivity) and to longer exposure times. This problem can be completely overcome by exposing the blots at −70°C to preflashed X-ray film

(Laskey and Mills, 1977). Preflashing can be done by preexposing X-ray film to an instantaneous flash of light for approximately 1 msec as generated by a photographic flash gun. The optical density of the unexposed film should increase to $A_{540\ nm}$ = 0.1–0.2 (Laskey and Mills, 1977) to result in optimal hypersensitization of the X-ray film. In the case of ^{125}I-detected blots, the area on the membrane containing the band of interest may also be cut out and quantitated in a scintillation counter.

4. Pitfalls

1. If there is *no signal,* the problem may be (1) a poor electrophoretic transfer, (2) target protein degradation, (3) poor protein retention on the membrane, (4) too dilute antibody solutions, (5) a wrong secondary antibody (e.g., HRP–goat anti-rabbit for mouse primary antibodies, or protein A for non-protein A-binding antibodies), or (6) the presence of azide in the TBS-T washing buffer (HRP is strongly inhibited by azide). Thus, azide may only be added to Blotto, and primary antibody dilutions and must be omitted in all subsequent steps.

2. *High background* is the most common problem during ECL-based detection methods. In almost all of the cases, a unsatisfactorily high signal/noise ratio can be virtually eliminated by (1) increasing the length of TBS-T washes and raising the detergent concentration in TBS-T to up to 1%; (2) using higher dilutions of primary and/or secondary antibodies; or (3) using HRP–protein A, HRP–protein G (because some of the monoclonal IgG subclasses are not recognized by protein A), or HRP–F(ab′)$_2$ fragments instead of species-specific HRP–secondary antibodies (Harlow and Lane, 1988).

C. LIGAND BLOTTING AND REVERSE LIGAND BLOTTING

The sensitivity of ECL detection can be even further increased using biotinylated secondary antibodies or ligands followed by HRP–streptavidin; however, the basic ECL detection procedure remains the same as described in Section B. Thus, a basic and generalized protocol for ligand blotting (Daniel *et al.,* 1983) and reverse ligand blotting (Stifani *et al.,* 1990) experiments using either labeled (biotinylated or radiolabeled) or unlabeled ligands will be provided. These blotting experiments allow the identification and characterization of receptor–ligand interactions. The individual steps involved are very simple and can be easily adapted to a given experiment and to the individual investigator's needs. We want to emphasize that solutions used in this procedure were optimized for one particular kind of receptor–ligand interaction, the interaction of chicken oocyte membrane lipoprotein receptors with their cognate ligands (George *et al.,* 1987). It is realized that other receptors will require different binding buffers and/or binding conditions; however, the basic procedure remains the same, and the outline described below can be considered a starting point for setting up ligand blotting and reverse ligand blotting experiments.

1. Ligand Blotting Using ECL or [^{125}I]Iodine Detection

Solutions

1. *Ligand blot buffer (LBB):* 20 mM Tris–HCl, 90 mM NaCl, and 2 mM CaCl$_2$, pH 8. To make 1 liter of LBB, mix 20 ml of 1 M Tris–HCl, pH 8 (121.1 g of Tris base/liter, adjust pH with 10 M HCl), 22.5 ml of 4 M NaCl (233.8 g of NaCl/liter), and 2 ml of 1 M CaCl$_2$·2H$_2$O (147.02 g of CaCl$_2$·2H$_2$O per liter).

2. *Blocking solution (BS):* Dissolve 5 g of bovine serum albumin (fraction V)

in 100 ml of sterile LBB. Filter through 0.45-μm Millipore unit to sterilize and to remove any particles, and store at 4°C.

3. *Solubilized receptor:* Membrane receptors are solubilized by treating isolated membranes with desired detergents in appropriate solubilization buffers.

4. *Ligands:* Both labeled (biotinylated or ^{125}I) and unlabeled ligands, to which antibodies are available, can be employed.

Steps

1. Load 50–100 μg of solubilized membrane protein and run out on a 4.5–18% gradient, one-lane SDS–PAGE minigel. Transfer the proteins to nitrocellulose.

2. After transfer, briefly stain the membrane with Ponceau S and, using a scalpel, trim the margins of the nitrocellulose such that there is protein from vertical edge to vertical edge. Cut the membrane into vertical strips approximately 3 mm wide.

3. Number strips with a ballpoint pen and place into individual lanes in an eight-lane disposable Schleicher & Schuell incubation tray. Add 1.5 ml of BS and incubate on a shaker for 2 hr at room temperature or overnight at 4°C.

4. Add appropriate amount of labeled (biotin, ^{125}I-ligand) or unlabeled ligand freshly diluted in BS. Incubate for 1 hr at room temperature with gentle agitation. If conducting competition experiments, preincubate the strips with competing ligand(s) for 1 hr prior to adding the ligand (only possible with a labeled ligand).

5. Briefly rinse the strips using two changes of LBB, then wash three times for 10 min each with LBB. Ligand blots incubated with a ^{125}I-ligand can now be exposed to film.

6. To each lane, add 1.5 ml of diluted (1:750) HRP–streptavidin (for a biotinylated ligand) or primary antibody (at 1/200–1/1000 dilution in BS) against the unlabeled ligand and incubate for 1 hr at room temperature with gentle agitation.

7. Wash as in step 5, and perform ECL detection for the HRP–streptavidin as described in Section B1, steps 6–8. If unlabeled ligand was used, now add HRP-protein A at 1/2000 in BS and incubate for 30 min at room temperature.

8. Wash strips as in step 5. Perform ECL detection as described in Section B1, steps 6–8.

2. Reverse Ligand Blotting Using ECL or [^{125}I]Iodine Detection

The basic method is the same as for ligand blotting, except that a purified ligand immobilized on a nitrocellulose membrane is incubated with solubilized membranes containing the receptor of interest.

Solutions

1. *Ligand blot buffer with detergent (LBB-T):* Add appropriate detergent (e.g., Triton X-100 or Tween 20) to LBB, at desired concentrations.

2. *Antireceptor primary antibody:* Use labeled (biotin or ^{125}I-iodinated) or unlabeled purified antibodies (e.g., IgG) against receptor to be studied.

Steps

1. Load and run an optimized amount of ligand (usually 0.1–5 μg protein per lane) on an SDS–PAGE gel, transfer the protein to a nitrocellulose membrane, and block the membrane for 2 hr in BS at room temperature or overnight at 4°C.

2. To 10 ml of LBB-T, add solubilized membrane protein (amount depends on receptor abundance) and incubate on a shaker for 1 hr.

3. Briefly rinse the membrane using two changes of LBB-T, then wash three times for 10 min each in LBB-T.

4. Dilute primary antibody against the receptor (determine optimal dilution) in LBB-T and incubate membrane in 10 ml of this solution for 1–2 hr at ambient temperature.

5. Wash membrane as in step 4 and, if the primary antibody is unlabeled, add diluted HRP–protein A or HRP–secondary antibody (1:5000 in LBB-T containing 5% BSA). Incubate with agitation in 10 ml of this solution for 1 hr. If the primary antibody is biotinylated, add HRP–streptavidin; if the primary antibody is iodinated, wash as described in Section B1, step 5, and expose to X-ray film.

6. Wash membrane as in step 4 and perform ECL detection as described in Section B1, steps 6–8.

3. Pitfalls

1. The high calcium content makes Blotto unsuitable as blocking buffer in most ligand blotting experiments.

2. Always check for nonspecific binding of HRP–streptavidin by running a lane of receptor without biotinylated ligand.

3. All incubations with biotinylated ligand should be done in the dark.

ACKNOWLEDGMENT

We thank Wolfgang Schneider for critical and helpful comments on the manuscript.

REFERENCES

Daniel, T., Schneider, W., Goldstein, J., and Brown, M. (1983) Visualization of lipoprotein receptors by ligand blotting. *J. Biol. Chem.* **258**, 4606–4611.

Fraker, P., and Speck, J. (1978) Protein and cell membrane iodinations with a sparingly soluble chloroamide, 1,3,4,6-tetrachloro-3α,6α-diphenylglycoluril. *Biochem. Biophys. Res. Commun.* **80**, 849–857.

George, R., Barber, D. L., and Schneider, W. J. (1987) Characterization of the chicken oocyte receptor for low and very low density lipoproteins. *J. Biol. Chem.* **262**, 16838–16847.

Harlow, E., and Lane, D. (1988) "Antibodies: A Laboratory Manual." Cold Spring Harbor Laboratory Press, Cold Spring Harbor, NY.

Laskey, R., and Mills, A. (1977) Enhanced autoradiographic detection of ^{32}P and ^{125}I using intensifying screens and hypersensitized film. *FEBS Lett.* **82**, 314–317.

Roach, P., and Noël, S.-P. (1987) Biotinylation of low density lipoproteins via free amino groups without loss of receptor binding activity. *J. Lipid Res.* **28**, 1508–1514.

Stifani, S., Nimpf, J., and Schneider, W. J. (1990) Vitellogenesis in *Xenopus laevis* and chicken: Cognate ligands and oocyte receptors. *J. Biol. Chem.* **265**, 882–888.

Swanstrom, R., and Shank, P. (1978) X-ray intensifying screens greatly enhance the detection by autoradiography of the radioactive isotopes ^{32}P and ^{125}I. *Anal. Biochem.* **86**, 184–192.

Enzyme-Linked Immunosorbent Assay

Hedvig Perlmann and Peter Perlmann

I. Introduction

The enzyme-linked immunosorbent assay (ELISA) (Engvall and Perlmann, 1971) is a highly versatile and sensitive technique which can be used for qualitative or quantitative determinations of practically any antigen or antibody. Reagents are stable, nonradioactive, and, in many cases, commercially available. The use of microtiter plates as the solid phase and the availability of microtiter plate readers have undoubtedly added to the usefulness and popularity of the method. In the following we give three examples of protocols. These are *indirect ELISA to determine antibodies, competitive ELISA to define antigenic specificities*, and *sandwich ELISA to detect antigens*. Enzyme-conjugated reagents are also used to determine antigen expression on the surface of cells in tissue culture or antibodies to these (Koho *et al.*, 1984). For the many modifications and applications the literature should be consulted (e.g., see Hornbeck, 1991a,b; Maloy *et al.*, 1991; Nutman, 1991).

II. Materials and Instrumentation

Flat-bottomed microtiter plates: Maxisorp from Nunc or High Binding from Costar

Round-bottomed microtiter plates for preparation of dilutions

Micropipet, multichannel pipet, and disposable pipet tips (Finnpipette, Lab Systems OY)

V_{max} Kinetic Microplate Reader with computer program SOFTmax from Molecular Devices Corporation

Microplate washer (Titertek, ICN Biomedicals)

III. Procedures

A. ALKALINE PHOSPHATASE CONJUGATION

See Engvall and Perlmann (1972).

Solutions

1. *ALP:* Alkaline phosphatase, type VII-S, 10,000 U = 3–5 mg protein (Cat. No. P-5521, Sigma Chemical Co.).

2. *PBS (phosphate-buffered saline) 10× stock solution:* 40 g Na$_2$HPO$_4$·12H$_2$O, 5 g KH$_2$PO$_4$, 81 g NaCl, H$_2$O to 1000 ml.

3. *Glutardialdehyde:* From Merck, for electron microscopy.

4. *Tris buffer, pH 8.0:* 4.44 g Tris–HCl, 2.65 g Tris base, 203 mg MgCl, 200 mg NaN$_3$, and H$_2$O to 1000 ml.

Steps

1. Centrifuge (2000 rpm) 3–4 mg ALP. Discard supernatant.

2. Add 1 mg of affinity-purified polyclonal antibodies or monoclonal antibodies purified by ammonium sulfate precipitation to the pellet.

3. Dialyze against PBS (1× concn) 4 hr at room temperature.

4. Weigh dialysate and add 8 μl 25% glutardialdehyde per gram of solution.

5. Mix on roller drum at 4°C overnight.

6. Dialyze against PBS (1× concn) at 4°C overnight and then against Tris buffer, pH 8.0.

7. Add 0.5% BSA and store at 4°C.

B. BIOTINYLATION OF IMMUNOGLOBULIN

See Herzman and Richards (1974).

Solutions

1. *0.1 M NaHCO$_3$:* 84.01 g/1000 ml H$_2$O.

2. *DMF:* N,N-dimethylformamide (BDH).

3. *Biotin:* D-biotinyl-ε-aminocaproic acid N-hydroxysuccinimide ester (Boehringer-Mannheim, Cat. No. 1008960).

Steps

1. Dialyze affinity-purified polyclonal antibodies or monoclonal antibodies purified by ammonium sulfate precipitation against 0.1 *M* NaHCO$_3$ at 4°C overnight, and adjust to 1 mg/ml.

2. Dissolve 1 mg biotin in 100 μl ice-cold DMF in a glass tube (keep dark). Immediately before the next step, add 900 μl ice-cold, filtered 0.1 *M* NaHCO$_3$.

3. Mix 1 ml antibody (1 mg/ml) with 200 μl biotin (1 mg/ml). Keep the tube dark in an ice bath for 2 hr and then 4 hr at room temperature with occasional shaking.

4. Dialyze overnight at 4°C against PBS containing 0.02% NaN$_3$.

5. Add 0.5% BSA and store at 4°C.

C. OPTIMAL REAGENT CONCENTRATIONS

1. *Concentration of coating reagent:* The plastic solid phase is practically saturated when coated with the reagent at a concentration of 10 μg/ml. Try 10 μg/ml down to 1 μg/ml in coating buffer, pH 9.6. (Some proteins adhere better to

the plate at lower pH. For unknown antigens or monoclonals, try PBS or a buffer of pH ~ 5.)

2. *Concentration of test reagent.* If possible use one known positive, one known negative, and a standard. Find the concentration at which the known positive sample gives a good positive reading and responds to dilution.

3. *Concentration of developing reagent.* Commercial enzyme conjugates usually have a recommended concentration. Try a few dilutions around that, e.g., 1/500, 1/1000, 1/2000, and 1/4000. Choose the lowest concentration ensuring excess; the only limiting factor in the setup should be the amount of test reagent.

D. ELISA PROTOCOLS

Solutions

1. *Coating buffer, pH 9.6:* 1.59 g Na_2CO_3, 2.93 g $NaHCO_3$, 200 mg NaN_3, H_2O to 1000 ml.

2. *Incubation (diluent) buffer:* 100 ml PBS stock (10×), 5 g BSA (bovine serum albumin), 0.5 ml Tween 20, 1 ml 20% NaN_3, H_2O to 1000 ml.

3. *Washing buffer:* 45 g NaCl, 2.5 ml Tween 20 (0.05%), H_2O to 5000 ml.

4. *Enzyme substrate buffer:* 97 ml diethanolamine, 800 ml H_2O, 1 ml 20% NaN_3, 101 mg $MgCl_2 \cdot 6H_2O$ (should be added last). Adjust to final pH 9.8 with 1 M HCl (~100 ml).

5. *Substrate for ALP:* NPP (*p*-nitrophenyl phosphate, 5-mg tablets, Sigma Chemical Co.), 1 tablet/5 ml of enzyme substrate buffer.

6. *Streptavidin–ALP:* From Sigma Chemical Company.

1. Indirect ELISA for Screening Specific Antibodies in Serum or Hybridoma Supernatants

Reactants

1. *Antigen.*

2. *Antibody specific for test antigen.*

3. *Anti-immunoglobulin enzyme conjugate.*

4. *Substrate.*

Steps

1. Coat plate with 50 μl/well antigen, diluted in coating buffer, pH 9.6, overnight at 4°C.

2. Block with 100 μl/well incubation buffer for 1 hr at 37°C. Wash four times with washing buffer.

3. Add 50 μl/well immune serum, e.g., 1/1000, or hybridoma supernatant, e.g., 1/5, in incubation buffer. Incubate for 1 hr at 37°C. Wash four times with washing buffer.

4. Add 50 μl/well ALP-conjugated relevant anti-immunoglobulin (e.g., goat anti-human γ chains, rabbit anti-mouse Ig) diluted in incubation buffer. Incubate for 1 hr at 37°C. Wash four times with washing buffer.

5. Develop with fresh NPP, 50 μl/well, and read absorbance at 405 nm.

2. **Competitive ELISA for Defining Antigenic Specificities and Determining Possible Antigenic Cross-Reactivity between Antigens**

Reactants

1. *Antigen.*
2. *Serial dilutions of test antigen + antibody specific for test antigen.*
3. *Anti-immunoglobulin enzyme conjugate.*
4. *Substrate.*

Steps

1. Coat plate with 50 μl/well antigen, diluted in coating buffer, pH 9.6, overnight at 4°C.

2. Block with 100 μl/well incubation buffer, 1 hr at 37°C. Wash four times with washing buffer.

3. Mix 40 μl of serial dilutions of test antigen diluted in incubation buffer and 40 μl/well of an immune serum with known specificity, diluted in incubation buffer in round-bottomed microtiter plates. Incubate for 1 hr at 37°C and transfer 50 μl of the mixtures to the coated plate; incubate for 4 hr at room temperature. Wash four times with washing buffer.

4. Add 50 μl/well relevant ALP-conjugated anti-immunoglobulin diluted in incubation buffer. Incubate for 1 hr at 37°C. Wash four times with washing buffer.

5. Develop with fresh NPP, 100 μl/well, and read absorbance at 405 nm.

3. **Sandwich ELISA for Detecting Antigens**

Reactants

1. *Capture antibody specific for test antigen.*
2. *Antigen.*
3. *Biotinylated antibody specific for test antigen:* See Section IV.
4. *Streptavidin–ALP.*
5. *Substrate.*

Steps

1. Coat plate overnight at 4°C with 50 μl/well antigen-specific monoclonal antibody diluted in PBS or antigen-specific polyclonal antibody diluted in coating buffer.

2. Block with 100 μl/well incubation buffer for 1 hr at 37°C. Wash four times with washing buffer.

3. Add 50 μl/well test antigen (e.g. cell culture supernatants or serum dilutions). Incubate for 1 hr at 37°C. Wash four times with washing buffer.

4. Add 50 μl/well biotinylated monoclonal antibody specific for a different determinant of the antigen, or biotinylated polyclonal antibody of the same antigen specificity as used for coating (see Section IV) diluted in incubation buffer. Incubate for 1 hr at 37°C. Wash four times with washing buffer.

5. Add 50 μl/well ALP-conjugated streptavidin, 1/2000 in incubation buffer, 1 hr at 37°C. Wash four times with washing buffer.

6. Develop with fresh NPP, 50 μl/well, and read absorbance at 405 nm.

IV. Comments

A. CONTROLS

Four to eight wells in every plate are used for blanks (substrate, but no reagents) and the mean value is subtracted from test values. All samples are set up in duplicates. Negative controls with incubation buffer replacing the reagents should always be included and should give OD readings well below OD 0.100. Particularly in the two-site sandwich applications (ELISA, Section IIID3) it is essential that the capture antibody does not bind to the second antibody and vice versa. For screening of unknown samples, and comparison between different runs, include a known positive sample as reference. For estimation of background, include expected negatives, e.g., nonimmune sera (ELISA, Section IIID1), cell culture medium, or irrelevant antigen (ELISA, Section IIID3).

B. BLOCKING

After coating, vacant protein binding sites on the plastic surface should be blocked. BSA, casein, milk powder, and gelatin are commonly used. To avoid cross-reactive antibody binding to the blocking protein the same protein as used for dilution of the reagents should be included in the incubation (diluent) buffer.

C. INCUBATION TIMES

Coating the plates overnight is often practical and the coated plates can be stored for several weeks at 4°C, wrapped in plastic film. Coating for 3–4 hr at room temperature or 1 hr at 37°C may often be enough. The same holds true for the specific binding of the reagents. The signal may be significantly increased by longer incubations, but shorter incubations at 37°C may suffice as well. Development of color with the substrate varies in time but requires usually between 10 and 60 min.

D. AMPLIFICATION

Amplification of the signal may be obtained, e.g., by use of an extra layer such as enzyme-conjugated anti-immunoglobulin as the developing reagent in the ELISA protocol described in Section IIID1 or biotinylated antibody followed by streptavidin–enzyme conjugate as developing reagent in the ELISA protocol described in Section IIID3.

E. SANDWICH ELISA

Antibody sandwich ELISAs are sensitive and very useful for detection of antigen, e.g., cytokines, in cell culture supernatants. As an example, for determining human interleukin-4 (IL-4) according to the ELISA protocol in Section IIID3, we use monoclonal antibodies of two different specificities against IL-4. For isotype determinations in human serum or lymphocyte culture supernatants we use goat or rabbit antibodies made highly Fc specific by affinity purification. The same polyvalent antibody preparation can be used both as capture antibody and as enzyme-conjugated or biotinylated second antibody. For IgG subclass determinations, we use monoclonal antibodies as capture antibodies and Fc-specific, affinity-purified (depleted of anti-mouse Ig reactivity) goat anti-human IgG as second antibody. For quantitation of isotypes or IgG subclasses, standard immunoglobulin preparations or myeloma protein solutions of known concentrations are commercially available.

F. QUANTITATION

For quantitation of specific antibodies (Section IIID1) a standard curve is prepared with serial dilutions (e.g., 300, 100, 30, 10, 3, and 1 ng/ml) of a relevant standard immunoglobulin in wells coated with affinity purified anti-immunoglobulin instead of the antigen. The linear range from a log–log curve is used for interpolation of the experimental values. Similarly, the amount of antigen can be determined in a sandwich ELISA (Section IIID3) with the help of a standard curve with known amounts of the antigen run in parallel. One standard curve can be used for several plates if care is taken that all plates are developed for the same time.

G. SYNTHETIC PEPTIDES

When the antigen is a short peptide (<20 amino acids) it may have to be coupled to a carrier protein for coating. This protein should also be used for blocking and in the incubation (diluent) buffer.

V. Pitfalls

A. HIGH BACKGROUNDS

Purity and specificity of the reagents are the basic requirements for reliable ELISA determinations. Furthermore the sensitivity of the assay depends on low background. Therefore low OD readings of the negative controls are absolutely essential. With appropriate controls it is possible to identify reagents giving rise to unwanted binding of the enzyme conjugate and to remove the possible cross-reacting antibodies by affinity purification and/or neutralization.

B. COMPETITIVE ANTIBODIES

When determining antigen-specific antibodies (Section IIID1) of a certain isotype or IgG subclass, problems may arise if antibodies of other isotypes with higher affinity do compete for the same antigenic sites. If the relative concentration of the test antibody is high enough, that problem may be solved by coating with a capture antibody specific for its isotype or subclass, followed by addition of the sample and then the antigen conjugated with enzyme or biotin.

C. ADSORPTION-INDUCED PROTEIN DENATURATION

Loss of functional activity of antibodies (as much as 90% for polyclonal antibodies and all for some monoclonal antibodies) due to adsorption to polystyrene requires serious consideration (Butler *et al.*, 1992). Changes in the conformation of antigens at coating may lead to masking of native epitopes as well as to exposure of "new" epitopes. Of interest in this context is the finding of Jitsukawa *et al.* (1980) that by mixing antigen or antibody with a stabilizing protein such as BSA (10 μg/ml), a considerably increased coating efficiency may be achieved.

REFERENCES

Butler, J. E., Ni, L., Nessler, R., Joshi, K. S., Suter, M., Rosenberg, B., Chang, J., Brown, W. R., and Cantarero, L. A. (1992) The physical and functional behavior of capture antibodies adsorbed on polystyrene. *J. Immunol. Methods* **150**, 77–90.

Engvall, E., and Perlmann, P. (1971) Enzyme-linked immunosorbent assay (ELISA). Quantitative assay of immunoglobulin G. *Immunochemistry* **18**, 871–874.

Engvall, E., and Perlmann, P. (1972) Enzyme-linked immunosorbent assay (ELISA). III. Quantitation of specific antibodies by enzyme-labeled anti-immunoglobulin in antigen-coated tubes. *J. Immunol.* **109**, 129–135.

Herzman, H., and Richards, R. M. (1974) Use of avidin–biotin complex for staining of biological membranes in electron microscopy. *Proc. Natl. Acad. Sci. USA* **71**, 3537.

Hornbeck, P. (1991a) Enzyme-linked immunosorbent assays. *In* "Current Protocols in Immunology" (J. E. Coligan, A. M. Kruisbeek, D. H. Margulies, E. M. Shevach, and W. Strober, NIH, eds.), pp. 2.1.1–2.1.22. Greene Publishing Associates and Wiley-Interscience, New York.

Hornbeck, P. (1991b) Isotype determination of antibodies. *In* "Current Protocols in Immunology" (J. E. Coligan, A. M. Kruisbeek, D. H. Margulies, E. M. Shevach, and W. Strober, NIH, eds.), pp. 2.2.1–2.2.6.

Jitsukawa, T., Nakajima, S., Sugawara, I., and Watanabe, H. (1980) Increased coating efficiency of antigens and preservation of original antigenic structure after coating in ELISA. *J. Immunol. Methods* **116**, 251–257.

Koho, H., Paulie, S., Ben-Aissa, H., Jonsdottir, I., Hansson, Y., Lundblad, M-L., and Perlmann, P. (1984) Monoclonal antibodies to antigens associated with transitional cell carcinoma of the urinary bladder. I. Determination of the selectivity of six antibodies by cell ELISA and immunofluorescence. *Cancer Immunol. Immunother.* **17**, 165–172.

Maloy, W. L., Coligan, J. E., and Paterson, Y. (1991) Indirect ELISA to determine antipeptide antibody titer. *In* "Current Protocols in Immunology" (J. E. Coligan, A. M. Kruisbeek, D. H. Margulies, E. M. Shevach, and W. Strober, NIH, eds.), pp. 9.4.8–9.4.11. Greene Publishing Associates and Wiley-Interscience, New York.

Nutman, T. B. (1991) Measurement of polyclonal immunoglobulin synthesis using ELISA. *In* "Current Protocols in Immunology" (J. E. Coligan, A. M. Kruisbeek, D. H. Margulies, E. M. Shevach, and W. Strober, NIH, eds.), pp. 2.12.1–2.12.6. Greene Publishing Associates and Wiley-Interscience, New York.

A Simple Solid-Phase Mutual Inhibition Assay Using Biotinylated Antigen for Analyzing the Epitope Specificities of Monoclonal Antibodies

Masahide Kuroki

I. Introduction

The most conventional method for epitope mapping of monoclonal antibodies (mAbs) is the competitive solid-phase assay in which the antigen is immobilized and a labeled antibody as well as competing unlabeled antibodies are mixed in solution (Kaufman and Goldsby, 1982; Wagener *et al.*, 1984). Although this method facilitates separation of free from bound antibody, it possesses the problem of labeling all antibodies to be tested. As the number of mAbs to be handled is usually large, this method is time consuming and tedious. This article describes a solid-phase mutual inhibition assay for determination of epitope specificities of mAbs by using 96-well plates coated with mAbs, competitor mAbs, biotinylated antigen (Bayer and Wilchek, 1990), and avidin–peroxidase conjugate. The exchange of competing and immobilized antibodies in this assay system does not demand additional labeling procedures (Kuroki *et al.*, 1992b). With carcinoembryonic antigen (CEA) as a model antigen, the mutual inhibition assay was developed for seven different anti-CEA mAbs tested.

II. Materials and Instrumentation

N-Hydroxysuccinimidobiotin (NHSB, MW = 341.4, Cat. No. H-1759) and *N,N*-dimethylformamide (Cat. No. D-4254) were obtained from Sigma Chemical Company. Hydrogen peroxide (H_2O_2, 30%, Cat. No. 13-1910), *o*-phenylenediamine (OPD, Cat. No. 24-1780), and two preservatives, methyl *p*-hydroxybenzoate (MHB, Cat. No. 19-3480) and propyl *p*-hydroxybenzoate (PHB, Cat. No. 24-6245), were from Katayama Chemical Industries Company, Ltd. Nonidet P-40 (NP-40, Cat. No. 71-5705) was from Iwai Kagaku Company, Ltd.; horseradish peroxidase (HRP)–avidin D from Vector Laboratories, Inc.; bovine serum albumin (BSA) from Boehringer-Mannheim GmbH; 96-well polystyrene plates (Immulon 2, Cat. No. 011-010-3450) from Dynatech Laboratories, Inc.; 1-ml small reaction vials with internal cone (Reacti-Vial, Cat. No. 13221) from Pierce Chemical Company; a microtiter plate reader (Titertek Multiskan MCC) and a plate washer (Titertek S8/12) from Flow Labs–ICN; and a plate shaker (Tomy Mixer Z) from Tomy Seiko Company, Ltd. CEA (MW = 180,000) was highly purified from a metastatic liver tumor from a colonic adenocarcinoma as previously described (Koga *et al.*, 1985).

Anti-CEA mAbs were prepared and purified as described elsewhere (Kuroki *et al.*, 1984, 1992a).

III. Procedures

A. BIOTINYLATION OF ANTIGEN

Solutions

1. *PBS:* 0.1 *M* sodium phosphate-buffered saline, pH 7.0.

2. *Antigen (CEA) solution for biotinylation:* 1 mg/ml (5.56 n*M*) in PBS.

3. *NHSB solution:* 3.5 mg/ml (10.25 m*M*) in dimethylformamide. Add 7.0 mg of NHSB, with stirring, to 0.5 ml dimethylformamide in a Reacti-Vial, and dilute the solution up to 2 ml with deionized distilled water. Prepare fresh just before use.

Steps

1. Add 54 μl (189.8 μg, 556 nmole) of freshly prepared NHSB solution to 0.1 ml (100 μg, 556 pmole) of CEA solution in a 1-ml Reacti-Vial with rapid stirring (NHSB/CEA molar ratio = 1000).

2. After incubation for 2 hr at room temperature, add PBS up to about 0.8 ml and dialyze exhaustively against PBS.

3. Determine the protein concentration of the biotin-labeled CEA by reading the optical density at 280 nm (the extinction coefficiency at 280 nm of the CEA used is 5.44) or by another method.

B. PREPARATION OF ANTIBODY-COATED PLATES

Solutions

1. *BBS:* 0.01 *M* borate-buffered saline, pH 8.0.

2. *Blocking solution:* 5% BSA/0.1% MHB/0.01% PHB in BBS.

3. *Washing buffer:* 0.05% NP-40 in BBS.

Steps

1. Dilute the mAbs to be tested in BBS at concentrations of 0.5 to 5 μg/ml. For the optimal concentration of each mAb, see Section IV.

2. Add 50 μl of each mAb solution into each well of 96-well plates and dry down at 37°C overnight.

3. Block nonspecific protein absorption by adding 200 μl of the blocking solution into each well and incubating for 1 hr at 37°C.

4. Remove the blocking solution and wash the plates three times with the washing buffer.

C. MUTUAL INHIBITION ASSAY

Solutions

1. *Sample buffer:* 1% BSA/0.1% MHB/0.01% PHB in BBS.

2. *Biotinylated CEA solution:* 200 ng/ml in the sample buffer.

3. *Competitor mAb solutions:* Make serial fivefold dilutions of the mAbs to be tested in the sample buffer. The starting concentration of each mAb is 100 μg/ml.

4. *HRP–avidin solution:* 0.25 μg/ml in the sample buffer.

5. *CPB:* 0.05 M citrate/0.1 M phosphate buffer, pH 5.0.

6. *OPD solution:* 4% OPD in methanol. Stock at −70°C.

7. *Substrate solution:* 0.04% OPD/0.006% H_2O_2 in CPB.

8. Dilute 150 μl of 4% OPD and 3 μl of 30% H_2O_2 up to 15 ml with CPB for one plate. Prepare fresh.

9. *Stopping solution:* 8 N H_2SO_4.

Steps

1. To each well of 96-well plates previously coated with a given mAb, add increasing amounts of competitor mAbs in 25 μl of the sample buffer and 5 ng of biotinylated CEA in 25 μl of the same buffer, and shake the plate for 20 sec on a plate shaker.

2. After a 1-hr incubation at 37°C, remove the mixed solutions and wash three times with the washing buffer.

3. Add 100 μl of the HRP–avidin solution and incubate for 1 hr at room temperature.

4. Remove the HRP–avidin solution and wash three times with the washing buffer.

5. Add 150 μl of the substrate solution and incubate for 20 to 30 min at room temperature.

6. Terminate the reaction by adding 20 μl of the stopping solution and read the optical density of each well at 492 nm in a plate reader.

7. Determine the amount of competitor mAb required to give half-maximal inhibition of binding of biotinylated CEA from the respective inhibition curves.

IV. COMMENTS

Biotin can be readily conjugated to a variety of molecules, such as antibodies, enzymes, and nucleic acids. The small size (MW = 341.4) of the biotin molecule prevents the biotinylation procedure from modifying the chemical, physical, or immunological properties of the molecules to which biotin is bound. Moreover, multiple biotinylation of the same molecule can be performed without any adverse effect.

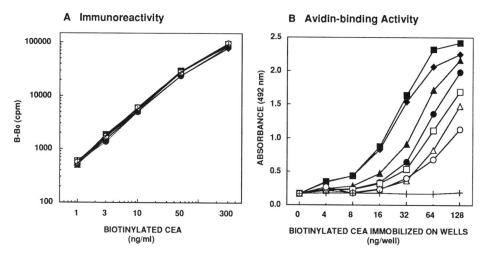

A Immunoreactivity

B Avidin-binding Activity

FIGURE 1   Immunoreactivity (A) and avidin binding activity (B) of CEA samples biotinylated at different NHSB-to-CEA molar ratios. Immunoreactivity was estimated by a sandwich-type solid-phase radioimmunoassay in which a polyclonal goat anti-CEA antibody immobilized on polystyrene beads was used as the catcher and another goat anti-CEA absorbed with NCA was labeled with ^{125}I and used as the tracer. B, radioactivity of samples; B_0, radioactivity of the control containing no CEA. Avidin binding activity was estimated using the CEA immobilized on 96-well polystyrene plates. Varying amounts of biotinylated CEA samples (in 50 μl of BBS) were dried in each well overnight at 37°C. After blocking and washing, the plates were successively incubated with 100 μl of HRP–avidin D for 30 min at room temperature and with 150 μl of the substrate solution for 25 min at room temperature. The final reaction was terminated by adding the stopping solution and the absorbance at 492 nm of each well was measured. NHSB-to-CEA molar ratio: 0 (+), 31.3 (○), 62.5 (△), 125 (□), 250 (●), 500 (▲), 1000 (■), 2000 (◆). [Adapted, with permission, from Kuroki *et al.* (1992*b*).]

Figure 1 shows the effect of biotinylation on the immunoreactivity and avidin binding activity of CEA. As shown in Fig. 1A, no apparent difference in antigenic reactivity was observed among the CEA preparations biotinylated at different NHSB-to-CEA molar ratios. When the effect of biotinylation on the binding of CEA to avidin–peroxidase was tested, optimal results were achieved with a NHSB-to-CEA ratio of 1000 (Fig. 1B). Thus, we have used this ratio for preparing biotinylated CEA.

The competitive inhibition curves of two group D anti-CEA mAbs, F33-13 and F33-20, are shown in Fig. 2. In the mAb F33-13 inhibition assay (Fig. 2A), of the seven mAbs used as competitors, four mAbs, including the homologous mAb, showed more than 80% inhibition, whereas three other mAbs demonstrated only trivial inhibition. As shown in Fig. 2B, however, in the mAb F33-20 inhibition assay, only the homologous mAb showed more than 80% inhibition at the highest input levels. To quantify the inhibitory effect of each mAb, the amounts of competitor mAbs required to inhibit the biotinylated CEA binding by 50% to each mAb dried on wells were determined from the respective inhibition curves (Table I). This presentation allows the comparison of the ability of each mAb to inhibit the binding of other mAbs to CEA with the reciprocal competition of each mAb binding to CEA by the other mAbs (Kuroki *et al.*, 1990).

This method alleviates the laborious procedures of labeling all antibodies to be tested and is convenient for mapping analysis of many mAbs if the corresponding purified antigen is available.

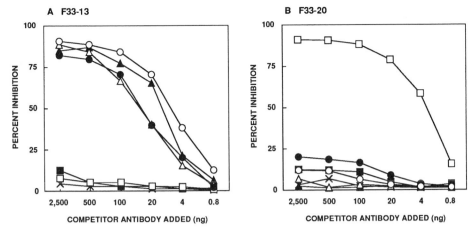

FIGURE 2 Mutual inhibition assays among group D anti-CEA mAbs using purified biotinylated CEA and purified mAb preparations. Two mAbs of group D, F33-13 (A) and F33-20 (B), were dried onto wells of 96-well plates. Purified IgGs from the mAbs were also used as competitors at the indicated quantities. Competitor mAbs tested: F33-13 (○), F34-171 (●), F82-35 (△), F36-68 (▲), F33-20 (□), F36-14 (■), F82-21 (X).

V. Pitfalls

1. The concentrations of mAbs used for coating the plates should be those at which 5 ng of biotinylated antigen (CEA) yields absorbencies ranging from 1.0 to 1.2 (less than 1.5) in the absence of competitor antibody, resulting in good inhibition results.

2. The competitor antibody solutions should be added into the antibody-coated plates before adding the biotinylated antigen solutions, also resulting in good inhibition results.

TABLE I Mutual Inhibition Assays among Group D Anti-CEA Monoclonal Antibodies[a,b]

Competitor mAb	mAb immobilized on polystyrene plate						
	F33-13	F34-171	F82-35	F36-68	F33-20	F36-14	F82-21
F33-13	+++[c]	+++	+++	—	—	—	—
F34-171	+++	+++	+++	—	—	—	—
F82-35	+++	+++	+++	—	—	—	—
F36-68	+++	+++	+++	+++	—	—	—
F33-20	—	—	—	—	+++	—	—
F36-14	—	—	—	—	—	+++	—
F82-21	—	—	—	—	—	—	+++
Epitope	D-a	D-a	D-a	D-b	D-c	D-d	D-e

[a] Adapted, with permission, from Kuroki *et al.* (1992b).

[b] The group D anti-CEA mAbs recognized the epitopes on domains A1–B1 of the CEA molecule (Kuroki *et al.*, 1992a; Ikeda *et al.*, 1992). The amount of competitor mAb required to give half-maximal inhibition of binding of biotinylated CEA was determined from the respective inhibition curves.

[c] +++, Half-maximal inhibition at <100 ng; ++, 100–500 ng; +, 500–2500 ng; —, 50% inhibition was not obtained, even at the highest amount (2500 ng) of competitor antibody.

REFERENCES

Bayer, E. A., and Wilchek, M. (1990) Protein biotinylation. *In* "*Methods in Enzymology*" (M. Wilchek and E. A. Bayer, eds.), Vol. 184, pp. 138–160. Academic Press, San Diego.

Ikeda, S., Kuroki, Ma., Haruno, M., Oikawa, S., Nakazato, H., Kosaki, G., and Matsuoka, Y. (1992) Epitope mapping of the carcinoembryonic antigen with various related recombinant proteins expressed in Chinese hamster ovary cells and 25 distinct monoclonal antibodies. *Mol. Immunol.* **29**, 229–240.

Kaufman, B. M., and Goldsby, R. A. (1982) Epitope ratio analysis (ERA): A simple radioimmunological method using monoclonal antibodies for the simultaneous analysis of several antigens. *J. Immunol. Methods* **54**, 1–7.

Koga, Y., Kuroki, Ma., Matsunaga, A., Shinoda, T., and Matsuoka, Y. (1985) Further comparative studies on chemical properties of carcinoembryonic antigen in tumor tissues and closely related antigens in adult feces and meconium. *Mol. Immunol.* **22**, 67–73.

Kuroki, Ma., Arakawa, F., Haruno, M., Murakami, M., Wakisaka, M., Higuchi, H., Oikawa, S., Nakazato, H., and Matsuoka, Y. (1992a) Biochemical characterization of 25 distinct carcinoembryonic antigen (CEA) epitopes recognized by 57 monoclonal antibodies and categorized into 7 groups in terms of domain structure of the CEA molecule. *Hybridoma* **11**, 391–407.

Kuroki, Ma., Fernsten, P. D., Wunderlich, D., Colcher, D., Simpson, J. F., Poole, D. J., and Schlom, J. (1990) Serological mapping of the TAG-72 tumor-associated antigen using 19 distinct monoclonal antibodies. *Cancer Res.* **50**, 4872–4879.

Kuroki, Ma., Kuroki, Mo., Koga, Y., and Matsuoka, Y. (1984) Monoclonal antibodies to carcinoembryonic antigen: A systematic analysis of antibody specificities by using related normal antigens and evidence for allotypic determinants on carcinoembryonic antigen. *J. Immunol.* **133**, 2090–2097.

Kuroki, Ma., Wakisaka, M., Murakami, M., Haruno, M., Arakawa, F., Higuchi, H., and Matsuoka, Y. (1992b) Determination of epitope specificities of a large number of monoclonal antibodies by solid-phase mutual inhibition assays using biotinylated antigen. *Immunol. Invest.* **21**, 523–538.

Wagener, C., Fenger, U., Clark, B. R., and Shively, J. E. (1984) Use of biotin-labeled monoclonal antibodies and avidin–peroxidase conjugates for the determination of epitope specificities in a solid-phase competitive enzyme immunoassay. *J. Immunol. Methods* **68**, 269–274.

DNA Immunoprecipitation: Application to Characterization of Target Sequences for a Human Centromere DNA-binding Protein (CENP-B)

Kenji Sugimoto

I. Introduction

DNA immunoprecipitation is a simple modification of the immunoprecipitation procedure designed for characterizing the interaction between protein and DNA (McKay, 1981). This technique is used to detect the *DNA binding activity* of proteins such as DNA replication factors and transcriptional factors. The procedure described below is a further application to isolate the target sequences of a centromere DNA-binding protein (CENP-B) from a replicable oligonucleotide library. The enrichment process is conveniently monitored by the color of the transformants. Here the recombinant CENP-B is expressed as a fusion protein to β-galactosidase in *Escherichia coli* so that the β-galactosidase moiety is used as the tagged antigen (Sugimoto *et al.*, 1992). When the specific antibodies are available, however, the same procedure is also applicable to any other DNA-binding proteins whose target sequences have not been well characterized.

II. Materials and Instrumentation

Deoxyadenosine [α-^{32}P]5'-triphosphate (Cat. No. NEG-012H) was from Du Pont NEN Products. Acetic acid (Cat. No. 002-12), agar (Cat. No. 010-28), 5-bromo-4-chloro-3-indolyl-β-D-galactoside (X-gal, Cat. No. 056-27), chloroform (Cat. No. 084-02), *N,N*-dimethylformamide (Cat. No. 130-16), dithiothreitol (DTT, Cat. No. 141-12), ethanol (Cat. No. 147-13), EDTA (CAT. No. 151-11), extract yeast (Cat. No. 368-02), glycerol (Cat. No. 170-18), Hepes (Cat. No. 175-14), isoamyl alcohol (Cat. No. 027-15), isopropyl-β-D-thiogalactopyranoside (IPTG, Cat. No. 197-35), kanamycin monosulfate (Cat. No. 198-39), lysozyme chloride (Cat. No. 208-41), 2-mercaptoethanol (Cat. No. 214-18), phenol (Cat. No. 267-19), phenylmethylsulfonyl fluoride (PMSF, Cat. No. 273-27), potassium chloride (Cat. No. 285-14), sodium acetate trihydrate (Cat. No. 311-15), sodium chloride (Cat. No. 313-20), and Tris (Cat. No. 354-10) were obtained from Nacalai Tesque, Inc. Competent *E. coli* (Cat. No. 314-02591), Hi-Competence Broth (Cat. No. 319-01343), *Hinf*I (Cat. No. 310-00192), Klenow fragment (Cat. No. 312-00814), and T4 DNA ligase (Cat. No. 311-00404) were products

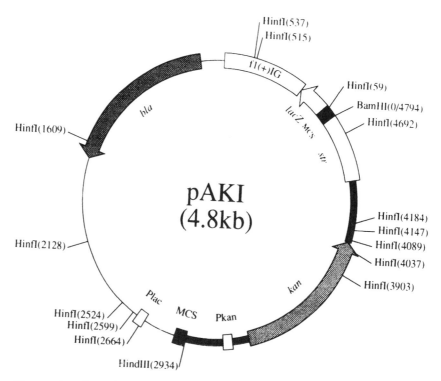

Figure 1 Physical map of pAKI plasmid used for construction of an oligonucleotide library. Transformants harboring this plasmid form white colonies on X-gal plates. The $(3n + 1)$-nucleotide insertion into the *Bam*HI site restores the reading frame for the β-galactosidase. The recombinant plasmid is conveniently discriminated from the empty plasmid by the color of the transformants on X-gal plates. The oligonucleotides used are

5′-GATCGCYYYYRYYRGAAACGGGAGC-3′

3′-CGRRRRYRRYCTTTGCCCTCGCTAG-5′

Y, pyrimidine; R, purine. Italics indicate the degenerated CENP-B box sequence (Sugimoto *et al.,* 1992).

from Nippon Gene. Poly(dI–dC)·poly(dI–dC) (Cat. No. 27-7880), protein A–Sepharose CL-4B (Cat. No. 17-0780-01), ribonucleic acid, transfer from *E. coli* (tRNA, Cat. No. R1753), and ultrapure dNTP set (Cat. No. 27-2035-01) were from Pharmacia LKB Biotechnology. Bovine serum albumin fraction V (BSA, Cat. No. A-8022) and β-galactosidase from *E. coli* (Cat. No. G-5635) were from Sigma Chemical Company. Polyoxyethylene (10) octylphenyl ether (Triton X-100, Cat. No. 168-11805), polypeptone (Cat. No. 394-00115), and sodium dodecyl sulfate (SDS, Cat. No. 191-07145) were from Wako Pure Chemical Industries. Plasmids pWa1-1 and pAKI (Fig. 1) are described elsewhere (Sugimoto *et al.,* 1992).

Glass beads 4 mm in diameter (Cat. No. 27-835-2140) were obtained from Argus Science. Program temperature control system PC700 was from Astec. Gene Pulser cuvettes with a path length of 0.2 cm (Cat. No. 165-2086), Gene Pulser (Cat. No. 165-2075), and Pulse Controller (Cat. No. 165-2098) were from Bio-Rad Laboratories. Microcentrifuge (MRX-150) and TA-4 rotor were from Tomy Seiko.

III. Procedures

A. PREPARATION OF CENP-B EXTRACT FROM IPTG-INDUCED CELL PELLETS OF Escherichia coli

Cell Pellets and Solutions

1. *IPTG-induced cell pellets of E. coli strain Y1-11:* Recombinant human CENP-B was expressed in *E. coli* strain Y1-11 which was constructed by lysogenizing a recombinant λ gt11 clone (λ 1–11) (Sugimoto *et al.*, 1992).

2. *Extraction buffer:* 50 mM Tris–HCl, pH 7.5, 10 mM EDTA, 10 mM 2-mercaptoethanol, 1 mM PMSF. Store at $-20°C$. PMSF should be added to the buffer immediately before use. PMSF is extremely toxic. To make 50 ml of extraction buffer, combine 2.5 ml 1 M Tris–HCl, pH 7.9; 1 ml 0.5 M EDTA-Na, pH 8.0; 0.035 ml 2-mercaptoethanol; 0.5 ml 0.1 M PMSF dissolved in isopropanol; and distilled water to 50 ml.

3. *Lysozyme solution:* Weigh 20 mg of lysozyme chloride and dissolve in 1 ml of extraction buffer before use.

4. *Triton X-100:* 20% (v/v) Triton X-100 in H_2O. To make 50 ml of the solution take 10 ml of Triton X-100 and fill up to 50 ml with distilled water.

Steps

1. Resuspend the IPTG-induced cell pellets (1-liter culture equivalent) completely with 18 ml of the extraction buffer in a 42-ml Nalgene centrifugation tube on ice.

2. Add 1 ml of lysozyme solution. Swirl gently and keep on ice for 15 min.

3. Add 1 ml of 20% Triton X-100 to the suspension. Mix gently and keep on ice for 15 min.

4. Sonicate the cell lysate on ice until the lysate becomes nonviscous.

5. Remove the cell debris by centrifuging for 20 min in a TA-4 rotor at 15,000 rpm at 4°C.

6. Aliquot into microcentrifuge tubes. Freeze in liquid nitrogen and store at $-80°C$.

B. CONSTRUCTION OF AN OLIGONUCLEOTIDE LIBRARY

Solutions

1. *Oligonucleotides:* Dissolve synthetic oligonucleotides 25mer in length (ca. 2 A_{260} units) in 200 μl of sterilized water. Calculate 10 OD as a concentration of 20 μg/ml DNA. Store at $-20°C$.

2. *BamHI-digested pAKI plasmid DNA:* Digest plasmid pAKI DNA with the restriction enzyme *Bam*HI according to the standard procedure (Sambrook *et al.*, 1989).

3. *10× annealing buffer:* 100 mM Tris–HCl, 500 mM NaCl, 10 mM EDTA. To make 1 ml of the solution, add 100 μl of a 1 M stock solution of Tris–HCl, pH 7.6; 20 μl of a 0.5 M stock solution of EDTA-Na, pH 8.0; 500 μl of 1 M NaCl; and 380 μl of sterile water.

4. *TE:* 10 mM Tris–HCl, pH 7.6, 1 mM EDTA. To make 100 ml of the solution, add 1 ml of a 1 M stock solution of Tris–HCl, pH 7.6; 0.2 ml of a 0.5

M stock solution of EDTA-Na, pH 8.0; and 98.8 ml of distilled water. Sterilize by autoclaving.

5. *3 M sodium acetate:* To make 100 ml of the solution dissolve 40.8 g of sodium acetate·3H$_2$O in 80 ml of water. Adjust pH to 5.2 with acetic acid and volume to 100 ml. Sterilize by autoclaving.

6. *LB medium:* To make 1 liter of LB medium, dissolve 10 g polypeptone, 5 g extract yeast, and 5 g NaCl, in 1 liter of distilled water. Adjust pH to 7.5 with 2 N sodium hydroxide. Add 20 mg of kanamycin monosulfate and sterilize by autoclaving.

Steps

1. Prepare the following annealing mixture in a 0.5-ml microcentrifuge tube:

    2.5 μg of upper-strand DNA (5'-GATCGCYYYYRYYRGAAACGGG-AGC-3')

    2.5 μg of lower-strand DNA (3'-CGRRRRYRRYCTTTGCCCTCGC-TAG-5')

    5 μl 10× annealing buffer

    Sterile water to 50 μl

2. Place the tube on a programmed temperature control system. Incubate at 80°C for 5 min and then cool gradually to 15°C at the rate of 1°C/5 min.

3. To ligate the oligonucleotides to a vector, prepare the following ligation mix on ice:

    0.8 μg of *Bam*HI-digested pAKI plasmid

    2 μl annealed oligonucleotides

    2 μl 10× ligation buffer

    Sterile water to 20 μl

4. Add 400 units of T4 DNA ligase to the reaction. Incubate overnight at room temperature.

5. To precipitate the ligated DNA, add 2 μl of 3 M sodium acetate and 60 μl ethanol to the ligation mixture. Leave the tube at −20°C for 20 min.

6. Spin the tube for 5 min at top speed. Wash pellet with 400 μl of 70% ethanol. Repeat this step three times and dry the pellet *in vacuo.*

7. Resuspend the pellet in 5 μl of TE buffer.

8. Thaw electrocompetent cells on ice. Transfer 40 μl into a microcentrifuge tube and add 2.5 μl of ligated DNA. Transfer the cell suspension into an electroporation cuvette.

9. Place the cuvette in the holder in an electroporation apparatus. Pulse at 2.5 kV with a 25-μF capacitance, connected by a pulse controller set at 200 Ω.

10. Dilute immediately the transfected cells in 1 ml of Hi-Competence Broth with a Pasteur pipette. Transfer the cell suspension into a microcentrifuge tube.

11. Incubate the cells for 1 hr at 37°C prior to inoculation into 50 ml LB medium containing 20 μg/ml of kanamycin. Plate 0.1–1 ml of the culture and estimate the number of transformants (see Section D). Grow the rest of the cells overnight.

12. Prepare plasmid DNA according to the standard procedure (Sambrook *et al.*, 1989).

C. DNA IMMUNOPRECIPITATION OF AN OLIGONUCLEOTIDE LIBRARY

Solutions

1. *4× binding buffer:* 48 mM Hepes-Na, pH 7.9, 16 mM Tris–HCl, pH 7.9, 240 mM KCl, 4 mM EDTA-Na, pH 8.0, 4 mM DTT, 48% glycerol, 0.4% Triton X-100. Store at −20°C. Make 40 ml of 4× binding buffer:

> 1.92 ml 1 M Hepes-Na, pH 7.9
>
> 0.64 ml 1 M Tris–HCl, pH 7.9
>
> 9.6 ml 1 M KCl
>
> 0.32 ml 0.5 M EDTA-Na, pH 8.0
>
> 19.2 ml glycerol
>
> 0.16 ml 1 M DTT
>
> 0.8 ml 20% Triton X-100
>
> Sterile water to 40 ml

2. *Washing buffer:* 12 mM Hepes-Na, pH 7.9, 4 mM Tris–HCl, pH 7.9, 120 mM KCl, 1 mM EDTA-Na, pH 8.0, 1 mM DTT, 0.2% Triton X-100. Prepare the buffer before use. Make 50 ml of washing buffer:

> 0.6 ml 1 M Hepes-Na, pH 7.9
>
> 0.2 ml 1 M Tris–HCl, pH 7.9
>
> 0.1 ml 0.5 M EDTA-Na, pH 8.0
>
> 0.05 ml 1 M DTT
>
> 6 ml 1 M KCl
>
> 0.5 ml 20% Triton X-100
>
> Distilled water to 50 ml

3. *BSA:* Weigh 5 mg of BSA and dissolve in 1 ml of sterile water. Store at −20°C.

4. *Rabbit anti-β-galactosidase serum:* To produce rabbit serum against β-galactosidase from *E. coli,* follow the standard procedure (Amero *et al.,* 1988).

5. *Protein A–Sepharose:* Resuspend 0.1 g of protein A–Sepharose CL-4B in 1 ml of washing buffer. Store at 4°C.

6. *TES:* 10 mM Tris–HCl, pH 7.6, 1 mM EDTA, 1% (w/v) SDS, 10 μg/ml tRNA. To make 10 ml of TES, add 0.1 g of SDS and 0.01 ml of 10 mg/ml tRNA to 10 ml of TE.

7. *24:1 chloroform/isoamyl alcohol:* Mix chloroform and isoamyl alcohol at the ratio of 24:1 (v/v). Store at 4°C.

8. *Phenol/chloroform:* Phenol is highly corrosive. Melt at 68°C in a water bath. Extract three times with an equal volume of 0.5 M Tris–HCl, pH 7.6, followed by 0.1 M Tris–HCl, pH 7.6. Store at 4°C. Mix the phenol solution with an equal volume of 24:1 chloroform/isoamyl alcohol and leave for several minutes until water phase separates from phenol. Use a lower phase.

9. *10% (v/v) glycerol:* To 10 ml of glycerol, add 90 ml of an ultrapure water and mix well. Autoclave.

Steps

1. In a 1.5-ml microcentrifuge tube, combine the following:

> 20 μl 4× binding buffer
>
> 0.3 μg oligonucleotide plasmid library DNA (see Section B)
>
> 3–30 μg pWa1-1 plasmid DNA (Sugimoto *et al.*, 1992) as a competitor
>
> 10 μl 5 mg/ml BSA
>
> 2 μl CENP-B extract (see Section A)
>
> Sterile water to 80 μl

2. Incubate for 1 hr on ice.

3. Add 1 μl of rabbit anti-β-galactosidase serum to the reaction. Incubate for 1 hr on ice.

4. Add 10 μl of protein A–Sepharose suspension. Incubate for 1 hr on ice, mixing gently.

5. Spin the immunocomplexes for 1 min in a microcentrifuge at top speed. Remove the supernatant and resuspend the pellet in 400 μl of washing buffer. Repeat this four times.

6. Spin the tube, remove the supernatant, and resuspend the pellet in 200 μl of TES.

7. Add 200 μl of phenol/chloroform. Vortex the tube for 30 sec and centrifuge for 5 min.

8. Transfer the upper phase into a new tube. Add 200 μl of 24:1 chloroform/ isoamyl alcohol, vortex, and centrifuge.

9. Transfer the upper phase into a new tube. Add 20 μl of 3 M sodium acetate and 500 μl of ethanol. Leave the tube at $-20°C$ overnight.

10. Precipitate DNA by spinning the tube for 5 min. Rinse the pellet with 400 μl of ice-cold 70% ethanol. Repeat this three times and dry the pellet *in vacuo.*

11. Dissolve the pellet with 10 μl of 10% glycerol.

12. Proceed with steps 8–12 in Section B.

D. ESTIMATION OF THE FOLD ENRICHMENT OF THE TARGET SEQUENCES

Solutions and Plates

1. *2% X-gal solution:* Weigh 20 mg and dissolve in 1 ml of dimethylformamide. Store at $-20°C$ in the dark.

2. *0.5 M IPTG solution:* Weigh 238 mg and dissolve in 2 ml of sterile water. Store at $-20°C$.

3. *X-gal plates:* Add 12 g agar and 20 mg kanamycin monosulfate to 1 liter LB medium and sterilize by autoclaving. Cool to 55°C and then add 1 ml of a

TABLE I   Estimation of the Fold Purification in DNA Immunoprecipitation[a]

Cycle number of DNA immunoprecipitation	Oligonucleotide library number	Number of blue colonies	Number of white colonies	Ratio of blue/white	Fold purification
0	3.0	18	95	0.19	1.0
1	3.1	116	710	0.16	0.8
2	3.2	40	124	0.32	1.7
3	3.3	130	76	1.7	9
4	3.4	92	29	3.2	17
5	3.5	401	4	100	530

[a] Library 3.0 was constructed by inserting complementary synthetic oligonucleotides containing the degenerated CENP-B box sequences into the *Bam*HI site of plasmid pAKI. After one cycle of DNA immunoprecipitation, the precipitated DNA was recovered into *E. coli*, designated library 3.1. The plasmid DNA was prepared again from library 3.1 and applied for the second cycle of DNA immunoprecipitation, yielding library 3.2, and so on. The fold enrichment was calculated by counting blue and white colonies on X-gal plates (see text for the equation).

2% stock solution of X-gal and 0.2 ml of a 0.5 *M* stock solution of IPTG. Mix gently and pour 20-ml aliquots into 90-mm dishes.

Steps

1. Drop several pieces of sterilized glass beads on a X-gal plate. Spread a portion of transfected cells uniformly on the surface by rolling the beads.

2. Grow the transformants at 37°C overnight.

3. Count the numbers of blue and white colonies on the plates.

4. Calculate the fold enrichment according to the equation (Table I)

$$\text{fold enrichment} = \frac{\text{blue/white ratio after immunoprecipitation}}{\text{blue/white ratio before immunoprecipitation}}$$

E. DNA IMMUNOPRECIPITATION OF RESTRICTION DNA FRAGMENTS

Solution

1. *Poly(dI–dC)·poly(dI–dC):* Dissolve poly(dI–dC)·poly(dI–dC) in sterile water to 1 mg/ml. Store at −20°C.

Steps

1. In a 1.5-ml tube, combine 2 μl 10× *Hin*fI buffer, 10 μl miniprep plasmid DNA (0.3 ml culture equivalent), and sterile water to 20 μl.

2. Add 1 unit *Hin*fI and incubate at 37°C for 1 hr.

3. In a 1.5-ml microcentrifuge tube, combine 1 μl 10× Klenow buffer; 2 μl *Hin*fI-digested DNA mixture; 0.5 μl 2 m*M* dTTP, dCTP, and dGTP mixture; 0.15 μl of [α-^{32}P]dATP (3000 Ci/mmole, 10 μCi/μl); and sterile water to 10 μl.

4. Add 0.4 unit of Klenow enzyme and incubate at room temperature for 30 min.

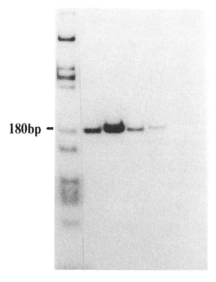

1 2 3 4 5 6 7

180bp –

Figure 2 Autoradiogram of immunoprecipitated DNA fragments harboring the CENP-B binding sequences resolved on a 5% polyacrylamide gel. The representative plasmid DNAs were isolated from an enriched plasmid library (library 3.3 shown in Table I). *Hin*fI-digested plasmid DNA fragments were labeled with ^{32}P and subjected to the DNA immunoprecipitation assay (see Section IIIE). Characterized sequences are CTTCGTTGGAAACGGGA from clone 33 (lane 2), TTTCGTT*A*GAAACGGGA from clone 36 (lane 3), C*T*TCGTT*A*GAAACGGGA from clone 38 (lane 4), TTT*T*GTTGGAAACGGGA from clone 44 (lane 5), TTT*TATTA*-GAAACGGGA from clone 34 (lane 6), and TTT*TATC*AGAAACGGGA from clone 37 (lane 7). Italics indicate substituted nucleotides from the authentic CENP-B box sequence, TTTCGTTGGAAACGGGA.

5. In a 1.5-ml tube, combine 8 μl 4× binding buffer, 5 μl ^{32}P-labeled DNA mixture, 1 μl 1 mg/ml poly(dI–dC)·poly(dI–dC), 2 μl 5 mg/ml BSA, 1 μl CENP-B extract (see Section A), and sterile water to 32 μl.

6. Leave on ice for 1 hr.

7. Add 68 μl of washing buffer.

8. Proceed to steps 3–10 in Section C.

9. Dissolve the pellet in 20 μl of TE.

10. Separate the DNA fragments on 5% acrylamide gel in TBE buffer (Sambrook *et al.*, 1989). Dry the gel on a filter paper prior to autoradiography.

IV. Comments

Using the protocol described above, it is possible to isolate CENP-B binding sequences. Representative results are shown in Table I and Fig. 2. It is better to titrate the amount of competitor DNA in the binding reaction, as the greater the amount of competitor included, the greater the enrichment achieved (Sugimoto *et al.*, 1992). When a sufficient fold enrichment is not obtained after repeated cycles of DNA immunoprecipitation, the quality of the oligonucleotide library should be in doubt. The library may not contain the candidate sequences. The standard procedures for induction of recombinant proteins in λgt11 lysogen, plasmid DNA preparation, restriction digestion of plasmid DNA, and production of antibodies are described elsewhere (Huynh *et al.*, 1985; Amero *et al.*, 1988; Sambrook *et al.*, 1989).

REFERENCES

Amero, S. A., James, T. C., and Elgin, S. C. R. (1988) Production of antibodies using proteins in gel bands. *In* "Methods in Molecular Biology" (J. M. Walker, ed.), Vol. 3, pp. 355–362. Humana Press, Clifton, NJ.

Huynh, T. V., Young, R. A., and Davis, W. D. (1985) Construction and screening cDNA libraries in λgt10 and λgt11. *In* "DNA Cloning I" (D. M. Glover, ed.), pp. 49–78. IRL Press, Oxford.

McKay, R. D. G. (1981) Binding of a simian virus 40 T antigen-related protein to DNA. *J. Mol. Biol.* **145,** 471–488.

Sambrook, J., Fritsch, E. F., and Maniatis, T. (1989) "Molecular Cloning: A Laboratory Manual," 2nd ed. Cold Spring Harbor Laboratory Press, Cold Spring Harbor, NY.

Sugimoto, K., Wakisaka, E., and Himeno, M. (1992) Cycled DNA immunoprecipitation procedure to enrich the target sequences for DNA binding proteins with the fold purification monitored. *Anal. Biochem.* **207,** 114–120.

Immunofluorescence Microscopy of Cultured Cells

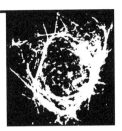

Mary Osborn

I. Introduction

Immunocytochemistry is the method of choice for locating an antigen to a particular structure or subcellular compartment provided that an antibody specific for the protein under study is available. Immunofluorescence is a sensitive method requiring only one available antigenic site on the protein. Usually the indirect technique is used. In this technique the first antibody is unlabeled and can be made in any species. After it has bound to the antigen a second antibody, made against IgGs of the species in which the first antibody is made and coupled to a fluorochrome such as fluoroscein isothiocyanate, is added. The distribution of the antigen can then be viewed in a microscope equipped with the appropriate filters.

Immunofluorescence as a method to study cytoarchitecture and subcellular localization gained prominence with the demonstration that antibodies can be produced to actin even though it is a ubiquitous components of cells and tissues (Lazarides and Weber 1974). Cytoskeletal structures visualized in cells in immunofluorescence microscopy include the three filamentous systems: microfilaments, microtubules, and intermediate filaments (Color Plates 18–20 and micrographs in the article by Monika Herzog, Annette Draeger, Elisabeth Ehler, and J. Victor Small, this volume). In addition proteins can be located to other cellular subcompartments and organelles, e.g., the plasma or nuclear membranes (Fig. 1), the Golgi apparatus, or the endoplasmic reticulum (Fig. 2), or to other cellular structures such as mitochondria (Fig. 3) and vesicles. Other proteins can also be localized to subcompartments of the nucleus or even of the nucleolus. In addition to its use in identifying cytoskeletal structures and organelles, immunocytochemistry has proved useful in building up a biochemical or protein chemical anatomy of a structure. Examples include the location of the microfilament-associated proteins to the stress fiber and the description of the biochemical anatomy of such structures as microvilli and stereo cilia. A third and very important use of the technique has been to demonstrate heterogeneity in mixed cultures, e.g., of neuronal cultures, or of other primary cell cultures (cf. Color Plate 19 and Fig. 4).

The micrographs that accompany this article show not only the beauty of some of the structures, but also some of the advantages of the technique. First in such micrographs only the arrangement of the particular protein against which the antibody is made is visualized. Second, for those proteins that form part of the supramolecular structures, the arrangement of those structures throughout the cell is revealed. Third, numerous cells can be visualized at the same time, and therefore it is relatively easy to determine how the structures under study vary under particular conditions. Immunofluorescence microscopy is also a useful method to establish appropriate

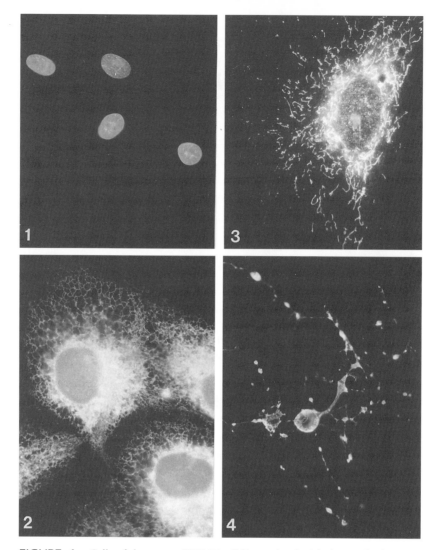

FIGURE 1 Cells of the mouse HEL37 cell line stained with the antibody 346 which recognizes lamins A/C. Only the nuclear membrane is stained. ×400.

FIGURE 2 CV-1 cells stained with the ID3 antibody against protein disulfide isomerase to reveal the endoplasmic reticulum (cf. Vaux *et al.*, 1990). ×600.

FIGURE 3 FIGURE 3A mouse 3T3 cell stained with an antibody to cytochome oxidase to show the arrangement of mitochondria. ×600.

FIGURE 4 An oligodendrocyte in a rat optic nerve primary culture stained with antibodies to galactoceroboside. Other cells present in the same field are not stained. (cf. Raff *et al.*, 1978). ×400.

conditions to study a structure at higher resolution in the electron microscope. A 1:1 correspondence has been shown for a parallel-processed or even the same specimen when studied under fluorescence and under the electron microscope. Electron microscopic methods not only allow location of the antigen to a particular structure at higher resolution but may also allow the determination of interactions between a structure that is immunolabeled and other unlabeled structures in the cell.

Other reviews of immunofluorescence of cultured cells that may be helpful include those of Osborn (1981) and Osborn and Weber (1981), and for live cells, Wang and Taylor (1989). For an overview of the different cytoskeletal and motor proteins, see Kreis and Vale (1993).

II. Materials and Instrumentation

A. ANTIBODIES

Antibodies to many cellular proteins can now be purchased commercially. Firms offering a variety of antibodies to cytoskeletal and other proteins include Amersham, Biomakor, Dako, Sigma, and Novocastra; other firms have put together specialized collections emphasizing one or another narrower area.

Primary antibodies may be monoclonal antibodies made in mice or polyclonal antibodies made in species such as guinea pigs and rabbits. The appropriate dilution is established by a dilution series. Monoclonal antibodies supplied as hybridoma supernatants can often be diluted 1:1 to 1:20 for immunofluorescence or even more if other more sensitive immunocytochemical procedures are used (see article by Mary Osborn and Susanne Isenberg in this volume). Monoclonal antibodies supplied as ascites fluid can be diluted in the range 1:100 to 1:1000. Polyclonal antibodies supplied as sera should be diluted in the range 1:20 to 1:100. Note that many rabbits have relatively high levels of autoantibodies against keratins and/or other cellular proteins, so check presera. Affinity purification in which the antigen is coupled to a support and the polyclonal antibody is then put through the column usually results in a dramatic improvement in the quality of the staining patterns. Affinity-purified antibodies should work in the range of 5–20 μg/ml.

Secondary antibodies directed against IgGs of the species in which the first antibody is made are usually purchased already coupled to FITC or rhodamine (for list of suppliers, see above). The working dilution for the secondary antibody is established by running a dilution series. Usually 1:50 to 1:150 dilutions of the commercial products are appropriate. An essential control is to check that the second antibody is negative when used alone. If nonspecific staining is present, it can sometimes be removed by absorbing the antibody on fixed monolayers of cells or on an acetone cell powder.

Antibodies other than IgMs should be stored in the freezer (−70°C for valuable primary antibodies and affinity-purified antibodies, −20°C for the rest). Antibodies should be stored in small aliquots and repeated freezing/thawing should be avoided. IgMs may be inactivated by freezing/thawing and are better kept in 50% glycerol in a freezer set at −20 to −25°C. If dilutions are made in a suitable buffer (e.g., phosphate-buffered saline, 0.5 mg/ml BSA, 10^{-3} M sodium azide) diluted antibodies are stable for several months at 4°C.

B. REAGENTS AND OTHER USEFUL ITEMS

Methanol is of reagent grade. *Formaldehyde* can be diluted 1:10 from a concentrated 37% solution (e.g., Analar-grade BDH Chemicals). As such solutions usually contain 11% methanol it may be better to make the formaldehyde solution from paraformaldehyde. In this case, heat 18.5 g paraformaldehyde in 500 ml PBS to 60°C and filter through a 0.45-μm filter. Store at room temperature.

Phosphate-buffered saline contains per liter 8 g NaCl, 0.2 g KCl, 0.2 g KH$_2$PO$_4$, and 1.15 g Na$_2$HPO$_4$, adjusted to pH 7.3 with NaOH. With respect to *mounting medium*, polyvinyl alcohol-based mounting media have the advantage in that although they are liquid when the sample is mounted, they solidify within several hours of application. In addition, the fluorescence is stable if the sample is held in the dark and at 4°C. Samples can be reexamined and photographed after months or even years. Commonly used mounting media include Elvanol 51-05 (Serva) and Mowiol (4-88) (Hoechst). Place 6 g analytical-grade glycerol in a 50-ml plastic conical centrifuge tube, add 2.4 g of Mowiol 4.88 or Elvanol 51-05, and stir for 1 hr to mix. Add 6 ml distilled water and stir for a further 2 hr. Add 12 ml of 0.2 M Tris buffer (2.42 g Tris/100 ml water, pH adjusted to 8.5 with HCl as FITC has maximal fluorescence emission at this pH), and incubate in a water bath at 50°C for 10 min, stirring occasionally to dissolve the Mowiol. Clarify by centrifugation at 1200 g for 15 min, and aliquot. Store at −20°C; unfreeze as required. Once unfrozen, the solution will be stable for several months at room temperature.

Other useful items include round (12-mm) or square (12 × 12-mm) glass coverslips (thickness 1½). Ten round coverslips fit in a petri dish of diameter 5.5 cm. For screening purposes or when a large number of samples are needed (e.g., for hybridoma screening), microtest slides that contain 10 numbered circles 7 mm in diameter (Flow Labs, Cat. No. 6041805) are useful. Tweezers (e.g., Dumont No. 7) are used to handle the coverslips. Ceramic racks into which coverslips fit (Cat. No. 8542E40, A. Thomas) and matching glass containers are also needed. Glass beakers (30 ml) are used to wash the specimens. Cells growing in suspension can be firmly attached to microscope slides using a cytocentrifuge such as the Cytospin (Shandon Instruments).

C. INSTRUMENTATION

The essential requirement is access to a microscope equipped with appropriate filters to visualize the fluorochromes in routine use. The Zeiss inverted microscope, Photomicroscope III, or Axiophot is suitable, as are models from other manufacturers. An automatic camera, with spot and whole field options for photography, is a useful accessory. Epifluorescence, an appropriate high-pressure mercury lamp (HBO 50 or HBO 100), and appropriate filters (so that specimens doubly labeled with fluorescein and rhodamine can be visualized) are basic requirements. Lenses should also be selected carefully. The depth of field of the lens will decrease as the magnification increases. Round cultured cells will be in focus only with a 25× or 40× lens, whereas flatter cells can be studied with a 63× or 100× lens. To enable phase and fluorescence to be studied on the same specimen, some lenses should have phase optics. Only certain lenses transmit the Hoechst DNA stain (e.g., Neofluar lenses) and this stain also requires a separate filter set.

Confocal microscopy is being increasingly used, particularly for rounded cells and for structures in or near the nucleus.

III. Indirect Immunofluorescence Procedure

Steps

1. Trypsinize cells 1–2 days prior to the experiment onto glass coverslips or on multitest slides that have been washed in 100% ethanol and oven sterilized. For most applications choose coverslips or multitest slides on which cells are two-thirds or less confluent. Drain coverslip or slide on filter paper to remove excess medium, but do not allow it to dry.

2. Place coverslips in ceramic rack and multitest slides in metal racks, and immerse in methanol precooled to −10 to −20°C. Leave 6 min.

3. Make a wet chamber by lining a 13-cm-diameter (for coverslips) or a 24 × 24-cm square petri dish (for slides) with two or three sheets of filter paper, and add sufficient water to moisten the filter paper.

4. Wash the fixed specimens briefly in PBS, remove excess PBS by touching to dry filter paper, and place cell side up over the appropriate number in the wet chamber.

5. Add 5–10 μl of an appropriate dilution of the primary antibody with an Eppendorf pipette. Use the tip to spread the antibody over the coverslip without touching the cells. Replace the top of the wet chamber, transfer to a 37°C incubator with humidity, and incubate for 45 min.

6. Wash by dipping each coverslip individually three times into each of three 30-ml beakers containing PBS. Wash slides by replacing slides in metal rack and transferring through three PBS washes (180 ml each, leave for 2 min in each). Remove excess PBS with filter paper.

7. Replace specimens in wet chamber. Add 5–10 μl of an appropriately diluted second antibody carrying a fluorescent tag. Return to 37°C incubator for a further 30–45 min.

8. Repeat step 6.

9. Identify microscope slides with small adhesive labels on which date, specimen number, antibody, or other information is written. Place slides in cardboard microslide folders (e.g., 6708-M10 Thomas Scientific). Mount two coverslips per slide by inverting each coverslip and placing cell side down on a drop of mounting medium placed on the slide, with a disposable ring micropipette. Cover with filter paper and press gently to remove excess mounting medium. For samples on multitest slides, use 6 × 2.5-cm glass coverslips on which a drop of mounting medium has been placed. Secure the coverslips with nail polish.

10. Photograph. Use a fast film (e.g., Kodak 35-mm Tri-X) and push the development, e.g., with Diafine (Acufine).

IV. Comments

Specimens should not be allowed to dry out at any stage in the procedure. If coverslips are accidentally dropped, the side on which the cells are can be identified by focusing on the cells under an upright microscope and scratching gently with tweezers.

A. FIXATION

The procedure given above results in good results with many cytoskeletal and other antigens; however the optimal fixation protocol depends on the specimen, the antigen, and the location of the antigen within the cell. There are three requirements. First, the fixation procedure must retain the antigen within the cell. Second, ultrastructure must be preserved as far as possible without destroying the antigenic determinents recognized by the antibody. Third, the antibody must be able to reach the antigen; i.e., the fixation and permeabilization steps must extract sufficient cytoplasmic components so the antibodies can penetrate the fixed cells. In the procedure given above, fixation and permeabilization are achieved in a single step, i.e., with methanol. Alternative fixation methods include the following:

1. Formaldehyde–methanol: 3.7% formaldehyde in PBS for 10 min (to fix the cells), then methanol at −10°C for 6 min (to permeabilize the cells).

2. Formaldehyde–Triton: 3.7% formaldehyde in PBS for 10 min, then PBS

with 0.2% Triton X-100 for 1 min at room temperature (see also article by Monika Herzog, Annette Draeger, Elisabeth Ehler, and J. Victor Small in this volume).

3. Glutaraldehyde: Fix in 1% glutaraldehyde (electron microscopic grade) in PBS for 15 min, then methanol at −10°C for 15 min. Immerse in fresh sodium borohydride solution (0.5 mg/ml in PBS) for 3 × 4 min. Wash with PBS 2 × 3 min each. Note that the sodium borohydride step is necessary to reduce the unreacted aldehyde groups; without this step the background will be very high.

Note that formaldehyde treatment destroys the antigenicity of many antigens. Alternatively in a very few cases positive staining may be observed only after formaldehyde fixation. Very few antigens react after glutaraldehyde fixation.

B. SPECIAL SITUATIONS

1. Fluorescently labeled phalloidin, a phallotoxin that binds to filamentous actin, is usually used to reveal the distribution of filamentous actin in cells (Color Plate 16). To obtain good staining patterns, fix cells 10 min in 3.7% formaldehyde in PBS. Wash with PBS. Incubate for 1 min in 0.2% Triton X-100 in PBS, and wash with PBS. Incubate with an appropriate dilution of rhodamine-labeled phalloidin (e.g., Sigma Cat. No. P-5157) for 30 min at 37°C, wash with PBS, and mount in Mowiol.

NOTE   *Caution: Phalloidin is extremely poisonous.*

---

2. To stain endoplasmic reticulum use either an antibody, e.g., ID3 against a sequence in the tail region of protein disulfide isomerase (Vaux *et al.*, 1990) (Fig. 6), or the lipophilic cationic fluorescent dye $DiOC_6$ (3,3-dihexyloxacarbocyanine iodide, Kodak 14414) (Terasaki *et al.*, 1984). To stain with dye fix 5 min in 0.25% glutaraldehyde in 0.1 M cacodylate, 0.1 M sucrose buffer, pH 7.4. Wash. Stain for 80 sec with dye, mount in buffer, and observe using a 63× or 100× lens and the fluorescein filter. Reticular structures should be apparent. Note that mitochondria will also be stained. To stain only mitochondria use either an antibody, e.g., to cytochrome oxidase (Fig. 3), or the dye rhodamine 123.

3. Special fixation procedures may also be needed for other membrane structures in cells. In addition, lectins can be used to stain carbohydrate-containing organelles, e.g., staining of Golgi apparatus with fluorescently labeled wheat germ or other agglutinins.

4. To stain DNA immerse coverslips in Hoechst dye (20 μg/ml bisbenzamide, Cat. No. H-33342, Sigma) in 25% ethanol, 75% PBS for 1–2 min, drain excess dye, and mount directly in Mowiol. Or stain with Hoechst between steps 8 and 9 in the immunofluorescence procedure.

5. Some cellular structures such as microtubules are sensitive to calcium. In this case add 2–5 mM EGTA to the 3.7% formaldehyde solution in Section IVA and to the methanol in Section III, step 2.

6. Sometimes for cell surface components it may be advantageous to stain live cells. Expose such cells to antibody for 25 min, and proceed with steps 6–8 in Section III. Then fix cells in 5% acetic acid/95% ethanol for 10 min at −10°C (Fig. 4, cf. Raff *et al.*, 1979).

7. It is often advantageous to visualize two or three antigens in the same cell. See the article by Monika Herzog *et al.* in this volume for methods to do this.

C. STEREOMICROSCOPY

Fluorescence microscopy gives an overview of the whole cell. With practice specimens can be seen in three dimensions when looking through the microscope. Stereo micrographs can be made using a simple modification of commercially available parts (Osborn *et al.*, 1978a). Alternatively, confocal microscopy is increasingly being used and is particularly useful for round cells, which are not in focus with the higher-power 63 or 100 lenses, or to document arrangements and obtain greater resolution at different levels in the cell (cf. Fox *et al.*, 1991).

D. LIMIT OF RESOLUTION

Theoretically this is ~200 nm when light of wavelength 515 nm and a numerical aperture of 1.4 is used. Objects with dimensions above 200 nm will be seen at their real size. Objects with dimensions below 200 nm can be visualized provided they bind sufficient antibody but will be seen with diameters equal to the resolution of the light microscope (cf. visualization of single microtubules in Osborn *et al.*, 1978b). Thus, objects closer together than 200–250 nm cannot be resolved by fluorescence microscopy, e.g., microtubules in the mitotic spindle or ribosomes.

V. Pitfalls

Occasionally no specific structures are visualized even though the cell is known to contain the antigen. This may be because:

1. Antibodies can be species specific. This can be a particular problem with monoclonal antibodies, which, for instance, may work with human but not with other species. If in doubt check the species specificity with the supplier before purchase.

2. The fixation procedure may inactivate the antigen. For instance, many intermediate filament antibodies no longer react after fixation protocols such as those in Section IVA.

3. The antigen can be poorly fixed or extracted by the fixation procedure.

4. The antibody may not be able to gain access to the antigen; e.g., antibodies to tubulin often do not stain the intracellular bridge.

5. The specimens may be generally fluorescent and it can be hard to decide whether this is due to specific or nonspecific staining.

REFERENCES

Fox, M. H., Arndt-Jovin, D. J., Jovin, T. M., Baumann, P. H., and Robert-Nicoud, M. (1991) Spatial and temporal distribution of DNA replication sites localized by immunofluorescence and confocal microscopy in mouse fibroblasts. *J. Cell Sci.* **99**, 247–253.

Kreis, T., and Vale, R. (1993) "Guidebook to the Cytoskeletal and Motor Proteins." Oxford University Press, London/New York.

Lazarides, E., and Weber, K. (1974) Actin antibody: The specific visualization of actin filaments in non-muscle cells. *Proc. Natl. Acad. Sci. USA* **71**, 2268–2272.

Osborn, M. (1981) Localization of proteins by immunofluorescence techniques. *Techniques Cell. Physiol.* **P107**, 1–28.

Osborn, M., Born, T., Koitzsch, H.-J., and Weber, K. (1978a) Stereo immunofluorescence microscopy. I. Three-dimensional arrangement of microfilaments, microtubules and tonofilaments. *Cell* **13**, 477–488.

Osborn, M., and Weber, K. (1981) Immunofluorescence and immunochemical procedures with affinity purified antibodies. *In* "Methods in Cell Biology," Vol. 23, Part A: "The Cytoskeleton." Academic Press, New York.

Osborn, M., Webster, R. E., and Weber, K. (1978b) Individual microtubules viewed by immunofluorescence and electron microscopy in the same PtK2 cell. *J. Cell Biol.* **77**, R27–R34.

Raff, M. C., Mirsky, R., Fields, K. L., Lisak, R. P., Dorfman, S. H., Pilbenberg, D. H., Gregeon, N. A., Leibowitz, S., and Kennedy, M. C. (1978) Galactocereboside is a specific cell surface antigenic marker for oligodendrocytes in culture. *Nature* **274**, 813–816.

Terasaki, M., Song, J., Wong, J. R., Weiss, M. J., and Chen, L. B. (1984) Localization of endoplasmic reticulum in living and glutaraldehyde fixed cells with fluorescent dyes. *Cell* **38**, 101–108.

Vaux, D., Tooze, J., and Fuller, S. (1990) Identification by anti-idiotype antibodies of an intracellular membrane protein that recognizes a mammalian endoplasmic reticulum retention signal. *Nature* **345**, 495–502.

Wang, Y.-L., and Taylor, D. L. (1989) "Methods in Cell Biology," Vols. 29 and 30: "Fluorescence Microscopy of Living Cells in Culture." Academic Press, New York.

Immunofluorescence Microscopy of the Cytoskeleton: Double and Triple Immunofluorescence

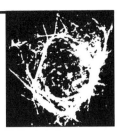

Monika Herzog, Annette Draeger, Elisabeth Ehler, and J. Victor Small

I. Introduction

Cells possess an extensive scaffolding of fibrillar elements, collectively referred to as the *cytoskeleton*. The components of the cytoskeleton are involved in diverse cellular functions ranging from mitosis to cell motility to signal transduction. In cultured cells, the three primary components of the cytoskeleton—actin filaments, microtubules, and intermediate filaments—can be readily visualized using immunofluorescence microscopy. Here we describe a protocol for double and triple labeling of the cytoskeleton that can also be applied to the localization of proteins putatively associated with one or more of its components.

The use of antibodies to localize proteins within cells requires that the cells be chemically fixed and rendered permeable to the antibody molecules. The pitfalls of this approach are as numerable as the different techniques employed. The compromises that must, by necessity, be made should thus be recalled when drawing conclusions about the results obtained. In general, one aims to achieve optimal structural preservation combined with intense antibody labeling. But the properties of many antibodies do not allow us this luxury. As a rule, stronger fixation, giving better structural preservation, leads to weaker antibody labeling. Inorganic solvents (normally acetone or methanol) serve as weak fixatives and aldehydes (formaldehyde and glutaraldehyde) as stronger fixatives, and various recipes employing these alone or in combination have been described in studies of the cytoskeleton (e.g., Fujiwara and Pollard, 1980; Lazarides, 1982; Osborn and Weber, 1982; see also the article by Mary Osborn). Permeabilization of the cell membrane is achieved either with inorganic solvents or with anionic detergents. We have had good experience with techniques involving the use of aldehyde–detergent mixtures that effect simultaneous penetration of the cell and fixation of the cytoskeleton and the structures bound to it. The same protocols yield good preservation of the cytoskeleton also in the electron microscope (e.g., Small, 1988), but at the expense of a major loss of the membrane-bound organelles. A method involving aldehyde fixation followed by detergent permeabilization is also described.

II. Materials and Reagents

1. *Coverslips:* Round glass coverslips 10 or 12 mm in diameter, cleaned with lint-free paper, and sterilized for tissue culture by exposure to ultraviolet light in the culture dish.

2. *Humid chamber*: Large petri dish 14 cm in diameter, or similar container with lid, containing a glass plate (around 9 cm square) coated with a layer of Parafilm and supported on a moistened piece of filter paper on the bottom of the dish. A few drops of water on the glass plate facilitate spreading and flattening of the Parafilm.

3. *Washing reservoir*: Two multiwell dishes, 24 wells each (e.g., Falcon or Nunc).

4. *Rotary shaker*. Rotating–tilting table for washing (optional).

5. *Filter paper:* Whatman No. 1, 9 cm in diameter.

6. *Forceps:* Dumont No. 4 or 5 or equivalent watchmaker forceps.

7. *Pipettes:* Set of automatic pipettes (0–20 μl, 20–200 μl, 50–1000 μl) or capillary pipettes for diluting and aliquoting antibodies. Pasteur pipettes.

8. *Phalloidin:* Rhodamine (TRITC)-, fluorescein-, or coumarin-conjugated phalloidin from Sigma. Store as 0.1 mg/ml stocks in methanol at $-20°C$.

9. *Secondary antibodies:* Commercial secondary antibodies carrying fluorescein, Texas red, Cy-3, or coumarin conjugates are in our experience of generally good quality. Rhodamine-conjugated antibodies are best when homemade (see Brandtzaeg, 1973). We store our antibodies in a refrigerator at 4°C. The antibodies and other probes used here are listed under Solutions in Section III.

10. *Gelvatol, Vinol:* The basic ingredient of the mounting medium is polyvinyl alcohol (MW 10,000, around 87% hydrolyzed), which is sold under various tradenames: Elvanol, Mowiol, Gelvatol, etc. We use Vinol 203 from Air Products and Chemicals Inc.

III. Procedures

A. DOUBLE AND TRIPLE IMMUNOFLUORESCENCE MICROSCOPY OF THE CYTOSKELETON

Solutions

1. *0.5 M EGTA stock solution:* For 500 ml stock, weight out 95.1 g EGTA (Sigma Cat. No. E-4378) into 400 ml H_2O. Adjust pH to 7.0 with 1 N NaOH and make up to 400 ml with H_2O. Store at room temperature in a plastic bottle.

2. *1 M MgCl$_2$ stock solution:* For 500 ml stock, weigh out 101.6 g $MgCl_2 \cdot 6H_2O$, add H_2O to 500 ml, dissolve, and store at 4°C.

3. *Cytoskeleton buffer (CB):* 10 mM Mes (Sigma Cat. No. M-8250), 150 mM NaCl, 5 mM EGTA, 5 mM MgCl$_2$, 5 mM glucose. For 1 liter add to 800 ml H_2O the following amounts: Mes, 1.95 g; NaCl, 8.76 g; 0.5 M EGTA, 10 ml; 1 M MgCl$_2$, 5 ml; glucose, 0.9 g. Adjust pH to 6.1 with 1 N NaOH and fill up to 1 liter. Store at 4°C. For extended storage, add 100 mg streptomycin sulfate (Sigma Cat. No. S-6501).

4. *Tris-buffered saline (TBS), 10× concentrated stock solution:* 200 mM Tris (Merck Cat. No. 8382), 1.54 M NaCl, 20 mM EGTA, 20 mM MgCl$_2$, pH 7.5 at room temperature. For 1 liter add the following components to 800 ml H_2O: Tris, 24.2 g; NaCl, 89.9 g; 0.5 M EGTA, 40 ml; 1 M MgCl$_2$, 20 ml. Adjust pH to 7.5 with 1 N HCl and make up to 1 liter. Store at 4°C. Dilute required amount 1:9 with H_2O before use.

5. *Triton X-100 (T):* Make up 10% aqueous stock and store at 4°C.

TABLE I

Combination	Tubulin Vimentin Actin	Myosin Vinculin Actin
First antibody	Rabbit antitubulin,[1][a] 1:30[b] Mouse antivimentin,[2] 1:20	Rabbit antimyosin,[7] 1:25 Mouse antivinculin,[8] 1:5
Second antibody		Sheep anti-mouse, biotinylated,[3] 1:10
Third antibody	Goat anti-rabbit coumarin,[4] 1:10 Horse anti-mouse Texas red,[5] 1:50 FITC-phalloidin,[6] 1:100	AMCA avidin D, coumarin,[9] 1:50 Goat anti-rabbit Texas red,[10] 1:50 FITC-phalloidin,[6] 1:100

[a] (1) Provided by Dr. T. Kreis, Geneva; (2) provided by Dr. M. Osborn (Sigma clone V-9, Cat. No. V-6630); (3) Amersham (Cat. No. RPN 1001); (4) Dako (Cat. No. W478); (5) Vector Laboratories (Cat. No. TI-2000); (6) Sigma (Cat. No. P-8543); (7) Biomedical Technologies Inc. (nonmuscle myosin, Cat. No. BT-561); (8) Sigma clone hVin 1 (Cat. No. V-9131); (9) Vector Laboratories (Cat. No. A-2008); (10) Vector Laboratories (Cat. No. TI-1000).
[b] Dilution.

6. *Glutaraldehyde (GA):* Make up 2.5% solution of glutaraldehyde by diluting 25% glutaraldehyde EM grade (Agar Scientific Ltd, Cat. No. R-1020 or equivalent) in CB. Readjust pH to 6.1 and store at 4°C.

7. *$NaBH_4$, 0.5 mg/ml in cold TBS or CB:* Make up fresh: weigh out 5-mg aliquots of $NaBH_4$ (Sigma Cat. No. S-9125) into dry 10-ml tubes and add 10 ml of chilled buffer just before use.

8. *Fixative mixtures:*

a. *Paraformaldehyde* (PFA): Make up stock 3% solution of paraformaldehyde (analytical-grade, Merck Cat. No. 4005). To make 100 ml, heat 80 ml of CB to 60°C, add 3 g paraformaldehyde, and mix for 30 min. Add a few drops of 10 *M* NaOH until the solution is clear, cool, adjust pH to 6.1, and make up to 100 ml with CB. Store in aliquots at −20°C.

b. *Paraformaldehyde–Triton mixture (3% PFA/0.3% T):* Add Triton X-100 from 10% aqueous stock to stock 3% paraformaldehyde.

c. *Paraformaldehyde–glutaraldehyde-Triton mixture (3% PFA/0.1% GA/ 0.3% T).* Make up by diluting stock solutions in CB.

9. *Blocking solution:* Combine 1% bovine serum albumin and 2% normal goat serum in TBS.

10. *Antibody mixtures:* These are made up in TBS or in the blocking solution. To remove any unwanted particles, centrifuge (10,000 *g* for 10 min) the diluted mixtures before use. Typical antibody (Ab) mixtures used for triple immunofluorescence are given in Table I.

11. *Mounting medium:* Mix 2.4 g of polyvinyl alcohol with 6 g glycerol (87%) and then add 6 ml H_2O. After at least 2 hr at room temperature, add 0.2 ml 0.2 *M* Tris–HCl, pH 8.5, to the mixture and further incubate the solution for 10 min at 60°C. Remove any precipitate by centrifugation at 17,000 *g* for 30 min. Store in aliquots at −20°C. [As antibleach agents added to mounting medium, additives are available that considerably reduce bleaching and thus enable multiple pictures to be taken of the same cells. We use *n*-propyl gallate (Giloh and Sedat, 1982) at

2.5–5 mg/ml or phenylenediamine (Johnson *et al.*, 1982) at 1–2 mg/ml in the mounting medium. After dissolving additive, degas mounting medium before storage.]

Steps

1. Seed the cells onto coverslips in the petri dish and allow them to attach and spread for several hours or overnight in an incubator.

2. Aspirate growth medium and rinse dish gently with CB (warmed to room temperature), taking care not to shift the coverslips over each other. Aspirate CB and replace with one of the following fixative solutions:

    a. 3% PFA/0.3% T, 5 min; wash CB; 3% PFA, 20 min
    b. 3% PFA, 10 min; wash CB; 0.1% T, 1 min
    c. 3% PFA/0.1% GA/0.3% T, 10 min; wash with CB, 3 × 5 min; NaBH$_4$ on ice (ensure that coverslips remain submerged)

3. Rinse twice with CB (can be stored for several days at 4°C).

4. Block. Invert each coverslip onto a 20-μl drop of blocking solution on Parafilm in the humid chamber. Before transfer to drop, dry the back side of the coverslip by holding it briefly on filter paper with a pair of forceps, taking care not to allow the cell side to dry. Drain any excess solution from the cell side by touching the edge of the coverslip to the filter paper. Incubate on blocking solution for 5 min or until first antibody mixtures are prepared. (Back side of coverslip should not be wet or coverslip will sink during the washing step.)

5. Apply drops (10–20 μl) of first antibody mixture to unused part of Parafilm and transfer coverslips to appropriate drops after draining excess blocking solution on filter paper. Replace lid on petri dish and leave at room temperature for 30 min.

6. Wash. To ease removal of coverslips for washing, pipette 10 μl TBS under their edge to lift them up from the Parafilm. Using forceps, transfer coverslips to multiwell dish in which the wells are filled to the brim with TBS so that the liquid surface is flat. The coverslips will float well, cell side down, as long as the back side remains dry. For efficient washing, transfer dish gently to a tilting–rotating table for 10 min. Repeat washing steps after transfer of coverslips to a second dish containing fresh TBS.

7. Change Parafilm in humid chamber and apply drops of second antibody mixture. Transfer coverslips to drops after briefly draining excess TBS with filter paper and incubate for 30 min.

8. Wash as described in step 6.

9. Apply third antibody as described in step 7.

10. Wash as described in step 6.

11. Mount. Add a small drop of mounting medium to a cleaned glass slide using, for example, a plastic disposable pipette tip. Drain excess TBS from coverslip and gently invert onto drop. *Note:* The mounting medium dries quite fast so the drops should be applied singly and not in batches. If necessary, remove excess medium after mounting by applying small pieces of torn filter paper to the coverslip edge.

12. Observe directly in fluorescence microscope with a dry lens. An oil immersion lens can be used the next day when the mounting medium has solidified (Fig. 1).

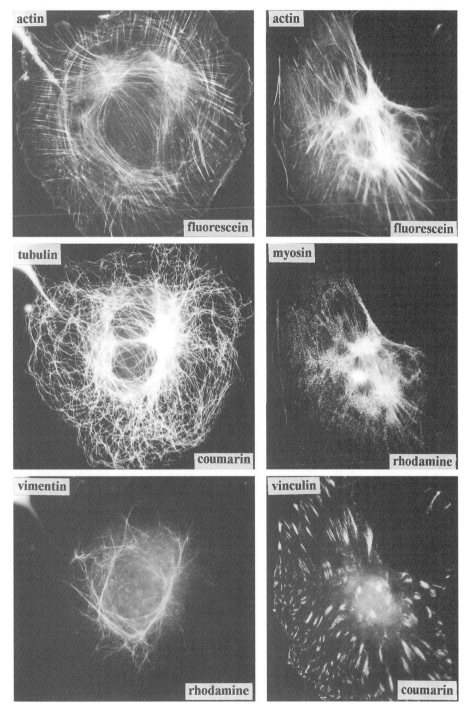

Figure 1 Triple immunofluorescence labeling of the cytoskeleton using rhodamine-, fluorescein-, and coumarin-conjugated probes, as indicated. Actin is labeled with phalloidin. The two cells shown (left and right) are labeled according to the two different combinations given in Table I.

IV. Filters

For double immunofluorescence microscopy with FITC and rhodamine (or Texas red or Cy3), standard filter sets are available. If bleed-through of one color into the wrong channel is observed the filter combinations should be rechecked by the manufacturer. When using coumarin in a triple combination, an ultraviolet excitation filter is used together with a barrier filter that excludes green fluorescence arising from UV excitation of fluorescein. A filter combination supplied on request by Zeiss that is suitable for coumarin comprises G365 for excitation and BS 450–490 as a barrier filter (see, e.g., Small *et al.,* 1988).

V. Pitfalls

If problems arise from sinking of coverslips during washing use another washing protocol, for example, immersion of coverslips cell side up in separate petri dishes containing TBS. Damaged cells normally arise from inadvertently allowing the coverslip to dry at any stage of the procedure or by touching the cell side with filter paper. Labeling with phalloidin can be improved by including this probe also in the first antibody. Successful double or triple immunofluorescence labeling requires that the individual antibody combinations each produce intense staining with a clean background, when used alone.

REFERENCES

Brandtzaeg, P. (1973) Conjugates of immunoglobulin G with different fluorochromes. I. Characterization by anionic exchange chromatography. *Scand. J. Immunol.* **2,** 273–290.

Fujiwara, K., and Pollard, T. D. (1980) Techniques for colocalizing contractile proteins with fluorescent antibodies. *In* "Current Topics in Developmental Biology," Vol. 14, pp. 271–296. Academic Press, New York.

Giloh, H., and Sedat, J. W. (1982) Fluorescence microscopy: Reduced photobleaching of rhodamine and fluorescein protein conjugates by *n*-propyl gallate. *Science* **217,** 1252–1255.

Johnson, G. D., Davidson, R. S., McNamee, K. C., Russell, G., Goodwin, D., and Holborow, F. J. (1982) Fading of immunofluorescence during microscopy: A study of the phenomena and its remedy. *J. Immun. Methods* **55,** 231–242.

Lazarides, E. (1982) Antibody production and immunofluorescent characterization of actin and contractile proteins. *In* "Methods in Cell Biology" (L. Wilson, ed.), Vol. 24, pp. 313–331. Academic Press, New York.

Osborn, M., and Weber, K. (1982) Immunofluorescence and immunocytochemical procedures with affinity purified antibodies: Tubulin-containing structures. *In* "Methods in Cell Biology" (L. Wilson, ed.), Vol. 24, pp. 97–132. Academic Press, New York.

Small, J. V. (1988) The actin cytoskeleton. *Electron Microsc. Rev.* **1,** 155–174.

Small, J. V., Zobeley, S., Rinnerthaler, G., and Faulstich, H. (1988) Coumarin–phalloidin: A new actin probe permitting triple immunofluorescence microscopy of the cytoskeleton. *J. Cell Sci.* **89,** 21–24.

Immunocytochemistry of Frozen and of Paraffin Tissue Sections

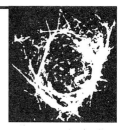

Mary Osborn and Susanne Isenberg

I. Introduction

Immunocytochemistry of tissue sections can yield valuable information as to the location of antigens. Thus it can determine whether the antigen is ubiquitous or is present only in certain tissues. It can further determine whether all cells in a given tissue are positive for a given antigen, or whether the antigen is restricted to one or a few specialized cell types within the tissue. Its uses are not limited to normal tissues, and testing of tumor tissues in immunocytochemistry can yield information important for determination of tumor type. As in the article on immunocytochemistry of cultured cells (by Mary Osborn), choice of antibodies and of fixation method can be of critical importance. New antibodies should be tested on both frozen sections and on paraffin sections of a variety of tissues in which the antigen is thought to be present. In general more antibodies will react on frozen sections than on paraffin sections; however, morphology is better preserved in the paraffin sections.

For other reviews of methods, see Denk (1987) and Sternberger (1979), and for overviews of the use of these methods in histopathology, see Osborn and Weber (1983), Tubbs *et al.* (1986), Jennette (1989), and Osborn and Domagala (1990).

II. Materials and Instrumentation

Antibodies
See the article by Mary Osborn in this volume. Dilute monoclonal antibodies 1:5 to 1:30, ascites fluid 1:100 to 1:1000, and polyclonal antibodies 1:20 to 1:40. Dilute both primary and secondary antibodies as far as possible to save money and to avoid unspecific reactions.

Cryostat
Use, e.g., a Reichert-Jung Cryostat Frigocut Model 2700. A useful accessory is a freezing head with variable temperature control. Use a C-knife and resharpen when necessary.

Tissue-tek
OCT compound from Miles Laboratories.

Paraffin Embedding
Automatic machines are useful only for laboratories that process a large number of samples. Check equipment for paraffin embedding in the local pathology department.

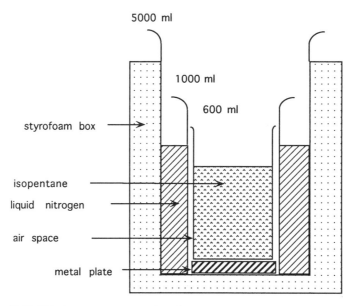

plastic   beakers

5000 ml

1000 ml

600 ml

styrofoam box

isopentane

liquid   nitrogen

air space

metal plate

FIGURE 1   Apparatus used to freeze tissues.

Sliding Microtomes

These are relatively cheap, e.g., Reichert-Jung Model H.40, and can be used with disposable knives.

Water Baths for Histology

These are thermostatically controlled and relatively shallow, e.g., 20 cm in diameter and 4 cm deep.

Microscopes

For a microscope to view immunofluorescence specimens see the article by Mary Osborn this volume. To view peroxidase- or streptavidin–biotin-stained specimens only a simple light microscope is required.

III. Procedures

A. CRYOSTAT SECTIONS

Steps

1. Freezing of Tissue Blocks

1. Fill the inner beaker of the freezing apparatus with isopentane and the outer beaker with liquid nitrogen about 30 min before freezing tissues (Fig. 1). Use reagent-grade isopentane. Wait until isopentane reaches −120 to −130°C. At −155°C the isopentane will freeze.

2. Dissect tissues. Cut into small blocks (∼4–7 mm) using a scalpel. Place block on a prenumbered square of paper, with the surface that will be sectioned furthest away from the paper. For small specimens, e.g., vessels, place a drop of Tissue-tek on the paper, then add the tissue.

3. Drop tissue blocks into iospentane. Leave for at least 30 sec. Remove blocks with plastic tweezers and transfer directly to plastic vials (scintillation vials ∼6 ×

2.5 cm work well) or metal cans (~3 × 3 cm) with screw tops that have been precooled on dry ice. Close vials and store in a −70°C freezer. Tissue blocks are stable for several years.

2. Cutting Cryostat Sections

1. Wash microscope slides by dipping in acetone, air-dry, and store at room temperature. Store plastic tweezers and brush in the cryostat. Precool cryostat and freezing head.

2. Place Tissue-tek on precooled freezing head, and mount block so that the larger side of the cut section is at 90° to the knife blade.

3. The optimal cutting temperature is different for different tissues. Most tissues cut well at −15 to −20°C. For liver, use −10°C. If the sections wrinkle as they are cut and look mushy decrease the temperature. If the sections have cracks and look brittle increase the temperature.

4. To cut sections use the C-knife. First trim the block to get a good cutting surface. Then adjust the section thickness to 5 μm, and use the automatic advance. Now cut three or four sections so that the preset section thickness is achieved. Then bring the antiroll plate on the knife to stop the section from rolling up and to keep it flat on the knife. The antiroll plate must be parallel to the knife edge, and should only protrude very slightly over the edge.

5. For optimal sections the knife and the antiroll plate must be kept clean (use a soft cloth dipped in acetone). Always clean the knife in the cutting direction and never the reverse, so as not to damage the cutting edge of the knife.

6. Remove the antiroll plate and hold the microscope slide over but not touching the cut section. The section should now spring on to the slide because of the difference in temperature between knife and slide. The quality of the section can be checked using toluidine blue or hematoxylin–eosin staining (see below).

7. Dry the sections at room temperature for 30 min. Then either use directly or place in a slide box and put in −70°C freezer. Cut sections are stable for months at −70°C.

8. Sections from a few tissues may not stick firmly enough to slides, and may come off during subsequent processing. If this happens try coating slides with 0.1% polylysine (e.g., Sigma Cat. No. 8920) in water.

B. PARAFFIN SECTIONS

Steps

1. Embedding Tissues in Paraffin

Human material is often received from the clinic already embedded in paraffin. Protocols vary depending on the clinic, with time of fixation in formaldehyde being very variable (e.g., 4 hr to over the weekend). To embed animal tissue in the lab cut into 4 to 7-mm blocks and place it for 4–8 hr in 3.7% formaldehyde in water or PBS, 1 hr in 50% ethanol, 2 × 1 hr in 70% ethanol, 2 × 1 hr in 96% ethanol, 2 × 1 hr in 100% ethanol, 1 × 1 hr in xylene, 1 × 2 hr in xylene, and 2 × 2 hr in Paraplast Plus (Shandon).

2. Cutting Paraffin Sections

1. To obtain very thin sections (1–2 μm) put the paraffin blocks in a freezer at −20°C for around 30 min. Mount the block in the holder of a sliding microtome.

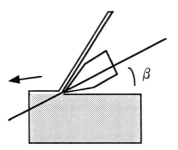

FIGURE 2 Correct adjustment of knife and of cutting angle to cut paraffin sections.

If the block cuts well do not use the automatic advance, but rely instead on the natural expansion of the block as it warms up to advance the block. If the block is not easy to cut use the automatic advance set at a thickness of 1–2 μm. Correct adjustment of the knife and of the cutting angle is very important. Use an inclination angle (β) of 15° (Fig. 2). If the inclination angle is less than 10° the knife will not cut the block, and if it is greater than 15° the block will break.

2. Trim the block until the cutting surface is optimal. Then cut a section, using a paint brush to draw the section onto the knife so that it does not roll up.

3. Dip a second paint brush in water, so that the section will adhere to it, and move the section to a water bath held at 40–45°C. If the section is placed with the shiny smooth surface touching the water the warmth will smooth out the section and wrinkles will vanish!

4. Place a microscope slide under the section, and using a brush position the section on the slide.

5. Dry the sections. For immunohistochemical methods dry overnight at 37°C. For normal histological methods set drying oven to 60°C so that the paraffin melts in part during the drying step, and dry for 1–2 hr.

3. Deparaffinization

Immerse sections 2 × 10 min in xylene, 1 × 3 min in 100% ethanol, 1 × 3 min in 95% ethanol, and air-dry.

4. Trypsinization

Some laboratories routinely use trypsinization or other proteolytic treatment of formalin-fixed, paraffin-embedded tissues prior to immunohistochemistry, e.g., 5 min in 0.1% trypsin (Sigma Cat. No. T-8128) in PBS at room temperature. As stressed by Ordonez *et al.* (1988) this can enhance the staining by certain antibodies but may also result in false-negative staining with other antibodies. Thus, control trypsinization conditions carefully.

5. Treating Sections in a Microwave Oven

Cut sections onto Superfrost or similar slides. After deparaffinization immerse slides in citrate buffer (2.1 g citric acid monohydrate/liter adjusted to pH 6.0 with NaOH). Microwave for two cycles of 5 min each at a setting of 650 or 700 W. Add more buffer between cycles so slides stay covered during the microwave step. Cool to room temperature (cf. Cattoretti *et al.*, 1992).

C. HISTOLOGIC STAINING OF SECTIONS

Stain frozen sections directly. Deparaffinize paraffin sections (see above), substituting a wash with distilled water for the air-drying step.

Solutions

1. *Toluidine blue:* Immerse sections in 1% toluidine blue for approximately 1 min. Wash with distilled water. Mount in water-soluble embedding medium, e.g., Glycergel (Dako Cat. No. C563).

2. *Hemotoxylin–eosin:* Immerse sections for 10 min in Hemalum (Merck Cat. No. 9249) solution. Wash for 10 min under running tap water, for 5 min in eosin, (Merck Cat. No. 15935) and twice with distilled water, and then run through an alcohol series (e.g. 75%, 95% for 2 min each, then 100% for 5 min, then 2 × 5 min in xylol) and mount in Eukitt (Riedel de Haën Cat. No. 33949) or Entellan (Merck Cat. No. 7960.0100).

C. IMMUNOCYTOCHEMISTRY

Three methods are described in detail: immunofluorescence, the immunoperoxidase method, and the more sensitive streptavidin–biotin method. The two latter methods have the advantage that nuclei can be counterstained with hemotoxylin and that only a simple light microscope is required to visualize the stain; however, fluorescence generally gives greater resolution.

As noted for cells, many antibodies that react well on cryostat sections may not react on the same tissue after it has been fixed in formaldehyde and embedded in paraffin. In such a case it may be advantagous to try fixing tissue, e.g., in B5, Bouin's or Zenker's fixative or alcohol, prior to paraffin embedding. An interesting alternative is to use sections of formaldehyde-fixed, paraffin-embedded material that have been treated in a microwave oven.

For all methods mark the position of the section after fixation; either use a diamond pencil or circle the section with a water-repellent marker (Dako Cat. No. 52002). Remove excess buffer after rinsing steps with Q-Tips. Use 10 μl of antibody per section. Apply with an Eppendorf pipette and use the pipette tip to spread the antibody over the section without touching the section. Several manufacturers (e.g., Dako) produce excellent protocol sheets for each immunocytochemical method.

Steps

1. Immunofluorescence

1. Fix cryostat sections or paraffin sections deparaffinized as above for 10 min in acetone at −10°C. Air-dry.

2. Use steps 2–9 of the protocol given in the article by Mary Osborn in this volume for multitest slides. Nuclei can be counterstained with Hoechst dye (see Osborn's article). Positively stained cells will be green (see Color Plate 20), if an FITC-labeled second antibody is used, or red, if a rhodamine-labeled second antibody is selected.

2. Peroxidase Staining

1. Fix cryostat sections for 10 min in acetone at −10°C, air-dry, and wash in PBS.

2. Deparaffinize paraffin sections, and incubate for 30 min at room temperature in 100 ml methanol containing 100 μl H_2O_2 to block endogenous peroxidase activity. Wash in PBS.

3. Incubate for 10 min at 37°C with normal rabbit serum diluted 1:10 in PBS, 0.5 mg/ml BSA. Drain but do not wash after this step.

4. Incubate with primary antibody (e.g., mouse monoclonal) for 30 min at 37°C.

5. Wash three times in PBS.

6. Incubate with second antibody coupled to peroxidase, e.g., rabbit anti-mouse for a monoclonal first antibody (Cat. No. P260 from Dako diluted 1:10 to 1:20).

7. Wash three times in PBS and once in Tris buffer (6 g NaCl, 6 g Tris/liter, pH 7.4).

8. Develop for 10 min at room temperature using freshly made solutions (e.g., 0.06 g diaminobenzidine, Fluka Cat. No. 32750 in 100 ml Tris buffer, 0.03 ml H_2O_2). *Note*: Diaminobenzidine is a carcinogen; handle with care.

9. Wash in tap water.

10. Apply a light counterstain by immersing the slide in Hemalum for 1 to 10 sec. Remove when staining reaches the required intensity.

11. Wash in tap water.

12. Mount in Glyergel (Dako Cat. No. C563).

Notes

1. Structures that are positively stained will be dark brown, whereas nuclei will be light blue (Color Plates 23 and 24).

2. The method can be made more sensitive by using an additional step with a peroxidase–antiperoxidase complex (see Sternberger, 1979).

3. Streptavidin–Biotin Stain

Buy the reagents separately or use the Histostain-SP kit from Zymed Laboratories (Cat. No. 95-6543 for mouse primary antibody, Cat. No. 95-6143 for rabbit primary antibody). These kits are based on the strong binding between streptavidin, a 60,000-kDa protein isolated from *Streptomyces avidinii*, and biotin, a water-soluble vitamin (MW 244, $K_d = 10^{-15}$ M). Instructions are given for the mouse kit.

1. Fix cryostat sections for 10 min in acetone at -10°C and air-dry. Sections can be treated with 0.23% periodate for 45 sec. Go to step 3.

2. Deparaffinize paraffin sections and air-dry. Incubate 10 min in PBS at room temperature, then 10 min in H_2O_2 solution (9 parts methanol to 1 part 30% H_2O_2 in water). Wash 3 × 2 min in PBS.

3. Reduce nonspecific background staining by blocking for 10 min in 10% goat serum at room temperature. Then drain but do not wash.

4. Incubate with primary antibody, e.g., mouse monoclonal antibody, in wet chamber for 30 min at 37°C.

5. Wash 3 × 2 min in PBS.

6. Add biotinylated second antibody, e.g., goat anti-mouse, for 10 min at room temperature and repeat step 5.

7. Add enzyme conjugate streptavidin–peroxidase diluted 1:20 for 5 min at room temperature. This binds to the biotin residues on the second antibody.

8. Develop by adding substrate–chromogen mixture for 5 min at 37°C or 15 min at room temperature. The enzyme peroxidase catalyzes the substrate hydrogen peroxide and converts the chromogen aminoethylcarbazole to a red, colored deposit.

9. Wash 3 × 2 min in distilled water.

10. Counterstain with Hemalum between 1 and 10 sec.

11. Wash 7 min in tap water.

12. Mount in Glycergel.

Notes

1. Structures that are positively stained will be red, whereas nuclei will be light blue (Color Plates 22 and 25).

2. Optimal dilution of primary antibody has to be determined for each antibody.

3. The streptavidin–peroxidase conjugate is the same for all species; the blocking serum and second antibody vary according to the species in which the first antibody is made.

4. The alkaline phosphatase–antialkaline phosphatase technique is also a very sensitive method (Color Plate 21).

IV. Comments

If possible, include (1) a positive control, i.e., a section of a tissue known to contain the antigen; (2) a negative control, i.e., a section known not to have the antigen; and (3) a reagent control, i.e., a section stained with nonimmune serum instead of the primary antibody. Ideally, (1) should be positive and (2) and (3) negative. If high backgrounds are obtained, it may help to adjust the antibody concentrations by increasing the length of time for washing steps or by including 0.5 M NaCl or 5% BSA in the antibody solutions.

REFERENCES

Cattoretti, G., Becker, M. H. G., Key, G., Duchrow, M., Schlüter, C., Galle, J., and Gerdes, J. (1992) Monoclonal antibodies against recombinant parts of the Ki-67 antigen (MIB 1 and MIB 3) detect proliferating cells in microwave processed formalin-fixed paraffin sections. *J. Pathol.* **168**, 357–363.

Denk, H. (1987) Immunohistochemical methods for the demonstration of tumor markers. *In* "Morphological Tumor Markers" (G. Seifert, ed.), pp. 47–70. Springer-Verlag, Berlin.

Jenette, J. C. (1989) "Immunohistology in Diagnostic Pathology." CRC Press, Boca Raton, FL.

Ordonez, N. G., Manning, J. T., and Brooks, T. E. (1988) Effect of trypsinization on the immunostaining of formalin-fixed, paraffin-embedded tissues. *Am. J. Surg. Pathol.* **12**, 121–129.

Osborn, M., and Domagala, W. (1990) Immunocytochemistry in diagnostic cytopathology. *In* "Comprehensive Cytopathology" (M. Bibbo, ed.), pp. 1011–1051. W. B. Saunders, Philadelphia.

Osborn, M., and Weber, K. (1983) Tumor diagnosis by intermediate filament typing: A novel tool for surgical pathology. *Lab. Invest.* **48**, 372–394.

Sternberger, L. A. (1979) "Immunohistochemistry," 2nd ed. John Wiley & Sons, New York.

Tubbs, R. R., Gephardt, G. N., and Petras, R. E. (1986) "Atlas of Immunohistology." American Society of Clinical Pathologists Press, Chicago.

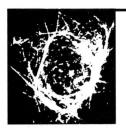

Fluorescent Labeling of Nascent RNA in the Cell Nucleus Using 5-Bromouridine 5'-Triphosphate

Derick G. Wansink, Alison M. Motley, Roel van Driel, and Luitzen de Jong

I. Introduction

Three different RNA polymerases are responsible for nuclear transcription (Sentenac, 1985; Bautz and Petersen, 1989). 5-Bromouridine 5'-triphosphate (BrUTP), an artificial UTP analog, is efficiently incorporated into RNA by RNA polymerases I and II and possibly III (Nakayama and Saneyoshi, 1984; Wansink et al., 1993). Antibodies specifically recognizing BrUTP have been developed and are commercially available (Gratzner et al., 1975; Vanderlaan and Thomas, 1985). Here, we describe the use of BrUTP as a marker for RNA synthesis in the interphase cell nucleus. BrUTP is incorporated into nascent RNA during run-on transcription in permeabilized cells (Marzluff and Huang, 1984) or after microinjection of BrUTP directly into the cell. Incorporated BrUTP is detected using a BrUTP-specific monoclonal antibody followed by fluorescently labeled secondary antibodies and fluorescence microscopy. Fluorescently labeled RNA is observed in several hundreds of domains in the interphase nucleus (Fig. 1) (Wansink et al., 1993; Jackson et al., 1993). Run-on transcription in permeabilized cells and short-term in vivo labeling result in similar staining patterns. Sites containing incorporated BrUTP reflect sites of RNA synthesis (Wansink et al., 1993). Labeling RNA with BrUTP is sensitive, rapid, and simple, and has been successfully applied in many different cell types from several species (e.g., chicken, rat kangaroo, hamster, mouse, rat, and human). It offers many possibilities in combination with other immunocytochemical techniques in double-labeling experiments (Wansink et al., 1993).

II. Materials and Instrumentation

BrUTP (Cat. No. B-1633), digitonin (Cat. No. D-1407), L-α-lysolecithin (Cat. No. L-4129), Triton X-100 (Cat. No. X-100), PMSF (Cat. No. P-7626), BSA (Cat. No. B-7906), gelatin from cold water fish skin (Cat. No. G-7765), Hoechst 33258 (Cat. No. B-2883), p-phenylenediamine (Cat. No. P-6001), and α-amanitin (Cat. No. A-2263) are from Sigma Chemical Company. Paraformaldehyde (Cat. No. 4005) and dithiothreitol (DTT, Cat. No. 11474) are from Merck. RNasin ribonuclease inhibitor (Cat. No. N2512) is from Promega. S-Adenosylmethionine (Cat. No. 102415), ATP (Cat. No. 126888), CTP (Cat. No. 103845), GTP (Cat. No. 106399), and UTP (Cat. No. 110221) are from Boehringer-Mannheim. Rat monoclonal antibody (mAb) against BrUTP (Cat. No. MAS 250C, originally raised against bromodeoxyuridine) is from Sera-Lab. Normal

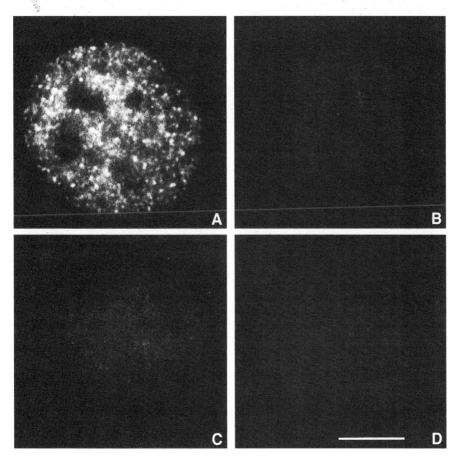

FIGURE 1 Localization of BrUTP-labeled RNA in Triton X-100-permeabilized human bladder carcinoma cells. Nascent RNA was fluorescently labeled during 30 min run-on transcription as described in this article. (A, C, D) Run-on transcription in the presence of BrUTP. (B) BrUTP was substituted with UTP to examine the specificity of the mAb. (C) α-Amanitin (1 μg/ml) was included during run-on transcription to block RNA polymerase II transcription. (D) Before fixation cells were incubated with 50 μg/ml RNase A for 10 min at room temperature. Bar = 5 μm. (Reproduced from the *Journal of Cell Biology* (1993), **122**:283–293, by copyright permission of the Rockefeller University Press.)

donkey serum (Cat. No. 017-000-121), biotin-conjugated donkey anti-rat IgG(H + L) (Cat. No. 712-065-138), and FITC-conjugated streptavidin (Cat. No. 016-090-084) are from Jackson ImmunoResearch Laboratories. DME (Cat. No. 074-02100), FCS (Cat. No. 011-06290), L-glutamine (Cat. No. 043-05030), and penicillin–streptomycin (Cat. No. 043-05140) are from Gibco.

Coverslips (16-mm diameter, No. 1) are from Chance Propper. Microscope slides (Cat. No. 011101) are from Menzel Gläser. Replica dishes (Cat. No. 638102) are from Greiner. A humidified chamber is made from a large petri dish (22 × 22 cm), Parafilm, and wet tissues.

III. Procedures

A. PREPARATION OF STOCK SOLUTIONS

Solutions

1. *TBS:* 10 mM Tris–HCl, pH 7.4, 150 mM NaCl, 5 mM MgCl$_2$. Dissolve 0.6 g Tris, 4.4 g NaCl, and 0.5 g MgCl$_2 \cdot$6H$_2$O in distilled water, adjust pH to 7.4, and bring to a total volume of 500 ml. Store at 4°C.

2. *Glycerol buffer:* 20 mM Tris–HCl, pH 7.4, 5 mM $MgCl_2$, 0.5 mM EGTA, 25% glycerol. Dissolve 1.2 g Tris, 0.5 g $MgCl_2 \cdot 6H_2O$, 0.1 g EGTA, and 144 ml glycerol (87%) in distilled water, adjust pH to 7.4, and bring to a total volume of 500 ml. Store at 4°C.

3. *2× Synthesis buffer:* 100 mM Tris–HCl, pH 7.4, 20 mM $MgCl_2$, 1 mM EGTA, 200 mM KCl, 50% glycerol. Dissolve 1.2 g Tris, 0.4 g $MgCl_2 \cdot 6H_2O$, 0.04 g EGTA, 1.5 g KCl, and 57.5 ml glycerol (87%) in distilled water, adjust pH to 7.4, and bring to a total volume of 100 ml. Store at 4°C.

4. *NTP:* 10 mM NTP. Stock solutions of ribonucleotides are prepared according to Sambrook *et al.* (1989). Dissolve 30 mg NTP in 3 ml distilled water and adjust to pH 7.0 with 50 mM solution of Tris base (approximately 1.5 ml). Dilute an aliquot of neutralized NTP appropriately and read optical density at the wavelength given below. The actual concentration (approximately 10 mM) can be calculated using the corresponding extinction coefficient (sources: Nakayama and Saneyoshi, 1984; Sambrook *et al.*, 1989). Aliquot and store at −20°C.

	ATP	BrUTP	CTP	GTP	UTP
λ_{max} (nm)	259	280	271	253	260
Extinction coefficient ($10^3\ M^{-1}\ cm^{-1}$)	15.4	9.3	9.0	13.7	10.0

5. *Injection buffer:* 0.1 M BrUTP, 140 mM KCl, 2 mM Pipes, pH 7.4. Dissolve 6 mg BrUTP in 100 μl of 140 mM KCl, 2 mM Pipes, pH 7.4. Adjust pH to 7.4 if necessary. Aliquot and store at −20°C.

6. *SAM:* 10 mM *S*-adenosylmethionine. Dissolve 5 mg *S*-adenosylmethionine hydrogen sulfate in 1 ml distilled water, aliquot, and store at −20°C.

7. *PMSF:* 100 mM PMSF. Dissolve 174 mg PMSF in 10 ml isopropanol, aliquot, and store at −20°C.

8. *10× PBS:* Dissolve 81.8 g NaCl, 2.0 g KCl, 11.6 g $Na_2HPO_4 \cdot 2H_2O$, and 2.0 g KH_2PO_4 in distilled water and bring to a total volume of 1 liter. Store at room temperature.

9. *PBS:* 140 mM NaCl, 2.7 mM KCl, 6.5 mM $Na_2HPO_4 \cdot 2H_2O$, 1.5 mM KH_2PO_4): Add 50 ml 10× PBS to distilled water, adjust pH to 7.4, and bring to a total volume of 500 ml. Store at 4°C.

10. *PBG:* PBS containing 0.5% (w/v) BSA and 0.05% (w/v) gelatin. Dissolve 2.5 g BSA and 0.6 g gelatin from cold water fish skin (45%) in 500 ml PBS. Aliquot and store at −20°C.

11. *10% BSA:* Dissolve 2 g BSA in 20 ml PBS. Remove debris by centrifugation, aliquot, and store at −20°C.

12. *Hoechst 33258:* Dissolve 1 mg Hoechst 33258 in 5 ml distilled water. Store at 4°C.

13. *Embedding medium:* Dissolve 25 mg *p*-phenylenediamine in a mixture of 2.5 ml 10× PBS and 22.5 ml glycerol (87%). Protect from light and air as much as possible. Adjust pH to 8.0 using 0.5 M $NaHCO_3$, pH 9.0. Embedding medium should be colorless. Aliquot and store at −20°C. Discard and prepare new when solution turns brownish.

B. CELL CULTURE

Human bladder carcinoma cells were grown at 37°C under a 10% CO_2 atmosphere in DME supplemented with 10% (v/v) heat-inactivated FCS, 2 mM L-glutamine, 100 IU/ml penicillin, and 100 μg/ml streptomycin. For each experiment cells were transferred onto coverslips placed in a replica dish and allowed to grow for 24–48 hr.

C. LABELING OF NASCENT RNA WITH BRUTP IN PERMEABILIZED CELLS

Solutions

Prepare fresh for 20 coverslips.

1. *10% Triton X-100:* Add 150 mg Triton X-100 to 1350 ml distilled water and mix until solution is homogeneous.

2. *Glycerol buffer containing 0.05% Triton X-100:* Mix 10 μl 10% Triton X-100 and 1.99 ml glycerol buffer.

3. *TBS containing 0.05% Triton X-100:* Mix 10 μl 10% Triton X-100 and 1.99 ml TBS.

4. *Transcription buffer:* 50 mM Tris–HCl, pH 7.4, 10 mM $MgCl_2$, 0.5 mM EGTA, 100 mM KCl, 25% glycerol, 25 μM S-adenosylmethionine, 0.5 mM ATP, BrUTP, CTP, and GTP. Mix 1 ml 2× synthesis buffer, 5 μl SAM, 100 μl of each of the four NTPs, and 595 μl distilled water. Place on ice.

5. *RNasin:* 1 U/μl RNasin ribonuclease inhibitor. To make a 1 U/μl solution, add 2 μl RNasin ribonuclease inhibitor (40 U/μl) to 78 μl PBS containing 5 mM DTT. Place on ice.

Steps

All steps are done at room temperature unless specified otherwise. The coverslips are placed on Parafilm in a humidified chamber. Each solution is carefully added onto the coverslip (approximately 100 μl per coverslip). After incubation the solution is carefully but adequately removed by aspiration and replaced by the next solution. The coverslips may not become dry. *Note:* Shortly before use, add PMSF and RNasin to the final concentrations indicated below.

1. Take coverslips out of culture medium and place them on Parafilm (cells facing upward) in a humidified chamber. Rinse in TBS. Directly proceed to step 2.

2. Incubate 3 min in glycerol buffer containing 1 mM PMSF.

3. Permeabilize cells for 3 min in glycerol buffer containing 0.05% Triton X-100, 1 mM PMSF, and 10 U/ml RNasin.

4. Allow run-on transcription for 5–60 min in transcription buffer containing 1 mM PMSF and 20 U/ml RNasin.

5. Rinse 3 min in TBS containing 0.05% Triton X-100, 1 mM PMSF, and 5 U/ml RNasin.

6. Rinse 3 min in TBS containing 1 mM PMSF and 5 U/ml RNasin.

7. Fix cells (see Section E).

D. LABELING OF NASCENT RNA WITH BRUTP IN LIVING CELLS BY MICROINJECTION

Steps

1. Take coverslip out of replica dish and place it in a petri dish containing culture medium at 37°C to maintain normal growth conditions during injection.

2. Inject injection buffer into the cytoplasm (about 5% of the total cell volume). Some 300 cells are injected in 10 min (see also articles by M. Graessmann and A. Graessmann, by Yu-Li Wang, and by Rainer Pepperkok, Rainer Saffrich, and Wilhelm Ansorge). Note that incorporation of BrUTP into nascent RNA starts immediately after injection of BrUTP into the cell.

3. If longer incorporation after finishing injection is desired, place the petri dish back in the incubator for some time.

4. Incorporation is stopped by fixation (see Section E), or alternatively follow steps 5–7:

5. Stop incorporation by rinsing coverslip 3 min in TBS containing 0.05% Triton X-100, 1 mM PMSF, and 5 U/ml RNasin.

6. Rinse 3 min in TBS containing 1 mM PMSF and 5 U/ml RNasin.

7. Fix cells (see Section E).

E. FIXATION, IMMUNOLABELING, AND EMBEDDING

Solutions

Prepare fresh.

1. *2% Formaldehyde in PBS:* Formaldehyde solution is prepared by depolymerizing paraformaldehyde. Add 1 g paraformaldehyde to 10 ml distilled water in a beaker containing a stirring bar. Stir and heat to 65°C. Add 10-μl aliquots of 1 N NaOH until all paraformaldehyde has dissolved (approximately 50 μl). Add 5 ml 10× PBS and 35 ml distilled water. Adjust pH to 7.4.

2. *PBS containing 0.5% Triton X-100:* Mix 100 μl 10% Triton X-100 and 1.9 ml PBS.

3. *PBS containing 100 mM glycine:* Dissolve 75 mg glycine in 10 ml PBS.

4. *Anti-BrUTP (1:500 in PBG):* Dilute 4 μl rat mAb against BrUTP in 2 ml PBG.

5. *Biotin-conjugated anti-rat IgG (1:300 in PBG):* Dilute 7 μl biotin-conjugated donkey anti-rat IgG(H + L) in 2.1 ml PBG.

6. *FITC-conjugated streptavidin (1:500 in PBG):* Dilute 4 μl FITC-conjugated streptavidin in 2 ml PBG.

7. *25% Normal donkey serum:* Mix 0.5 ml normal donkey serum with 1.5 ml PBS.

8. *PBS containing 0.4 μg/ml Hoechst 33258:* Mix 4 μl Hoechst 33258 and 2 ml PBS.

Steps

1. Fix cells for 15 min in 2% formaldehyde in PBS.
2. Rinse twice for 3 min in PBS.
3. Extract for 5 min in PBS containing 0.5% Triton X-100.
4. Rinse twice for 3 min in PBS.
5. Block for 10 min in PBS containing 100 mM glycine.
6. Block for 10 min in 10% BSA.
7. Incubate overnight in anti-BrUTP at 4°C.
8. Rinse 4 × 5 min in PBG.
9. Block for 10 min in 25% normal donkey serum.
10. Incubate 1.5 hr in biotin-conjugated anti-rat IgG.
11. Rinse 4 × 5 min in PBG.
12. Incubate 30 min in FITC-conjugated streptavidin in the dark.
13. Rinse twice for 5 min in PBG and twice for 5 min in PBS.
14. Stain DNA for 3 min in PBS containing 0.4 μg/ml Hoechst 33258. Then place coverslip in PBS.
15. Mount coverslips in 10 μl embedding medium per coverslip on microscope slides. Remove excess embedding medium with a tissue. Seal with nail polish. View directly. Store samples at −20°C.

IV. Comments

The BrUTP labeling described in this article gives a punctated nuclear staining *in vitro* as well as *in vivo*. Similar patterns have been observed in all cell lines tested. Only the number of spots per nucleus and the labeling intensity differ between cell lines. Cells with a relatively short cell generation time generally contain more spots per nucleus.

Usually we label permeabilized cells for 15–30 min. Longer labeling results in a more intense, but similar staining pattern. For visualization of sites of RNA synthesis *in vivo* labeling time should be kept to a minimum (5–15 min) because the *in vivo* transcription rate is higher than the transcription rate in permeabilized cells. When cells are labeled for a longer time *in vivo* sites of RNA processing may be labeled in addition to sites of transcription.

Control experiments are very important (see Fig. 1). Nuclear staining is sensitive to 1 μg/ml amanitin (when present in the transcription buffer). This demonstrates that the staining represents transcripts of RNA polymerase II (Roeder, 1976). No labeling is observed when cells are treated with RNase A before fixation. In contrast, labeling is not sensitive to DNase I. This proves that BrUTP is incorporated into RNA and not into DNA. Finally, no labeling is observed when UTP instead of BrUTP is present in the transcription buffer. This demonstrates the specificity of the antibodies.

In many cell lines nucleoli are not labeled under the conditions described here, although radioactive experiments have shown that RNA polymerase I (exclusively located in the nucleolus) does incorporate BrUTP. We attribute this absence of labeling to the dense structure of the nucleolus, which prevents the antibodies from binding to BrUTP incorporated into nucleolar RNA (see also Wansink *et al.*, 1993).

Permeabilizing agents other than Triton X-100 have been successfully used, e.g., digitonin (40 μg/ml) and L-α-lysolecithin (0.1 mg/ml). The optimal concentration for efficient permeabilization should be tested for each cell type and each permeabilizing agent (permeable cells no longer exclude trypan blue).

Glutaraldehyde may also be used as a fixative. Fixation in methanol is not recommended, because this does not preserve the labeling.

Visualization of BrUTP that is incorporated into nascent RNA can be combined with immunolabeling of other nuclear components in dual immunofluorescence experiments (see Wansink *et al.*, 1993).

V. Pitfalls

1. Use cells from an actively growing culture. The cell layer on the coverslip should not be confluent. Confluent cultures result in a dramatic reduction of permeabilization efficiency and in a decrease in transcriptional activity.

2. Preferentially, cells should attach firmly to the coverslips. Otherwise many cells may be lost during the procedure. Use of digitonin as a permeabilizing agent may partly overcome this problem.

3. RNase activity during the procedure will decrease labeling intensity (especially when present before fixation). In practice this does not appear to be a major problem. If no clear labeling is observed RNase activity may have been present and additional precautions may be necessary.

REFERENCES

Bautz, E. K. F., and Petersen, G. (1989) Eukaryotic RNA polymerases. *In* "Molecular Biology of Chromosome Function" (K. W. Adolph, ed.), pp. 157–179. Springer Verlag, Heidelberg.

Gratzner, H. G., Leif, R. C., Ingram, D. J., and Castro, A. (1975) The use of antibody specific for bromodeoxyuridine for the immunofluorescent determination of DNA replication in single cells and chromosomes. *Exp. Cell Res.* **95**, 88–94.

Jackson, D. A., Hassan, A. B., Errington, R. J., and Cook, P. R. (1993) Visualization of focal sites of transcription within human nuclei. *EMBO J.* **12**, 1059–1065.

Marzluff, W. F., and Huang, R. C. C. (1984) Transcription of RNA in isolated nuclei. *In* "Transcription and Translation, a Practical Approach" (B. D. Hames and S. J. Higgins, eds.), pp. 89–129. IRL Press, Oxford.

Nakayama, C., and Saneyoshi, M. (1984) Utilizations of various uridine 5′-triphosphate analogues by DNA-dependent RNA polymerases I and II purified from liver nuclei of the cherry salmon (*Oncorynchus masou*). *J. Biochem.* **96**, 1501–1509.

Roeder, R. G. (1976) Eukaryotic nuclear RNA polymerases. *In* "RNA Polymerase" (R. Losick and M. Chamberlin, eds.), pp. 285–329. Cold Spring Harbor Press, Cold Spring Harbor, NY.

Sambrook, J., Fritsch, E. F., and Maniatis, T. (1989) "Molecular Cloning, a Laboratory Manual," 2nd ed. Cold Spring Harbor Press, Cold Spring Harbor, NY.

Sentenac, A. (1985) Eukaryotic RNA polymerases. *CRC Crit. Rev. Biochem.* **18**, 31–90.

Vanderlaan, M., and Thomas, C. B. (1985) Characterization of monoclonal antibodies to bromodeoxyuridine. *Cytometry* **66**, 501–505.

Wansink, D. G., Schul, W., van der Kraan, I., van Steensel, B., van Driel, R., and de Jong, L. (1993) Fluorescent labeling of nascent RNA reveals transcription by RNA polymerase II in domains scattered throughout the nucleus. *J. Cell Biol.* **122**, 283–293.

Labeling of Endocytic Vesicles Using Fluorescent Probes for Fluid-Phase Endocytosis

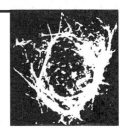

Esther L. Racoosin and Joel A. Swanson

I. Introduction

Cultured cells such as fibroblasts and murine macrophages endocytose solutes from their extracellular medium at high rates (Steinman *et al.*, 1976). This process has been studied using a variety of fluorescent solute probes that may be enclosed within clathrin-coated or uncoated vesicles forming at the cell surface. These probes also report the transport of solute within membrane vesicles into other organellar compartments of the endocytic pathway, such as early endosomes and lysosomes. They are readily soluble in many different types of cell culture medium and do not bind to the plasma membrane. Because of their efficient transport throughout the organellar compartments of the endocytic pathway, fluorescent probes for fluid-phase endocytosis can be used either to localize specific organelles along the endocytic pathway, using fluorescence microscopy (Racoosin and Swanson, 1993), or to measure bulk fluid endocytosis in larger populations of cultured cells (Swanson, 1989a). The methods described below provide a stepwise technical guide to labeling of endocytic vesicles. A more detailed discussion of labeling strategies and interpretation of results has been published elsewhere (Swanson, 1989b).

II. Materials and Instrumentation

The fluorescent probes lucifer yellow CH (LY, potassium salt, Cat. No. L-1177), fluorescein dextran (MW 10,000, FDx10, Cat. No. D-1821), fixable fluorescein dextran (MW 10,000, FDx10f, Cat. No. D-1820), and Texas red dextran (MW 10,000, TRDx10, Cat. No. D-1828) are from Molecular Probes. Bovine serum albumin (BSA, fraction V, Cat. No. A-9647), paraformaldehyde (Cat. No. P-6148), L-lysine–HCl (Cat. No. L-1262), and phenylenediamine are from Sigma Chemical Company. Glutaraldehyde is from Polysciences (8% solution) and formaldehyde is from Baxter Scientific (37% solution). Goat serum is from Gibco. Glass coverslips, of 12- or 25-mm circular diameter or 22 mm square, No. 1 or 0 thickness, are from Fisher Scientific.

A microscope equipped for epi-illumination of fluorescent specimens is required. For observation of living cells it is sometimes desirable to maintain the cell preparation at 37°C. Thermostatically controlled heaters are available for this purpose.

III. Procedures

A. LABELING ENDOCYTIC COMPARTMENTS WITH A FLUORESCENT PROBE: MICROSCOPIC OBSERVATION OF LIVING CELLS

Solutions

1. *Medium containing fluorescent probe:* Dissolve fluorescent dextran in the growth medium or saline most suitable for the cell type. For macrophages, prepare 1 mg/ml FDx10 or 0.5 mg/ml LY in Dulbecco's modified essential medium (DMEM) + 10% heat-inactivated fetal bovine serum (HIFBS) or in Ringer's solution containing 0.2% bovine serum albumin. Other cell types, with lower constitutive rates of endocytosis, may require higher concentrations of fluorophore. Thus, it may be appropriate initially to test different concentrations of the fluorescent probe and different labeling times. LY is sometimes difficult to dissolve, especially if purchased as a potassium salt. In such cases, it may be sonicated and warmed slightly as a more concentrated stock solution in water, before mixing with medium.

2. *VALAP:* Melt 1 part petroleum jelly (Vasoline), 1 part paraffin (Fisher Scientific, Cat. No. P31-500), and 1 part lanolin (Cat. No. 2252-01 anhydrous, Baker Chemical Co.) together in a beaker.

3. *Buffer (Ringer's solution + BSA):* 155 mM NaCl, 5 mM KCl, 2 mM CaCl$_2$, 1 mM MgCl$_2$, 2 mM NaH$_2$PO$_4$, 10 mM Hepes, 10 mM D-glucose, pH 7.2, + 0.2% BSA.

Materials

1. *Coverslip fragments:* Obtain No. 1 thickness, 22-mm-square coverslips. Place 10 coverslips into a plastic petri dish and mash, using the blunt end of a forceps, until the coverslip fragments are 2–5 mm.

Steps

1. Plate cells onto coverslips at low density. Store in wells of tissue culture cluster dishes containing tissue culture medium.

2. Before adding to cells, warm medium containing the fluorescent probe to 37°C. For cells on coverslips in 16-mm-diameter tissue culture wells, replace culture medium with at least 0.25 ml of medium containing the fluorescent probe. Swirl the dishes to distribute medium. Incubate cells at 37°C for various times. A 2- to 5-min incubation will label primarily pinosomes or early endosomes; a 2- to 5-min incubation followed by a 5- to 15-min "chase" incubation in the absence of the probe should label late endosomes. A 60-min incubation should label nearly all compartments (pinosomes, endosomes, and lysosomes), and a 60-min incubation followed by a long chase (30 min or more) should label primarily lysosomes (Fig. 1). These labeling times vary with cell type and are therefore simply good approximations.

3. First, arrange several coverslip fragments on a microscope slide such that they can support, like table legs, the coverslip with cells. At the end of the incubation, wash excess fluorescent probe from cells using warm medium or warm buffer. Washing should be done as quickly as possible. Use buffers that are at incubation temperature (i.e., 37°C) to maintain the distribution of endocytic vesicles. The intracellular distribution of vesicles is often dependent on the integrity of the cold-labile microtubule cytoskeleton. Next, place the coverslip, cell side down, on top of the coverslip fragments arranged on the slide. Using a

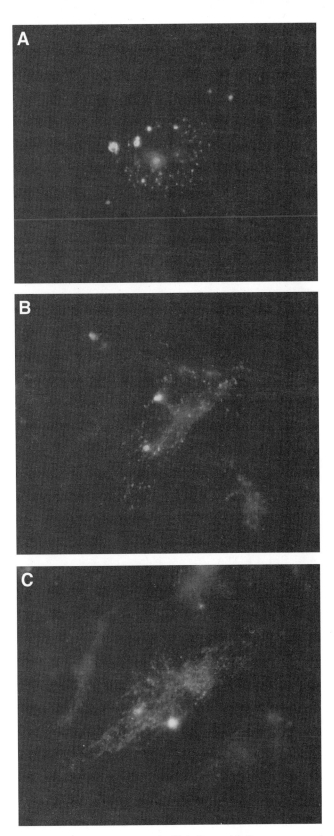

FIGURE 1 A short period of labeling with fluorescent probes followed by increasing chase times labels different endocytic compartments. Macrophages were incubated for 2 min in medium containing 0.5 mg/ml FDx10, then washed and fixed immediately (A), washed and chased in the absence of FDx10 for 15 min (B), or washed and chased in the absence of FDx10 for 30 min (C). These protocols result in the labeling of pinosomes (A), late endosomes (B), and lysosomes (C).

Pasteur pipette, quickly add warm Ringer's/BSA to the space between the coverslip and the slide. Absorb excess buffer from around the coverslip with a paper towel. To seal the preparation, heat a clean Pasteur pipette over a Bunsen burner flame, then poke it into a beaker containing solid VALAP to melt and draw VALAP into the pipette (carefully reheat the pipette containing VALAP over the Bunsen burner if necessary). Next, touch the tip of the Pasteur pipette around the borders of the coverslip, allowing the liquified VALAP to flow out and seal the coverslip to the slide. Repeat this procedure until the chamber is completely sealed.

4. Once the coverslip chamber is prepared, it should be viewed immediately. During microscopic examination, it may be necessary to attenuate the light, as intense light can cause photochemical damage to living cells. Too intense illumination can cause explosions of endocytic vesicles containing fluorescent probes, resulting in the release of those probes into the cell cytoplasm. Observation of very dim fluorescent organelles can be aided by darkening the room and by the use of image-intensifying video cameras (Hamamatsu Photonics Systems Corp.) mounted on the microscope.

B. LABELING ENDOCYTIC COMPARTMENTS WITH A FLUORESCENT PROBE: MICROSCOPIC OBSERVATION OF FIXED CELLS

Solutions

1. *FG fixative:*

   a. *Stock A (2× stock):* 0.5 M sucrose, 2 mM EGTA, 1 mM EDTA, 40 mM Hepes, 0.02% sodium azide. Mix all reagents in 90 ml water, adjust pH to 7.4, then bring to final volume of 100 ml. This stock may be stored at −20°C.

   b. *Final working solution (10 ml):* 5 ml stock A, 1 ml 37% formaldehyde, 64 μl of 8% glutaraldehyde, and distilled water to final 10 ml. Concentrations of working solution: 3.7% formaldehyde, 0.05% glutaraldehyde, 0.25 M sucrose, 1 mM EGTA, 0.5 mM EDTA, 20 mM Hepes, pH 7.4

2. *PLPS fixative:* This fixative is modified from the periodate–lysine–paraformaldehyde fixative of McLean and Nakane (1974).

   a. *Stock 1—8% paraformaldehyde in distilled water:* Make this solution in a chemical hood. Add 8 g paraformaldehyde to 90 ml distilled water in a beaker with a stir bar; put the beaker in a metal pan containing water. Heat the mixture to 70°C while stirring. Add one drop of 1 N NaOH to the mixture. Let mixture clear for a minute, then add another drop of 1 N NaOH. The solution should clear more after another minute. Allow the clear solution to cool, then increase volume to 100 ml and filter. The 8% paraformaldehyde may be kept in aliquots at −20°C.

   b. *Stock 2—10× PLPS:* Small volumes (50 ml) of this concentrated solution are made at a time because it should be discarded after 2 weeks at 4°C. Concentrations for the 10× stock are the following (g/50 ml solution): 200 mM Mes (1.952 g), 700 mM NaCl (2.045 g), 50 mM KCl (0.1864 g), 700 mM lysine–HCl (6.42 g), 50 mM MgCl$_2$ (2.5 ml of a 1 M stock solution), 20 mM EGTA (5 ml of a 0.2 M stock solution). Mix all reagents except MgCl$_2$ and EGTA in 30 ml of water until completely dissolved. Next, add EGTA and then MgCl$_2$. Adjust pH to 7.5, bring to 50 ml, and filter.

c. *Working solution:* The final concentration is 1× PLPS solution, 3.7% para-formaldehyde, 4.5% sucrose, 10 mM sodium periodate (NaIO$_4$). For 10 ml of fixative, mix 1 ml 10× PLPS solution, 0.45 g sucrose, and 4.38 ml distilled water. After the sucrose is dissolved, add 4.62 ml 8% paraformaldehyde, then 21.4 mg NaIO$_4$.

3. *Tris-buffered saline + sucrose (TBS–sucrose):* 20 mM Tris–HCl, 150 mM NaCl, 4.5% sucrose (w/v), pH 7.5. For prolonged storage at 4°C, add sodium azide to a final concentration of 0.05%.

4. *TBS–GS:* TBS + sucrose, + 2% heat-inactivated goat serum.

5. *Mounting medium:* To make 10 ml of mounting medium, dissolve 10 mg phenylenediamine in 1 ml of 1× phosphate-buffered saline in a 15-ml tube. Add 9 ml glycerol. As this mixture is light sensitive, wrap tube with aluminum foil and let mix overnight on rotating wheel. Aliquot medium into darkly colored microfuge tubes and store at −20°C. Warm to room temperature before use. Discard when solution becomes brown.

Steps

1. Incubate cells in medium containing fluorescent probes, as described above. If one intends to extract cells following fixation for subsequent immunolabeling experiments, incubate in higher concentrations of fluorescent dextrans or LY. Nonfixable dextrans are often lost by extraction procedures; thus, fixable dextrans may be preferable for use.

2. Wash away excess fluorescent probe with buffer.

3. Aspirate buffer from cells and replace with warm fixative. Cells that will not be prepared for immunolabeling can be fixed using either FG or PLPS fixatives. Cells that will be prepared for immunolabeling (see step 6 below) should be fixed with PLPS. Rapidly swirl dishes to distribute fixative evenly.

4. Cells treated with FG fixative should be incubated for 20 min at 37°C, whereas those in PLPS should be incubated for 0.5–1.5 hr at room temperature.

5. Following fixation, remove fixative and wash 3 × 5 min with TBS–sucrose. If no further processing is needed (i.e., no immunofluorescence), then mount coverslips on slides using mounting medium (see step 7 below), and observe.

6. To extract cells for immunolabeling, one should use methanol stored at −20°C over molecular sieves, which remove water. Methanol should be poured into a glass beaker on dry ice. Using jeweler's forceps to hold the coverslip, blot off excess TBS–sucrose, then immerse in the methanol. One should extract long enough to permeabilize cells, but not so long as to extract all the fluorescent probe from endocytic vesicles; 20–60 sec should suffice. Blot off excess methanol and replace in the well. When all coverslips have been extracted, wash cells with TBS–GS, 3 × 5 minutes. Coverslips can then be incubated with antibodies, diluted in TBS–GS. The length of time and temperature of antibody incubations will vary depending on the affinity of the antibody and the accessibility of the antigen. We incubate with primary antibody at 4°C for 12–16 hr (overnight) and with secondary antibody at 37°C for 3–4 hr. Following incubation with primary antibody, coverslips are washed 3 × 5 minutes with TBS-GS. Following incubation with secondary antibody, coverslips should be washed with TBS–GS, followed by TBS–sucrose. Coverslips can then be mounted on slides.

7. To prepare a slide for fluorescence microscopy, remove a coverslip from its culture well using jeweler's forceps and place it, cell side down, on a droplet of mounting medium (10 μl for a 12-mm circular coverslip) that has been placed on

the slide. Take care not to trap air bubbles under the coverslip. Seal the coverslip to the slide using nail polish.

IV. Pitfalls

1. If fixable fluorescent probes stick nonspecifically to cells or coverslips, try pretreating coverslips with serum before plating cells.

2. Prolonged examination of live cells under the fluorescence microscope may damage labeled endocytic vesicles. Use the lowest light intensity and light exposure that permits observation.

3. Extractions with methanol may deplete fluorescent label from endocytic vesicles. Shorten extraction time or try fixable fluorescent probes.

4. Some probes may be difficult to see using standard fluorescence filter sets. LY, for example, can be seen with some fluorescein filter sets (wide bandpass), but not with others. Check to be sure the probe can be visualized with your microscope, or purchase the appropriate filter combinations.

REFERENCES

McLean, I. W., and Nakane, P. K. (1974) Periodate–lysine–paraformaldehyde fixative. A new fixative for immunoelectron microscopy. *J. Histochem. Cytochem.* **22**, 1077–1083.

Racoosin, E. L., and Swanson, J. A. (1993) Macropinosome maturation and fusion with tubular lysosomes in macrophages. *J. Cell Biol.* **121**, 1011–1020.

Steinman, R., Brodie, S. E., and Cohn, Z. A. (1976) Membrane flow during pinocytosis. *J. Cell Biol.* **68**, 665–687.

Swanson, J. A. (1989a) Phorbol esters stimulate macropinocytosis and solute flow through macrophages. *J. Cell Sci.* **94**, 135–142.

Swanson, J. A. (1989b) Fluorescent labeling of endocytic compartments. *In* "Methods in Cell Biology," Vol. 29: "Fluorescence Microscopy of Living Cells in Culture: Part A" (Y.-l. Wang and D. L. Taylor, eds.), pp. 137–151. Academic Press, New York.

Labeling of the Endoplasmic Reticulum with DiOC$_6$(3)

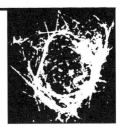

Mark Terasaki

I. Introduction

The endoplasmic reticulum (ER) is the site of synthesis of membrane proteins, secreted proteins, and membrane lipids, and it is the principal intracellular calcium store. The ER can be localized in living or fixed cells or in cell-free membrane preparations with simple procedures using the fluorescent dye DiOC$_6$(3) (Terasaki et al., 1984). The dye is particularly easy to use because it permeates through the plasma membrane and because its fluorescence is bright and stable.

DiOC$_6$(3) is a general membrane dye; that is, DiOC$_6$(3) is not a specific dye for the ER. When the technique is successful, the ER is recognized by its characteristic morphology and continuity. When the technique is not successful, it is often because the ER cannot be distinguished from the other organelles, or because the ER has a dense three-dimensional structure which cannot be resolved by the light microscope. It is very important to remember the nonspecificity of staining by DiOC$_6$(3). If the ER is not imaged clearly, then one cannot claim that the fluorescence image "shows" the distribution of ER; the fluorescence could just as well be due to mitochondria, lysosomes, or other organelles. These issues are discussed in more detail elsewhere (Terasaki and Reese, 1992).

The best results have been obtained with cells that have regions where the ER has a two-dimensional organization. Examples are certain fibroblasts or epithelial cells in culture, which have a large thin peripheral region, or certain plant cells, which have a distinct cortical ER network adjacent to the plasma membrane. The technique is not as useful in cells or regions of cells in which the ER has a three-dimensional distribution, though in a few cases, confocal microscopy has been useful in these regions.

General directions on how to stain with DiOC$_6$(3) are given here. More details about staining mechanisms were reported in an early review (Terasaki, 1989), and a later review contains more recent references (Terasaki, 1993). A different method for labeling ER, which requires microinjection of DiI (a long-chain dicarbocyanine dye), is described elsewhere (Terasaki and Jaffe, 1991; Jaffe and Terasaki, 1993; Terasaki and Jaffe, 1993).

II. Materials and Instrumentation

DiOC$_6$(3) can be obtained from Molecular Probes (Cat. No. D-273) or Eastman Kodak (Cat. No. 136 8141). A stock solution of 0.5 mg/ml in ethanol, protected from light, can be stored at room temperature for at least 1 year.

To image the fluorescence staining, a high-numerical-aperture lens (1.2–1.4) is required. A standard fluorescein filter works with this dye. To document the staining in fixed cells, 35-mm photographic film is sufficient. To document changes of the ER in living cells, it is best to have an electronic imaging system such as an SIT camera with imaging processing hardware or confocal microscope.

III. Procedures

A. LIVING CELLS

Two alternate methods are used: Observe cells in a low concentration of $DiOC_6(3)$, or stain cells briefly with a high dye concentration then observe them in dye-free medium.

1. First Method

Solution

1. 0.5 μg/ml $DiOC_6(3)$ in growth medium, diluted from stock $DiOC_6(3)$ in ethanol (see Materials and Instrumentation).

Steps

1. Mount the cells in growth medium containing $DiOC_6(3)$.

2. After about 5 min, observe staining, without washing out the dye. If there is only mitochondrial staining, wait longer or make another sample with a higher dye concentration. If the cells start to round up and detach, make another sample with a lower dye concentration.

2. Second Method

Solution

1. 2.5 μg/ml $DiOC_6(3)$ in growth medium, diluted from stock $DiOC_6(3)$ in ethanol (see Materials and Instrumentation).

Steps

1. Incubate the cells in 2.5 μg/ml $DiOC_6(3)$ for 5 min.

2. Wash the coverslip and mount it in dye-free medium.

3. Observe the staining, and change the dose or length of incubation if required.

A potential disadvantage of the first method is that the dye in the medium will contribute too much background fluorescence, and a potential disadvantage of the second method is that the dye will eventually leak out of the cells, reducing staining intensity.

For whole tissues, immerse the tissue in 0.5 μg/ml $DiOC_6(3)$ and observe after 5 min. Change the concentration if staining is not optimal. Alternatively, stain the tissue in 2.5 μg/ml for 5–10 min, wash, mount, and observe.

B. FIXED CELLS

For fixation, glutaraldehyde is required because formaldehyde often vesiculates the ER. It might be best to use EM-grade glutaraldehyde from a freshly opened vial, but less high quality glutaraldehyde seems to work well also; the main criterion is whether the ER is vesiculated. For mammalian cultured cells, 0.25% glutaraldehyde has worked well. This concentration is sufficient to fix well but is relatively low so that autofluorescence takes longer to develop. It is important to pay attention to the osmolarity of the buffer, even after fixation. Twice hypertonic buffers cause the ER to shrink. Twice hypotonic buffers seem to leave the ER intact, but more dilute buffers cause the ER to vesiculate. For cultured cells, a buffer consisting of 100 mM sucrose, 100 mM sodium cacodylate, pH 7.4 has worked well; Hepes or phosphate buffers will probably work well also. Lastly, it is important not to let the coverslip dry out at any time.

Once the cells have been stained, the coverslip must be mounted in some way to allow microscopic observations. For living cells, the main consideration is to keep the conditions so that the cells are as healthy as possible. For fixed cells, glycerol (or any detergents) and nonpolar solvents, such as those in nail polish used to seal coverslips, should be avoided because these extract the staining. Another consideration for mounting coverslips is that there must be good access for a high-numerical-aperture (i.e., oil immersion) objective lens. One way to mount fixed or living cells on coverslips is to use a chamber made of silicon rubber gasket material (Ronsil). Cut a small hole in it with a cork borer. Fill the chamber with buffer and quickly place the coverslip over the hole, pressing it down so as to make a seal. Then wipe off the excess with a Kimwipe. This is not airtight, and small bubbles will start to appear at the edge of the chamber after 30 min to 1 hr. As the staining quality also decreases with time, this is usually not a problem.

Solutions

1. *Sucrose cacodylate buffer:* 100 mM sucrose, 100 mM sodium cacodylate, pH 7.4. Adjust sucrose concentration for correct osmolarity of the cells being stained. This can be stored at room temperature.

2. *0.25% glutaraldehyde in sucrose cacodylate buffer.*

3. *2.5 μg/ml DiOC$_6$(3) in sucrose cacodylate buffer:* Use the stock DiOC$_6$(3) in ethanol (see Materials and Instrumentation).

Steps

1. Fix the cells in the glutaraldehyde solution for 3–5 min.

2. Stain the cells in DiOC$_6$(3) in sucrose cacodylate buffer for 10 sec.

3. Wash the cells and mount them in dye-free sucrose cacodylate buffer.

4. Look at cells immediately because staining becomes less optimal after about 10–20 min and then slowly deteriorates. The deterioration consists of development of autofluorescence and dye redistribution to some large vesicles at the expense of the ER.

C. CELL FRACTIONS

Solution

1. *0.5 μg/ml DiOC$_6$(3) in the buffer used to isolate the cell fractions.*

Step

1. Mount the fractions in the DiOC$_6$(3)-containing buffer. Try to use fractions dilute enough so that the membranes can be easily distinguished from each other.

D. PHOTOGRAPHY

What to aim for is a print that looks as good or almost as good as what your eyes see in the eyepiece. If the image in the microscope eyepiece looks blurry or dim to your eyes, then photography will probably not improve it. Use a 100× lens if possible, with a 63× lens as second choice. Figure 1 was taken with a 100× lens.

$DiOC_6(3)$ fluorescence is bright, and it should be possible to obtain a fairly good image on photograph film. To get an optimum image, it may be necessary to experiment with the photographic conditions. Films with higher ASA are more sensitive to light but are more grainy. Try a black and white ASA 400 film first. Push the processing about one stop to increase the sensitivity (e.g., for TMAX film, develop for 10 min instead of 7.5 min). In this author's opinion, there is a greater range of adequate exposure times for fluorescence than for transmitted light so that the light exposure meter is less necessary for obtaining good exposures of fluorescence images. Try exposures of 1, 2, 4, or 8 sec. Try not to expose longer than about 10 sec because vibrations during long exposures can blur the image. Once a good exposure time has been determined, take as many photographs as possible to increase the chance of getting good images. Try to work fast so that there is less bleaching. With fixed cells, it is also good to work fast because the staining quality seems to deteriorate gradually after about 10–20 min. If possible, try to develop the film soon to get feedback on what adjustments in the photographic procedures can be done. When printing negatives, recall that film has greater dynamic range than paper, so that details that can be seen in the brightest and darkest regions of the negative can sometimes be reproduced on print paper only in the brightest or the darkest regions but not both.

E. VIDEO MICROSCOPY

With video imaging, it is possible to obtain many images of the same cell, though video image quality is usually poorer than photographic image quality. To collect useful data, it is important to optimize the amount of illumination with respect to photodynamic damage versus image quality.

F. DOUBLE LABELING USING IMMUNOFLUORESCENCE

Localization of intracellular antigens requires permeabilization, but $DiOC_6(3)$ staining is extracted by the usual methods of permeabilizing cells (detergents, methanol). Double labeling has been accomplished in a procedure where cells are stained with $DiOC_6(3)$, photographed, permeabilized, processed for immunofluorescence, and then photographed again (Terasaki et al., 1986; Terasaki and Reese, 1992). Probably the most difficult part of this rather arduous effort, is to find the same cells again. One way to do this is as follows. Scrape a cross on the coverslip using a rubber policeman or any other thin implement, such as a pipetman tip. Break off a small corner of the coverslip to keep track of orientation. Using a phase-contrast inverted microscope at low magnification (i.e., 10–16×), draw the positions of cells near the cross. Under high magnification, it is possible to find the intersection of the cross by scanning the coverslip, finding a scraped pathway, and following it to the center of the coverslip where it intersects with the other pathway. Record on the map which cells were photographed, and use this map to find the same cells after immunofluorescence.

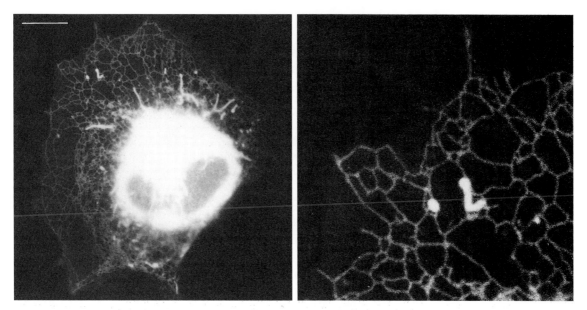

FIGURE 1 A CV-1 cell (monkey kidney epithelial cell line) fixed in glutaraldehyde, then stained with DiOC$_6$(3). Left: The ER is the network in the thin spread periphery of the cell. Several mitochondria (which are much thicker and usually unbranched) are seen. No details in the central region can be seen because of the overlap of many organelles. Right: Higher magnification of the same cell (printed from the same negative) shows more details of the ER network. Two brightly stained objects are near the center of the image; the longer one is a mitochondrion, and the round one to the left is either a small mitochondrion or a lysosome. Bar = 10 μm for (left); Bar = 3.1 μm (right).

IV. Comments

To troubleshoot problems or to devise procedures for staining in new situations, it is useful to know about staining mechanisms of DiOC$_6$(3). DiOC$_6$(3) is a lipophilic cationic molecule that is permeable to the plasma membrane. In living cells exposed to low concentrations of dye, DiOC$_6$(3) accumulates only in the mitochondria, due to the large negative membrane potential there. At higher concentrations, the dye stains the ER and other organelles, presumably because the mitochondria are saturated with the dye. In fixed cells, the dye stains mitochondria, ER, and other organelles at all concentrations. DiOC$_6$(3) very probably is in the membrane bilayer of stained cells. Any treatment that extracts bilayers will also extract the dye.[1]

It can also be useful to compare fixation for DiOC$_6$(3) staining with fixation for conventional electron microscopy and for immunofluorescence of intracellular proteins. The aldehydes glutaraldehyde and formaldehyde are chemical fixatives that permeate through the plasma membrane. For electron microscopy, glutaraldehyde is preferred because formaldehyde tends to vesiculate membranes. Both do not "fix" membranes because lipids are still able to diffuse in the bilayer. Osmium does fix membranes, but in the process, prevents membranes from being stained with DiOC$_6$(3). Osmium also destroys fluorescence in prestained cells. For immunofluorescence, formaldehyde is used more often because glutaraldehyde-fixed cells develop autofluorescence. Antibodies do not cross membranes of aldehyde-fixed cells. Therefore, either aldehyde cells must be permeabilized with detergents such as Triton X-100, or living cells can be fixed and permeabilized by using other agents such as cold methanol. Both these treatments extract membranes and make it impossible to use DiOC$_6$(3) staining.

[1] Koning, *et al.* (*Cell Motil. Cytoskeleton* **25**, 111–128, 1993) is a good article about staining living yeast cells with DiOC$_6$(3).

REFERENCES

Jaffe, L. A., and Terasaki, M. (1993). Structural changes of the endoplasmic reticulum of sea urchin eggs during fertilization. *Dev. Biol.* **156,** 556–573.

Terasaki, M. (1989) Fluorescent labeling of endoplasmic reticulum. *In* "Methods in Cell Biology," Vol. 29: "Fluorescence Microscopy of Living Cells in Culture" (Y.-L. Wang and D. L. Taylor, eds.), pp. 125–135. Academic Press, San Diego.

Terasaki, M. (1993) Probes for endoplasmic reticulum. *In* "Fluorescent Probes of Living Cells: A Practical Manual" (W. T. Mason, ed.), pp. 120–123. Academic Press, London.

Terasaki, M., Chen, L. B., and Fujiwara, K. (1986) Microtubules and the endoplasmic reticulum are highly interdependent structures. *J. Cell Biol.* **103,** 1557–1568.

Terasaki, M., and Jaffe, L. A. (1991) Organization of the sea urchin egg endoplasmic reticulum and its reorganization at fertilization. *J. Cell Biol.* **114,** 929–940.

Terasaki, M., and Jaffe, L. A. (1993) Imaging of the endoplasmic reticulum in living marine eggs. *In* "Methods in Cell Biology," Vol. 37: "Cell Biological Applications of Confocal Microscopy" (B. Matsumoto, ed.). Academic Press, Orlando, FL.

Terasaki, M., and Reese, T. S. (1992) Characterization of endoplasmic reticulum by co-localization of BiP and dicarbocyanine dyes. *J. Cell Sci.* **101,** 315–322.

Terasaki, M., Song, J. D., Wong, J. R., Weiss, M. J., and Chen, L. B. (1984) Localization of endoplasmic reticulum in living and glutaraldehyde fixed cells with fluorescent dyes. *Cell* **38,** 101–108.

Use of Fluorescent Analogs of Ceramide to Study the Golgi Apparatus of Animal Cells

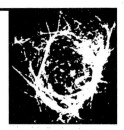

Richard E. Pagano and Ona C. Martin

I. Introduction

Studies of lipid traffic at the Golgi complex have recently been made possible using fluorescent analogs of ceramide (Cer), N-[7-(4-nitrobenzo-2-oxa-1,3-diazole)]-6-aminocaproyl D-*erythro*-sphingosine (C$_6$-NBD-Cer) and N-[5-(5,7-dimethyl BODIPY)[1]-1-pentanoyl]-D-*erythro*-sphingosine (C$_5$-DMB-Cer) (reviewed in Pagano, 1989, 1990; Rosenwald and Pagano, 1993). These molecules are vital stains for the Golgi apparatus (Lipsky and Pagano, 1985a; Pagano *et al.*, 1991). In living cells they are metabolized to the corresponding fluorescent analogs of sphingomyelin (SM) and a glycolipid, glucosylceramide (GlcCer). These fluorescent metabolites are subsequently transported to the plasma membrane from the Golgi complex by a vesicle-mediated process analogous to the transport of newly synthesized membrane and secretory proteins (Lipsky and Pagano, 1983, 1985b; Kobayashi and Pagano, 1989). Using fluorescence video imaging, C$_6$-NBD-Cer has been used to study the dynamics of the Golgi apparatus in cultured astrocytes (Cooper *et al.*, 1990). C$_6$-NBD-Cer also stains the Golgi apparatus of fixed cells, most likely through interaction(s) with endogenous lipids and cholesterol, and serves as a trans-Golgi marker for both light and electron microscopy (Pagano *et al.*, 1989). In polarized cells, C$_6$-NBD-Cer is metabolized to fluorescent analogs of SM and GlcCer, and the latter is preferentially delivered to the apical cell surface (van Meer *et al.*, 1987; van't Hof and van Meer, 1990). This polarized delivery is consistent with the known enrichment of glycosphingolipids in apical membranes, and indicates that C$_6$-NBD-Cer and its metabolites are recognized by the cellular sorting and transport machinery in a manner similar to their natural counterparts.

In this article, we describe procedures for the (1) preparation and storage of fluorescent Cer/BSA complexes for incubation with cells; (2) incubation of living cells with fluorescent Cer analogs; (3) incubation of fixed cells with fluorescent Cer analogs; and (4) examination of the distribution of the fluorescent Cer and its metabolites at the electron microscopic (EM) level.

---

[1] The BODIPY fluorophore has an approximately two- to threefold higher fluorescence yield and greater photostability than NBD (Johnson *et al.*, 1991). The BODIPY Cer analog is also useful because its fluorescence emission spectrum is dramatically red-shifted as the probe concentrates in membranes. Thus, with the appropriate microscope filters, the Golgi apparatus can be observed within living cells without interfering fluorescence from other intracellular membranes.

II. Materials and Instrumentation

C_6-NBD-Cer (Cat. No. N-1154) and C_5-DMB-Cer (Cat. No. D-3521) are from Molecular Probes, Inc. The lipids are stored at $-70°C$ in chloroform/methanol (19/1, v/v), and should appear as single fluorescent spots following thin-layer chromatography in chloroform/methanol/15 mM $CaCl_2$ (60/35/8, v/v/v). Defatted BSA (Cat. No. A-6003) is from Sigma Chemical Company. 3,3'-Diaminobenzidine tetrahydrochloride (DAB) is purchased from Polysciences, preweighed in 10-mg aliquots in sealed serum vials. Unless indicated, all other materials are from Sigma Chemical Company.

Microscopy is performed with a conventional fluorescence microscope. We routinely use a Zeiss IM-35 (Carl Zeiss, Inc.) equipped with a Planapo 100× (1.3 NA) objective and an electronic shutter at the mercury lamp (100 W) housing. To minimize exposure to the exciting light, the samples are briefly focused with a neutral density filter (1 OD) in the light path. The filter is then removed, and the sample is exposed for 2–4 sec using full illumination for photomicroscopy. For NBD-labeled specimens, samples are excited at 450–490 nm and the fluorescence is observed at 520–560 nm. For BODIPY-labeled specimens, samples are excited at 450–490 nm and the fluorescence is observed either at ≥520 nm (green + red wavelengths) or at ≥590 nm (red wavelengths) (see Pagano *et al.,* 1991). Black and white photomicrographs are obtained using Tri-X film (Eastman Kodak Co.) and processed at ASA 1600 with Diafine developer (Acufine, Inc.); color photomicrographs are obtained using either Ektachrome 400 or Kodachrome 200 film.

III. Procedures

A. PREPARATION OF NBD– OR BODIPY–Cer/BSA COMPLEXES

These complexes are used for subsequent labeling of living or fixed preparations of cells (see below). We routinely prepare them as either dilute (5 nmol/ml) or concentrated (0.5 nmol/μl) stock solutions.

1. Dilute (5 nmol/ml) Stock Solutions

Solutions

1. Approximately 1 mM C_6-NBD-Cer or C_5-DMB-Cer stock solution in chloroform/methanol (19/1, v/v).
2. 10 ml serum-free balanced salt solution[2] containing 0.34 mg defatted BSA/ml in a 50-ml plastic centrifuge tube.
3. 500 ml serum-free balanced salt solution for dialysis.

Steps

1. Dispense 50 nmole C_6-NBD-Cer or C_5-DMB-Cer in chloroform/methanol into a small glass test tube and dry, first under a stream of nitrogen and then *in vacuo* for at least 1 hr.
2. Dissolve dried Cer in 200 μl absolute ethanol.
3. Inject Cer into the 10 ml BSA solution (while vortex mixing).

[2] We use HMEM, 10 mM 4-(2-hydroxyethyl)-1-piperazineethanesulfonic acid-buffered minimal essential medium, pH 7.4, without indicator.

4. Rinse Cer/ethanol tube with a little of the Cer/BSA solution and combine with the Cer/BSA complex.

5. Dialyze overnight at 4°C against 500 ml serum-free balanced salt solution.

6. Recover in 10 ml balanced salt solution and store in a plastic tube at −20°C.

2. Concentrated (0.5 nmol/μl) Stock Solutions

Solutions

1. Approximately 1 mM C_6-NBD-Cer or C_5-DMB-Cer stock solution in chloroform/methanol (19/1, v/v).

2. 450 μl serum-free balanced salt solution[3] containing 250 nmol DF-BSA in a small glass test tube.

Steps

1. Dispense 250 nmole C_6-NBD-Cer or C_5-DMB-Cer from the chloroform/methanol stock solution into a small glass test tube and dry down, first under a stream of nitrogen and then *in vacuo* for at least 1 hr.

2. Add 50 μl ethanol to the dried Cer. Vortex mix to completely dissolve the sample.

3. Using a micropipette, add the ethanol solution of the fluorescent Cer to the DF-BSA solution while vortex mixing.

4. Rinse the tube that contained the ethanol solution with an aliquot of the fluorescent Cer/DF−BSA complex.

5. Transfer the Cer/DF−BSA complex to a plastic conical centrifuge tube and store at −20°C.

B. STAINING THE GOLGI APPARATUS WITH FLUORESCENT CERAMIDES

1. Living Cells

Solutions

1. 5 nmol/ml or 0.5 nmol/μl C_6-NBD- or C_5-DMB-Cer/BSA complex.

2. HMEM for cell incubations.

Steps

1. Rinse cells grown on glass coverslips or on plastic tissue culture dishes in HMEM and transfer to an ice water bath at 2°C.

2. Incubate the cells for 30 min at 2°C with 5 nmol/ml C_6-NBD-Cer/BSA or C_5-DMB-Cer/BSA in HMEM.

3. Rinse the samples several times with ice-cold HMEM, transfer to 37°C, and further incubate for 30 min.

4. Wash the samples in HMEM and observe under the fluorescence

[3] We use HCMF, 10 mM 4-(2-hydroxyethyl)-1-piperazineethanesulfonic acid-buffered Puck's saline without calcium and magnesium.

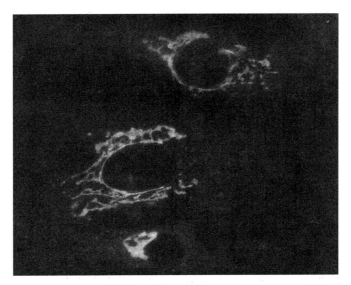

FIGURE 1 Living human skin fibroblasts were incubated with C_6-NBD-Cer as described in Section IIIB. Note prominent fluorescence at the Golgi apparatus and weaker labeling at other intracellular membranes.

microscope. Prominent labeling of the Golgi apparatus and weaker labeling of other intracellular membranes by the fluorescent Cers should be seen (Fig. 1).

2. Fixed Cells

Solutions

1. HMEM for rinsing cells.

2. 0.5% glutaraldehyde/10% sucrose/100 mM Pipes, pH 7.0.

3. HCMF.

4. Freshly prepared NaBH$_4$ in HCMF (0.5 mg/ml) (*optional*).

5. 5 nmol/ml or 0.5 nmol/μl C_6-NBD-Cer/BSA complex (do not use C_5-DMB-Cer/BSA complex) (see Section IV).

6. 3.4 mg/ml DF-BSA in HCMF.

Steps

1. Rinse cells grown on glass coverslips or on plastic tissue culture dishes in HMEM and fix for 5–10 min at room temperature in 0.5% glutaraldehyde/10% sucrose/100 mM Pipes, pH 7.0.

2. Wash the cells in HCMF. [*Optional:* The samples can be transferred to an ice water bath and incubated (3 × 5 min) with NaBH$_4$ in ice-cold HCMF to reduce glutaraldehyde-induced autofluorescence. For most cell types and fixation conditions, the staining of the Golgi apparatus is so prominent and the autofluorescence is so low that this step is not necessary.]

3. Rinse the samples several times with ice-cold HCMF, transfer to an ice water bath, and incubate for 30 min at 2°C with 5 nmol/ml C_6-NBD-Cer/BSA complex.

4. Rinse the samples several times with HCMF and incubate at room temperature (4 × 30 min) with 3.4 mg/ml defatted BSA in HCMF. [This

incubation serves to remove ("back-exchange") excess C_6-NBD-Cer from the fixed cells (Pagano *et al.,* 1989)].

5. Wash the samples in HCMF and observe under the fluorescence microscope. Prominent labeling of the Golgi apparatus by C_6-NBD-Cer is seen.

C. METHOD FOR EXAMINING DISTRIBUTION OF THE FLUORESCENT Cer AND ITS METABOLITES AT THE EM LEVEL

See Pagano *et al.* (1989, 1991).

Solutions

1. 0.1 *M* Tris, pH 7.6.
2. 1.5 mg DAB/ml 0.1 *M* Tris, pH 7.6, freshly prepared and kept on ice.
3. 0.1 *M* Na cacodylate, pH 7.4.
4. 1% OsO_4 in 0.1 *M* Na cacodylate, pH 7.4.

Steps

Caution: DAB is a potent carcinogen. Always wear gloves when handling DAB solutions and immerse all materials that contact DAB in bleach before disposing of them.

NOTE

---

1. Cells should be grown in 35-mm-diameter plastic tissue culture dishes, not on glass coverslips.

2. Label living or fixed cells according to desired protocol (e.g., as in Section IIIB above). Living cells should be fixed after labeling (see Section IIIB). Always include a sample that has not been treated with the fluorescent lipid as a control.

3. Wash cells in 0.1 *M* Tris (pH 7.6) and add 0.9 ml DAB solution to the culture dish. Cover dish and place in the dark at room temperature for ≥ 10 min.

4. Irradiate sample for 30 min at room temperature using the 476.5-nm line of an argon laser operating at 50-mW power. To obtain a large area of irradiated cells, the laser beam is expanded to a line approximately 1 mm wide × 1 cm long using a cylindrical lens. [Alternatively, the specimen may be irradiated using a 6.3× objective and filters appropriate for NBD fluorescence (Zeiss Cat. No. 487717), although only a very small area of the culture dish (≤ 1 mm in diameter) is irradiated.]

5. After irradiation, wash the sample five or more times in 0.1 *M* Tris (pH 7.6) and observe using phase optics for evidence of a DAB reaction product. Using a dissecting scope and a needle, circumscribe on the inside of the culture dish the region of cells that are DAB-positive.

6. Rinse the sample in 0.1 *M* cacodylate buffer (pH 7.4) and treat with 1% OsO_4 in 0.1 *M* cacodylate buffer for 60 min at room temperature.

7. Wash in cacodylate buffer, dehydrate, and embed.

8. After polymerization is complete, the area of DAB-positive cells should be readily identified by the scratch made in step 6. Cut out this region of the dish

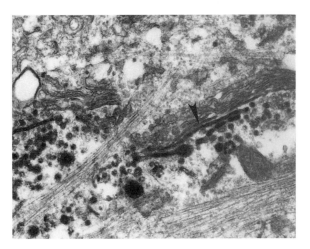

FIGURE 2 Living human skin fibroblasts treated with C₅-DMB-Cer as described in Section IIIB were fixed, photobleached in the presence of diaminobenzidine (Section IIIC), processed for thin-section electron microscopy, and photographed. Note the black deposition product in the Golgi stacks and in Golgi-associated vesicles (at arrows).

and mount for thin-section electron microscopy. A typical result using this procedure on human skin fibroblasts after treatment with C_5-DMB-Cer is shown in Fig. 2.

IV. Comments

By use of the protocols in this article, the Golgi apparatus of cells can be readily stained. The prominent labeling of this organelle by fluorescent Cer analogs has been observed in all cell types tested to date. We believe this labeling results from the spontaneous transfer of the lipid into cells followed by molecular trapping at the Golgi apparatus (Pagano, 1989; Pagano *et al.*, 1989). Although C_6-NBD-Cer or C_5-DMB-Cer can be delivered to cells from either lipid vesicles (Lipsky and Pagano, 1983, 1985a,b) or a BSA complex (Pagano and Martin, 1988; Pagano *et al.*, 1989), the use of fluorescent Cer/BSA complexes as described in this article is especially convenient because they can be prepared in advance of an experiment and stored frozen. In addition, repeated freezing and thawing do not affect cell labeling or the purity of the fluorescent lipids.

Although both C_6-NBD-Cer and C_5-DMB-Cer are vital stains for the Golgi apparatus, only C_6-NBD-Cer is suitable for staining of fixed cells. In using C_6-NBD-Cer for staining fixed cells, we found that fixation time, temperature, and buffer composition are not critical; however, brief treatment of fixed cells with detergents or fixation with methanol/acetone at $-20°C$ eliminates labeling of the Golgi apparatus.

Visualization of C_6-NBD-Cer and C_5-DMB-Cer at the electron microscope level is performed using methods adapted from Maranto (1982) and Sandell and Masland (1988) in which cells treated with various fluorescent compounds were photobleached in the presence of DAB. The photooxidation products catalyze the polymerization of DAB to yield a high-molecular-weight osmiophilic compound which is visualized at the EM level. Double-label experiments indicate that both C_6-NBD-Cer and C_5-DMB-Cer label a subset of Golgi membranes that corresponds to the trans-Golgi elements (Pagano *et al.*, 1989, 1991).

REFERENCES

Cooper, M. S., Cornell-Bell, A. H., Chernjavsky, A., Dani, J. W., and Smith, S. J. (1990) Tubulovesicular processes emerge from trans-Golgi cisternae, extend along microtubules, and interlink adjacent trans-Golgi elements into a reticulum. *Cell* **61**, 135–145.

Johnson, I. D., Kang, H. C., and Haugland, R. P. (1991) Fluorescent membrane probes incorporating dipyrromethenboron difluoride fluorophores. *Anal. Biochem.* **198,** 228–237.

Kobayashi, T., and Pagano, R. E. (1989) Lipid transport during mitosis: Alternative pathways for delivery of newly synthesized lipids to the cell surface. *J. Biol. Chem.* **264,** 5966–5973.

Lipsky, N. G., and Pagano, R. E. (1983) Sphingolipid metabolism in cultured fibroblasts— Microscopic and biochemical studies employing a fluorescent analogue of ceramide. *Proc. Natl. Acad. Sci. USA* **80,** 2608–2612.

Lipsky, N. G., and Pagano, R. E. (1985a) A vital stain for the Golgi apparatus. *Science* **228,** 745–747.

Lipsky, N. G., and Pagano, R. E. (1985b) Intracellular translocation of fluorescent sphingolipids in cultured fibroblasts: Endogenously synthesized sphingomyelin and glucocerebroside analogs pass through the Golgi apparatus en route to the plasma membrane. *J. Cell Biol.* **100,** 27–34.

Maranto, A. R. (1982) Neuronal mapping: A photooxidation reaction makes Lucifer Yellow useful for electron microscopy. *Science* **217,** 953–955.

Pagano, R. E. (1989) A fluorescent derivative of ceramide: Physical properties and use in studying the Golgi apparatus of animal cells. *In* "Methods in Cell Biology," Vol. 29, pp. 75–85. Academic Press, San Diego.

Pagano, R. E. (1990) The Golgi apparatus: Insights from lipid biochemistry. *Biochem. Soc. Trans.* **18,** 361–366.

Pagano, R. E., and Martin, O. C. (1988) A series of fluorescent N-(acyl)-sphingosines: Synthesis, physical properties, and studies in cultured cells. *Biochemistry* **27,** 4439–4445.

Pagano, R. E., Martin, O. C., Kang, H. C., and Haugland, R. P. (1991) A novel fluorescent ceramide analog for studying membrane traffic in animal cells: Accumulation at the Golgi apparatus results in altered spectral properties of the sphingolipid precursor. *J. Cell Biol.* **113,** 1267–1279.

Pagano, R. E., Sepanski, M. A., and Martin, O. C. (1989) Molecular trapping of a fluorescent ceramide analog at the Golgi apparatus of fixed cells: Interaction with endogenous lipids provides a trans-Golgi marker for both light and electron microscopy. *J. Cell Biol.* **109,** 2067–2079.

Rosenwald, A. G., and Pagano, R. E. (1993) Intracellular transport of ceramide and its metabolites at the Golgi complex: Insights from short-chain ceramides. *Adv. Lipid. Res.* **26,** 101–118.

Sandell, J. H., and Masland, R. H. (1988) Photoconversion of some fluorescent markers to a diaminobenzidine product. *J. Histochem. Cytochem.* **36,** 555–559.

Van Meer, G., Stelzer, E. H. K., Wijnaendts-van-Resandt, W., and Simons, K. (1987) Sorting of sphingolipids in epithelial (Madin–Darby canine kidney) cells. *J. Cell Biol.* **105,** 1623–1635.

Van't Hof, W., and van Meer, G. (1990) Generation of lipid polarity in intestinal epithelial (Caco-2) cells: Sphingolipid synthesis in the Golgi complex and sorting before vesicular traffic to the plasma membrane. *J. Cell Biol.* **111,** 977–986.

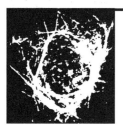

Vital Staining of Mitochondria with Rhodamine 123 and of Acidic Organelles with Acridine Orange

Julio E. Celis and Kurt Dejgaard

I. Introduction

Visualization of cellular organelles using vital dyes provides a convenient way to observe *in vivo* these structures under various physiological conditions. Here, we describe the staining of mitochondria and acidic organelles in human dermal fibroblasts exposed to rhodamine 123 (Johnson *et al.*, 1980; Chen, 1989, and references therein) and acridine orange (Matteoni and Kreiss, 1985), respectively.

II. Materials

Rhodamine 123 (Cat. No. R-804) and acridine orange (Cat. No. A-6014) were obtained from Sigma. All other reagents and materials were as described in the article by Ariana Celis and Julio E. Celis in Volume 1. Besides standard equipment for tissue culture (see article by Ariana Celis and Julio E. Celis in Volume 1) the procedure requires a fluorescent microscope equipped with rhodamine and FITC filters.

III. Procedures

A. STAINING OF MITOCHONDRIA WITH RHODAMINE 123

This procedure is adapted from that of Johnson *et al.* (1980).

Solutions

1. *Complete Dulbecco's modified Eagle's medium (DMEM):* Prepare as described in the article by Ariana Celis and Julio E. Celis in Volume 1.

2. *Hanks' buffered saline solution (HBSS) without Ca^{2+} and Mg^{2+}:* 10× stock solution. To make 1 liter, weigh 4 g of KCl, 0.6 g of KH_2PO_4, 80 g of NaCl, and 0.621 g of $Na_2HPO_4 \cdot 2\ H_2O$. Complete to 1 liter with distilled water.

3. *1× HBSS without Ca^{2+} and Mg^{2+}:* To make 1 liter of HBSS take 100 ml of the 10× stock solution and complete to 1 liter with distilled water.

4. *Rhodamine 123 stock solution:* Weigh 10 mg of rhodamine 123 and dissolve in 10 ml of distilled water.

5. *Rhodamine 123 (10 µg/ml):* Take 0.1 ml of the stock rhodamine 123 solution and add 9.9 ml of HBSS.

Steps

1. Plate human dermal fibroblasts in sterile 12-mm round glass coverlips placed in 40-mm tissue culture dishes containing complete DMEM (see also articles by Robert T. Dell'Orco and by Vincent J. Cristofalo, Roberta Charpentier, and Paul D. Phillips in Volume 1). Wash and sterilize glass coverslips as described in the article by Ariana Celis and Julio E. Celis in Volume 1.

2. When the cells have reached the desired cell density, wash the coverslips twice with HBSS.

3. Pick up the coverslip with sterile Dumont No. 5 forceps (see Fig. 3F in the article by Ariana Celis and Julio E. Celis in Volume 1) and place it in a 40-mm tissue culture dish containing 1 to 2 ml of rhodamine 123 (10 µg/ml) in HBSS. Leave for 10 min at room temperature.

4. Wash the cells gently by dipping the coverslips sequentially in three 40-mm tissue culture dishes filled with HBSS.

5. Place the coverslip, cell side up, on an object glass containing a drop of HBSS. Add a drop of HBSS on top of the cells and cover with a rectangular cover glass. Do not apply pressure or slide the coverslip and cover glass on top of each other as the cells may be damaged.

6. Observe in a fluorescence microscope using a FITC filter (Fig. 1A).

B. STAINING OF ACIDIC ORGANELLES WITH ACRIDINE

This procedure is adapted from that of Matteoni and Kreiss (1985).

Solutions

1. *Acridine orange stock (0.6 mg/ml):* To make 10 ml, weigh 6 mg of acridine orange and complete to 10 ml with distilled water. Keep at 4°C protected from light.

2. *Hanks' buffered saline solution (HBSS) without Ca^{2+} and Mg^{2+}:* See Section A.

Steps

1. Take one of the seeded coverslips prepared in Section A and place it in a 40-mm tissue culture dish containing 2 ml of a 1:100 dilution of the acridine orange stock solution in HBSS. Leave 4–5 min at room temperature (protect from light).

2. Wash the cells by dipping the coverslips sequentially in three 40-mm tissue culture dishes filled with HBSS.

3. Place the coverslip, cell side up, on a object glass containing a drop of HBSS. Add a drop of HBSS on top of the cells and cover with a rectangular cover glass. Do not apply pressure or slide the coverslip and cover glass on top of each other.

4. Observe in a fluorescence microscope using a rhodamine filter (Fig. 1B).

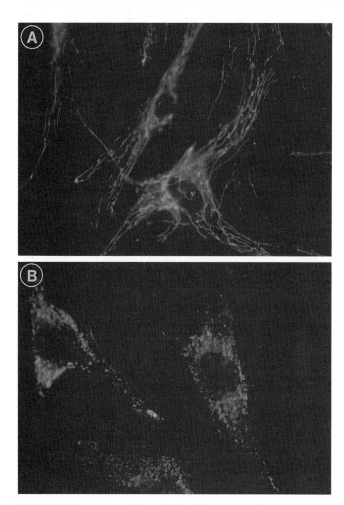

FIGURE 1 Human dermal fibroblasts stained with (A) rhodamine 123 and (B) acridine orange.

IV. Comments

The procedures as described here can also be used to stain epithelial cells.

V. Pitfalls

1. As the cells are not fixed, care should be taken not to apply pressure when mounting the coverslip.
2. The monolayer should be carefully washed after staining to reduce the background.

REFERENCES

Chen, L. B. (1989) Fluorescent labeling of mitochondria. *In* "Fluorescence Microscopy of Living Cells in Culture" (Y. L. Wang and D. L. Taylor, eds.), pp. 103–123. Academic Press, San Diego.
Johnson, L. V., Walsh, M. L., and Chen, L. B. (1980) Localization of mitochondria in living cells with rhodamine 123. *Proc. Natl. Acad. Sci. USA* 77, 990–994.
Matteoni, R., and Kreiss, T. (1985) Translocation and clustering of endosomes and lysosomes depends on microtubules. *J. Cell Biol.* 105, 1253–1265.

PART 9

INTRACELLULAR MEASUREMENTS

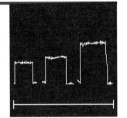

Measuring Membrane Potential in Single Cells with Confocal Microscopy

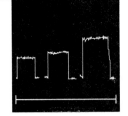

Leslie M. Loew

I. Introduction

The use of fluorescent voltage-sensitive dyes to measure membrane potential was originally introduced by L. B. Cohen and his colleagues to measure rapid changes from multiple sites in complex neuronal systems (Cohen and Salzberg, 1978). The method has been extended and is now widely used to measure membrane potential of nonexcitable cells in bulk suspensions (Waggoner, 1985; Freedman and Laris, 1988). More recently, voltage-sensitive dyes were applied to measure the membrane potential of single cells via high-resolution quantitative fluorescence microscopy (Loew *et al.*, 1990; Loew, 1993). This approach allows one to determine voltages from many individual cells more conveniently and less invasively than the well-established microelectrode-based methods. In one version of the approach it is even possible to measure variations in membrane potential along the surface of individual cells (Montana *et al.*, 1989; Bedlack *et al.*, 1992). The methods described in this article employ a lipid-permeable cationic dye and confocal microscopy to measure the relative concentration gradient of dye across the membrane of single cells; the membrane potential can then be determined via application of the Nernst equation (Ehrenberg *et al.*, 1988; Farkas *et al.*, 1989). The theory and rationale behind this method are described by Loew (1993).

II. Materials and Instrumentation

A confocal microscope (MRC-600) is obtained from Bio-Rad. A high-resolution NA 1.4 63X plan apochromat objective (Cat. No. 440762) and an inverted microscope (Axiovert 135) are obtained from Carl Zeiss. A thermoregulated microscope chamber equipped for perfusion and solution exchange is obtained from Biophysica Technologies. Coverslips (No. 1, 31 mm in diameter) are also obtained from Biophysica Technologies.

Tetramethylrhodamine ethyl ester perchlorate (TMRE, Cat. No. T-669) is obtained from Molecular Probes. Hepes (Cat. No. H7523) and valinomycin (V-0627) are obtained from Sigma.

III. Procedures

Solutions

1. *Normal buffer (NB):* 130 mM NaCl, 5.5 mM KCl, 1.8 mM CaCl$_2$, 1.0 mM MgCl$_2$, 25 mM glucose, 20 mM Hepes buffer adjusted to pH 7.4 with NaOH.

Sterilize and store at 4°C. To make 1 liter dissolve 7.6 g NaCl, 0.41 g KCl, 0.2 g CaCl$_2$, 0.2 g MgCl$_2$, 4.5 g glucose, and 4.8 g Hepes in distilled water and titrate with 1 N NaOH to pH 7.4; adjust to a total volume of 1 liter.

2. *Valinomycin stock:* 10 mM valinomycin in 95% ethanol. To make 1 ml, dissolve 10 mg of valinomycin in 1 ml of 95% ethanol. Store at −20°C.

3. *TMRE stock:* 0.5 mM tetramethylrhodamine ethyl ester in 95% ethanol. To make 10 ml, dissolve 2.5 mg of TMRE perchlorate in 10 ml of 95% ethanol. Store at −20°C.

4. *Normal TMRE buffer (NTB):* 100 nM TMRE in NB. Add 20 μl TMRE stock to 100 ml of NB. Use on the day of preparation.

5. *High-potassium buffer (KB):* 130 mM KCl, 5.5 mM NaCl, 1.8 mM CaCl$_2$, 1.0 mM MgCl$_2$, 25 mM glucose, 20 mM Hepes buffer adjusted to pH 7.4 with KOH. Sterilize and store at 4°C. To make 1 liter dissolve 0.32 g NaCl, 9.7 g KCl, 0.2 g CaCl$_2$, 0.2 g MgCl$_2$, 4.5 g glucose, and 4.8 g Hepes in distilled water and titrate with 1 N KOH to pH 7.4; adjust to a total volume of 1 liter.

6. *Depolarizing TMRE buffer (DTB):* 100 nM TMRE, 1 μM valinomycin in KB. Add 20 μl TMRE stock and 10 μl valinomycin stock to 100 ml KB. Use on the day of preparation.

Steps

1. Grow cells to 25% confluence on No. 1 glass coverslips.

2. Turn on the temperature control circuitry on the microscope chamber to begin thermal equilibration.

3. Gently wash a coverslip with NB three times and with NTB once. Return the coverslip to the culture dish and incubate in 5 ml NTB for 10 min.

4. Remove the coverslip from the dish and wipe the underside with a Q-tip or a Kimwipe. Mount the coverslip on the microscope chamber and fill with NTB. Mount the chamber on the confocal microscope stage.

5. Refer to the Bio-Rad MRC-600 manual for general instructions on the operation and tuning of the confocal microscope. Adjustments and settings specific for this method are listed here.

6. Adjust the confocal pinhole to an aperture equivalent to a z-axis depth of focus that is less than one-fourth the thickness of the cells to be analyzed.

7. The *gain* and *black level* controls on the photomultiplier should be set to manual operation throughout these measurements. Set the gain to 0 and start scanning with the laser shutter closed; set the black level until there is a barely visible signal appearing on the system monitor. This procedure will ensure that light signals are not being improperly offset and that photometric measurements will be possible.

8. Locate and focus on a field of view containing several cells using the conventional bright-field microscope light path. Switch to the confocal light path.

9. With a 1% T neutral density filter in the laser excitation path and the system set for fast scanning, raise the gain control until mitochondrial fluorescence begins to approach saturating gray levels. Some readjustment of the focus will probably be necessary as well.

10. Find a new field of view by moving the stage to a region that has not been exposed to light. Use an appropriate averaging mode and scan speed to obtain a noise-free signal while minimizing light exposure. Save this image to the hard disk for subsequent analysis of mitochondrial membrane potential.

11. Change the neutral density filter in the laser excitation path to achieve sufficient signal for a plasma membrane potential measurement; a 10% T filter is usually adequate. Alternatively, the gain may be set to a higher calibrated value. Acquire and save an image with a single fast scan to minimize light exposure.

12. Repeat steps 10 and 11 on several fresh fields of view and in conjunction with any desired solution changes to test for membrane potential responses to experimental treatments.

13. Repeat steps 10 and 11 after flushing the chamber with DTB and incubating for 5 min.

14. Acquire background images using the settings of steps 10 and 11 on a clean chamber filled with dye-free medium (i.e., NB).

15. Obtain intensities from different regions of these images using the *stats* command in the Bio-Rad MRC-600 software. Subtract the background intensity derived from the images in step 14 from the measurements to derive the signal due to TMRE fluorescence. The required intensities are:

F_{in} Mean intensity from an intracellular region free of mitochondrial fluorescence (the nucleus is often a convenient region for this measurement)

F_{out} Mean intensity from an extracellular region

B Ratio F_{out}/F_{in} for depolarized cells (step 13); corrects for any nonpotentiometric binding of the TMRE

16. Determine the membrane potential for the plasma membrane from the following equation using the fluorescence intensities determined in step 15:

$$\Delta V = -60 \, \log\left(\frac{F_{in} \cdot B}{F_{out}}\right) mV$$

17. Repeat the analysis of steps 15 and 16 on mitochondrial regions from images saved in step 10. F_{in}, in this context, is the maximum intensity within a mitochondrion; F_{out} is the intracellular fluorescence intensity. Be sure to normalize these intensities for any differences in excitation light or gain during image acquisition. Use these results qualitatively because the small size of the mitochondria precludes accurate determination of intramitochondrial fluorescence intensities without additional correction procedures (Loew, 1993).

IV. Comments

The procedures described above can be used to measure the plasma membrane potential of any glass-adherent cell line. This key measure of the physiological state of the cell is involved in many signal transduction mechanisms; the procedures described herein offer a convenient alternative to microelectrode-based techniques for elucidating the role of membrane permeability changes in signaling events. Also, mitochondrial membrane potential can be assessed qualitatively, permitting the study of how the physiological state of this important organelle is regulated.

The procedures above call for two steps to separately acquire images used for mitochondrial and plasma membrane potential. These steps can be combined if data are accumulated into a 16-bit image (i.e., 65,000 gray levels) with sufficient dynamic range to offer the necessary precision for fluorescence measurements from mitochondria, cytosol, and extracellular space. Of course, such data must be exported to software capable of dealing with 16-bit images; the Bio-Rad software can produce 16-bit images, but can only analyze 8-bit images.

Adhesion to a glass substrate can be enhanced by pretreatment of coverslips with polylysine, collagen, fibronectin, laminin, or any of a number of other reagents as appropriate for the particular cells to be studied.

This laboratory currently employs a Bio-Rad confocal laser scanning unit attached to a Zeiss microscope with a high-numerical-aperture objective. As this equipment is very expensive, a central confocal facility is found at many institutions; the procedures described here may be easily adapted to comparable available equipment manufactured by other companies. Likewise, any microscope chamber capable of temperature control and solution replacement would be suitable for these studies, including easily fabricated homemade devices (cf. Loew, 1993).

V. Pitfalls

1. The high intensity of laser excitation can easily lead to photobleaching and phototoxic effects involving singlet oxygen (Tsien and Waggoner, 1990). Therefore, exposure to the exciting light should be minimized and control experiments devised to check for photodamage.

2. The kinetics of dye redistribution following a change in membrane potential is quite variable depending on the particular cell type under study (Farkas *et al.*, 1989). If the kinetics of a change in membrane potential is being studied, it is necessary to determine the dye equilibration rate to be sure that it does not become limiting. This may be achieved by treating the cells with DTB and monitoring the rate of loss of fluorescence.

3. As stated above, changes in mitochondrial potential can be monitored but the absolute amplitude cannot be obtained. This is because the smallest depth of focus achievable with confocal microscopes is still wider than the diameter of most mitochondria. Even if only qualitative comparisons are desired, however, care should still be taken that an analyzed mitochondrion is centered within the optical slice; a mitochondrion that is off-center may be quite visible but will be insufficiently sampled and display artifactually low intensities. Also, mitochondria in many cell types can be quite motile; it is therefore important that the laser scan rate be sufficiently fast that the mitochondria not produce a blurred and, thus, artifactually low intensity image.

REFERENCES

Bedlack, R. S., Wei, M.-d., and Loew, L. M. (1992) Localized membrane depolarizations and localized intracellular calcium influx during electric field-guided neurite growth. *Neuron* 9, 393–403.
Cohen, L. B., and Salzberg, B. M. (1978) Optical measurement of membrane potential. *Rev. Physiol. Biochem. Pharmacol.* 83, 35–88.
Ehrenberg, B., Montana, V., Wei, M.-d., Wuskell, J. P., and Loew, L. M. (1988) Membrane potential can be determined in individual cells from the Nernstian distribution of cationic dyes. *Biophys. J.* 53, 785–794.
Farkas, D. L., Wei, M., Febbroriello, P., Carson, J. H., and Loew, L. M. (1989) Simultaneous imaging of cell and mitochondrial membrane potential. *Biophys. J.* 56, 1053–1069.
Freedman, J. C., and Laris, P. C. (1988) Potentiometric indicators in nonexcitable cells. *In* "Spectroscopic Membrane Probes" (L. M. Loew, ed.), Vol. 3, pp. 1–50. CRC Press, Boca Raton, FL.
Loew, L. M. (1993) Confocal microscopy of potentiometric fluorescent dyes. *In* "Methods

in Cell Biology," Vol. 38: "Cell Biological Applications of Confocal Microscopy" (B. Matsumoto, ed.), pp. 194–209. Academic Press, Orlando, FL.

Loew, L. M., Farkas, D. L., and Wei, M.-d. (1990) Membrane potential imaging: Ratios, templates, and quantitative confocal microscopy. *In* "Optical Microscopy for Biology" (B. Herman and K. Jacobson, eds.), pp. 131–142. Wiley–Liss, New York.

Montana, V., Farkas, D. L., and Loew, L. M. (1989) Dual wavelength ratiometric fluorescence measurements of membrane potential. *Biochemistry* **28**, 4536–4539.

Tsien, R. Y., and Waggoner, A. (1990) Fluorophores for confocal microscopy: Photophysics and photochemistry. *In* "Handbook of Biological Confocal Microscopy" (J. B. Pawley, ed.), pp. 169–178. Plenum, New York.

Waggoner, A. S. (1985). Dye probes of cell, organelle, and vesicle membrane potentials. *In* "The Enzymes of Biological Membranes" (A. N. Martonosi, ed.), pp. 313–331. Plenum, New York.

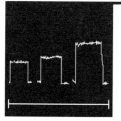

Measurement of Cytosolic pH in Single Cells by Dual-Excitation Fluorescence Spectrometry: Simultaneous Visualization Using Hoffman Modulation Contrast Optics

Robert Romanek, Ori D. Rotstein, and Sergio Grinstein

I. Introduction

The cytosolic pH of intact, viable cells (pH_i) can be measured with minimal interference to cellular function using pH-sensitive fluorescent dyes. The fluorescence of the pH indicator can be monitored at a single emission wavelength while undergoing single-wavelength excitation. pH-independent decreases in the fluorescence signal can, however, result from photobleaching or leakage of the dye out of the cells. Such artifacts can be overcome through the use of dual-wavelength ratio spectroscopy. By use of a dye that is differentially sensitive to pH at two separate wavelengths, with one wavelength being either insensitive, much less sensitive, or sensitive in the opposite direction of the other, a ratio of the fluorescence changes at the two chosen wavelengths can be generated. This ratio normalizes the measurements with respect to the amount of fluorophore and is truly representative of pH_i (Taylor and Wang, 1989; Grinstein and Putnam, 1993). The fluorescence ratio can be calibrated *in situ* by equilibrating the pH_i with the extracellular pH using nigericin, a K^+/H^+ ionophore (see Thomas *et al.*, 1979, for details).

2′, 7′-Bis(carboxyethyl)-5(or 6)-carboxyfluorescein (BCECF) has been the fluorescent dye of choice for measurement of pH_i near the physiological range. While the acid form of BCECF is poorly permeant, acetoxymethylation of the carboxyl residues renders the dye lipid soluble and facilitates entry into the cell. Once in the cell, the ester (BCECF-AM) is hydrolyzed by endogenous esterases, releasing BCECF, which is captured in the cytoplasm (Grinstein *et al.*, 1989).

Changes in cell size or shape can affect the fluorescence signal generated during pH_i determinations. In the case of motile cells, physical displacement of the cells can also occur during the course of a measurement. While wavelength ratioing in principle corrects for some of these events, simultaneous monitoring of cellular morphology is highly recommended. For this reason, the system described below combines the use of BCECF fluorescence excitation ratio determinations with continuous visualization of the cells using red light and Hoffman modulation contrast optics.

II. Materials and Instrumentation

Mes (Cat. No. M-8250), Hepes (Cat. No. H-3375), RPMI-1640 medium (bicarbonate-free, Cat. No. R-4130), DMSO (Cat. No. D-8779), and poly-L-lysine (Cat.

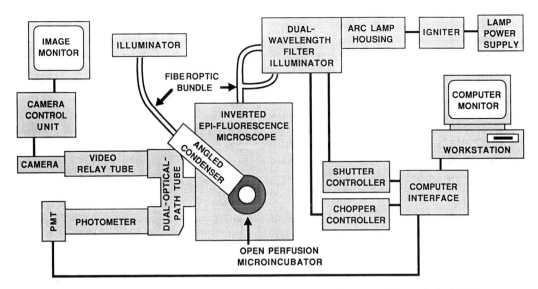

FIGURE 1 Configuration of hardware for simultaneous visualization of the cells by Hoffman modulation contrast optics and measurement of fluorescence ratio. Details of the light path are shown in Fig. 2.

No. P-1524) are obtained from Sigma. Tris (Cat. No. 604-207) is from Boehringer-Mannheim. Potassium chloride (Cat. No. P217-500) and type FF microscopy immersion oil (Cat. No. 12-371-1A) are from Fisher Scientific. Nigericin (Cat. No. N-1495) and the acetoxymethyl ester form of 2′, 7′-bis(2-carboxyethyl)-5(and 6)-carboxyfluorescein (BCECF-AM, Cat. No. B-1150) are purchased from Molecular Probes.

The Diaphot-tmd microscope and the dual-optical-path tube including 510- and 550-nm dichroic mirrors and an infrared filter are purchased from Nikon Canada Instruments Inc. The Hoffman imaging system, composed of the illuminator, condenser with 620-nm barrier filter, and video relay tube, are from Modulation Optics. The CCD-72 camera and corresponding controller are from Dage-MTI Inc., and the image monitor is a Panasonic WV-5370A, Matsushita Electric. The fluorescence detection system is the M-Series MS-600-2 package from Photon Technologies Inc. and includes the dual-wavelength filter illuminator, 490 p10 and 440 p10 nm filters, arc lamp with igniter and power supply, photometer, photomultiplier tube (PMT), shutter controller, optical chopper controller, computer interface, computer, and software. The open-perfusion microincubator (OPMI) with a Leiden coverslip holder and the TC-202 temperature controller are from Medical Systems Corporation (Cat. No. MS-200D). The coverslips are Thomas Red Label Micro Cover Glasses (Cat. No. 6662-F70) from Thomas Scientific. The 535 df 25-nm bandpass and 520-nm barrier filters are from Omega Optical. The configuration of the equipment listed above is illustrated in Figs. 1 and 2. The Hoffman modulation contrast and fluorescence light paths are detailed in Fig. 2.

III. Procedures

A. LOADING CELLS WITH THE DYE

Solutions

1. *RPMI-1640:* To make 1 liter, add 16.4 g of RPMI-1640 powder (1 bottle) to distilled water, adjust the pH to 7.4, and bring to a total volume of 1 liter. Adjust osmolarity to 290 ± 5 mOsm using NaCl. Store frozen at −20°C.

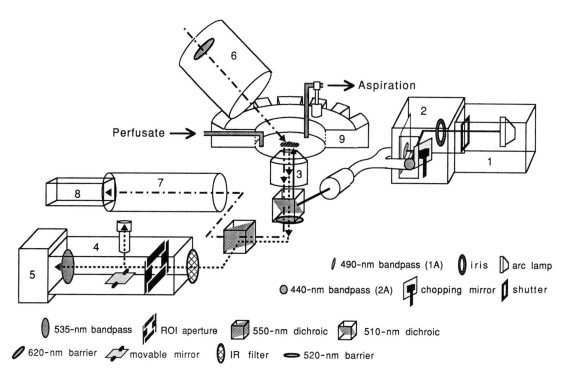

490-nm bandpass (1A)   **iris**   **arc lamp**

440-nm bandpass (2A)   **chopping mirror**   **shutter**

535-nm bandpass   **ROI aperture**   **550-nm dichroic**   **510-nm dichroic**

620-nm barrier   **movable mirror**   **IR filter**   **520-nm barrier**

FIGURE 2   Details of the perfusion system and of the light path used for Hoffman modulation contrast optics and for BCECF fluorescence ratio determinations. The light path used for Hoffman optics is indicated by the dash-dot line. The solid line represents the alternating (chopped) 490- and 440-nm excitation beam and the dashed line is the emitted light. To help relate this figure to Fig. 1, hardware components have been identified by the following numbering scheme: (1) arc lamp housing; (2) dual-wavelength filter illuminator; (3) 40× oil immersion objective of the inverted epifluorescence microscope; (4) photometer tube; (5) PMT (photomultiplier tube); (6) angled Hoffman condenser; (7) video relay tube; (8) camera; (9) open-perfusion microincubator. For clarity, we have omitted the housing of the dual-optical-path tube that contains the 550-nm dichroic mirror and the infrared filter along with the mirrors that direct light to the video relay tube and the photometer. The body of the inverted microscope, which houses the 510-nm dichroic mirror and the 520-nm barrier filter, was also omitted for simplicity.

2. *BCECF-AM stock solution:* Dissolve 1 mg of BCECF-AM in 1 ml of DMSO. Store at −20°C in 10-μl aliquots.

Steps

1. Incubate cells in a suitable medium (for macrophages use $5-10 \times 10^5$ cells/ml bicarbonate-free RPMI-1640) with 1 μg/ml BCECF-AM for 10–20 min at 37°C. Cells in suspension should be gently rotated to prevent sedimentation. For cells grown on coverslips no mixing is required.

2. Wash the cells twice to remove unhydrolyzed BCECF-AM and extracellular hydrolysis products. Maintain cells in the medium of choice until ready for use. Cells should preferably be used within 30 min of loading.

B. PREPARING CELLS FOR PHOTOMETRY

Solutions

1. RPMI-1640 is used as the incubation and wash solution.

2. *Poly-L-lysine:* Dissolve 1.2 mg/ml in distilled water; make fresh each time.

Steps

Load the Leiden coverslip dish using one of the following protocols.

a. Adherent cells grown on coverslips

1. Place freshly loaded cells directly into the Leiden coverslip dish, orienting the coverslip so that cells face upward. Ensure that a good seal exists between the coverslip and the O-ring by wiping away excess medium from the underside of the coverslip and checking for leaks.

2. Add 0.5 ml of incubation medium to the dish.

b. Adherent cells grown in suspension

1. Place a clean coverslip into the Leiden coverslip dish.

2. Overlay with 0.5 ml of the loaded cell suspension and allow sufficient time for the cells to attach ($\approx$15 min for macrophages).

3. Wash twice with incubation medium to remove nonadherent cells.

4. Overlay cells with 0.5 ml of desired incubation medium and check underside of dish for leaks as above.

c. Nonadherent cells grown in suspension

1. Before loading the cells, coat coverslips with an agent that will promote attachment of nonadherent cells. Poly-L-lysine and Cell-Tak (Collaborative Research Inc.) have been used extensively. Wash excess adhesive agent.

2. Place washed, coated coverslips into the Leiden coverslip dish and proceed as described in Section Bb, steps 2–4.

Place a drop of oil on the immersion objective and position the loaded Leiden dish in the open perfusion microincubator over the objective (No. 9 in Fig. 2).

C. MONITORING CELL MORPHOLOGY BY HOFFMAN MODULATION CONTRAST OPTICS

Steps

1. Turn on the illuminator connected to the Hoffman angled condenser, the camera control unit, and the image monitor.

2. Direct the outgoing light to the dual-optical-path tube by selecting the appropriate microscope mirror setting.

3. Select the appropriate 620-nm barrier filter (located in the angled condenser) for the objective being used. The red light chosen for Hoffman illumination is separated from the light emitted by BCECF by a 550-nm dichroic mirror located in the dual-optical-path tube (Fig. 2) and is directed through the video relay tube (No. 7 in Fig. 2) to the camera (No. 8 in Fig. 2). The image is then processed by the camera control unit and displayed in the image monitor (see Fig. 1).

4. Adjust the height and position of the angled condenser, the settings of the camera control unit, and the focus of the microscope, until a sharp image of the cell is obtained.

5. Position the cell to be studied at the center of the image monitor by displacing the microscope stage. Adjust the camera alignment to ensure that the

direction of movement of the stage corresponds to the displacement seen on the image monitor.

D. MEASUREMENT OF FLUORESCENCE RATIO

Steps

1. Turn off room lights or use a dark curtain around the microscope to eliminate stray light from entering the optical system. Red light can be used for dim illumination of the room.

2. Turn on the lamp power supply; then start the arc lamp. It is important to start the lamp before turning the computer on, to eliminate possible damage from power surges.

3. Turn on the computer and launch the PTI program; then turn on the optical chopper and the shutter controller, ensuring that the shutter is toggled off.

4. Configure the software for data acquisition as follows (see PTI manual for details):

Hardware configuration	Excitation chopper	Yes
	All others	No
Data acquisition setup	Screen plot 1	1A
	Screen plot 2	1A/2A
	Data rate	2
	Scan duration	600
	Shutter control	Manual
	Time display window	600
	All others	off

5. Place the 490- and 440-nm bandpass filters (1A and 2A respectively) in the appropriate positions, as indicated in Fig. 2. The excitation light from the arc lamp traverses a shutter and an iris before being alternately directed to the two excitation filters through a chopping mirror. The excitation beam then travels down the fiberoptic bundle into the microscope, where it is reflected at the cells by a 510-nm dichroic mirror. Fluorescence emitted from the cells traverses this dichroic mirror and is filtered by a 520-nm barrier (see Fig. 2). The emitted light is reflected to the photometer by a 550-nm dichroic mirror in the dual-optical-path tube (see Figs. 1 and 2). After the light travels through an infrared filter a "region of interest" (ROI) can be selected using a variable aperture. The light either can be deflected to an eyepiece used for visual adjustment of the ROI aperture, or can undergo a final selection using a 525-nm bandpass filter, before entering the photomultiplier tube (see Figs. 1 and 2).

6. To select the cell of interest set the movable mirror in the photometer to the "view" position, which directs the light path to the eyepiece. With the cell on the image monitor in focus ensure that the image at the eyepiece is parfocal, using the adjustment ring located in the dual-optical-path tube. Using the ROI aperture controls, adjust the viewing field to bracket the cell to be studied. This cell should correspond to the one previously centered on the image monitor.

7. Using a felt-tip marker draw a box corresponding to the ROI on the image monitor to aid in properly positioning cells for study.

8. Return the movable mirror in the photometer to the "measure" position.

E. ENSURING PARFOCALITY OF HOFFMAN AND FLUORESCENCE IMAGES

Steps

1. Use the stage controls to move the desired cell into the ROI box marked on the image monitor.

2. Start data collection by the computer, displaying both 1A and 1A/2A.

3. Manually toggle the shutter to the *on* position. Signals should appear on both the 1A and 1A/2A screens.

4. Adjust the iris of the dual-wavelength filter illuminator and the gain of the PMT to achieve a maximal signal with minimal rate of fluorescence decay, indicative of dye photobleaching (see Section V).

5. While monitoring the 1A signal, adjust the focus on the microscope until the 1A signal is maximal.

6. Check the image on the video monitor. If it is no longer in focus, adjust the parfocal control located on the video relay tube until the image is sharp.

F. CALIBRATION OF pH$_i$ VERSUS FLUORESCENCE

Solutions

All solutions contain 140 mM KCl and are adjusted to the desired pH using 10 mM concentrations of the appropriate buffers. Five solutions of varying pH in the 6 to 8 interval provide satisfactory calibration of BCECF fluorescence (e.g. Fig. 3). Nigericin (5 μM) is added immediately prior to use.

Steps

1. After setting the open-perfusion microincubator to the desired temperature, perfuse the dish with the initial calibration solution. Set the aspirator level to limit the volume to 0.5 ml.

2. With a cell situated in the ROI, start data collection.

3. After perfusing the chamber with ≈4 vol (i.e., ≈2 ml) of solution, open the excitation shutter for 20 to 30 sec. Monitor the fluorescence to ensure establishment of a stable ratio (see Fig. 3), indicating equilibration of pH$_i$ with the external pH.

4. Once a steady-state ratio has been collected, shutter off the fluorescence, change the perfusate to the next solution, and repeat step 3. Continue until fluorescence ratios have been recorded for all the calibration solutions.

5. Using the PTI software create a lookup table relating fluorescence ratio values to pH$_i$. This will allow for the subsequent on-screen conversion of experimental ratio values to their corresponding pH$_i$ values.

IV. Comments

Because the pK_a of BCECF is 6.97, the fluorescence ratio varies nearly linearly with pH between 6.5 and 7.5, encompassing most of the physiologically relevant range. Together with the ease and specificity of cytoplasmic loading and its slow rate of leakage from the cells, these properties make BCECF at present the probe of choice for fluorometric measurement of pH$_i$. Other dyes such as SNARF and

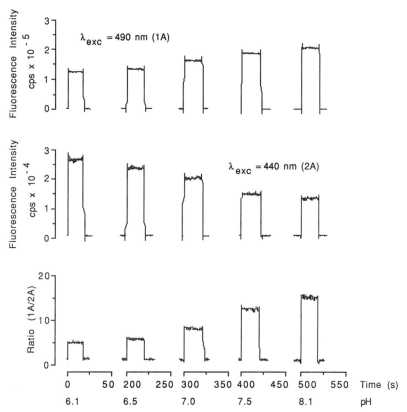

FIGURE 3   Representative calibration of a BCECF-loaded cell, relating the fluorescence to pH. The cytosolic pH was clamped at the indicated values using nigericin, a K^+/H^+ ionophore (Thomas *et al.*, 1979), and the fluorescence emission at 535 nm was measured while alternately exciting the cell at 490 and 440 nm. The intensity of emitted light with excitation at 490 nm (1A) is shown in the top panel. The intensity of emitted light with excitation at 440 nm (2A) is shown in the middle panel. The ratio of the two signals (490/440, 1A/2A) is displayed in the third panel. These values can be plotted against the corresponding pH to generate a calibration curve. Note the progressive decrease in 2A signal due to leakage and bleaching.

SNAFL ($pK_a \approx 7.5$ and 7.7, respectively) can be used to extend the range of measurable pH_i in the alkaline direction.

Calibration of the fluorescent dye versus pH_i should ideally be performed on the same batch of cells used for experimental analysis. This method is most accurate, yet is labor intensive and time consuming. If calibrations are reproducible from one experiment to the next, external calibration can be considered. A standard calibration curve, with statistically defined deviation ranges, can be constructed in advance for a specific cell type. Such a curve can then be applied to cells studied separately, provided that the loading conditions (i.e., cell density, dye concentration, temperature) are strictly maintained. It must, however, be borne in mind that depending on the length of the experiments, parameters such as dye leakage and photobleaching (see next section) may affect the validity of the calibration.

V. Pitfalls

1. It is important that the filters used to compose the light path be carefully chosen. Specifically, some bandpass filters such as those used to select the

fluorescence emission wavelength allow the passage of the red light used by the Hoffman optics.

2. Fluorescent signals from neighboring cells can leak into the ROI. Plating the cells sparsely allows more liberal definition of the ROI, overcoming this problem.

3. The extent of BCECF loading varies according to cell type, cell density, temperature, dye concentration, and time. Loading is also different for cells that are plated versus cells in suspension. All these conditions must be optimized for each individual biological system and maintained constant for external calibration to be applicable.

4. Leakage and photobleaching of BCECF tend to reduce its fluorescence in a pH-independent manner. This becomes apparent as a time-dependent decrease in the fluorescence intensity when exciting at 440 nm, which is a near-isosbestic point and is in principle expected to remain constant at varying pH. This effect is illustrated in Fig. 3 (middle trace).

5. Photobleaching of BCECF can induce cellular photodynamic damage. Bleaching and photodynamic damage can be minimized by reducing the intensity of the excitation beam and/or by minimizing the time of exposure of the cells to the excitation light, using the shutter which can be programmed to open for only brief intervals.

REFERENCES

Grinstein, S., and Putman, R. (1993) Measurement of Intracellular pH. *In* "Membrane Transport in Biology" (J. Schafer, H. Ussing, P. Kristensen, and G. Giebisch, eds.), Vol. 6. Springer-Verlag, Heidelberg.

Grinstein, S., Cohen, S., Goetz-Smith, J. D., and Dixon, S. J. (1989) Measurements of cytoplasmic pH and cellular volume for detection of Na^+/H^+ exchange in lymphocytes. *In* "Methods in Enzymology" (S. Fleischer and B. Fleischer, eds.), Vol. 173, pp. 777–790. Academic Press, San Diego.

Taylor, D. L., and Wang, Y. (1989) "Methods in Cell Biology," Vol. 30: "Fluorescence Microscopy of Living Cells in Culture." Academic Press, San Diego.

Thomas, J. A., Buchsbaum, R. N., Zimniak, A., and Racker, E. (1979) Intracellular pH measurements in Ehrlich ascites tumor cells utilizing spectroscopic probes generated *in situ. Biochemistry* **18**, 2210–2218.

PART 10

CYTOGENETICS AND *IN SITU* HYBRIDIZATION

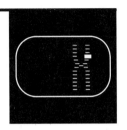

Basic Cytogenetic Techniques: Culturing, Slide Making, and G-Banding

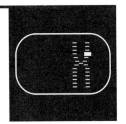

Chih-Lin Hsieh

I. Introduction

Study of human chromosomes has been carried out since the end of the last century. Numerous developments have made cytogenetics an increasingly exciting field in the last 40 years. The use of colchicine as a mitotic block (Levan, 1938) and the application of hypotonic treatment (Hsu, 1952) to obtain mitotic spread, the development of an air-drying approach to slide making (Moorehead *et al.*, 1960), the observation that phytohemagglutinin stimulates mitosis in leukocytes (Nowell, 1960), and the development of several staining procedures laid the technical foundation for cytogenetics today. Since the correct determination of the human chromosome number (Tijo and Levan, 1956) and the identification of trisomy-21 in Down syndrome (Lejeune *et al.*, 1959), cytogenetics has become an increasingly important component of clinical medicine, prenatal diagnosis, biomedical research, and cancer diagnosis and prognosis. In recent years, the application of molecular biology has expanded the capabilities of cytogenetic approaches even more.

Mitosis, which lasts about 30 min, is the only period of the cell cycle in which chromosomes are condensed and visible by light microscopy. In general, cytogenetic analysis involves blocking the cell cycle at metaphase of mitosis, followed by harvesting, slide preparation, staining, and visualization. Twenty-three pairs of human chromosomes are classified into seven groups (Fig. 1) and the International System for Human Cytogenetic Nomenclature (ISCN, 1985) is the definitive reference for classification and nomenclature.

Peripheral blood is the most commonly used source of cells for postnatal chromosome analysis. Phytohemagglutinin (PHA), first used by Nowell (1960), is used as a mitogen for stimulating the T cells in peripheral blood for chromosome analysis. Alternative methods are available when there is a specific need to obtain chromosomes from some other cell lineages (for lymphocyte mitogens, see Tizard, 1992). The slide-making section explains how to produce microscope slide preparations from the harvested cell culture suspensions. The mitotic chromosomes obtained can be used to identify numerical and structural chromosome abnormalities as well as normal chromosome variations by various classical staining techniques. High-resolution chromosome preparations are used for more detailed analysis of microdeletions or rearrangements, fine breakpoint analysis, and refined mapping.

II. Materials and Instrumentation

Fetal bovine serum (Cat. No. A-1111-D) is from HyClone. RPMI-1640 medium (Cat. No. 11875-051), L-glutamine (Cat. No. 25030-024), gentamicin (50 mg/ml,

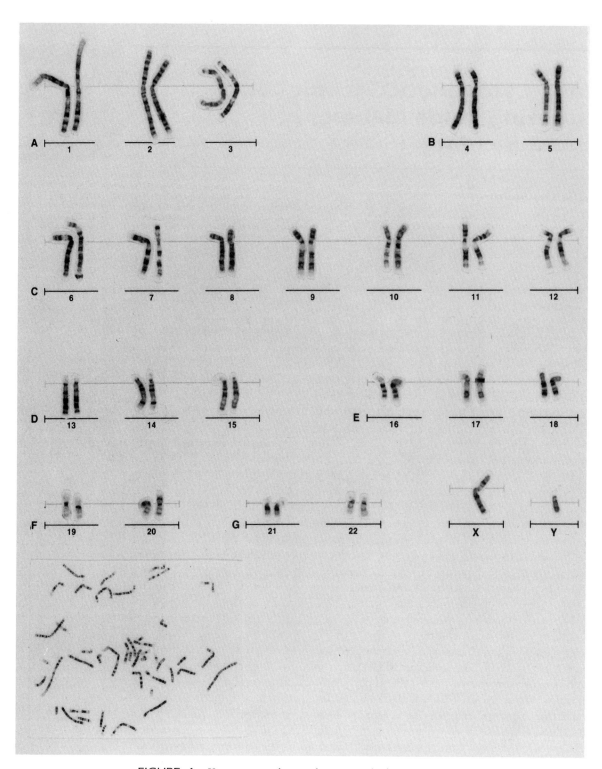

FIGURE 1   Karyotype and metaphase spread of a normal male karyotype.

Cat. No. 15750-011), phytohemagglutinin-M (PHA, Cat. No. 670-0576), Colcemid (10 μg/ml, Cat. No. 120-5211), and Hanks' balanced salt solution (HBSS, Cat. No. 24020-042) are from Gibco-BRL.

Amethopterin (Cat. No. A-6770), thymidine (Cat. No. T-9250), potassium chloride (KCl, Cat. No. P-4504), ethidium bromide (Cat. No. E-8751), and sodium chloride (Cat. No. S-9625) are from Sigma.

Sodium heparin vacutainer (B-D No. 6386, Cat. No. 02-683-69) and one-end-frosted microscope slides (Corning 2949-75x25, Cat. No. 12-533-15) can be purchased from Fisher Scientific. Slides should be hydrophilic and can hold a thin film of water across the slide. Tuberculin syringe (Cat. No. BD9626), 15-ml sterile conical centrifuge tubes (Corning 25319-15, Cat. No. 21008-6780), 21-gauge needles (Cat. No. BD5167), trypsin (Cat. No. DF0153-60), Wright's stain (Cat. No. EM-WX0025-3), Whatman No. 1 filter paper (Cat. No. 28450-160), mounting medium (Cat. No. 48212-290), and cover glass No. 1 (Cat. No. 48393-081) can be purchased from VWR. The pHydrion capsule, pH 6.8 (Cat. No. 9070-01), is from J. T. Baker.

A table-top centrifuge is needed for harvesting cells and a phase-contrast microscope is needed for slide making.

III. Procedures

A. CULTURE AND METAPHASE HARVEST OF PERIPHERAL BLOOD

T cells in whole blood cultures are stimulated with PHA to proliferate. After 2 or 3 days the cultures have gone through one or two rounds of mitosis, respectively. Cells are treated with colchicine, which prevents formation of the mitotic spindle fiber apparatus, and mitotic cells in metaphase accumulate. Cells are then treated with hypotonic solution and fixed with methanol–acetic acid fixative. The hypotonic treatment is essential.

Solutions

1. *Supplemented medium RPMI-1640:* To each 100 ml of RPMI-1640, add 11 ml fetal bovine serum (~10% FBS), 1.2 ml 200 mM L-glutamine (2 mM final concentration), and 0.1 ml gentamicin, 50 mg/ml (50 μg/ml final concentration). Fresh L-glutamine needs to be added to the medium every 2–4 weeks.

2. *Amethopterin (methotrexate, 10^{-5} M stock):* 0.5 mg in 98 ml of Hanks' BSS. Aliquots can be stored at −20°C for 1 year or at 4°C for 1 month.

3. *Thymidine (10^{-3} M stock):* 25 mg in 100 ml of Hanks' BSS. Aliquots can be frozen for up to 1 year or at 4°C for 1 month.

4. *Hypotonic solution (0.075 M KCl):* Add H_2O to 0.56 g KCl to make 100 ml.

5. *Fixative:* Make fresh, 3:1 methanol:glacial acetic acid.

Steps

1. Collect peripheral blood into a sodium heparin vacutainer. Blood in sodium heparin can be held for up to 5 days and still be successfully cultured.

2. From a tuberculin syringe with a 21-gauge needle, add 0.25 ml of whole blood (0.2 ml for newborns up to 3 weeks) to a sterile 15-ml centrifuge tube containing 5.0 ml of supplemented RPMI-1640 medium (Section II). Add 0.05 ml of reconstituted PHA solution to each tube. A single culture will typically yield three to five full slide preparations or more if only a portion of the slide is used.

3. Incubate the cultures at a shallow angle at 37°C for 2, 3, or 4 days. Three-day cultures are optimal but 2- or 4-day cultures can be used to accommodate scheduling concerns. Newborn blood usually works well after 2 days of culturing.

Synchronization is optional and can be omitted by skipping steps 4 and 5, but will result in longer chromosomes.

4. Twenty-one hours prior to harvest (the exact time is not critical, but do not exceed 22 hr), block the culture by adding 50 μl of 10^{-5} M amethopterin (final 10^{-7} M). Reincubate at 37°C.

5. Four and one-half hours prior to harvest (this interval is important), release the culture by adding 50 μl of 10^{-3} M thymidine (final 10^{-5} M). Reincubate at 37.0°C.

6. Thirty minutes prior to harvest, add Colcemid to a final concentration of 0.05 μg/ml. Reincubate for 30 min.

7. Begin harvest by centrifuging at 180 g for 8.0 min and aspirate supernatant.

8. Add 6 ml of 0.075 M KCl hypotonic solution at room temperature to the tube and gently resuspend. Incubate at room temperature for 15 min.

9. Add 10–12 drops of 3:1 methanol:acetic acid fixative from a Pasteur pipette and mix well. Centrifuge as above. The pellet will appear brown and clumpy due to the hemoglobin.

10. Draw off all but the last 0.5 ml of the supernatant overlaying the pellet. Resuspend the pellet by tapping the bottom of the tube gently. Bring the volume up to 5 ml by adding fixative slowly. Mix well. Centrifuge as above.

11. Repeat step 10.

12. Remove the supernatant and resuspend the pellet in an appropriate volume of fixative for slide making. The volume is dependent on pellet size and should result in a light milky suspension (generally, no more than 1.5 ml).

13. Make slides.

B. CULTURE AND HARVEST FOR HIGH-RESOLUTION PROMETAPHASE CHROMOSOMES

Synchronizing the cell cycle and inhibiting chromosome condensation allow the enrichment of mitotic cells at prophase or prometaphase with more than 750 G-bands per haploid karyotype level. Synchronization is accomplished by blocking cultures in S phase of the cell cycle with amethopterin, an inhibitor of thymidylate synthesis. The block is released by addition of thymidine, and a wave of late prophase or prometaphase cells are captured by a series of sequential harvests with short mitotic arrest. Chromosome condensation can also be inhibited by adding DNA intercalating agents, such as ethidium bromide, before harvest.

Solutions

1. See Section A.

2. *Ethidium bromide (1.25 × 10^{-3} M):* 4.9 mg in 10.0 ml of Hanks' BSS. Protect the solution from light with foil and store at 4°C.

Steps

1. Initiate multiple cultures, as in step 2 of the basic protocol, and incubate on a shallow angle at 37°C for 3 or 4 days. Follow the basic protocol through

step 5.

2. One hour before harvest, add 50 μl of 1.25×10^{-3} M ethidium bromide (final 1.25×10^{-5} M) to cultures.

3. Harvest one culture according to step 6 of the basic protocol.

4. The rest of the cultures should be harvested sequentially at 10- to 15-min intervals spanning a period of 30 min to 1 hr. Add colcemid 10 min before each harvest, as in step 6 of the basic protocol, but only reincubate at 37°C for 10 min and proceed with the harvest from step 7 of the basic protocol.

NOTE

The optimal interval between release and addition of Colcemid, usually 4 to 5 hr, for the sequential harvests should be determined. Once the optimal interval is determined, four cultures around this optimal time are generally harvested at 10-min increments.

C. SLIDE PREPARATION

Solution

1. *Fixative:* Make fresh 3:1 methanol:glacial acetic acid.

Steps

1. Soak slides in a Coplin jar of 100% methanol. Remove the slide from methanol and polish the side that you plan to drop the harvest suspension onto (front side) with a Kimwipe. Dip the slide back into methanol briefly and swirl it in a beaker of deionized water until a uniform thin film of water covers the slide.

2. Hold the frosted end with the index and middle fingers on the front side and thumb on the back side of the slide, and blot the long edge of the slide on a paper towel to draw off excess water by capillary action. Keep the long edge in contact with the paper towel, and lower the top edge of the slide toward you until your thumb touches the bench top (approximately a 30° angle between the slide and the bench top).

3. Hold the Pasteur pipette horizontally, about 1–2 in. above the slide; place 3 drops of cell suspension, evenly spaced, onto the slide starting from the free end and moving successively toward the frosted end touching your fingers. The drops should strike the slide one-third of the width from the top of the slide and should burst on the water film as they strike the slide and spread out evenly. Flood the slide by applying fixative across the top of the slide from the free end toward the frosted end. A consistent dispersal of cells across the entire surface of the slide is the objective. Adjust the number of drops per slide according to the density of the suspension and the need of the project.

4. Raise the slide, blot the long edge, wipe off the back, and air-dry the slide by placing it on a 30° angle lengthwise with the front side up (the side with the cells) and the frosted end downhill. Mark the slide with a No. 3 pencil.

The method described here is not the only approach to chromosome slide preparation, but it has been successfully used in many laboratories. Air drying is the most critical and the most variable part of slide making. A humidity of 50% is often sufficient to prepare the slide exactly as the protocol above. The drying process can be manipulated (such as by drying slides on a wet paper towel or on a warm surface) relative to ambient temperature and humidity. The contrast of the chromosomes should be viewed by phase-contrast microscopy. Chromosomes with medium or dark contrast and sharp edge definition are the best (not dark and with a halo around the chromosomes).

5. Bake the slides at 90°C for 30 min before banding. (This step is omitted if the *in situ* hybridization method is used instead of the routine banding method.)

D. GTW BANDING

Solutions

1. *Trypsin:* Rehydrate a vial with 10 ml H_2O, and store 1-ml aliquots at −20°C. Mix 1 ml of the trypsin solution and 49 ml of 0.9% NaCl before use (discard at the end of the day).

2. *Sodium chloride:* Make 0.9% solution (0.9 g in 100 ml of water).

3. *Wright's stain (0.2%):* Add 0.8 g of stain in 400 ml absolute methanol, swirl briefly to mix, and then let the mixture stand for few minutes. Filter through Whatman No. 1 filter paper into a brown bottle. Store tightly capped at room temperature (discard after 30 days).

4. *pHydrion solution:* Dissolve content of one pHydrion 6.8 capsule in 100 ml H_2O to make the stock. The working solution is 5% of the stock solution.

Steps

1. Dip the slide in trypsin solution (see Section II) at room temperature for 3–60 seconds. Vary the time to adjust banding quality.

2. Rinse briefly twice in two Coplin jars containing 0.9% NaCl.

3. Flood the slide for 1–3 min with a mixture of 1 ml of 0.2% Wright's stain (see Section II) and 4 ml of pHydrion buffer (a stain rack is convenient).

4. Rinse with H_2O and blow-dry with compressed air, or press the slide between lens paper on a flat and hard surface.

5. Cover the slide with mounting medium and a coverglass.

IV. Pitfalls

1. Mitogen failure will result in very few or no mitotic cells, many polysegmented nuclei, and very few large nuclei on the slide. Addition of fresh PHA at the correct concentration is important.

2. Incorrect concentration of the hypotonic solution or poor slide making will result in no metaphases or knotted and encapsulated chromosome spreads on the slide. If the problem cannot be corrected by slide making, then make fresh hypotonic solution.

3. If in the synchronized harvests, the mitotic index is reduced with only sporadic metaphases with long chromosomes, fresh amethopterin and thymidine solutions should be made.

REFERENCES

Hsu, T. C. (1952) Mammalian chromosomes in vitro. 1. The karyotype of man. *J. Hered.* **43**, 167.

ISCN (1985) "An International System for Human Cytogenetic Nomenclature." S. Karger, Basel/New York.

Lejeune, J., Gautier, M., and Turpin, R. (1959) Etude des chromosomes somatiques de neuf enfants mongoliens. *C. R. Acad. Sci. Paris* **248**, 1721.

Levan, A. (1938) The effect of colchicine on root mitosis in *Allium. Heredity* **24**, 471.

Moorehead, P. S., Nowell, P. C., Mellman, W. J., Battips, D. M., and Hungerford, D. A. (1960) Chromosome preparations of leukocytes cultured from human peripheral blood. *Exp. Cell Res.* **20**, 613.

Nowell, P. C. (1960) Phytohemagglutinin: An initiator of mitosis in cultures of normal human leukocytes. *Cancer Res.* **20**, 462.

Tijo, J. H., and Levan, A. (1956) The chromosome number of man. *Hereditas* **42**, 1.

Tizard, I. R. (1992) "Immunology: An Introduction," 3rd ed., p. 107. Saunders College, Philadelphia.

SUGGESTED READING

Barch, M. J. (ed.) (1991) "The ACT Cytogenetics Laboratory Manual," 2nd ed. Raven Press, New York.

Rooney, D. E., and Czepulkowski, B. H. (eds.) (1992) "Human Cytogenetics," Vol. I: "Constitutional Analysis," 2nd ed. Oxford University Press, New York.

Verma, R. S., and Babu, A. (1989) "Human Chromosomes." Pergamon Press, New York.

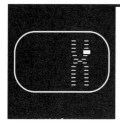

Production of Viable Hybrids between Adherent Cells

Doris Cassio

I. Introduction

Somatic cell hybridization was introduced by Barski *et al.* (1960) and Sorieul and Ephrussi (1961).This technique allows one to examine the result of introducing various genomes in different functional states and from different species into the **same** cell. Hybrid cells have been widely used in various fields (genetics, cell biology, tumor biology, virology). The most important applications of somatic cell hybridization are production of monoclonal antibodies and chromosomal gene assignment, in particular human gene mapping.

Spontaneous fusion of cells in culture occurs at a very low frequency. To obtain hybrid cells, inactivated Sendai virus, or more commonly polyethylene glycol (PEG) introduced by Pontecorvo (1976), is used as a fusogen. The inital products of fusion contain within a common cytoplasm two or more distinct nuclei from one single parent (homokaryons) or from both parents (heterokaryons). Only a small proportion of these polykaryons progress to nuclear fusion and then through mitosis. The formation of viable hybrids from heterokaryons is thus a rare event and the use of selective methods that favor the survival of the hybrids at the expense of the parental cells is often a requisite.

The best known of such methods is the application of HAT (hypoxanthine + aminopterine + thymidine) selection for the fusion of HGPRT− and TK− cells (Littlefield, 1964) but different combinations of selectable markers can be used (Hooper, 1985), provided that the two selective systems do not interfere. If the lines that will be fused have no selective markers, a good strategy is to select sequentially for HGPRT deficiency and ouabain resistance in one parental cell line. Then this marked cell line may be fused with any unmarked cell line and hybrids selected in HAT + ouabain (Jha and Ozer, 1976). For producing primate–rodent hybrids the selection of an HGPRT− rodent parent is sufficient, because rodent cells are more resistant to ouabain than primate cells. Moreover, hybrid cells can also be isolated on the basis of their size, morphology, growth parameters, and DNA content.

Whatever the method used to isolate hybrids, the most important is to optimize the fusion conditions to obtain the highest number of viable hybrids possible. In the best cases the fusion of several million parental cells leads to the formation of only a few hundred hybrids and often the yield of viable hybrids is much lower. The protocol described here has been routinely used to produce large amounts of hybrid clones between differentiated rat hepatoma cells and various cells of different histogenetic origin and of different species, in particular mouse and human fibroblasts (Sellem *et al.*, 1981). Moreover, some of the hybrids obtained have been themselves used as partners of fusion and new hybrids were successfully generated using exactly the same method. Two parameters have to be considered in fusion experiments: the yield of viable and growing hybrids and their stability. Thus, defining optimal fusion conditions and analyzing hybrid clones regularly for their phenotype and chromosomal content are recommended.

II. Materials

PEG 1000 ultrapure (Merck, Cat. No. 9729)

Trypsin (United States Biochemical Corp., Cat. No. 22715)

Complete growth medium (available from local suppliers)

Serum-free growth medium (available from local suppliers)

Selective complete growth medium (available from local suppliers)

35- and 50-mm tissue culture dishes (Falcon, Cat. Nos. 3001 and 3002)

22 × 22-mm sterile glass coverslips

III. Procedure

A. BEFORE THE FUSION

Solutions

1. *50 % PEG (for fusion):* Autoclave PEG 1000. This both liquifies and sterilizes the PEG. Cool it to 37°C and mix with an equal volume of sterile serum-free medium prewarmed at 37°C. Adjust, if necessary, to the desired pH with 1.0 M NaOH (range of pH generally used 7.2–7.9). This solution can be stored at 4°C for up to 2 weeks.

2. *0.25 and 0.05% trypsin (to detach the fusion products):* To make 100 ml of solution, solubilize 0.8 g of NaCl, 0.04 g of KCl, 0.058 g of $NaHCO_3$, 0.1 g dextrose, and 0.25 g (0.25%) or 0.05 g (0.05%) of trypsin. Complete to 100 ml with distilled water. Incubate at 37°C for 1–2 hr. Sterilize by filtration and store at 4°C (rapid use) or −20°C.

Step

1. Grow parental cells in nonselective medium for a short period.

B. FUSION

Steps

1. Inoculate the mixture of parental cells to be fused into several 50-mm tissue culture dishes containing complete growth medium. The total number of cells has to be adjusted to occupy the entire dish surface, such that the fusion will be done on cells that are in close contact. For 50-mm petri dishes the total cell number could vary from 5×10^5 to 4×10^6 depending on the density at confluence of the cell lines used. Although equal numbers of parental cells are

TABLE I Production of Rat Hepatoma × Human Fibroblast Hybrids[a]

Ratio of parental cells[b] (hepatoma:fibroblast)	Fusion conditions	Selection conditions	Hybrid yield[c]
1:1	PEG, pH 7.2	HAT, ouabain, pH 7.2	$<2.0 \times 10^{-6}$
4:1			5.0×10^{-6}
10:1			2.0×10^{-5}
1:1	PEG, pH 7.8	HAT, ouabain, pH 7.8[d]	1.5×10^{-5}
4:1			3.0×10^{-5}
10:1			1.5×10^{-4}
10:1	Sendai virus, pH 7.8	HAT, ouabain, pH 7.8[d]	1.0×10^{-4}
1:1	No fusogen, pH 7.8	HAT, ouabain, pH 7.8[d]	$<2.0 \times 10^{-6}$

[a] For details of the parental cell lines, see Sellem *et al.* (1981).
[b] 2×10^6 cells were plated per 50-mm petri dish.
[c] Hybrid yield = total number of hybrid clones/total cell number of minority parent.
[d] Cells were maintained at pH 7.8 for 6 days after fusion and then cultured at pH 7.2, as usual.

generally recommended, use different ratios of parental cells (see Table I and Section IV).

2. Incubate the mixed cultures a few hours (4 hr to overnight). This allows the cells to adhere to the support and to establish contacts with neighbors.

3. Warm the serum-free medium and the 50% PEG solution to 37°C.

4. Remove the medium thoroughly from the culture and wash once with 5 ml serum-free medium.

5. Add gently 3.0 ml of 50% PEG all over the cell layer.

6. After 45 sec aspirate the PEG.

7. Exactly 1 min after the PEG treatment, add 5 ml of serum-free medium.

8. Aspirate half the medium and add 2.5 ml of serum-free medium.

9. Repeat step 8 four times.

10. Aspirate all the medium.

11. Add 5 ml of serum-free medium and let the cells recover for at least 2 hr but no longer than 12 hr.

Steps 4 to step 11 must be done dish by dish. Include some control dishes. They will be treated as the others except that PEG solution will be replaced by serum-free medium.

C. AFTER THE FUSION

Steps

1. Aspirate the medium and add 3 ml of 0.25% trypsin per dish.

2. As soon as the cell layer begins to detach, add 3 ml of 0.05% trypsin and detach the cells by repeated pipetting.

3. Add the cell suspension in a tube containing 2 ml of complete growth medium (to arrest the trypsin action). Rinse, if necessary, the dish with 2 ml medium and add this medium to the tube containing the cells.

4. Centrifuge the cells at 500 g (1500 rpm) for 5 min at room temperature.

5. Resuspend thoroughly the cell pellet in complete growth medium and count cell number in a hemocytometer (see article by Ariana Celis and Julio E. Celis in Volume 1). Using the described protocol, generally at least 80% of the cells are recovered after the fusion.

6. Pool, if necessary, cells recovered from identical dishes and inoculate different numbers of cells (10^3 to 10^6) either in culture dishes or on 22-mm glass coverslips (in 35-mm dishes).

7. Incubate the cells at least overnight (eventually a few days) in complete growth medium, before adding selective medium that will kill the parental cells and let the hybrid cells survive.

8. At regular intervals, watch for the appearance of growing hybrid colonies. Count their number in dishes or coverslips that contain well-isolated colonies. From this number the yield of growing hybrids can be calculated. For one fusion, this yield is equal to the total number of hybrid clones obtained divided by the total cell number of the minority parent engaged in the fusion.

9. Use the dishes that contain a small number of colonies to isolate independent hybrid clones (one per dish will be scraped, subcultured, characterized, as soon as possible, frozen, and recharacterized). From the dishes that contain many colonies, if this situation arises, hybrid cell populations can be obtained in mass and rapidly studied.

10. Use the glass coverslips to control by cytogenetic methods the hybrid nature of the clones and to test if their chromosomal content is stable with time in culture. The karyotyping *in situ* method, described by Worton and Duff (1979), is highly recommended. This method is easy, is generally applicable to adherent cells, and can be performed on small colonies even a few generations after fusion (Fig. 1). The glass coverslips can also be used for phenotypic characterization of hybrid clones.

IV. Comments

The production of hybrid clones in large amounts greatly depends on the parental cells and on the fusion conditions. This last point is illustrated in Table I for rat hepatoma × human fibroblast hybrids. The frequency of occurrence of such hybrids was particularly low, compared with other hepatoma-derived hybrids. Various conditions were therefore tested. The use of unbalanced ratios of parental cells is one of the most important factors in improving the hybrid yield. Therefore to save time and to obtain the highest number of hybrid cells, fusion of parental cells in different ratios is recommended.

Mixed parental cell populations that have not been treated with PEG can give rise at low frequency to colonies that grow in selective medium. These colonies could be either spontaneous hybrids or revertants from parental cells.

V. Pitfalls

1. Some PEG preparations produce great lethality, whereas ultrapure PEG from Merck results in acceptable levels of lethality (generally below 20%).

2. Because it is impossible to predict if hybrid clones will be produced in high yield, once the fusion is performed and the products of fusion are detached, inoculate them at different concentrations (that could cover a 1000× range) such

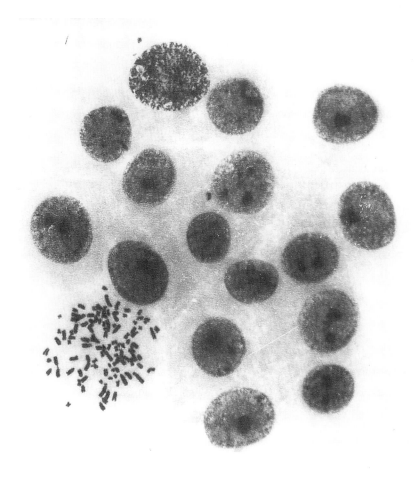

FIGURE 1 The *in situ* karyotyping method (Worton and Duff, 1979) was performed on rat hepatoma-derived hybrid colonies 8 days after fusion. The colony shown was composed of 17 cells, one of which was in metaphase. This metaphase contains a hundred chromosomes, corresponding to the expected sum of the mean chromosome numbers the parents (46 and 52, respectively).

that well-isolated hybrids could be obtained even if the yield varies from 10^{-6} to 10^{-3}.

3. A smaller number of hybrid clones is obtained if the cells are not detached after the fusion.

ACKNOWLEDGMENTS

I thank my colleagues C. H. Sellem, M. C. Weiss and particularly C. Hamon-Benais for the illustrations.

REFERENCES

Barski, G., Sorieul, S., and Cornefert, F. (1960) Production dans des cultures *in vitro* de deux souches cellulaires en association, de celules de caractère "hybride." *C. R. Acad. Sci. Paris* **251**, 1825–1827.
Hooper, M. (1985) In *"Mammalian Cell Genetics"* (E. Edward Bittar, ed.), pp. 77–81. Wiley–Interscience, New York.

Jha, K. K., and Ozer, H. L. (1976) Expression of transformation in cell hybrids. I. Isolation and application of density-inhibited Balb/3T3 cells deficient in hypoxanthine phosphoribosyl transferase and resistant to ouabain. *Somat. Cell Genet.* **2,** 215–233.

Littlefield, J. W. (1964) Selection of hybrid from matings of fibroblasts *in vitro* and their presumed recombinants. *Science* **145,** 709–710.

Pontecorvo, G. (1976) Production of indefinitely multiplying mammalian somatic cell hybrids by polyethylene glycol (PEG) treatment. *Somat. Cell Genet.* **1,** 397–400.

Sellem, C. H., Cassio, D., and Weiss, M. C. (1981) No extinction of tyrosine aminotransferase inducibility in rat hepatoma–human fibroblast hybrids containing the human X chromosome. *Cytogenet. Cell Genet.* **30,** 47–49.

Sorieul, S., and Ephrussi, B. (1961) Karyological demonstration of hybridization of mammalian cells *in vitro*. *Nature (London)* **190,** 653–654.

Worton, R. G., and Duff, C. (1979) Karyotyping. *In "Methods in Enzymology,"* (W. B. Jakoby, and I. H. Paston, eds.), Vol. 58, pp. 322–344. Academic Press, Orlando, FL.

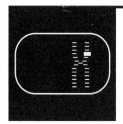

Microcell-Mediated Chromosome Transfer: Selective Transfer and Retention of Single Human Chromosomes into Recipient Cells of Choice

Michael J. Anderson and Eric J. Stanbridge

I. Introduction

Evidence for tumor suppression and its genetic basis emanated primarily from somatic cell fusion experiments (Harris *et al.*, 1969; Stanbridge, 1976). These studies involved fusion of normal cells with cancer cells resulting in nontumorigenic hybrids, and have led to the notion that normal cells harbor the genetic information necessary to suppress the malignant phenotype of neoplastic cells. In reducing the complexity associated with whole genome transfer, and thereby providing a genetically more focused approach, single chromosome transfer (Fig. 1) was subsequently developed as a refinement of this technique (Fournier and Ruddle, 1977; Saxon *et al.*, 1985). By "tagging" the relevant chromosome with a dominant selectable marker (i.e., with the bacterial *neo* or *gpt* gene), one can selectively transfer, and retain, single human chromosomes into recipient cells of choice. Since its discovery, the microcell transfer technique has been carried out with a number of different human tumor types to correlate tumor suppression with a particular chromosome (Saxon *et al.*, 1985; Oshimura *et al.*, 1990; Bader *et al.*, 1991; Tanaka *et al.*, 1991; Goyette *et al.*, 1992).

II. Materials and Instrumentation

Tissue culture flasks (25 cm², Cat. No. 25100; 75 cm², Cat. No. 25110-75), dishes (100 mm, Cat. No. 25070-100), and conical tubes (50 ml, Cat. No. 25330-50) were obtained from Corning. Nunclon 25-cm² flasks (Cat. No. T-3008-2) were purchased from Intermountain Scientific, and disposable syringes (30 ml, Cat. No. 14-823-20) from Fisher. Nucleopore polycarbonate filters (8 μm, Cat. No. 110614; 5 μm, Cat. No. 110613; 3 μm, Cat. No. 110612) were obtained from Costar. Colcemid (Cat. No. 234109) was purchased from Calbiochem, cytochalasin B (Cat. No. 85,777-7) from Aldrich, phytohemagglutinin-P (PHA-P, Cat. No. 3110-56-4) from Difco Laboratories, geneticin (G418 sulfate, Cat. No. 860-1811IJ) and fetal bovine serum (FCS, Cat. No. 16000-028) from Gibco-BRL, Dulbecco's modified Eagle's medium (DMEM, Cat. No. 04-550Q) from Whittaker, and trypsin/EDTA (Cat. No. 9340) from Irvine Scientific. Penicillin (Cat. No. P-3032), streptomycin sulfate (Cat. No. S-9137), amphotericin B (Cat. No. A-2411), hypoxanthine (Cat. No. H-9636),

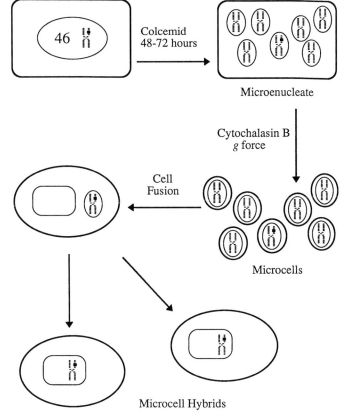

FIGURE 1 Schematic representation of the procedure for microcell-mediated transfer. The marked chromosome represents the human chromosome containing a dominant selectable gene (i.e., the bacterial *neo* gene or *gpt* gene).

thymidine (Cat. No. T-1895), DMSO (Cat. No. D-5879), methotrexate (Cat. No. M-8407), polyethylene glycol 1000 (PEG-1000, Cat. No. P-3515), sodium chloride (NaCl, Cat. No. S-3014), dibasic sodium phosphate (Na_2HPO_4, Cat. No. S-3264), and monobasic sodium phosphate (NaH_2PO_4, Cat. No. S-3139) from Sigma. Dowex AG 501-X8(D) resin (Cat. No. 143-6425) was obtained from Bio-Rad.

Swinnex disk filter holders (Cat. No. SX00 025 00) and silicone gaskets (Cat. No. SX00 025 01) were obtained from Millipore. To assemble the filter holders, a polycarbonate filter is placed on the bottom part of the filter holder so that there is no overhang. A silicone gasket is placed on top of the filter and the top part of the filter holder is screwed into place. Once assembled, the individual filter assembly is wrapped in aluminum foil and sterilized by autoclave (20 min, slow exhaust).

III. Procedures

A. CHROMOSOME TRANSFER INTO ADHERENT RECIPIENT CELLS

The procedure modified from that of Fournier and Ruddle (1977) according to Saxon *et al.* (1985).

Solutions

1. *Colcemid stock solution:* 100 μg/ml Colcemid in H_2O. To make 50 ml of this solution, add 5 mg of colcemid and 50 ml distilled water. After dissolving, filter-sterilize and store at 4°C.

2. *Cytochalasin B stock solution:* 10 mg/ml cytochalasin B in DMSO. To make 5 ml of this solution, add 50 mg of cytochalasin B and 5 ml DMSO. After dissolving, aliquot 1.0-ml portions and store at $-20°C$.

3. *Phytohemagglutinin-P (PHA-P) stock solution:* 10 mg/ml PHA-P in H_2O. To make 5 ml of this solution, add 50 mg of PHA-P and 5 ml distilled water. After dissolving, filter-sterilize and store at 4°C.

4. *Phosphate-buffered saline (PBS) solution:* 145 mM NaCl, 26 mM NaH_2PO_4, and 40 mM Na_2HPO_4. To make 1 liter of this solution, add 8.47 g of NaCl, 3.12 g of NaH_2PO_4, and 5.68 g of Na_2HPO_4. After dissolving, complete to 1 liter with distilled water and adjust to pH 7.2. Autoclave-sterilize and store at room temperature.

5. *Geneticin (G418) stock solution:* 40 mg/ml G418 sulfate in unsupplemented DMEM. To make 125 ml of this solution, add 5 g G418 sulfate and 125 ml DMEM. After dissolving, filter-sterilize and store at 4°C.

6. *HAT solution:* 100 μM hypoxanthine, 40 μM methotrexate, and 1.6 mM thymidine in DMEM. To make 1 liter of this solution, add 13.61 mg hypoxanthine, 20.34 mg methotrexate, and 387.52 mg thymidine. After dissolving complete to 1 liter with DMEM medium and filter-sterilize. Store at 4°C.

7. *Polyethylene glycol (PEG) solution:* To make "fusion-grade detoxified" polyethylene glycol, heat 1 kg PEG-1000 to 43°C in a water bath until melted. Once melted, pour 500 ml into an 800-ml beaker and adjust the pH to pH 7.4. Add 20 g Dowex AG 501-X8(D) resin and incubate for 4 hr in a 37°C water bath, mixing periodically. Slowly filter the PEG–resin slurry through 20 g of unexposed resin. Dilute "detoxified" PEG-1000 to 48% (v/v) with DMEM and aliquot into 10-ml portions. Store at $-20°C$.

Steps

To obtain the largest yield of microcells from a particular monochromosome donor cell line, it is best to determine the optimum Colcemid concentration and incubation time for that cell line. Cells should be cultured on coverslips and DAPI-stained at different times and Colcemid concentrations to establish optimum conditions for micronucleation. In general, rodent–human monochromosome hybrids should be exposed to 40 ng/ml Colcemid for 48 hr.

1. Trypsinize a confluent 75-cm² tissue culture flask containing the monochromosome donor cell line to be micronucleated. Seed half of the cells into six 25-cm² Nunclon flasks.

2. When the cells become approximately 70–90% confluent, aspirate off the medium and add 6 ml DMEM/10% FCS (supplemented with 100 IU/ml penicillin, 0.1 mg/ml streptomycin, and 0.05 μg/ml amphotericin B) containing 40 ng/ml Colcemid to each flask. Incubate the cells approximately 48 hr at 37°C in 5% CO_2.

3. The Colcemid treatment generally kills 25–35% of the cells, which float off. Aspirate off the Colcemid-containing medium and fill the flasks to the neck with unsupplemented DMEM containing 10 μg/ml cytochalasin B solution. Securely fasten the flask lids.

4. Fill each well of a Beckman JA-14 fixed-angle rotor with 100 ml of water (cushion). Place the six Nunclon flasks firmly into the individual rotor wells, with

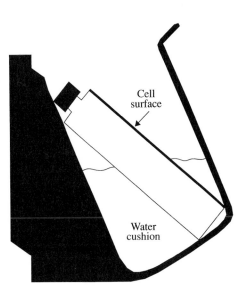

FIGURE 2 Diagram of a Beckman JA-14 rotor well containing a Nunclon flask with the monochromosome donor cells to be enucleated.

the cell surface pointed outward and the flask tilted so that the bottom is positioned at the outside corner (Fig. 2).

5. Enucleate by centrifuging the flasks at 14,000 rpm (in a Beckman J2-21 centrifuge) for 75 min at 34°C.

6. Following centrifugation, remove each flask and wipe the water away with an ethanol-soaked towel. Individually check the flasks for water leakage by examining the necks of the flasks for a clear discoloration (signifying the presence of water). Flasks that exhibit signs of leakage are routinely discarded.

7. Most of the microcells will pellet at the bottom corner of each flask. Carefully pour off all but 2–4 ml of the DMEM/cytochalasin B solution, taking care not to disrupt the pellet. The DMEM/cytochalasin B solution should be filtered and reused in future experiments. Using a 2-ml disposable pipette, resuspend each of the microcell pellets.

8. Assemble the filter assembly as shown in Fig. 3.

9. Transfer the resuspended microcells from each of the Nunclon flasks to the 30-ml syringe (Fig. 3). When all of the microcells have been pooled in the syringe, use the plunger to slowly filter the resuspended microcells through the polycarbonate filter series. All large microcells (greater than 3 μm in diameter), contaminating whole cells, and karyoplasts should be eliminated.

10. Pour the filtrate into a sterile 50-ml conical tube and pellet the microcells by centrifuging for 10 min at 3200 rpm. Aspirate off the supernatant and resuspend the microcell pellet in 2.5 ml unsupplemented DMEM containing 50 μg/ml PHA-P.

11. The day prior to fusion, seed the recipient cell line into two 25-cm^2 tissue culture flasks (experimental and negative control). The flasks should be 80–90% confluent on the day of the fusion.

12. Aspirate off the medium from the two flasks containing the recipient cell line. Add 2 ml of the microcell suspension to one of the flasks and allow 20–30 min (at room temperature) for the microcells to attach to the recipient cells. Add 2 ml of unsupplemented DMEM containing 50 μg/ml PHA-P to the second flask (this serves as a negative control for selection). Add the remaining

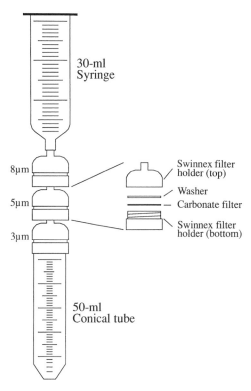

30-ml
Syringe

8μm

Swinnex filter
holder (top)

5μm

Washer
Carbonate filter

3μm

Swinnex filter
holder (bottom)

50-ml
Conical tube

FIGURE 3 Schematic representation of the filter assembly. Once the Swinnex filter holders and the 30-ml syringe are stacked firmly on top of each other, they are placed on top of a 50-ml conical tube and taped into place.

0.5 ml of microcell suspension to a 25-cm^2 flask containing 5 ml DMEM/10% FCS (this latter flask serves as a control for whole-cell "breakthrough" during filtration).

13. Once the microcells have attached to the recipient cells, aspirate off the excess PHA-P and add 2 ml PEG-1000 solution. Allow the PEG-1000 to remain for exactly 60 sec and then rapidly rinse the cells with 5 ml PBS. Repeat washing twice more. Add 6 ml DMEM/10% FCS and incubate overnight at 37°C in 5% CO$_2$. Repeat this step with the negative control flask.

14. Trypsinize the cells from the experimental and negative control flasks on the following day, seed into 100-mm dishes, and feed with DMEM/10% FCS. Twenty-four to forty-eight hrs later aspirate the medium off and replace it with selective medium (G418, HAT, or hygromycin, depending on which selectable marker was used to "tag" the transferred chromosome).

15. Refeed cells every 3–4 days until clones appear, which usually requires 14–21 days.

IV. Comments

By following the procedure described in this article it should be possible to generate a representative number of microcell hybrids using different transferred chromosomes and a variety of recipient cells.

V. Pitfalls

1. Faster growing monochromosome donor cell lines may have a tendency to shear from the 25-cm^2 Nunclon flasks during centrifugation, possibly resulting in a greater degree of breakthrough. This can be prevented by applying the Colcemid solution to the donor cells when they are less confluent.

2. If too few microcell hybrids are generated by the standard protocol, a greater number of microcells can be applied to the recipient cells (by simply harvesting more 25-cm² Nunclon flasks containing the monochromosome donor cell line). The authors have had the greatest success by pooling twelve 25-cm² Nunclon flasks.

3. If "breakthrough" does not represent a serious problem, substitution of a 5-µm filter for the 3-µm filter may increase overall microcell hybrid yields.

4. If "breakthrough" represents a serious and continuous problem, whether using the 8–5–3 µm or 8–5–5 µm filter series, the microcells collected following the initial filtration can be passed through a single 5-µm filter. Although this further filtration step does not generally affect overall yields, it may be helpful in eliminating contaminating whole cells.

5. The authors have observed that plating the recipient cells several hours prior to fusion, instead of the previous day, works equally well and may actually be preferred for certain cell lines.

6. Although failure to generate any microcell hybrids may be due to several reasons related to fusion, a number of reports (Bader *et al.*, 1991; Goyette *et al.*, 1992) have demonstrated that transfer of the relevant chromosome is incompatible with continued proliferation of the recipient cells *in vitro*. Therefore, to discriminate between chromosome incompatibility and fusion-related problems, a so-called "irrelevant" chromosome(s) should be transferred.

7. Lengthy exposure to PEG-1000 (greater than 60 sec) can result in the fusion of two recipient cells as well as the microcell containing the selectable human chromosome (Goyette *et al.*, 1992; Anderson *et al.*, 1994). Appearance of a large percentage of "tetraploid" microcell hybrids may be an indication that the fusion time is too long. Shortening the exposure time to PEG may solve this problem.

REFERENCES

Anderson, M. J., Casey, G., Fasching, C. L., and Stanbridge, E. J. (1994) Evidence that wild-type TP53, and not genes on either chromosome I or II, controls the tumorigenic phenotype of the human fibrosarcoma HT1080. *Genes, Chromosomes, Cancer* 9, 266–281.

Bader, S. A., Fasching, C., Brodeur, G. M., and Stanbridge, E. J. (1991) Dissociation of suppression of tumorigenicity and differentiation *in vitro* effected by transfer of single human chromosomes into human neuroblastoma cells. *Cell Growth Diff.* 2, 245–255.

Fournier, R. E. K., and Ruddle, F. H. (1977) Microcell-mediated transfer of murine chromosomes into mouse, Chinese hamster, and human somatic cells. *Proc. Natl. Acad. Sci. USA* 74, 319–323.

Goyette, M. C., Cho, K., Fasching, C. L., Levy, D. B., Kinzler, K. W., Paraskeva, C., Vogelstein, B., and Stanbridge, E. J. (1992) Progression of colorectal cancer is associated with multiple tumor suppressor gene defects but inhibition of tumorigenicity is accomplished by correction of any single defect via chromosome transfer. *Mol. Cell. Biol.* 12, 1387–1395.

Harris, H., Miller, O. J., Klein, G., Worst, P., and Tachibana, T. (1969) Suppression of malignancy by cell fusion. *Nature (London)* 223, 363–368.

Oshimura, M., Kugoh, H., Koi, M., Shimizu, M., Yamada, H., Satoh, H., and Barrett, J. C. (1990) Transfer of a normal human chromosome 11 suppresses tumorigenicity of some but not all tumor cell lines. *J. Cell. Biochem.* 42, 135–142.

Saxon, P. J., Srivatsan, E. S., Leipzig, G. V., Sameshima, J. H., and Stanbridge, E. J. (1985)

Selective transfer of individual human chromosomes to recipient cells. *Mol. Cell. Biol.* **5,** 140–146.

Stanbridge, E. J. (1976) Suppression of malignancy in human cells. *Nature (London)* **260,** 17–20.

Tanaka, K., Oshimura, M., Kikuchi, R., Seki, M., Hayashi, T., and Miyaki, M. (1991) Suppression of tumorigenicity in human colon carcinoma cells by introduction of normal chromosome 5 or 18. *Nature (London)* **349,** 340–342.

Microcell Transfer of Chromosomes from Mitotic Cells

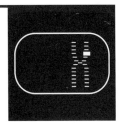

Elton Stubblefield and Mark Pershouse

I. Introduction

Microcell transfer refers to the ability to move an intact chromosome of interest from one cell line to another (see also article by Michael J. Anderson and Eric J. Stanbridge). This technique has been instrumental in several diverse scientific investigations. Key among these is the use of microcell transfer to produce hybrid cells containing a single human chromosome. The ability to produce such hybrids has made a profound impact on the human genome mapping effort and, more recently, has allowed the functional mapping of tumor suppressor genes (Stanbridge, 1990).

The application of the microcell transfer method has, since its inception, relied on the ability to induce micronucleation in a donor cell line (Ege and Ringertz, 1974). Although this is straighforward in most lines, sufficient micronucleate cells can be very difficult to achieve in some human cell lines or primary cultures, limiting the usefulness of this technique. The method described here provides an alternative in such cases, by using mitotic cells, rather than micronucleate cells as a starting material; however, mitotic cells do not attach to a substrate, so this approach depends on an enucleation procedure developed for unattached cells (Sanford and Stubblefield, 1987; Stubblefield and Pershouse, 1992).

The use of mitotic cells provides two distinct advantages. First, this technique can be applied to lines or cultures that micronucleate poorly. Additionally, because all microcells produced from mitotic cells are theoretically in early G_1 phase, fragmentation of the transferred chromosome can be avoided or can be enhanced by changing the cell cycle phase of the recipient culture to avoid the induction of prematurely condensed chromatin (PCC) or to enhance this phenomenon.

II. Instrumentation and Materials

Percoll (Cat. No. 17-0891-01) is obtained from Pharmacia Biotech Inc. Cytochalasin B (Cat. No. C-6762), and Hanks' balanced salt solution (Cat. No. H-4641) are obtained from Sigma Chemical Company. Colcemid (Cat. No. 234109) is obtained from Calbiochem Corporation. Giemsa stain (Cat. No. SG28-100) is obtained from Fisher Scientific. Phytohemagglutinin-P (Cat. No. 3110-57-3) is obtained from Difco Laboratories. Polyethylene glycol 1500 (PEG), 50% solution (Cat. No. 783641), and Hepes (Cat. No. 242608) are obtained from Boehringer–Mannheim. Oak Ridge centrifuge tubes (50 ml, Cat. No. 321-307) and NaCl (Cat. No. 832-008) are obtained from Curtin Matheson Scientific, Inc. Gravity filter holders (47 mm in diameter, Cat. No. 420400), 3-μm polycarbonate filters (47 mm in diameter, Cat. No. 111112), and 5-μm polycarbonate filters (47 mm in diameter, Cat. No. 111113) are obtained from Costar Nuclepore. Polycarbonate filters of 90-mm diameter and 3-μm pore size (Cat. No. 15565) are obtained from Poretics Corp. The stirred filter chamber for 90-mm filters was obtained from Costar Nuclepore, but is no longer available. It can be replaced by a 90-mm-diameter stirred cell (Cat. No. UHP90 TF #345400) from Micro Filtration Systems.

Microcell gradients are centrifuged in a Sorvall RC-2B centrifuge (Cat. No. RC-2B) using an SS-34 fixed-angle rotor (Cat. No. SC-8396) from DuPont, Sorvall. Equivalent equipment can be used.

III. Procedure

Solutions

1. *1 M Hepes buffer pH 7.2:* Dissolve 139.6 g of Hepes powder in 400 ml of water. Adjust the pH to 7.2 with 10 N NaOH. Bring to 500 ml with water. Filter-sterilize and store at 4°C.

2. *3 M NaCl:* Dissolve 87.7 g of NaCl in 500 ml of deionized water, filter-sterilize, and store at 4°C.

3. *Colcemid stock (100 μg/ml):* Dissolve 2 mg of Colcemid powder in 20 ml of culture medium without serum, filter-sterilize, and store in 2 ml aliquots at −20°C.

4. *PHA-P stock (10 mg/ml):* Reconstitute powdered PHA-P (50 mg) in 5 ml of sterile distilled water, divide into 100-μl aliquots, and store at −135°C.

5. *Cytochalasin B stock (2 mg/ml):* Dissolve powdered cytochalasin B (25 mg) in 12.5 ml of DMSO, divide into 0.8-ml aliquots, and store at −20°C.

6. *Hanks' balanced salt solution (1×):* Add 10 ml of Hanks' balanced salt solution (10×) to 90 ml of deionized water and adjust the pH to 7.2. After filter sterilization this solution is stored at 4°C.

Steps

1. Add Colcemid (0.1 μg/ml final concentration, 1:1000 dilution of stock) to an exponentially growing donor cell line.

2. After an optimal mitotic index is reached (4–12 hr), shake off loosely attached mitotic cells with a sharp slap to the side of the tissue culture flask(s).

3. Pellet mitotic cells by centrifugation at 500 g for 4 min.

4. Resuspend mitotic cells in the microcell gradient mixture. Use two (42 ml) gradients for up to 20 tissue culture flasks (75-cm² growing area). *To make 42 ml of microcell gradient mixture,* combine 19.6 ml culture medium with 5–10% serum, 20.0 ml Percoll, 1.0 ml 3 M NaCl, 1.0 ml 1 M Hepes buffer, pH 7.2, 0.4 ml cytochalasin B (2 mg/ml stock), and 0.04 ml Colcemid (100 μg/ml stock). Filter through a 0.45-μm filter to sterilize before adding the mitotic cells.

5. Centrifuge the gradients at 43,500 g for 70 min at 37°C.

6. Remove the top 5 ml of gradient in each tube and discard.

7. Remove the remaining gradient material with the exception of the most dense 5 ml near the bottom, and dilute 1:4 with culture medium without serum.

8. Gravity filter the gradient mixture through a 3-μm-pore-size filter.

9. Collect the filtrate and centrifuge for 15 min at 500 g.

10. Resuspend microcells in 2 ml of Hanks' balanced salt solution with PHA-P (Mercer and Schlegel, 1979). *To make Hanks' with PHA-P,* add 1.95 ml Hanks' balanced salt solution (1×) to 0.05 ml PHA-P (10 mg/ml stock).

11. Add the microcell–PHA mixture to a 50% confluent culture of recipient cells. (Cells should be rinsed free of any serum and drained just prior to microcell addition.)

12. Incubate the recipient cells and microcells for 20 min at 37°C in a 5% CO_2, humidified incubator.

13. Remove unattached microcells by aspiration.

14. Add 1 ml of PEG 1500 and spread across the recipient cells by tilting the flask.

15. After 45 sec (at 23°C) has elapsed, tilt the flask to pool the PEG in one corner.

16. After 60 sec has elapsed, immediately remove the PEG by aspiration. Quickly add 40 ml of culture medium with no serum to the flask, taking care not to pour or pipette across the monolayer of recipient cells.

17. Gently tilt the flask to allow the medium to rinse the fused cell layer.

18. Remove the first wash of medium and replace with a fresh 20 ml of culture medium.

19. Repeat steps 17 and 18 an additional two times.

20. Remove the last wash and replace with optimal medium with serum and an appropriate antibiotic.

21. Allow at least 24 hr for fusion to be complete and apply selective medium (HAT, G418, hygromycin, etc.).

IV. Comments

At step 10 in the procedure, two important assays must be done. One aliquot of the microcell suspension (0.5 ml) should be diluted into 10 ml of growth medium with serum and put into a culture flask under conditions in which the donor cells will clone. If the donor cells will only grow into clones on a feeder layer, then this should be done. You want to be sure that no whole cells have passed through the filter. If whole cells have contaminated the preparation, you can be sure that karyoplasts from interphase cells are present also. A drop of the concentrated microcell suspension also can be examined on a microscope slide as a temporary mount under a coverslip. Any gross contamination of the uniformly small microcell particles by the much larger whole cells or karyoplasts should be obvious under phase-contrast microscopy.

For some experiments, you will want to calculate the microcell yield and concentration in the final preparation. The undiluted microcell suspension can be counted by phase-contrast microscopy on a standard hemocytometer. In large experiments, it may be necessary to dilute the sample before counting. Depending on the donor cells used, some of the particles may not contain micronuclei, so in initial experiments, one should make a cytospin preparation of the microcell suspension and stain the air-dried sample with Giemsa or Wright's stain. Cytoplast fragments do not interfere with chromosome transfer, but they may confuse a true quantitation of the microcell concentration. More precise quantitation probably will require fluorescent stains and a flow cytometer.

If all has gone well, you have inserted donor chromosomes into some of the recipient cells. The task remaining is to find and isolate those cells that contain the specific chromosome(s) you are studying. This is usually done by inserting a selectable marker gene, such as *neo*, into the specific donor chromosome of choice, using DNA transfection. The neomycin resistance gene, *neo*, confers on the cells the ability to survive in medium containing the drug G418. Thus, any cell that gained the chromosome containing this marker gene will grow into a clone; all the other cells will die. Standard cytological procedures can be used to confirm that the proper donor chromosome is present in the surviving cells, if the chromosomes differ from those of the recipient, as in a human donor to mouse recipient. Proving that a human chromosome has been inserted into a human cell is much more difficult, but it can be done using analysis of the gain of restriction fragment length polymorphism (RFLP) or microsatellite repeat polymorphism markers (Pershouse *et al.*, 1993).

In heterospecific transfers, one can directly analyze the transfer frequency using cytogenetic analysis and species-specific chromosomal probes. Two days after microcell transfer, you can directly examine Colcemid-blocked metaphase chromosomes and find donor chromosomes in about 1% of the cells (Sanford and Stubblefield, 1989).

This methodology allows you to use any combination of cells, normal or transformed, attached or unattached, as donors and recipients in a microcell transfer experiment. The fusion step is somewhat more tedious to perform if the recipient cell does not form a monolayer, but it can be done. Such unattached cells can still be cloned in a soft agar, of course. Obviously, both cells must grow in culture, so that you may obtain mitotic cells as donors and have a growing population of recipient cells from which to select clones containing the desired chromosome.

Some of the selected clones will contain one or two whole chromosomes from the donor cells. Because the microcell was made from a metaphase chromosome composed of two chromatids, one would expect each transfer to result in two identical donor chromosomes in the recipient cell. Usually, however, only one is seen, so we suspect that the second copy is lost as the selected clone evolves. Selection pressure requires only one chromosome to be retained.

The transferred chromosome(s) is by definition in the G_1 phase of the cell cycle. If it is inserted into a cell in the S or G_2 phase of the cell cycle, it should undergo premature chromosome condensation when the recipient cell enters mitosis (Johnson and Rao, 1970). This will result in fragmentation, so that only small parts of the chromosome will be found in the selected clone. In some experiments, this may be a useful result, if you are seeking to localize a marker gene. We think fragmentation may be regulated by using synchronized G_1 cells as recipients when an intact donor chromosome is preferred and asynchronous recipient cells when chromosome fragments are desired. Of course, this must be tested for each combination of donor and recipient cells.

V. Pitfalls

1. *Step 1:* Colcemid is toxic to some lymphocytic cell lines. Velban (0.1 μg/ml) can be used instead in such cases.

2. *Step 2:* Cells in mitosis can be removed preferentially by the shake-off method or by a brief trypsin treatment (Stubblefield, 1968). The cell population need not all be in mitosis; the procedure can be used if 10% or more of the cells are in mitosis.

3. *Step 5:* We use a Sorvall RC-2B centrifuge. The tubes are placed in the SS-34 Sorvall rotor without adapters. We add 0.5 ml of water into the space around each tube to cushion the tube and prevent deformation of the tube during centrifugation. The temperature control is adjusted to 37°C, and the centrifuge is brought up to a speed of 19,000 rpm. Within the first 5 min the rotor warms to

37°C by friction with the air. In a centrifuge with a vacuum chamber, the rotor must be warmed to the desired temperature before centrifugation. After centrifuging for 70 min, the rotor is decelerated without using the brake. The tubes are carefully removed from the rotor to avoid stirring the gradient. Each tube contains a pellet of silica gel at the bottom and several distinct bands of cellular material that can be seen when the tube is illuminated from behind (Fig. 1). The material in the main band clumps together because it consists of cells with long fibrous strands that entangle as the gradient rotates during deceleration of the rotor (Fig. 2). Microcells do not have a predictable density and will be found throughout the gradient; karyoplasts usually form a distinct band below the main band of whole cells. In some cell lines, cytoplasts form a diffuse band near the top of the gradient.

4. *Step 8:* The filtration step separates whole cells and karyoplasts from the microcells and small cytoplasts, which pass through the 3-μm pores of the filter (McNeil and Brown, 1980). The pooled gradient material is drained through the filter tubing by gravity feed from a reservoir made from a 50-ml disposable syringe barrel mounted about 40 cm above the filter. No additional pressure can be applied, or the karyoplasts and whole cells will deform and penetrate the filter pores. This is a very critical part of the procedure, as any contaminating karyoplasts or whole cells will produce whole-cell hybrids and drug-resistant clones of donor cells, which may defeat the purpose of the experiment.

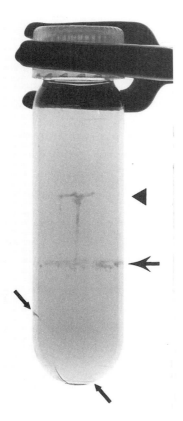

FIGURE 1   Percoll gradient centrifuged for 70 min as described in the text. The gradient is designed to provide the force necessary to separate the microcells from the donor mitotic cell. The resulting microcells are to be found throughout the gradient. The arrowhead marks the position of whole cells, tangled together by fine filaments of cytoplasm (see Fig. 2). The arrow marks the band of karyoplasts that originate from enucleation of interphase cells. The two small arrows at the bottom show the position of the silica gel pellet that forms during centrifugation of Percoll.

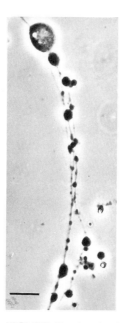

FIGURE 2 A mitotic cell removed from a gradient centrifuged for 30 min only. In the presence of cytochalasin B the cell forms strings of microcells that break free in the centrifugal field. The smallest microcells contain single mitotic chromosomes that quickly revert back to interphase. Phase contrast. Bar = 10 μm.

Purification of the microcells requires filtration through a 3-μm polycarbonate filter. We use a 90-mm-diameter filter mounted in a chamber that is stirred by a magnetic bar mounted near the filter surface. This alleviates clogging of the pores by whole cells and debris. Unstirred filters and filters of smaller diameter tend to clog before the whole sample can be filtered. We use a single sample pass through the 3-μm pores. Several unstirred filters can be used until they clog in sequence. Sequential passes through 5-μm pores, followed by a 3-μm filter in unstirred chambers, has been used successfully. The filters must be autoclaved before use.

5. *Step 9:* The filtrate containing the microcells is collected in sterile 50-ml plastic centrifuge tubes. These tubes are capped and centrifuged at 500 g for 15 min at room temperature. The microcells are fragile and do not survive centrifugation at higher gravities.

6. *Step 11:* The recipient monolayer must be prepared in advance; on the day of the experiment they should be about one-half confluent. The cells must not be packed together in a dense monolayer, but cell processes can be touching. After PEG treatment, some cell-to-cell fusion is inevitable, but most of the fusion should be between the microcells and the recipient cells.

7. *Step 12:* The monolayer can be examined briefly by phase-contrast microscopy at each stage in the process. After the microcells have settled and attached to the recipient cells, they should be evident as a scattered stippling in a low-power field of cells. Several hours after treatment with PEG, some binucleate cells can be seen. This is reassurance that the fusion process has occurred. If the recipient cells do not attach to form a monolayer, then they should be cosedimented with the microcells at each step in the procedure. This is not as efficient as using monolayer cells, but it has been done successfully. This procedure is complex, and many things can and will go wrong. One should not approach a project involving microcell transfer as a simple 2-week exercise for a graduate student. One should expect to make a number of tries (learning curve) before obtaining even limited success. With careful evaluation of the results at

each step, however, one should be able to find where the problems are and take corrective action.

REFERENCES

Ege, T., and Ringertz, N. R. (1974) Preparation of microcells by enucleation of micronucleated cells. *Exp.Cell Res.* **87,** 378–382.

Johnson, R. T., and Rao, P. N. (1970) Mammalian cell fusion: Induction of premature chromosome condensation in interphase nuclei. *Nature* **226,** 717–722.

McNeil, C. A., and Brown, R. L. (1980) Genetic manipulation by means of microcell-mediated transfer of normal human chromosomes into recipient mouse cells. *Proc. Natl. Acad. Sci. USA* **77,** 5394–5398.

Mercer, W. E., and Schlegel, R. A. (1979) Phytohemagglutinin enhancement of cell fusion reduces polyethylene glycol cytotoxicity. *Exp. Cell Res.* **120,** 417–421.

Pershouse, M. A., Stubblefield, E., Hadi, A., Killary, A. M., Yung, W. K. A., and Steck, P. A. (1993). Analysis of the functional role of chromosome 10 loss in human glioblastomas. *Cancer Res.* **53,** 5043–5050.

Sanford, J. A., and Stubblefield, E.(1987) General protocol for microcell-mediated chromosome transfer. *Somat. Cell Mol. Genet.* **13,** 279–284.

Sanford, J. A., and Stubblefield, E. (1989) Human oncogenes in mouse/human microcell hybrids. *Oncogene Res.* **1,** 195–204.

Stanbridge, E. J. (1990) Human tumor suppressor genes. *Annu. Rev. Genet.* **24,** 615–657.

Stubblefield, E. (1968) Synchronization methods for mammalian cell cultures. *In "Methods in Cell Physiology,"* (D. M. Prescott, ed.), Vol. 3, pp. 25–43. Academic Press, New York.

Stubblefield, E., and Pershouse, M. (1992) Direct formation of microcells from mitotic cells for use in chromosome transfer. *Somat. Cell Mol. Genet.* **18,** 485–491.

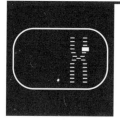

Chromosome Painting Using Degenerate Oligonucleotide-Primed Polymerase Chain Reaction-Amplified, Flow-Sorted Human Chromosomes

Nigel P. Carter

I. Introduction

Unmodified, modern flow cytometers are capable of high-resolution bivariate flow karyotype analysis such that all of the human chromosomes, with the exception of chromosomes 9–12, can be resolved and sorted. Application of simple polymerase chain reaction (PCR) amplification techniques to small numbers of sorted chromosomes enables chromosome paints to be generated rapidly without the need for the cloning of DNA libraries. Used with fluorescence *in situ* hybridization (FISH), these chromosome paints are finding an increasingly important role in cytogenetic investigations of human cells. In addition to normal human chromosomes, aberrant chromosomes can also often be resolved and sorted. Chromosome paints from the aberrant chromosomes can be hybridized to normal metaphase spreads. In this way the origin of the aberrant chromosomes can be visualized directly from the hybridization pattern on normal chromosomes, a process we have termed *reverse chromosome painting* (Carter *et al.*, 1992; Telenius *et al.*, 1992a,b).

II. Materials and Instrumentation

Spermine tetrahydrochloride (Cat. No. S-2876), spermidine trihydochloride (Cat. No. S-2501), Hoechst 33258 (Cat. No. B-2883), chromomycin A3 (Cat. No. C-2659), gentian violet (Cat. No. 3886), 4,6-diamidino-2-phenylindole (DAPI, Cat. No. D-1388), propidium iodide (Cat. No. P-4170), Triton X-100 (Cat. No. X-100), Tween 20 (Cat. No. P-1379), human AB serum (Cat. No. S-7148), tris(hydroxymethyl)methylaminopropanesulfonic acid (Taps, Cat. No. T5130), polyoxyethelene ether W-1 (Cat. No. P-7516), and mineral oil (Cat. No. M-5904) are obtained from Sigma. Biotin-16-dUTP (Cat. No. 1093-070) is obtained from Boehringer-Mannheim. Deoxynucleotide triphosphates (Cat. No. 27-2035-01) are obtained from Pharmacia. Taq polymerase (Cat. No. 75210-B) is obtained from New Brunswick Sciences Biologicals. Primer 6MW (5′ CCG ACT CGA GNN NNN NAT GTG G 3′, where N = any base in any primer, i.e., complete synthesis wobble), cartridge purified, is obtained from Genosys Biotechnologies or other primer synthesis companies. Cot-1 DNA (Cat. No. 5279SA) is obtained from Gibco-BRL. RPMI-1640 medium, fetal bovine serum, L-glutamine (200 m*M*), penicillin–streptomycin

(10,000 U/ml and 10,000 μg/ml, respectively), and colcemid solution (10 μg/ml) are obtained from locally preferred sources of tissue culture reagents.

A typical requirement for high-resolution bivariate flow karyotype analysis is a dual-laser optical bench flow cytometer with provision for dual-beam operation with spatial separation of the laser beams. The two lasers should be argon ion, one capable of maintaining 250 mW in UV multiline mode (351–364 nm), the other capable of maintaining 250 mW at 457.9 nm, both in TEM 00. The analog-to-digital converters should be at least 10-bit (1024-channel resolution) and bivariate plots capable of display at a minimum of 256 $\times$ 256 resolution.

III. Procedures

A. FLOW ANALYSIS AND SORTING

The lasers should be positioned such that the chromosomes pass first through the UV beam and then through the 457.9-nm beam. The spatial separation and optical alignment of the instrument should be carried out according to the manufacturer's recommended procedures. The laser beam focusing lens should be selected, where available, to maximize the light intensity at the detection point (i.e., without lateral beam expansion). Laser powers ideally should be 250 mW or higher. UV-excited Hoechst fluorescence is collected at the first detector through a UV-blocking filter (400-nm long pass) combined with a 480-nm short-pass filter. The 457.9-nm-excited chromomycin fluorescence is collected at the second detector through a 490-nm long-pass filter. Dual-beam delay and sorting settings should be adjusted according to the instrument manufacturer's recommendations. Operate the instrument with sterile sheath fluid comprising 100 mM sodium chloride, 10 mM Tris, 1 mM EDTA, adjusted to pH 7.2 with hydrochloric acid. A nozzle orifice diameter of 50–75 μm is recommended.

B. TISSUE CULTURE AND CHROMOSOME PREPARATION

Solutions

1. *Culture medium:* To 500 ml of RPMI-1640 medium add 100 ml of fetal bovine serum, 5 ml of 200 mM L-glutamine, and 5 ml of penicillin–streptomycin solution.

2. *Polyamine buffer and stain stock solutions:*

   a. Dissolve 1.18 g of Tris and 832 mg of EDTA in sterile distilled water, adjust pH to 8.0, and bring total volume to 100 ml.

   b. Dissolve 1.18 g of Tris and 190 mg of EGTA in sterile distilled water, adjust pH to 8.0, and bring total volume to 100 ml.

   c. Dissolve 5.96 g of potassium chloride in sterile distilled water and bring total volume to 100 ml.

   d. Dissolve 1.17 g of sodium chloride in sterile distilled water and bring total volume to 100 ml.

Solutions and should be sterile-filtered and stored at 4–10°C for up to 1 month.

   e. Dissolve 1.39 g of spermine in sterile distilled water and bring total volume to 10 ml. Aliquot and store at −20°C.

f. Dissolve 2.55 g of spermidine in sterile distilled water and bring total volume to 10 ml. Aliquot and store at $-20°C$.

g. Dissolve 3.15 g of sodium sulfite in sterile distilled water and bring total volume to 100 ml. Do not store.

h. Dissolve 2.94 g of trisodium citrate in sterile distilled water and bring total volume to 100 ml. Do not store.

i. Dissolve 10 mg of Hoechst 33258 in sterile distilled water and bring total volume to 10 ml. Sterile-filter and store in the dark at $4-10°C$.

j. Dissolve 5 mg of chromomycin A3 in ethanol and bring total volume to 2.5 ml. Aliquot and store at $-20°C$.

k. Add 1 ml of glacial acetic acid and 10 mg of gentian violet to sterile distilled water and bring total volume to 100 ml (Turck's stain). Store at $4-10°C$.

Steps

1. Grow the lymphoblastoid cell line for study to confluence in 20 ml of tissue culture medium in a gassed (5% CO_2) incubator.

2. Add an additional 30 ml of medium to the flask and gently break up any cell clumps. Incubate for 24 hr.

3. Add 0.5 ml of colcemid solution and mix gently. Incubate for 5 hr.

4. Transfer the cells into a 50-ml centrifuge tube and centrifuge at 200 g for 10 min. Decant the supernatant and place the tube, inverted, on an absorbent paper towel.

5. Dilute 4.7 ml of stock 800 mM potassium chloride solution to 50 ml with sterile distilled water and filter through a sterile 0.2-μm filter. Add 10 ml to the cell pellet and resuspend gently. Incubate at room temperature for 15 min.

6. Swelling can be monitored by staining 10 μl of the cell suspension with an equal volume of Turck's stain and viewing in a hemocytometer with phase-contrast microscopy.

7. To make the polyamine buffer, dilute together 10 ml of each of the stock solutions and, 50 μl of spermine, 50 μl of spermidine, 250 μl of Triton X-100, and 100 μl of β-mercaptoethanol with sterile distilled water, adjust pH to 7.2 with hydrochloric acid, and bring to a total volume of 100 ml. Pass through a sterile 0.2-μm filter.

8. Centrifuge cell preparation at 400 g for 5 min.

9. Discard the supernatant and invert the tube on a absorbent paper towel for a few seconds. Add 3 ml of the polyamine buffer and incubate on ice for 10 min.

10. Vortex for 10 sec at a speed that produces a swirling film of suspension on the wall of the tube.

11. Remove 10 μl of suspension onto a microscope slide and add 1 μl of Hoechst stain. Using fluorescence microscopy, check that the majority of chromosomes are free in solution and not clumped. If clumps are apparent, vortex for further periods of 5 sec until few clumps are present. Overvortexing will increase the number of broken chromosomes.

12. Centrifuge 850 μl of chromosome suspension at 100 g for 1 min. Transfer 740 μl of the supernatant to a tube suitable for use on the flow cytometer, add 20 μl of chromomycin solution, and mix immediately.

13. Add 20 μl of 100 mM magnesium sulfate. Dilute 5 μl of Hoechst stain with 45 μl of sterile distilled water and add 20 μl to the chromosome suspension. Mix well. Incubate for at least 2 hr on ice.

14. Add 100 μl of sodium citrate solution and 100 μl of sodium sulfite solution 15 min prior to analysis.

C. CHROMOSOME ANALYSIS AND SORTING

1. Data Acquisition

Run the stained chromosome preparation on the flow cytometer and acquire a bivariate plot of Hoechst fluorescence (y axis) versus chromomycin fluorescence (x axis) for a total of 50,000 events. Sample flow rate should be adjusted to about 300 chromosomes per second for best resolution, but sorting is possible at speeds of up to 2000 per second if separation of the desired peak can be maintained.

2. Chromosome Sorting

From the bivariate flow karyotype, identify the peak representing the chromosome from which a paint is required and set appropriate sorting gates. Sort 300–500 chromosomes directly into sterile 500-μl PCR tubes containing 33 μl of sterile distilled water.

D. DEGENERATE OLIGONUCLEOTIDE-PRIMED (DOP) PCR AMPLIFICATION AND LABELING

PCR Reagents

1. *Deoxynucleotide triphosphates (dNTPs):* Dilute dNTPs to 10 mM with 10 mM Tris buffer, pH 7.2. Mix equal volumes of dATP, dGTP, dCTP, and dTTP, aliquot, and store at $-20°$C. Mix 2 vol each of dATP, dGTP, and dCTP with 1 vol of dTTP (a 2:2:2:1 mix), aliquot, and store at $-20°$C.

2. *PCR buffer:* Dissolve 3.04 g of Taps, 1.86 g KCl, 203.3 mg MgCl$_2$, and 15.4 mg dithiothreitol in sterile distilled water, adjust pH to 9.3 with sodium hydroxide, and bring volume to 50 ml. Aliquot and store at $-20°$C.

3. *Primers:* Dissolve primer in sterile distilled water to give a concentration of 20 μM, aliquot, and store at $-20°$C.

4. *W-1 detergent:* Dissolve 100 μl of W-1 detergent in 10 ml of sterile distilled water, aliquot, and store at $-20°$C.

Steps

Primary DOP-PCR

1. Using a set of pipettes reserved for PCR use only, add to the tube containing the sorted chromosomes 5 μl of PCR buffer, 5 μl of primers, 4 μl of the equal mixture of dNTPs, 2.5 μl of W-1 detergent, and 0.5 μl of Taq polymerase. Vortex and spin in a microfuge briefly.

2. Add one drop of mineral oil to each tube and microfuge briefly.

3. Process in a thermal cycler using the following protocol

94°C for 9 min

9 cycles of
   94°C for 1 min
   30°C for 1.5 min
   ramp at 0.23°/sec to 72°C for 3 min
30 cycles of
   94°C for 1 min
   62°C for 1 min
   72°C for 1 min
72°C for 9 min

4. Analyze the PCR product by running 5–10 μl using 1% agarose gel electrophoresis. A smear of product from 200–2000 bp should be visible. Assess DNA concentration from the gel or using DNA fluorometry (typical yields are 50–120 ng/μl).

Secondary DOP-PCR (Labeling)

1. Using a set of pipettes reserved for PCR use only, add to a sterile 500 μl PCR tube a volume of sterile distilled water equivalent to 29.5 μl minus the volume of 150 ng of primary PCR product.

2. Add 5 μl of PCR buffer, 5 μl of primers, 3.5 μl of the 2:2:2:1 mixture of dNTPs, 5 μl of biotin-16-dUTP, 2.5 μl of W-1 detergent, and 0.5 μl of Taq polymerase. Using a different set of pipettes and at a different laboratory bench, add 150 ng of primary DOP-PCR product. Vortex and spin in a microfuge briefly.

3. Add one drop of mineral oil and microfuge briefly.

4. Process in a thermal cycler using the following protocol

94°C for 4 min
25 cycles of
   94°C for 1 min
   62°C for 1 min
   72°C for 1 min
72°C for 9 min

5. Analyze the PCR product by running 5–10 μl using 1% agarose gel electrophoresis. A smear of product from 200–2000 bp should be visible. Assess DNA concentration from the gel or using DNA fluorometry (typical yields are 50–120 ng/μl).

E. FLUORESCENCE IN SITU HYBRIDIZATION

Reagents

1. *20X SSC:* Dissolve 175.3 g of sodium chloride and 88.2 g of sodium citrate in sterile distilled water, adjust pH to 7.4 with sodium hydroxide, and bring volume to 1 liter.

2. *Washing buffer 4XT:* Add 500 μl of Tween 20 to 200 ml of 20X SSC and bring volume to 1 liter. Mix well until the Tween 20 has dissolved.

3. *Hybridization buffer:* Mix 5 ml of deionized formamide, 2 ml of 10% dextran sulfate, 1 ml of 20X SSC, and 800 μl of 0.5 M sodium phosphate, pH 7.0, and bring volume to 10 ml with sterile distilled water. Store at −20°C and warm to room temperature before use.

Steps

Chromosome Spreads

1. Prepare metaphase spreads from methanol/acetic acid (3/1 v/v) fixed cell preparations prepared using standard cytogenetic techniques, ideally using a methotrexate block and bromodeoxyuridine release method (see Rooney and Czepulkowski, 1992).

2. Further fix slides in methanol/acetic acid (3/1 v/v) for 1 hr. Air-dry.

3. Dehydrate through an ethanol series (70, 70, 90, 90, 100%) and air-dry.

4. Fix in acetone for 10 min and air-dry.

5. Before use, age fresh slides by incubation in a oven set at 42°C overnight. Alternatively, slides can be stored desiccated at room temperature and used after 1 week.

In Situ *Hybridization*

1. Add 50 ng of labeled PCR product and 2 μg of Cot-1 DNA to hybridization buffer to give a total volume of 15 μl and mix well.

2. Denature by incubating in a water bath at 65°C for 10 min. Transfer immediately to a water bath set at 37°C and incubate for 30 min.

3. Meanwhile, denature metaphase spreads by incubation for exactly 2 min in 70% formamide diluted in 2X SSC preheated in a water bath to 65°C. Transfer immediately to ice-cold 70% ethanol.

4. Dehydrate through an ethanol series (70, 90, 90, 100%) and air-dry.

5. Pipette the probe/hybridization buffer onto the metaphase spread and cover with a 22 × 32-mm clean glass coverslip. Seal the edges of the coverslip with rubber cement and incubate overnight in an oven set at 42°C.

6. Remove the rubber cement and soak off the coverslips in 2X SSC.

7. Incubate slides at 42°C for 5 min in each of two changes of 50% formamide diluted in 1X SSC followed by two changes of 2X SSC.

8. Incubate for 2 min in 4XT at room temperature.

9. Dilute 2 μl of avidin–FITC in 498 μl of 4XT/15% human AB serum. Dilute 4 μl of FITC-conjugated antiavidin in 496 μl of 4XT/15% human AB serum. Incubate for 10 min at room temperature and spin in a microfuge for 10 min.

10. Mix equal volumes of the two supernatants and incubate at room temperature for 10 min.

11. Pipette 100 μl of the mixed supernatants onto the slide and cover with a 22 × 32-mm piece of Nesco film. Incubate at room temperature for 30 min in a humidified box.

12. Wash slides in three changes of 4XT for 2 min each, dehydrate through an ethanol series (70, 70, 90, 90, 100%) and air-dry.

13. Pipette 10 μl of antifade mountant containing 3 μg/ml of DAPI plus 0.6 μg/ml of propidium iodide onto the spread, cover with a 22 × 32-mm glass coverslip, and seal with nail varnish.

14. View using an epifluorescence microscope with standard or dual filter blocks for FITC and propidium iodide as recommended by the microscope manufacturer.

IV. Comments

With the protocols described in this article, chromosome paints for use with FISH can be rapidly made from normal chromosomes for forward chromosome painting and from abnormal chromosomes for reverse chromosome painting. A typical investigation is illustrated in Color Plates 26–28.

As with all FISH experiments, the quality of the metaphase spreads, the concentration and incubation time of the competitor Cot-1 DNA, and the stringency of the posthybridization washes all affect the specificity and accuracy of the hybridization signals. While the protocols described in this article will in the majority of cases produce clear hybridization signals, adjustment of these three parameters may be required on occasion.

Cells types other than lymphoblastoid can be used to produce chromosome preparations for sorting. For a review of cell types and isolation protocols see Gray (1989).

Haptens other than biotin and fluorochromes other than FITC can be used to label chromosomes by DOP-PCR. We have used successfully, for DOP-PCR labeling, digoxigenin-11-dUTP, FITC-12-dUTP, and hydroxycoumarin-6-dUTP from Boehringer-Mannheim, and FluoroRed, FluoroGreen, and FluoroBlue from Amersham International. Chromosome paints labeled with different haptens or fluorochromes can be used together in a single hybridization for simultaneous multiple chromosome identification (see Dauwerse *et al.*, 1992).

V. Pitfalls

The presence of high-molecular-weight product (>3 kb) in the DOP-PCR will produce a high level of nonspecific background signals in hybridizations. This problem is caused by a very low primer concentration, too much target DNA, or too much Taq polymerase. In such cases, the amplifications should be repeated, adjusting one or more of these parameters.

ACKNOWLEDGMENTS

The protocols described here have been developed with support from the Medical Research Council of the United Kingdom, the U.K. Human Genome Project, and the Cancer Research Campaign. In particular, I acknowledge the support of Professor M. A. Ferguson-Smith; H. Telenius, who designed the DOP-PCR primers; A. H. Pelmear-Telenius, M. T. Perryman, and M. A. Leversha, for technical support; Dr. J. R. W. Yates, for referral of the illustrative case; and the staff of the East Anglian Regional Cytogenetics Laboratory, for cytogenetic analysis of the patient.

REFERENCES

Carter, N. P., Ferguson-Smith, M. A., Perryman, M. T., Telenius, H., Pelmear, A. H., Lerversha, M. A., Glancy, M. T., Wood, S. L., Cook, K., Dyson, H. M., Ferguson-Smith, M. E., and Willatt, L. R. (1992) Reverse chromosome painting: A method for the rapid analysis of aberrant chromosomes in clinical cytogenetics. *J. Med. Genet.* **29**, 299–307.

Dauwerse, J. G., Wiegant, J., Raap, A. K., Breuning, M. H., and van Ommen, G. J. J. (1992) Multiple colors by fluorescence *in situ* hybridisation using ratio-labelled DNA probes create a molecular karyotype. *Hum. Mol. Genet.* **1**, 593–598.

Gray, J. W. (1989). "Flow Cytogenetics." Academic Press, San Diego.

Rooney, D. E., and Czepulkowski, B. H. (1992) "Human Cytogenetics, A Practical Approach." IRL Press at Oxford University Press.

Telenius, H., Carter, N. P., Bebb, C. E., Nordenskjold, M., Ponder, B. A. J., and Tunnacliffe,

A. (1992a) Degenerate oligonucleotide-primed PCR (DOP-PCR): General amplification of target DNA by a single degenerate primer. *Genomics* **13**, 718–725.

Telenius, H., Pelmear, A .H., Tunnacliffe, A., Carter, N. P., Behmel, A., Ferguson-Smith, M. A., Nordenskjold, M., Pfragner, R., and Ponder, B. A. J. (1992b) Cytogenetic analysis by chromosome painting using degenerate oligonucleotide-primed polymerase chain reaction amplified flow-sorted chromosomes. *Genes, Chromosomes and Cancer* **4**, 257–263.

Fluorescence *in Situ* Hybridization of Human and Mouse DNA Probes to Determine the Chromosomal Contents of Cell Lines and Tumors

James D. Tucker, John W. Breneman, Denise A. Lee, Marilyn J. Ramsey, and Roy R. Swiger

I. Introduction

Fluorescence *in situ* hybridization (FISH) is used on an increasingly frequent basis for basic research and for clinical diagnostic purposes. For most applications, the sensitivity and specificity of fluorescent labeling exceed those of radiolabeling. Hybridization results can now be performed quickly and with relative ease. This article describes a general approach for accomplishing FISH using chromosome-specific composite DNA probes. Applications of the method described here include the analysis of constitutional and induced chromosome translocations and the evaluation of the chromosomal contents of cell lines and tumors.

II. Materials and Instrumentation

A. MATERIALS

1. Hybridization Setup: Probe and Slide Denaturation

The humidity box is a shallow plastic box with a tight-fitting lid, lined with a few sheets of filter paper or paper towels to hold moisture, and containing glass rods or plastic caps to hold the slides above the paper.

Floaters are small rectangular pieces of Styrofoam with holes cut to size to hold microcentrifuge tubes afloat in the water bath.

Plastic coverslips can be prepared by cutting up plastic bags; the material should be free of wrinkles and thick enough so it will lay flat.

Sterile distilled water is also needed.

Coplin jars with lids (Cat. No. S7660), 22 × 22-mm² glass coverslips (Cat. No. M6045-2), 24 × 60-mm glass coverslips (Cat. No. M6045-10), permanent ink markers, (Cat. No. P1224-x), labeling tape (Cat. No. L1599-xx), and a diamond-point engraving pen (Cat. No. P1230) were obtained from Baxter. Dextran sulfate (Cat. No. D-8906), herring sperm DNA (Cat. No. D-6898), and human placental DNA (Cat. No. D-7011) were obtained from Sigma. HCl (Cat. No. 9535-02), NaOH (Cat. No. 3727-01), NaCl (Cat. No. 3624-01), and trisodium citrate (Cat. No. 3646-01) were obtained from Baker. Ethanol (200 proof) was obtained from

Quantum Chemical Corporation. Carter's brand rubber cement is available from Avery Denison. Syringes, 5 and 10 ml, are available from Becton Dickinson. Formamide (Cat. No. 47670) was obtained from Fluka. Mouse Cot 1 blocking DNA was obtained from Gibco (Cat. No. 8440SA).

2. Removal of Unbound Probe, and Detection of Bound Probe

(This list includes only those supplies that are needed in addition to those listed above.)

Pasteur pipettes (Cat. No. P5216-1) and bulbs (P5215) were obtained from Baxter. Nonidet P-40 (Cat. No. N-6507), sodium azide (Cat. No. S-2002) p-phenylenediamine dihydrochloride (Cat. No. P-1519), 4,6-diamidino-2-phenylindole (DAPI, Cat. No. D-9542), and propidium iodide (PI, Cat. No. P-4170) were obtained from Sigma. Dulbecco's phosphate-buffered saline (Cat. No. 310-4040AJ) was obtained from Gibco. $NaHCO_3$ (Cat. No. 3506-01), Na_2HPO_4 (Cat. No. 3824-01), and NaH_2PO_4 (Cat. No. 3818-01) were obtained from Baker.

Also needed are lint-free blotting paper or absorbent paper towels, distilled water, forceps, and a beaker.

B. INSTRUMENTS

The single most critical instrument needed for fluorescence *in situ* hybridization is the microscope. For best results, especially for ease of hybridization detection and analysis, the microscope should be a relatively recent model that is optimized for detection of fluorescent signals. A 100-W mercury lamp provides optimal illumination. Although many older microscopes have fluorescence capability, newer models have better optical and filter designs which substantially improve their ability to detect bound probe.

Other required items include a thermal-regulated water bath, 37°C oven or incubator, microcentrifuge, pH meter, slide-warming plate capable of maintaining a temperature of 37°C, Vortex mixer, micropipettes and tips, thermometers, graduated cylinders, and a humidity box (small plastic box for holding slides horizontal during hybridizations). If microscope slides will be stored for more than a few weeks prior to hybridization, then a source of nitrogen gas, granular desiccant, and a −20°C freezer are also necessary.

III. Procedures

A. PREPARATION OF THE MICROSCOPE SLIDES

The first critical step for successful hybridizations is preparation of the microscope slides. A full description of the various methods by which this can be accomplished is beyond the scope of this chapter, although a few specific suggestions are given in Section V. In general, most methods that yield high-quality metaphase spreads *free of cytoplasm* will produce successful hybridizations. Because cytoplasm is a physical barrier to successful DNA probe penetration, it is essential that the preparations be as free of this material as possible. Our most common method of slide preparation uses a shallow plastic tray into which several paper towels have been placed. The towels are soaked in water and the excess water is drained off. The tray is then placed over a 50°C water bath to provide humidity, and allowed to become warm. The slides are placed in the tray and gently sprayed with water to produce a fine speckled pattern of droplets. The fixed cells are then dropped from a height of 2 to

4 cm. It is *not* necessary for the cells to be dropped from a greater height; this frequently results in the loss of too much material.

B. HYBRIDIZATION SETUP: PROBE AND SLIDE DENATURATION

Solutions

1. *20× SSC (3.0 M NaCl and 0.3 M Na citrate):* Prepare by dissolving 175.3 g NaCl in 800 ml of sterile double-distilled water. Add 88.2 g of trisodium citrate and bring volume up to 1 liter. Adjust the pH to 5.0 (when diluted to 2× SSC in subsequent steps, the pH will change to near 7.0).

2. *Hybridization Master Mix I:* Prepare by mixing together 5 ml formamide, 1 g dextran sulfate, and 1 ml 20× SSC. Heat to 70°C for several hours in a water bath to dissolve the dextran sulfate, cool to room temperature, adjust the pH to 7.0, and bring the volume up to 7 ml.

3. *Probe DNA:* This should be labeled with biotin, and be at a final concentration of approximately 20 to 100 ng of DNA per chromosome to be painted. The hybridization method described here assumes the DNA probe is biotinylated. Other types of labeling the probe are also available, and the method of detecting these is generally similar to the method described here.

4. *DNA blocker:* For the human, use placental DNA at a concentration of 1 mg/ml. For mouse hybridizations, use 1 mg/ml mouse Cot 1 blocking DNA.

5. *Carrier (herring sperm) DNA:* Dissolve in sterile distilled water at a concentration of 1 mg/ml. This DNA should be sonicated to an average length of 400 bp.

6. *2× SSC, pH 7.0:* Dilute 1 part of 20× SSC with 9 parts sterile distilled water. This solution is stable and can be stored for months at room temperature. We find it helpful to make very large amounts of 2× SSC and store it on a shelf in a large plastic container. A stopcock at the bottom allows easy removal.

7. *70% formamide/2× SSC:* Prepare by mixing 35 ml formamide, 5 ml 20× SSC, and 10 ml distilled water. Adjust the pH to between 7.0 and 7.3. This solution can be used for up to 1 week when stored at 4°C.

Steps

1. Prepare the DNA probe cocktail (for 22 × 22-mm² coverslips). Place 10.5 μl of hybridization mix in a microcentrifuge tube. Add 1.5 μl probe DNA, 1.5 μl human placental (blocking) DNA (or mouse Cot 1 blocking DNA if using a mouse probe), and 1.5 μl herring sperm (carrier) DNA, for a total volume of 15 μl. If the size of the coverslips is different, the volume of probe cocktail should be adjusted accordingly. *Note that these DNA reagents are given in volumes, not concentrations. The method given here is based on using the reagents at the concentrations given above.*

2. Place the 70% formamide solution in a Coplin jar with a lid and put it in the water bath. Turn the water bath temperature to 70°C. Make sure the temperature *inside* the jar is 70°C before proceeding. This can be accomplished by inserting a small clean thermometer into the jar; however, do not keep the lid off the jar any longer than necessary because the solution may absorb water from the bath.

3. Take the DNA probe cocktail prepared in step 1 above and vortex it

briefly to mix the DNA probe in the solution thoroughly. Place the tube in a microcentrifuge and *briefly* spin the probe cocktail to the bottom.

4. Place the tube containing the cocktail in a floater, and put the floater into the 70°C water bath for 5 min to denature the DNA. If the floater is large enough (5 cm^2), it will keep the tubes from tipping over. Make sure the tubes are *tightly* capped, that the bottoms of the tubes are completely immersed in the water, and that the lip of the tube is above the top of the Styrofoam.

5. Gently vortex the DNA solution and spin the probe cocktail to the bottom.

6. Put the probe cocktail in a 37°C oven for 30 min. This permits the repetitive elements of the DNA to anneal, and decreases undesirable hybridization signals. *If a human repetitive probe is being used (e.g., one that hybridizes only to the centromeres or telomeres), this step* must *be omitted.* This annealing step is also not necessary for mouse hybridizations.

7. Using the diamond-point engraver, gently etch the microscope slides that are to be hybridized on the *back* side to indicate where the drop(s) of material are located. This will assist in placement of the DNA probe and coverslip. If the drops are not readily visible, they can be readily located by breathing on the slide.

8. Place the slides in the 70°C, 70% formamide/2× SSC solution for 5 min.

9. Transfer the slides to a Coplin jar containing 70% ethanol at 4°C. After 2–5 min put the slides into another jar with 85% ethanol for another 2–5 min. Finally, transfer slides to a jar with 100% ethanol for 2–5 min.

10. Rinse the glass coverslips in 100% ethanol and dry.

11. Remove the slides from the last ethanol rinse and dry them using a gentle stream of room-temperature nitrogen gas. The purpose of this step is to ensure uniform drying of the slide, which minimizes undesired labeling.

12. Place the slides on the slide warmer at 37°C.

13. Retrieve the probe cocktail from the oven, then vortex and spin it in the microcentrifuge briefly.

14. Using a micropipette, measure 15 μl of probe cocktail and place it on the slide. Be sure to place the cocktail in the center of the drop of cells, between the etch marks, and take care to minimize the number of small air bubbles.

15. Immediately cover the probe cocktail with a cleaned glass coverslip. If bubbles are present they should be removed by using a small slender object, such as a micropipette tip, to push them gently to the edge of coverslip. Make sure the coverslip is laying completely on top of the slide, with no overhanging edges.

16. Using a syringe filled with rubber cement, seal the edges of the coverslips onto the slide with copious amounts of cement. Figure 1 shows this being performed on a 37°C warm plate.

17. After the rubber cement has completely dried (approximately 30 min), put the slides into a humidified box with several sheets of paper towels or filter paper on the bottom, as shown in Fig. 1 (the white semicircles are filter paper). The paper should be *damp, not soaked*. If there is standing water in the box the rubber cement will come loose and the hybridization mix will absorb water from the air and dilute the probe cocktail, ruining the hybridization.

18. Place the box in the 37°C oven. The optimum hybridization time may vary, but generally, the longer the hybridization the brighter the signal. For most applications, hybridization overnight is the minimum acceptable time, and longer times (up to 3 days) may be advantageous.

FIGURE 1 Illustration of steps B16 and B17. Rubber cement is shown being applied to the edges of coverslips on slides, which are lying on a 37°C warm plate. Shown on the right is a plastic box which will maintain the slides in a humid atmosphere during the hybridization.

C. REMOVAL OF UNBOUND PROBE AND DETECTION OF BOUND PROBE

Solutions

1. *Carbonate–bicarbonate buffer:* Add 0.42 g $NaHCO_3$ to 9 ml distilled water. Adjust the pH to 9.0 using 1 N NaOH, and bring the volume to 10 ml.

2. *Antifade mounting medium:* Prepare by adding 100 mg of *p*-phenylenediamine dihydrochloride to 10 ml Dulbecco's phosphate-buffered saline. Filter with 0.2-μm filter to remove any undissolved chemical. Adjust the pH to 8.0 using 0.5 *M* carbonate–bicarbonate buffer (this requires about 10 ml). Add this to 90 ml of glycerol. Store in the dark at −20°C. The solution will darken with time, but this will not affect the quality.

3. *Antifade mounting medium plus DAPI and/or propidium iodide stain:* By adding a counterstain directly to the mounting medium, it is possible to mount and counterstain the slides in a single step. To accomplish this, add 0.6 μg/ml final concentration of 4,6-diamidino-2-phenylindole (DAPI) or 0.2 μg/ml final concentration of propidium iodide (PI). If desired, both counterstains can be added.

4. *Avidin-conjugated with fluorescein isothiocyanate (FITC):* Prepare by making a 1:400 dilution in PNM of the 1 mg/ml stock.

5. *Anti-avidin:* Prepare by making a 1:100 dilution in PNM of the 1 mg/ml stock.

6. *PN buffer:* Prepare by dissolving 25.2 g $Na_2HPO_4 \cdot 7H_2O$ and 0.83 g $NaH_2PO_4 \cdot H_2O$ in 1 liter double-distilled H_2O. Add 0.6 ml Nonidet P-40 (NP-40). Mix thoroughly to dissolve the Nonidet detergent. Adjust the pH to 8.0 if necessary.

7. *2× SSC with 0.05% NP-40, pH 7.0:* To prepare, add 0.05 ml NP-40 to 100 ml 2× SSC.

8. *PNM buffer solution:* Prepare by adding 5% nonfat dry milk and 0.02% (w/v) sodium azide to PN buffer. Incubate at 37°C for 2 hr; then allow mixture to incubate overnight at room temperature. Spin in a centrifuge just long enough to settle the precipitate. Remove the supernatant and store at 4°C. This keeps for several months.

9. *50% formamide/2× SSC washing solution:* Prepare 150 ml immediately prior to washing the slides. Add 14 ml of 20× SSC to 70 ml formamide in a beaker, and then add 56 ml of double-distilled water. Adjust the pH to between 7.0 and 7.3.

Steps

1. Aliquot 50 ml of the 50% formamide/2× SSC washing solution into each of three Coplin jars labeled 1, 2, and 3. These solutions may be used several times in the course of a week if they are stored at 4°C, provided the order of the wash solutions remains the same. The solutions should be discarded if the amount of nonspecific background labeling appears high.

2. Place 50 ml of 2× SSC into another Coplin jar and label it No. 4.

3. Place 50 ml of 2× SSC containing 0.1% NP-40 into another Coplin jar and label it No. 5.

4. Preheat the water bath containing all five Coplin jars to 45°C. The solution in jar 5 turns cloudy at 45°C; this is normal.

5. When the interior of the Coplin jars has reached 45°C, remove the slides from the incubator and use the forceps to remove the rubber cement from around the coverslips.

6. Gently remove each coverslip by sliding a corner over the edge of the slide. Slowly lift each one *up* and away from the slide with forceps.

7. Set the slides in the first wash solution for 5 min. Agitate them frequently, and repeat for each of the subsequent four washes.

8. Wash each slide in PN buffer for 5 min at room temperature, repeat this step once.

9. Remove the slides from the final wash, drain them, and lay them flat.

10. Place at least 150 μl of PNM buffer onto each slide, cover it with a plastic coverslip large enough to cover the entire slide, and let the slides sit for 5 min at room temperature. The purpose of the PNM is to provide nonspecific blocking of protein. This enhances the specificity of the avidin and antiavidin reaction by reducing nonspecific background labeling.

11. Remove the coverslips, being careful to avoid scratching the slide. (Plastic coverslips tend to scratch the slide less than glass coverslips, but care must still be taken to avoid making scratches by other means.)

12. Place 120 μl of avidin–FITC (diluted 1:400 in PNM) onto each slide, and cover with a plastic coverslip. Allow the slides to incubate for a minimum of 30 min in a humidified box at 37°C. Remove the coverslips.

13. Rinse the slides sequentially in three Coplin jars containing room temperature PN buffer for 5 min each. Agitate each slide gently during this step.

14. Place 120 μl of antiavidin conjugated with biotin (diluted 1:100 in PNM) onto each slide, and cover with a plastic coverslip. Allow the slides to incubate for a minimum of 30 min in a humidified box at 37°C. Remove the coverslips.

15. Change PN buffer solutions and rinse the slides as described in step 13.

16. Add another layer of avidin–FITC as described in step 12.

17. Rinse the slides as described in step 13.

18. Remove the slides from the final rinse and lay them horizontally on the countertop, hybridized side *up*. Place 120 μl (or 2 to 3 drops from a Pasteur pipette) of antifade solution containing the counterstain PI, DAPI, or both, on the slide and cover with a glass coverslip. It is most convenient to use a large (24 × 60 mm) coverslip, even if only part of the slide has been hybridized.

19. Mix the counterstain with the residual water. This can be accomplished by holding down one edge of the coverslip while raising and lowering the other end five or six times. After the mixing is complete, remove any air bubbles by gently pushing them to the edge with a blunt object.

20. Remove the excess mounting medium by laying the slide on the countertop between sheets of absorbent paper towels. Gently press down on the paper over the slide, taking care not to break or move the coverslip around on the slide.

21. Remove the slide from the between the sheets of paper and clean off any mounting medium that may be on top of the slide. This is easily done with a damp absorbent paper towel. If a coverslip is particularly difficult to clean, it can be wiped with a corner of the towel on which a small amount of 100% ethanol is placed. The slides are now ready for viewing.

IV. Comments

A. ILLUSTRATIONS OF PAINTED METAPHASE CELLS

Color Plates 29–32 illustrate FISH with whole-chromosome probes on human and mouse metaphase cells using the method described in this article.

B. ALTERNATIVE PROCEDURES

If banding of the painted chromosomes is desired, the DAPI/actinomycin D procedure of Tucker *et al.* (1988) can be followed. The use of DAPI counterstain, with or without actinomycin D, is often helpful, particularly if centromere identification is important.

Commercially available human chromosome probes of very good quality can be obtained. Some of these are directly conjugated with the fluorochrome, i.e., instead of using biotinylated DNA and detecting the bound probe with avidin and antiavidin as described here, the fluorochrome itself is attached to the probe. When hybridizing these probes, steps 10 to 17 in Section IIIC can be eliminated. Color Plate 32 shows a human lymphocyte in metaphase with chromosomes 1, 2, and 4 painted simultaneously with the directly conjugated SpectrumOrange probe (manufactured by Imagenetics, Inc., and available through Gibco Life Technologies).

V. Pitfalls

A. SLIDE PREPARATION

In our experience, the most common difficulty encountered when attempting hybridizations is inadequate signal intensity. The usual cause of this is cytoplasm surrounding the chromosomes and acting as a mechanical barrier to penetration by the probe and/or avidin. For high-quality preparations it is essential that the slides be prepared with as little cytoplasm as possible. This requires control of the atmospheric humidity and adjustment of the concentration of acetic acid in the final fixation.

Following fixation of the cells in 3:1 (v/v) methanol:acetic acid, there are several additional steps by which excellent spreads may be achieved.

1. Our most common method uses a shallow plastic tray into which several paper towels have been placed. The towels are soaked in water and the excess water is drained off. The tray is then placed over a 50°C water bath to provide humidity and allowed to become warm. The slides are placed in the tray and gently sprayed with water to produce a fine speckled pattern of droplets. The fixed cells are then dropped from a height of 2 to 4 cm. It is *not* necessary for the cells to be dropped from a greater height; this frequently results in the loss of too much material. Of the three methods described here, this works the most consistently.

2. The cells can be fixed one additional time in glacial acetic acid, or in 1 part glacial acetic acid and 1 part 3:1 (v/v) methanol:acetic acid, and then dropped immediately onto dry slides. This method may be used in conjunction with *A* above.

3. The slides may be flooded with 100% acetic acid immediately after the cells are dropped.

B. SLIDE STORAGE

If the prepared slides are stored on a shelf at room temperature, over a period of months they will lose their ability to hybridize. Although the reasons for this are not completely clear, it is quite easy to prepare slides for long-term storage by placing them in slide boxes in sealed plastic bags with a N_2 atmosphere and a desiccant at -20°C. Limited experience with slides stored in this manner but kept at room temperature indicates that they lose their ability to hybridize.

ACKNOWLEDGMENT

This work was performed under the auspices of the U. S. Department of Energy by the Lawrence Livermore National Laboratory under Contract No. W-7405-ENG-48.

REFERENCES

Breneman, J. W., Ramsey, M. J., Lee, D. A., Eveleth, G. G., Minkler, J. L., and Tucker, J. D. (1993). The development of chromosome-specific composite DNA probes for the mouse and their application to chromosome painting. *Chromosoma* 102, 591–598.

Tucker, J. D., Christensen M. L., and Carrano, A. V. (1988) Simultaneous identification and banding of human chromosome material in somatic cell hybrids. *Cytogenet. Cell Genet.* 48,103–106.

SUGGESTED READING

Cremer, T., Popp, S., Emmerich, P., Lichter P., and Cremer, C. (1990) Rapid metaphase and interphase detection of radiation-induced chromosome aberrations in human lymphocytes by chromosomal suppression *in situ* hybridization. *Cytometry* 11, 110–118.

Johnson G. D., and Nogueira Araujo G. M. de C. (1981) A simple method of reducing the fading of immunofluorescence during microscopy. *J. Immunol. Methods* 43, 349–350.

Lichter, P., Cremer, T., Borden, J., Manuelidis, L., and Ward, D. C. (1988) Delineation of individual human chromosomes in metaphase and interphase cells by *in situ* suppression hybridization using recombinant DNA libraries. *Hum. Genet.* **80**, 224–234.

Pinkel, D., Landegent, J., Collins, C., Fuscoe, J., Segraves, R., Lucas J., and Gray, J. (1988) Fluorescence *in situ* hybridization with human chromosome-specific libraries: Detection of trisomy 21 and translocations of chromosome 4. *Proc. Natl. Acad. Sci. USA* **85**, 9138–9142.

Tucker, J. D., Ramsey, M. J., Lee, D. A., and Minkler, J. L. (1993) Validation of chromosome painting as a biodosimeter in human peripheral lymphocytes following acute exposure to ionizing radiation *in vitro*. *Int. J. Radiat. Biol.*, **64**, 27–37.

In Situ Hybridization Applicable to Abundantly Expressed mRNA Species

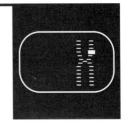

Roeland W. Dirks, Frans M. van de Rijke,
and Anton K. Raap

I. Introduction

RNA *in situ* hybridization techniques allow the study of gene expression at the individual cell level in a histocytomorphological context. RNA *in situ* hybridization studies are mostly performed with radioactive labeled probes, but these have resolution drawbacks that limit their applicability in the study of RNA distribution at the (sub)cellular level. From the early eighties several nonisotopic labeling methods based on the introduction of haptens (e.g., biotin and digoxigenin) or fluorochromes (fluorescein, rhodamine, coumarin) in the probe have been developed. Such probes provide a high spatial resolution and are now routinely used for the sensitive detection of unique DNA sequences in chromosome spreads and interphase cell nuclei (Lichter *et al.*, 1991; Wiegant *et al.*, 1991, 1993). Sensitive detection of mRNA molecules by nonisotopic *in situ* hybridization is, however, still under development (Singer *et al.*, 1986; Dirks *et al.*, 1989, 1990, 1991, 1992, 1993; Raap *et al.*, 1991). Here we describe a protocol that allows detection of abundantly expressed housekeeping gene mRNAs such as human elongation factor (HEF), glyceraldehyde-3-phosphate dehydrogenase (GAPDH), and actin in a variety of cell lines using digoxigenin-labeled DNA probes and fluorescence microscopy.

II. Materials and Instrumentation

Dulbecco's modified Eagle's medium without phenol red (DMEM, Cat. No. 041-01880 M), fetal calf serum (FCS, Cat. No. 011-06290), L-glutamine (Cat. No. 066-01051 H), penicillin–streptomycin (Cat. No. 043-05070 H), and trypsin (Cat. No. 043-05090 H) are from Gibco-BRL. Salmon testis DNA (Cat. No. D-7656), dithiothreitol (DTT, Cat. No. D-0632), thimerosal (Cat. No. T-5125), polyvinylpyrrolidone (PVP, Cat. No. PVP-40), mouse monoclonal antidigoxin (Cat. No. D-8156), rabbit anti-mouse fluorescein isothiocyanate (FITC) (Cat. No. F-7506), goat anti-rabbit FITC (Cat. No. F-9262) and 1,4-diazabicyclo-[2,2,2]-octane (DABCO, Cat. No. D-2522) are from Sigma. Ficoll 400 (Cat. No. 17-0400-01) is from Pharmacia. Bovine serum albumin fraction V (BSA, Cat. No. 44155) is from BDH. Formamide (Cat. No. 7042) and acetic acid (Cat. No. 6052) are from J. T. Baker. Amberlite MB1 ion exchanger (Cat. No. 40701) and 4,6-diamidino-2-phenylindol·2HCl (DAPI, Cat. No. 18860) are from Serva. Acid-free formaldehyde (Cat. No. 3999) is from Merck. dATP (Cat. No. 1051 440), dCTP (Cat. No. 1051 458), dGTP (Cat. No. 1051 466), dTTP (Cat. No. 1051 482), DNase I (Cat. No. 104 159), digoxigenin-11-dUTP (Cat. No. 1093 088), and blocking reagent (Cat. No. 1093 657) are from Boehringer–Mannheim. DNA polymerase I (Cat. No. M205A) is from Promega. Vectashield mounting medium (Cat. No. H-1000) is from Vector and Histo-clear from National Diagnostics. Staining jars (100 ml) for object slides (Cat. No. L4110) were obtained from Agar Aids Ltd.

Hybridization results were examined with a Leitz Dialux 20 fluorescence microscope equipped with a 100-W mercury arc lamp and standard excitation and emission filters for green, red, and blue fluorescence. Photographs were taken on 640 ASA Scotch 3M color slide film.

III. Procedures

A. LABELING OF DNA PROBES BY NICK TRANSLATION

Solutions

1. *Nick translation buffer (10×):* 0.5 M Tris–HCl, pH 7.8, 50 mM MgCl$_2$ and 0.5 mg/ml BSA. To make 10 ml of the solution, add 5 ml of an autoclaved 1 M stock solution of Tris–HCl, pH 7.8, 0.5 ml of an autoclaved 1 M solution of MgCl$_2$, 5 mg of nuclease-free BSA and complete to 10 ml with autoclaved distilled water. Aliquot in 100-μl portions and keep at -20°C.

2. *0.1 M DTT:* To make 10 ml, dissolve 150 mg of DTT in 10 ml of 0.01 M sodium acetate (pH 5.2). Filter the solution through a 0.2-μm filter, aliquot in 1-ml portions, and store at -20°C.

3. *Nucleotide mix:* 0.5 mM dATP, 0.5 mM dCTP, 0.5 mM dGTP, and 0.1 mM dTTP. To make 1 ml of the solution add, 5 μl each of 100 mM stock solutions dATP, dCTP, dGTP and 1 μl of 100 mM stock solution dTTP. Complete to 1 ml with autoclaved distilled water and store at -20°C.

4. *1 mg/ml DNase I:* To make 1 ml, add 1 mg of DNase, 20 μl of a 1 M stock solution of Tris–HCl, pH 7.6, 50 μl of a 1 M stock solution of NaCl, 10 μl of a 100 mM stock solution of DTT, 0.1 mg of BSA, and 0.5 ml of glycerol. Complete to 1 ml with autoclaved distilled water and store at -20°C.

5. *10 mg/ml Salmon testes DNA:* To make 10 ml, dissolve 100 mg DNA in 100 ml 0.3 M NaOH in TE, pH 7.8 (10 mM Tris–HCl, pH 7.8, 1 mM EDTA). Boil for 20 min at 100°C. Neutralize the solution by adding 5 ml 2 M Tris–HCl, pH 7.5, 7.5 ml 4 M HCl, and 12 ml 2 M sodium acetate. Precipitate the DNA by adding 2 vols of 100% -20°C ethanol and incubate for 1 hr on ice. Centrifuge for 10 min at 2600 g, remove the ethanol, and dissolve the DNA pellet in 10 ml TE buffer.

6. *Deionized formamide:* To make 100 ml, add 5 g of ion exchanger to 100 ml formamide. Stir for 2 hr and filter twice through Whatmann No. 1 filter paper. Aliquot in 1-ml portions and store at -20°C.

7. *20× SSC:* To make 1 liter, add 175.3 g NaCl and 88.24 g sodium citrate to distilled water. Adjust to pH 7.0 and complete to 1 liter. Autoclave the solution and store at room temperature.

8. *50× Denhardt's solution:* 1% PVP, 1% Ficoll (type 400), and 1% BSA. To make 500 ml of the solution, add 5 g Ficoll, 5 g PVP, 5 g BSA (fraction V), and distilled water to 500 ml. Sterilize the solution by filtration and store at -20°C.

Steps

1. Thaw the required stock solutions and keep them on ice. Prepare the labeling solution on ice and mix well. To make the labeling mixture, combine 26 μl autoclaved distilled water, 5 μl 10× nick translation buffer, 5 μl 100 mM DTT, 4 μl nucleotide mix, 2 μl digoxigenin-11-dUTP, 1 μl probe DNA (1 μg, e.g., cDNA), 2 μl DNA polymerase I, and 5 μl of a 1:1000 DNase I dilution from a 1 mg/ml stock solution.

2. Place the labeling mixture for 2 hr in a 16°C water bath.

3. Add 250 μl distilled water and precipitate the labeled probe by adding 30 μl 3 M sodium acetate, pH 4.8, 5 μl salmon testis DNA, and 750 μl −20°C ethanol. Mix well and place the solution for 30 min on ice.

4. Centrifuge for 30 min at 4°C in an Eppendorf centrifuge at maximum speed. Remove the ethanol completely and resuspend the pellet in 200 μl hybridization mixture to reach a probe concentration of 5 ng/μl. To make 10 ml hybridization mixture, combine 5 ml deionized formamide, 1 ml 20× SSC, 1 ml 0.5 M sodium phosphate buffer, pH 7.0, 1 ml 50× Denhardt's solution, and 2 ml autoclaved distilled water. The probe mixture can be stored at 4°C for at least 1 year.

B. CULTURING AND FIXATION OF CELLS

Solution

1. *10× PBS:* To make 10× PBS, pH 7.2, add 80 g NaCl, 2 g KCl, 15 g $Na_2HPO_4 \cdot 2H_2O$, and 1.2 g KH_2PO_4 and adjust to 1 liter. Autoclave the solution and store at room temperature.

Steps

1. Subconfluent cells that are growing in Falcon flasks as a monolayer in DMEM supplemented with 10% FCS, 100 U penicillin/ml, and 100 μg streptomycin/ml are trypsinized and seeded into petri dishes containing 5 microscopic object slides and 20 ml medium. Cells are grown to subconfluency at 37°C in a humidified 5% CO_2 atmosphere.

2. Wash the object slides containing cells in PBS for 1 min at room temperature.

3. Fix the cells in PBS containing 4% formaldehyde, 5% acetic acid for 20 min at room temperature. To make 100 ml fixative, combine 75 ml distilled water, 10 ml 10× PBS, 10 ml formaldehyde (37% stock), and 5 ml acetic acid.

4. Wash the cells in PBS for 5 min at room temperature and transfer the object slides to a 100-ml staining jar.

5. Wash the cells in 70% ethanol and store the object slides in 70% ethanol at 4°C until use.

C. PRETREATMENT AND HYBRIDIZATION

Solution

1. *0.1% pepsin:* To make 100 ml, dissolve 0.1 g pepsin in distilled water, adjust pH to 2.0, and bring to 100 ml. Make this solution about 15 min before use and place in a 37°C water bath.

Steps

1. Dehydrate the cells successively in 70, 90, and 100% ethanol for 3 min each.

2. Incubate for 10 min in Histo-clear at room temperature.

3. Wash in 100% ethanol for 5 min and rehydrate the cells successively in 100, 90, and 70% ethanol for 3 min each.

4. Wash the cells in PBS for 3 min at room temperature.

5. Incubate the cells in 0.1% pepsin solution for 5 min at 37°C.

6. Wash twice in PBS for 30 sec each.

7. Incubate in 1% formaldehyde in PBS for 5 min at room temperature.

8. Wash in PBS for 5 min and dehydrate as described in step 1.

9. Denature the probe dissolved in hybridization mixture for 5 min in a 80°C water bath.

10. Place the probe for 1 min on ice and spin down in an Eppendorf centrifuge.

11. Apply 10 μl of the denatured probe mixture on the object slide and cover the mixture with an 18 $\times$ 18-mm^2 coverslip.

12. Put the object glasses in a jar and hybridize overnight at 37°C in a moist chamber which consist of a 1-liter beaker covered with aluminum foil containing tissues moistened with 50% formamide/2$\times$ SSC, pH 7.0.

D. POSTHYBRIDIZATION WASHES

Solutions

1. *50% formamide/2$\times$ SSC wash solution:* To make 400 ml add, 200 ml formamide, 40 ml 20$\times$ SSC, and 160 ml distilled water and adjust the pH to 7.0.

2. *10$\times$ TBS:* To make 1 liter, dissolve 121.4 g Tris and 87.4 g NaCl in 800 ml distilled water. Adjust the pH to 7.4 with 6 *M* HCl and bring to a total volume of 1 liter.

Steps

1. Wash the slides in the 50% formamide/2$\times$ SSC solution at room temperature until the coverslips are released.

2. Transfer the slides to a new jar filled with 100 ml 50% formamide/2$\times$ SSC and wash for 10 min.

3. Wash the slides for 10 min each in 50% formamide/2$\times$ SSC at 42°C and in the same solution at room temperature.

4. Wash the slides in 2$\times$ SSC for 5 min at room temperature.

5. Wash the slides in 1$\times$ TBS for 5 min at room temperature.

E. IMMUNOCYTOCHEMICAL DETECTION

Solution

1. *Blocking solution:* To make 100 ml, add 0.5 g blocking reagent and 100 μl thimerosal (to prevent bacterial growth). Complete to 100 ml with 1$\times$ TBS. Heat

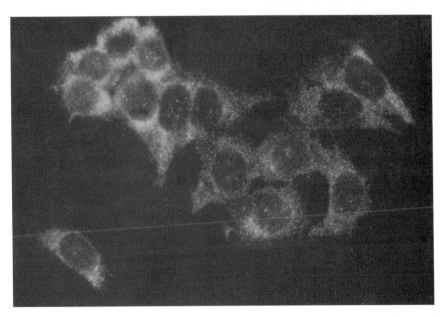

FIGURE 1 Demonstration of HEF mRNA as small fluorescent dots in the cytoplasm of HeLa cells.

the mixture for 1 hr at 60°C to dissolve the blocking reagent and aliquot in 10-ml portions. Store at −20°C.

Steps

1. Take a slide from the TBS solution and apply 100 μl blocking solution. Cover it with a 24 × 50-mm² coverslip and incubate for 30 min at 37°C in a moist chamber (1-liter beaker covered with aluminum foil containing tissue moistened with water).

2. Wash briefly with TBS to remove the coverslips.

3. Incubate the slides with mouse antidigoxin, diluted 1:500 in blocking solution, under a coverslip for 45 min at 37°C in a moist chamber.

4. Remove the coverslips by a brief wash in TBS and wash the slides 3 × 5 min with TBS at room temperature.

5. Incubate the slides with rabbit anti-mouse FITC, diluted 1:500 in blocking solution, as described in step 3.

6. Wash the slides as described in step 4.

7. Incubate the slides with goat anti-rabbit FITC, diluted 1:500 in blocking solution, as described in step 3.

8. Wash the slides as described in step 4.

9. Dehydrate the slides for 3 min each in 70, 90, and 100% ethanol and air-dry.

10. Apply 30 μl Vectashield containing 10 ng/μl DAPI (blue fluorescent DNA counterstain) on a slide and cover with a 24 × 50-mm² coverslip.

11. Examine the slides with a fluorescence microscope equipped with appropriate excitation and emission filters for FITC and DAPI fluorescence.

IV. Comments

The protocol described above allows the detection of abundant housekeeping gene mRNAs in cultured cells grown on object slides. A representative hybridization result of HEF mRNA in HeLa cells is shown in Fig. 1. Hybridization signals are

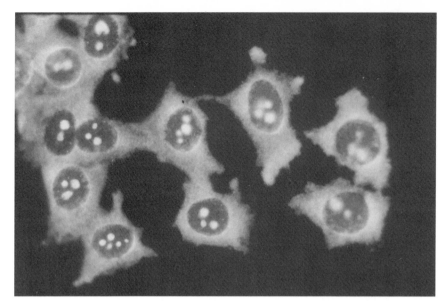

FIGURE 2 Detection of 28 S rRNA in HeLa cells with a digoxigenin-labeled 28 S rRNA plasmid probe.

visible as a large number of small fluorescent spots distributed throughout the cytoplasm. This hybridization protocol allows also bright-field microscopical visualization of hybridization signals when instead of fluorochrome antibody conjugates, conjugates with peroxidase or alkaline phosphatase are used (Dirks *et al.*, 1993).

As a positive control on the procedure, probes specific for rRNA, like 28 S rRNA, can be used. As illustrated in Fig. 2, cytoplasm and nucleoli of cells should give an intense fluorescent signal.

V. Pitfalls

1. The probe labeling can be checked by doing a spot test. Spot 1 μl of a dilution series of the labeled probe on a nitrocellulose filter and incubate with sheep antidigoxigenin–alkaline phosphatase. After performing the NBT/BCIP reaction a probe concentration of 5 to 1 pg/μl should be visible.

2. It is important to titrate the pepsin concentration and/or time of incubation to find a balance between loss of morphology and signal intensity.

3. For optimal results it is sometimes necessary to denature the target mRNA. This is done just before the hybridization, after applying the probe solution and coverslip on the slide, by placing the slide on an 80°C hot plate for 2 to 3 min.

REFERENCES

Dirks, R. W., Raap, A. K., Van Minnen, J., Vreugdenhil, E., Smit, A. B., and Van der Ploeg, M. (1989) Detection of mRNA molecules coding for neuropeptide hormones of the pond snail *Lymnaea stagnalis* by radioactive and non-radioactive in situ hybridization: A model system for mRNA detection. *J. Histochem. Cytochem.* 37, 7–14.
Dirks, R. W., Van Gijlswijk, R. P. M., Tullis, R. H., Smit, A. B., Van Minnen, J., Van der Ploeg, M., and Raap, A. K. (1990) Simultaneous detection of different mRNA sequences coding for neuropeptide hormones by double in situ hybridization using FITC- and biotin-labeled oligonucleotides. *J. Histochem. Cytochem.* 38, 467–473.

Dirks, R. W., Van Gijlswijk, R. P. M., Vooijs, M. A., Smit, A. B., Bogerd, J., Van Minnen, J., Raap, A. K., and Van der Ploeg, M. (1991) 3'-End fluorochromized and haptenized oligonucleotides as in situ hybridization probes for multiple, simultaneous RNA detection. *Exp. Cell Res.* **194**, 310–315.

Dirks, R. W., van Dorp, A. G. M., Van Minnen, J., Fransen, J. A. M., Van der Ploeg, M., and Raap, A. K. (1992) Electron microscopic detection of RNA sequences by non-radioactive in situ hybridization in the mollusk *Lymnaea stagnalis*. *J. Histochem. Cytochem.* **40**, 1647–1657.

Dirks, R. W., Van de Rijke, F. M., Fujishita, S., Van der Ploeg, M., and Raap, A. K. (1993) Methodologies for specific intron and exon RNA localization in cultured cells by haptenized and fluorochromized probes. *J. Cell Sci.* **104**, 1187–1197.

Lichter, P., Boyle, A. L., Cremer, T., and Ward, D. C. (1991) Analysis of genes and chromosomes by nonisotopic in situ hybridization. *Genet. Anal. Techn. Appl.* **8**, 24–35.

Raap, A. K., Van de Rijke, F. M., Dirks, R. W., Sol, C. J., Boom, R., and Van der Ploeg, M. (1991) Bicolor fluorescence in situ hybridization to intron and exon mRNA sequences. *Exp. Cell Res.* **197**, 319–322.

Singer, R. H., Lawrence, J. B., and Villnave, C. (1986) Optimization of in situ hybridization using isotopic and non-isotopic detection methods. *BioTechniques* **4**, 230–250.

Wiegant, J., Ried, T., Nederlof, P. M., Van der Ploeg, M., Tanke, H. J., and Raap, A. K. (1991) In situ hybridization with fluoresceinated DNA. *Nucleic Acids Res.* **19**, 3237–3241.

Wiegant, J., Wiesmeijer, C. C., Hoovers, J. M. N., Schuuring, E., d'Azzo, A., Vrolijk, J., Tanke, H. J., and Raap, A. K. (1993) Multiple and sensitive fluorescence in situ hybridization with rhodamine-, fluorescein-, and coumarin-labeled DNAs. *Cytogenet. Cell Genet.* **63**, 73–76.

In Situ Hybridization of Frozen Sections Using ^{35}S-Labeled Riboprobes

Daniel Carrasco and Rodrigo Bravo

I. Introduction

The study of gene products by biochemical and molecular techniques often uses tissue samples expressing a considerable amount of the target molecule. However, many genes with potential roles in the development of the mammalian embryo are expressed either in a minority of cells in complex tissues or for only brief periods during the differentiation of an organism or tissue, making the detection of their products difficult (Guant, 1991; Scholer, 1991). In these instances *in situ* hybridization has an advantage over other techniques as it allows not only the detection of minute amounts of mRNAs but also the identification of the cells in the tissue that express the gene product. It relies on the hybridization of a specifically labeled nucleic acid probe to the cellular mRNA in individual cells or tissue sections. Since the original studies of Cox *et al.* (1984), different adaptations have been successfully applied to allow the use of mouse tissues (Simmons *et al.,* 1989; Wilkinson and Green, 1990; Angerer and Angerer, 1992); however, the numerous methods available for tissue and probe preparations can make initiating *in situ* hybridization experiments daunting. Here we describe a detailed practical protocol that we routinely use for *in situ* hybridization of mRNA molecules in mouse embryos and other mouse tissues using ^{35}S-labeled single-stranded RNA. This protocol is optimized for the use of frozen sections, avoiding the time-consuming steps required for preparation and processing of wax-embedded tissues.

II. Materials

Acrylamide (Cat. No. A-9099), diethyl pyrocarbonate (DEPC, Cat. No. D-5758), Ficoll type 400 (Cat. No. F-4375), *N*, *N'*-methylenebisacrylamide (Cat. No. M-7256), Sephadex G-50 (Cat. No. G-50–80), polyvinylpyrrolidone (Cat. No. PVP-10), sodium chloride (Cat. No. S-3014), sodium dodecyl sulfate (SDS, Cat. No. L-4509), sodium phosphate (Cat. No. S-9390), Trizma base (Cat. No. T-1503), and toluidine blue (Cat. No. T-0394) are from Sigma. Dithiothreitol (DTT, Cat. No. 5508UA) is from Gibco-BRL. Acetic anhydride (Cat. No. A10–500), acetone (Cat. No. A949-1), ammonium acetate (Cat. No. A639-500), boric acid (Cat. No. A73-3), deionized formamide (Cat. No. BP228-100), glass wool (Cat. No. 11-390), paraformaldehyde (Cat. No. T353-500), sodium citrate (Cat. No. BP327-1000), sodium hydroxide solution (10 N, Cat. No. SS255-1), triethanolamine (Cat. No. T407-500), and xylene histological grade (Cat. No. UN1307) are from Fisher Scientific. Transcription optimized 5× buffer (Cat. No. P1181), RQ1 RNase-free DNase

(Cat. No. M6101), T7 RNA polymerase (Cat. No. P2076), T3 RNA polymerase (Cat. No. P2084), and rATP, rCTP, rGTP each at 10 mM (Cat. No. P1221) are from Promega. Bovine serum albumin (BSA Fraction V, Cat. No. 100 018), formamide (Cat. No. 100 144), RNase A (Cat. No. 109 169), RNasin (Cat. No. 786 349), and urea (Cat. No. 100 164) are from Boehringer-Mannheim. Developer (D-19, Cat. No. 146 4593), fixer (Cat. No. 197 1746), and NTB-2 emulsion (Cat. No. 165 4433) are from Kodak. Dextran sulfate (Cat. No. 17-0340-02) is from Pharmacia. Hydrochloric acid (Cat. No. 9535-01) is from J. T. Baker. [^{35}S]UTP (Cat. No. SJ.1303) is from Amersham. Yeast tRNA stock solution (20 mg/ml, Cat. No. 5302–977884) is from 5 Prime–3 Prime, Inc. Insulin syringe (1 ml) is from Becton Dickinson & Company. Tissue Freezing Medium (Cat. No. H-TFM) is from Triangle Biomedical Sciences. EDTA (Cat. No. 139-33-3) and desiccant (Cat. No. DX0016-3) are from EM Science. Ethyl alcohol 200 proof (Cat. No. 0290) is from Quantum Chemical Corporation. GeneClean kit (Cat. No. 3105) is from Bio 101, Inc. Cytoseal 60 mounting medium (Cat. No. 8310-4) is from Stephens Scientific.

Plastic molds (Cat. No. 1515–642), metallic tray and removable handle (Cat. No. 25445-011), glass staining dish and cover (Cat. No. 25445-009), glass coverslips (18 × 18 mm, Cat. No. 48368-040; 22 × 30 mm, Cat. No. 48394 026), and dust-off pressurized duster (Cat. No. 21899-100) are from VWR Scientific. Plastic staining dish (Cat. No. 195) and rack (Cat. No. 196) are from Shandon Lipshaw. Polyethylene tubes (50 ml, Cat. No. 25330-50) and polypropylene tubes (15 ml, Cat. No. 25319-15) are from Corning Incorporated. Paper filters (No. 58, Cat. No. 03720) are from Schleicher & Schuell. Silanated slides (Cat. No. H-08F-AP) are from Digene. Plastic boxes (Cat. No. 5700-0500) are from Nalgene. Wratten series II safelight system for dark room is from Kodak. Siliconized microcentrifuge tubes (Cat. No. B10607) are from Denville Scientific, Inc.

III. Procedures

Several precautions must be taken to prevent ribonuclease digestion of probe RNAs and mRNAs in tissue sections. Gloves must be worn at all times when handling both tissue and slides to avoid contact with skin secretions, the major source of RNase contamination. RNase inhibitors should be included in the probe synthesis reaction. Glassware and solutions must be RNase free. To avoid background, the autoradiographic emulsion and the dipped slides must be manipulated and stored away from light and penetrating radiation. Dust and particles in solution easily stick to the tissue or emulsion. This can be avoided by using clean coverslips, by working in a hood, and by using filtered solutions, whenever possible.

A. PREPARATION OF SINGLE-STRANDED RIBOPROBES

Solutions

1. *DEPC-treated water:* For 1 lt of deionized water, add 1 ml of DEPC, leave overnight and then autoclave at 121°C for 1 h. Store at room temperature (RT).

2. *1 M DTT stock solution:* To prepare 10 ml, solubilize 1.25 g of DTT in 8 ml of DEPC treated water and adjust to a total volume of 10 ml. Make 1-ml aliquots and store at −70°C.

3. *1 M Tris–HCl (pH 7.4) stock solution:* To make 100 ml, dissolve 12.11 g of Tris base in 80 ml of water. Adjust the pH by adding HCl and complete volume to 100 ml. Sterilize by autoclaving 30 min at 121°C.

4. *0.5 M EDTA (pH 8.0):* To prepare 100 ml, add 18.61 g of EDTA to 80 ml

of water. Stir vigorously on a magnetic stirrer. Adjust the pH to 8.0 with NaOH and complete volume to 100 ml. Sterilize by autoclaving 30 min at 121°C.

5. *TE buffer:* To make 100 ml, add 1 ml of 1 *M* Tris–HCl (pH 7.4) and 0.2 ml of 0.5 *M* EDTA (pH 8.0) to 99 ml of DEPC treated water.

6. *Sephadex G-50:* Leave 10 g of Sephadex G-50 to hydrate overnight in 100 ml of TE buffer. Then autoclave at 121°C for 30 min and store at 4°C.

7. *Glass wool:* Sterilize by autoclaving in a glass container covered with aluminum foil for 30 min at 121°C.

8. *10× Tris–borate–EDTA buffer (TBE):* To prepare 100 ml, dissolve 10.8 g of Tris base and 5.5 g of boric acid in 60 ml of deionized water. Add 4 ml of 0.5 *M* EDTA, pH 8.0, and adjust volume to 100 ml.

9. *6% Acrylamide/bisacrylamide solution:* To make 100 ml, dissolve 6 g of acrylamide, 0.3 g of bisacrylamide, and 48 g of urea in 60 ml of deionized water by stirring overnight. Add 10 ml of 10× TBE buffer and adjust the volume to 100 ml. Store the solution in dark bottles at room temperature.

Steps

Prepare single-stranded riboprobes by *in vitro* transcription of cDNA sequences cloned into vectors containing specific RNA polymerase initiation sites. After choosing the appropriate polymerase, prepare antisense and sense riboprobes. To avoid transcription of plasmid sequences and to obtain probes shorter than 300 base pairs (bp), linearize the construct using a restriction site that is distal to the RNA polymerase initiation site. In general, probes of 100–300 bp give a good hybridization signal and no alkaline hydrolysis of the riboprobe is required. Digest 5–10 μg of the plasmid with the selected restriction enzyme, run an agarose gel with the digested sample, and isolate the fully linearized plasmid with GeneClean. Measure the concentration of the linearized plasmid at 260 nm and store at −20°C.

1. Prepare the ^{35}S-radiolabeled probe by adding in a siliconized microcentrifuge tube in sequential order the following reagents:

Nuclease-free distilled water	2 μl
5 × transcription buffer	4 μl
0.1 *M* DTT	2 μl
10 m*M* rCTP	1 μl
10 m*M* rATP	1 μl
10 m*M* rGTP	1 μl
[^{35}S]UTP, 50 μCi	5 μl
RNasin	1 μl
T3 or T7 RNA polymerase	1 μl
Linearized DNA template, 200–300 ng	2 μl

2. Incubate at 37°C for 1 hr.

3. Add 1 μl of DNase and incubate 15 min at 37°C.

4. Add 5 μl of yeast tRNA stock solution and 75 ml of TE buffer with 10 m*M* DTT.

5. To purify the riboprobe, use a sterile glass wool to make a bed on the bottom of a 1-ml insulin syringe and fill the syringe with Sephadex G-50. Put the syringe in a 15-ml polypropylene tube and spin for 1 min at 2000 rpm in a RT-6000B Sorvall centrifuge at room temperature. Apply the sample and spin the syringe again at 2000 rpm for 1 min in a 15-ml tube containing inside a siliconized microfuge tube to collect the probe.

6. For analysis of the probe, run 1 μl on a 6% polyacrylamide gel and count 1 μl in a scintillation counter (200,000 to 1,000,000 cpm/μl is an expected yield). A significant amount of full-length transcripts and a smear of shorter fragments should be observed after autoradiography of the gel.

7. Dilute the probe to 100,000 cpm/μl in DEPC-treated water containing 100 mM DTT and divide into 10-μl aliquots in siliconized microcentrifuge tubes. Probes can last up to 1 month when kept at $-70°$C.

B. SECTION AND FIXATION

Solutions

1. *Phosphate-buffered saline stock solution (10$\times$ PBS):* For 1 liter, dissolve 80 g of NaCl, 2 g KCl, 14.4 g of Na$_2$HPO4, and 2.4 g of KH$_2$PO4 in 800 ml of DEPC-treated water. Adjust the pH to 7.4 with HCl. Add deionized water to 1 liter and sterilize by autoclaving for 30 min at 121°C. Store at room temperature.

2. *4% Paraformaldehyde solution:* To prepare 500 ml, heat 400 ml of DEPC-treated water to 50°C and add 20 g of paraformaldehyde. Stir the solution and heat to 60°C, add 2–3 drops of 10 N NaOH until the solution is clear. To a cylinder with 50 ml of 10$\times$ PBS, add the paraformaldehyde solution and adjust volume to 500 ml. Filter through filter paper into an aluminum foil-wrapped bottle and keep at 4°C. Discard this solution after 24 hr.

3. *0.85% NaCl solution:* To make 1 liter, solubilize 8.5 g of NaCl in deionized water and adjust to a total volume of 1 liter. Autoclave the solution for 30 min at 121°C. Store at room temperature.

4. *0.1 M triethanolamine solution:* To prepare 400 ml, add 5.5 ml of triethanolamine and adjust volume to 400 ml with sterilized water. Store at room temperature.

5. *Ethanol solutions (30, 50, 75, and 95%):* All ethanol solutions are prepared in DEPC-treated water.

Metallic tray, removable handle, glass dish, and cover are individually wrapped in aluminum foil and sterilized overnight at 200°C.

Steps

1. After dissection, immerse the embryo or tissue in Tissue Freezing Medium in plastic molds and immediately freeze the specimen by placing the plastic mold on the surface of liquid nitrogen for 1–2 min. Store the frozen specimen at $-70°$C.

2. Cut 10-μm sections at $-18°$C in a cryostat and collect individual sections on the center of silanated slides.

3. After air-drying the sections (10–20 min), put the slides in a metallic rack and fix the slides by immersing the rack in a glass staining dish containing 400 ml of cold (4°C) freshly prepared 4% paraformaldehyde for 1 hr. Keep this solution to be reused in step 6. The slides are kept in the metallic rack.

All subsequent steps are performed in glass staining dishes containing 400 ml of the indicated solutions. This allows the simultaneous processing of 30 slides.

4. Rinse slides in 1$\times$ PBS for 5 min.

5. Acetylate the sections by immersing the slides in a dish containing 0.1 M triethanolamine and a stirring bar. While stirring, add 1 ml of acetic anhydride and leave for 10 min.

6. Rinse by dipping the rack several times in 1× PBS. Then transfer the rack back to the 4% paraformaldehyde solution used in step 3. Keep at 4°C for 3 min.

7. Rinse the slides in 1× PBS and in 0.85% NaCl solution for 5 min each.

8. Dehydrate sections by dipping slides for approximately 2 min each in 30, 50, 70, and 95% and twice in 100% ethanol with occasional shaking. Keep these solutions to be reused in Section D, step 9.

9. Air-dry and use the sections for hybridization on the same day.

C. HYBRIDIZATION

Solutions

1. *20× SSC solution:* To make 1 liter, dissolve 175.3 g of NaCl and 88.2 g of sodium citrate in 800 ml of deionized water. Adjust the pH to 7.0 with a few drops of a 10 N NaOH solution and complete to 1 liter. Filter using filter paper and sterilize by autoclaving 30 min at 121°C. Store at room temperature.

2. *50× Denhardt's solution:* To prepare 50 ml, add 0.5 g of Ficoll, 0.5 g of polyvinylpyrrolidone, and 0.5 g of bovine serum albumin, dissolve, and adjust volume to a total 50 ml. Filter through filter paper and store at −20°C in 5-ml aliquots.

3. *4 M NaCl solution:* To make 100 ml, solubilize 23.4 g of NaCl in 80 ml of DEPC-treated water and adjust volume to a total of 100 ml. Store at room temperature.

4. *Hybridization buffer:* To prepare 10 ml, solubilize 1 g of dextran sulfate in 2.5 ml of DEPC-treated water at 50°C. Then add in the following order 0.2 ml 50× Denhardt's solution, 0.75 ml of 4 M NaCl, 0.2 ml of 1 M Tris–HCl (pH 7.4), 0.1 ml of 0.5 M EDTA (pH 8.0), 0.25 ml yeast tRNA stock solution, and finally 5 ml of deionized formamide. Mix well, make 1-ml aliquots and store at −20°C.

5. *Glass coverslips, 18 × 18 mm or 22 × 30 mm:* Clean the coverslips by dipping in acetone for 10 min, leave to dry on Whatman paper, and rinse twice in ethanol. Store in a glass container covered with aluminum foil and sterilize by autoclaving 30 min at 121°C.

6. *50% formamide–4× SSC:* To prepare 100 ml, add to 30 ml of deionized water 20 ml of 20× SSC solution and 50 ml of formamide. Make this solution fresh for each experiment.

7. *Humid chamber:* Prepare a humid chamber by wrapping the internal walls of a plastic box with tissue paper soaked in 50% formamide and 4× SSC.

Steps

1. Before starting the hybridization, dilute an aliquot of the radioactive probe by adding 9 vol of hybridization buffer. This dilution must be freshly prepared.

2. Place the slides on a slide warmer at 40°C. Heat the diluted probe at 80°C for 2 min, give a quick spin in a microcentrifuge, and apply 20–40 μl without touching the section.

3. At a slant, gently cover the section with a 18 × 18-mm or 22 × 30-mm clean coverslip avoiding to trap air bubbles.

4. Place the slide with the coverslip facing up in a humid chamber, close the lid tightly, and leave it in a humidified incubator overnight at 52°C.

D. WASHING

Solutions

1. *10× RNase stock buffer:* To prepare 500 ml, add 116.9 g of NaCl, 50 ml of 1 M Tris–HCl (pH 7.4), 50 ml of 0.5 M EDTA (pH 8.0), and adjust volume with deionized water to 500 ml. Store at room temperature.

2. *RNase A (10 mg/ml) solution:* To make 10 ml, dissolve 100 mg of RNase A in 1× RNase buffer. Make 1-ml aliquots and store at −20°C.

3. *Washing solution A (5× SSC–10 mM DTT):* To prepare 1 liter, add 200 ml of 20× SSC stock solution and adjust volume with deionized water to 1 liter. Just before use add 1 g of DTT.

4. *Washing solution B (50% formamide–2× SSC–10 mM DTT):* To make 1 liter, add 500 ml of formamide and 100 ml of 20× SSC stock solution and adjust volume with deionized water to 1 liter. Just before using, pour 400 ml into two staining glass dishes, warm up one of them to 65°C and the other to 37°C, and then add to both 0.4 g of DTT.

5. *RNase solution:* For 400 ml add 40 ml of 10× RNase buffer and 800 μl of 10 mg/ml RNase A and adjust volume with deionized water to 400 ml. Just before using transfer to a glass staining dish and warm up to 37°C in a water bath.

6. *Alcohol solutions:* Add 9.3 g of ammonium acetate to 30, 50, 70, and 95% ethanol solutions used in Section B, step 8.

Steps

1. Remove the slides one by one and place them vertically against the wall of a 250-ml beaker containing 200 ml of washing solution A in a water bath at 51°C. During this procedure, if the chamber was humid enough the coverslip covering the section should come off easily. If necessary, to aid detachment, push the coverslip gently. Then place the slide in a metallic rack submerged in a glass staining dish containing 400 ml of washing solution A at 51°C in a water bath. Leave for 30 min with constant agitation. All of the following steps are performed in glass staining dishes containing 400 ml of prewarmed solutions at the indicated temperature.

2. Remove metallic rack and place in washing solution B at 65°C in a water bath. Leave for 20–30 min with constant shaking.

3. Rinse slides by dipping the rack a few times in 1× RNase buffer.

4. Transfer rack to the RNase solution at 37°C and incubate for 30 min in a water bath. To remove air bubbles shake the rack manually vigorously two to three times during the incubation period .

5. Rinse slides in 1× RNase buffer at 37°C for 5 min.

6. Incubate in washing solution B at 50°C for 3 hr or overnight at 37°C. To remove air bubbles shake manually vigorously two to three times during the first 30 min of the incubation period.

7. Wash with 2× SSC at 37°C for 30 min.

8. Wash with 0.1× SSC at 37°C for 30 min.

9. Dehydrate sections by dipping for 2 min in 30, 50, 70, and 95% series of ethanol each containing ammonium acetate. Then dip twice in 100% ethanol without ammonium acetate.

10. After air-drying, slides are ready to use for autoradiography. Slides can be left in a glass staining dish with desiccant wrapped in aluminum foil for a few days.

E. AUTORADIOGRAPHY

Solutions

1. *NTB-2 emulsion:* Melt the emulsion in a water bath at 42°C for 30 min. In a safelight dark room dilute the emulsion 1:1 by adding 118 ml of deionized water. Make aliquots of approximately 50 ml in polyethylene tubes. Wrap the tube carefully with aluminum foil and store at 4°C.

2. *Plastic staining dish:* Add 5–6 spoons of desiccant to the compartment for the drying agent in the lid of the dish. Cover the perforated slide with tissue paper to prevent small particles of desiccant from falling on top of the emulsion.

Steps

1. In a safelight dark room melt the diluted NTB-2 emulsion (keep the container wrapped in aluminum foil) in a water bath at 42°C for 30 min. Mix by gentle inversion to avoid air bubbles. The emulsion can be reused five or six times if kept wrapped in aluminum foil at 4°C.

2. Dip the slides in the emulsion one at a time, allowing each to drain vertically for a few seconds, and place them in a plastic rack. Once all the slides are dipped, place rack in a plastic staining dish containing desiccant. Wrap the box in aluminum foil before taking it out of the dark room.

3. To allow the emulsion to dry, keep the sealed boxes at room temperature for 1 hr. Then leave them at 4°C for the desired period. Exposure time is determined empirically for each probe. A good practice is to work with two sets of slides and to develop the first set after 2 weeks of exposure.

F. DEVELOPING AND STAINING

Solutions

1. *Developer:* Heat 3.8 liters of water to 52°C on a hot stirring plate; slowly add 595 g of developer until dissolved. Keep at 4°C in a bottle wrapped with aluminum foil. Before use, take 400 ml and leave to warm up to 17°C in a glass staining dish.

2. *Fixer:* To 3.8 liters of water, add slowly 687 g of powder while on stirring plate until dissolved. Keep at 4°C in a bottle wrapped with aluminum foil. Before use take 400 ml and leave to warm up to 17°C in a glass staining dish.

3. *0.1% Toluidine blue:* To prepare 500 ml, dissolve 1 g of toluidine blue in 400 ml of deionized water and adjust to a total of 500 ml. Filter through filter paper and keep at room temperature.

4. *0.5% acetic acid solution:* To make 500 ml, add 50 ml of acetic acid to 450 ml of deionized water. Keep at room temperature.

5. *10% SDS:* To prepare 100 ml, solubilize 10 g of SDS in 80 ml of deionized water, adjust the pH to 7.0 with a few drops of a 10 N solution of NaOH, and complete to a total of 100 ml. Store at room temperature.

6. *Glass coverslips:* Clean the coverslips with a soft tissue paper and then remove the dust by dipping several times in ethanol. It is important to use clean coverslips because dust interferes with dark-field photomicrography.

Steps

All incubations and washings are performed in glass staining dishes containing 400 ml of the appropriate solutions.

1. Remove box with slides from the refrigerator and bring to room temperature.

2. In a safelight dark room, take the plastic rack with the slides out of the box and immerse in developer for 2 min, rinse in distilled water for 20 sec, and then fix for 5 min. All solutions must be at 17°C.

3. Wash in deionized water three to four times. The subsequent steps are performed under normal light conditions.

4. Immerse the sections in 0.1% toluidine blue for 30 sec to obtain a light blue staining. If overstaining occurs, destain in 0.5% acetic acid until background disappears in the emulsion around the tissues.

5. Dehydrate the sections by dipping for 2 min through a series of 30, 50, and 70% and twice in 100% ethanol.

6. Immerse in xylene and leave overnight to clear the sections.

7. Remove slides individually, let drain a little (do not let slides dry out), put a drop of mounting medium over the section, and carefully overlay with a clean coverslip. Remove the air bubbles from the mounting medium by gently pressing the coverslip. While the back of the slide is still wet, scrape the back of the slide with a razor blade, taking care not to scratch the glass. Slides are left for 1 day in a chemical hood to allow mounting medium to dry.

8. To eliminate residual emulsion slides should be carefully cleaned with a 0.1% SDS solution, then rinsed in deionized water and let to dry. Before observing the slides under the microscope it is convenient to clean once with 100% ethanol to eliminate dust particles.

IV. Comments

Using the protocol described in this article, we have obtained consistent results for *in situ* hybridization analysis of several families of genes. The protocol has been successfully used with mouse embryos in all the stages analyzed, from E7.5 to E17.5, and with different mouse tissue sections (Figs. 1A–D).

V. Pitfalls

Some of the most common problems encountered during *in situ* hybridization are listed below and exemplified in Fig. 2.

1. High background is always a potential problem and the most common when performing *in situ* hybridization. It is recognized by nonspecific labeling of the section hybridized with the sense-strand riboprobe and can be avoided if special care is taken in the following steps: During the hybridization procedure use freshly prepared humidifying solution, be sure that the chamber is humid enough and has been sealed properly to avoid evaporation of the hybridization

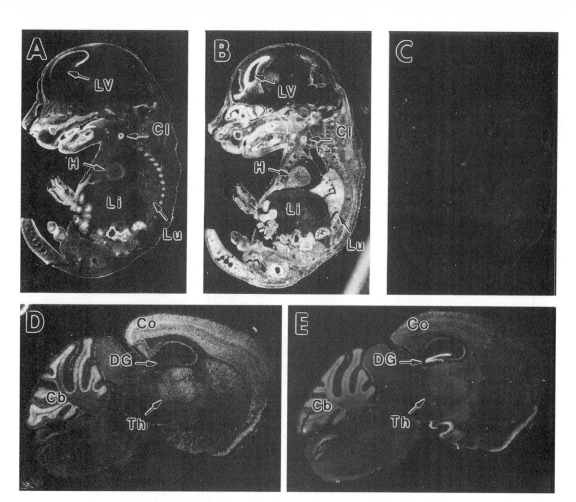

FIGURE 1 Examples of *in situ* hybridizations of embryos and mouse tissue sections. (A–C) Differential and specific signals obtained after hybridization of three different ^{35}S-labeled riboprobes to serial sections of a 16.5-day mouse embryo. (D, E) Hybridization signals of two different ^{35}S-labeled riboprobes hybridized to sagittal serial sections from a 6-week adult mouse brain. Cb, cerebellum; Cl, clavicle; Co, cortex; DG, dentate gyrus; H, heart; Li, liver; Lu, lung; LV, lateral ventricule; Th, thalamus.

solution. Leave the humid chamber during the hybridization step in a humidified incubator. During the washing, be sure to use prewarmed solutions and at the indicated temperatures, two or three degrees lower can make a big difference. Use constant shaking during the washes to increase interchange and to remove air bubbles. Figure 2A is an example of the background obtained when the hybridization solution has evaporated during overnight incubation at 52°C. High background is detected over the entire section and over the slide where the edges of the coverslip were located (arrows).

2. RNase contamination must always be kept in mind. In addition to the indications mentioned above, if *in situ* hybridization experiments will be performed routinely, the glass dish for RNase treatment should be labeled and kept apart from the rest. RNase contamination can be suspected if a known antisense positive control does not give the expected signal, or when differences in the intensity of the hybridization signal do not correlate with cellular density or the histology of the section. Figure 2B represents an example in which the hybridization signal does not correlate exactly with the corticomedullary structures found in the thymus.

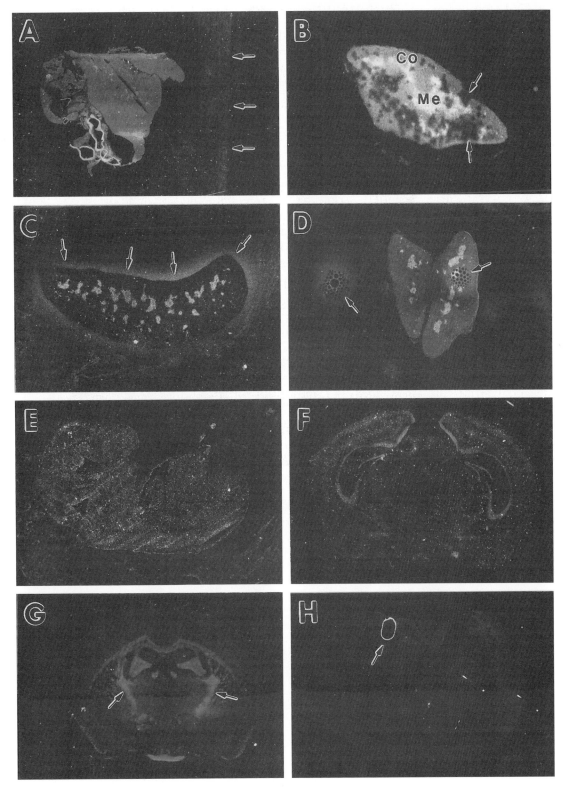

FIGURE 2 Examples of problems during *in situ* hybridization experiments. (A) High background due to evaporation of hybridization buffer. (B) Hybridization signal does not correlate with the histology of the section due to RNase contamination. (C) Nonspecific signal around the section produced by an uneven coating of the emulsion. (D) Air bubbles trapped in the emulsion. (E) High background produced by a siliconized slide. (F) Salt precipitation in the section due to poor extraction during the dehydration steps. (G) Artifactual signal from tissue structures due to overdehydration of section before fixation. (H) Signal produced by a pigmented structure. Co, cortex; Me, medulla.

3. The NTB-2 Kodak emulsion has an advantage over other emulsions in that it can be reused several times. The original stock solution must be diluted 1:1 with deionized water. The undiluted emulsion gives a nonspecific signal around the tissue due to uneven coating of the slide (Fig. 2C). Also, air bubbles are more easily trapped in the undiluted emulsion (Fig. 2D).

4. Dust particles and precipitated salt give a strong signal under dark-field illumination and can deteriorate or mask a good hybridization signal. To avoid this kind of problem, most of the steps are performed under the hood, all solutions are filtered, and coverslips are rinsed with ethanol. Some authors recommend the use of siliconized coverslips; however, we have not observed advantages with this procedure and in some cases using old siliconized coverslips we have obtained disastrous results with nonspecific signals all over the section and slide (Fig. 2E). During the dehydration step, after the washing, to efficiently extract the salts and avoid precipitation, the slides must be left for at least 2 min in each alcoholic solution and with constant shaking. In Fig. 2F is illustrated the type of background produced by salt precipitation when the section is not properly dehydrated. Artifactual signals are evenly distributed all over the section.

5. After fixation and dehydration, and before hybridization, the sections should appear almost transparent. If before fixation the sections are left air-drying for a long time, we have observed that they are not transparent, and under dark-field illumination some tissue structures become very apparent and these can be wrongly interpreted as a positive signal (Fig. 2G). Also, certain tissues like red blood cells, particularly in the heart chambers and pigmented structures like the eyeball, can give artifacts easily interpreted as a positive signal (Fig. 2H).

REFERENCES

Angerer, L. M., and Angerer, R. C. (1992) In "In Situ Hybridization" (D. G. Wilkinson, ed.), p. 15. IRL Press, Oxford.

Cox, H. K., Deleon, D. V., Angerer, L. M., and Angerer, R. C. (1984) Detection of mRNAs in sea urchin embryos by in situ hybridization using asymmetric RNA probes. Dev. Biol. 101, 485–502.

Guant, S. J. (1991) Expression patterns of mouse Hox genes: Clues to an understanding of developmental and evolutionary strategies. Bio Essays 13, 505–513.

Scholer, H. R. (1991) Octomania: The POU factor in murine development. Trends Biochem. Sci. 14, 52–56.

Simmons, D. M., Arriza, J. L., and Swanson, L. W. (1989) A complete protocol for in situ hybridization of messenger RNAs in brain and other tissues with radio-labeled single-standed RNA probes. J. Histotechnol. 12, 169–181.

Wilkinson, D. G., and Green, J. (1991) In "Postimplantation Mammalian Embryos" (A. J. Coop and D. L. Cockroft, eds.), p. 155. IRL Press, Oxford.

In Situ Detection of Human Papillomavirus DNA after Polymerase Chain Reaction Amplification

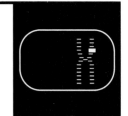

Gerard J. Nuovo

I. Introduction

Sensitive molecular biology techniques, such as Southern blot hybridization and the polymerase chain reaction (PCR) have greatly enhanced our understanding of infectious disease processes and oncogenesis. An important limitation of these techniques is that the DNA or RNA extraction prior to analysis precludes histologic correlation. This drawback is overcome by *in situ* hybridization; however, one cannot reliably detect low copy numbers in a given cell with *in situ* hybridization (Nuovo *et al.*, 1991a,b, 1992; Nuovo, 1992). Thus, a negative result with *in situ* hybridization does not disprove the presence of the target. It is now possible to do PCR in intact cell and tissue preparations and, thus, to combine the extreme sensitivity of PCR with the cell localizing ability of *in situ* hybridization (Nuovo *et al.*, 1991a,b, 1992; Nuovo, 1992).

II. Materials and Instrumentation

The silane-coated microscopic glass slides were obtained from ONCOR Corporation (Cat. No. S1308). As of this writing, it is recommended that one use autoclavable plastic coverslips from BelArt or ONCOR (Cat. No. S1370-14). The thermocyler was obtained from Perkin–Elmer Corporation. For most experiments the DNA Thermal Cycler (Cat. No. N801-0150) was used, although equivalent results were obtained with the 480 and 9600 models. All of the reagents for PCR are included in the GeneAmp kit from Perkin–Elmer (Cat. No. N801-0055). The human papillomavirus (HPV) probes and biotin detection system may be obtained from a variety of sources; we use the HPV *in situ* detection kits from Digene Diagnostics (Cat. No. 4206 0100) and ONCOR (Cat. No. S6800-KIT). The detection system, which employs a streptavidin–alkaline phosphatase conjugate, and the chromagen blue tetrazolium, which, in the presence of 5-bromo-4-chloro-3-indolynitrophosphate, yields a purple-blue precipitate at the site of hybridization, is from the HPV *in situ* kit available from Digene or ONCOR Corporation (Cat. No. S4200-Box). The counterstain, nuclear fast red, which stains nuclei pale pink and does not stain cytoplasm, is also part of the ONCOR HPV *in situ* kit. Pepsin (from Digene Diagnostics as part of their HPV *in situ* hybridization kit) was employed, although equivalent results were obtained with proteinase K (ONCOR, Cat. No. S4508). Formamide (Cat. No. S4117), dextran sulfate (Cat. No. S4010), 20× SCC (Cat. No. S2600), and HPV probes were obtained from ONCOR. HPV-infected tissues, either cervical, vulvar, or penile low- or high-grade squamous intraepithelial lesions, were obtained from the surgical pathology files. All tissues are fixed in 10% neutral buffered formalin; fixatives that contain heavy metals such as mercury and picric acid (e.g., Bouin's solution) will not allow for successful PCR *in situ* hybridization or *in situ* hybridization (Nuovo and Silverstein, 1988; Greer *et al.*, 1990).

III. Procedures

A. *IN SITU* HYBRIDIZATION

See Nuovo (1992).

Solutions

1. *Protease solution:* Add 2 mg/ml pepsin or trypsin to a solution of 0.1 *N* HCl in water. The solution can be kept at −20°C and thawed when ready to use.

2. *In situ hybridization probe cocktail* (for HPV genomic probes, although one may substitute other probes): Add 25 μl of formamide, 15 μl of 25% dextran sulfate, 5 μl of 20× SCC, and 5 μl of the probe (stock solution of 1 μg/ml biotin-labeled probe).

3. *Wash solution:* The wash solution contains 2.5% bovine serum albumin and 0.2× SSC (or 30 m*M* sodium chloride) and is heated to 45°C.

4. *Detection solution:* The detection solution contains 0.1 *M* Tris–HCl (pH 9 to 9.5) and 0.1 *M* NaCl.

5. *Substrate solution:* The substrate solution is the detection solution to which is added the chromagen. For every 200 ml of the substrate solution add 500 μl of nitroblue tetrazolium and 500 μl of 5-bromo-4-chloro-3-indolynitrophosphate.

Steps

1. Place several 4-μm paraffin-embedded sections on a silane-coated glass slide.

2. Wash slides in xylene for 5 min; wash slides in 100% ethanol for 5 min; then air-dry.

3. Digest in pepsin (2 mg/ml for 4 to 20 min).

4. Inactivate protease by washing in 0.1 *M* Tris (pH 7.5) and 0.1 *M* NaCl for 3 min.

5. Wash slides in 95% ethanol for 3 min and 100% ethanol for 5 min; then air-dry.

6. Add 5–10 μl of the probe cocktail to a given tissue section.

7. Overlay with a plastic coverslip cut slightly larger than the tissue section.

8. Place slide on a hot plate (95 to 100°C) for 5 min.

9. Remove bubbles over tissue gently with a toothpick.

10. Place slides in a humidity chamber at 37°C for 2 hr.

11. Remove coverslips; hold down one end with fingernail and lift off coverslip with toothpick.

12. Place in wash solution for 10 min at 40–60°C (higher temperature to determine HPV type or if background is a problem; lower temperature to increase detection rate of novel HPV types).

13. Wipe off excess wash solution and put slides in a humidity chamber; do not let slides dry out.

14. Add 50 μl of streptavidin–alkaline phosphatase conjugate per tissue section.

15. Incubate in humidity chamber for 20 min at 37°C.

16. Wash slides at room temperature for 3 min in a detection solution.

17. Place slides in substrate solution.

18. Incubate slides for 30 min to 2 hr, checking results periodically under microscope.

19. Counterstain with nuclear fast red and coverslip; view under microscope.

B. PCR *IN SITU* HYBRIDIZATION

See Nuovo (1992).

Solutions

1. *Amplifying solution:* Add 3 μl of the GeneAmp buffer, 5.6 μl of MgCl$_2$ (25 mM stock solution), 4.6 μl of dNTPs (stock prepared as per the GeneAmp kit), 1 μl of primer 1 and primer 2 (stock solution 20 μM), and 1 μl of bovine serum albumin (stock solution 2% w/v); add water to 29 μl. For three reactions, remove 6 μl and place in a separate tube.

2. *Protease, probe cocktail, wash, detection, and substrate solutions:* See Section A.

Steps

1–5. See Section A.

6. Add 10 μl of amplifying solution per tissue section. If possible, have three tissue sections per glass slide: one tissue, no PCR; one tissue PCR with Taq polymerase; and final tissue, PCR with no Taq.

7. Overlay solution with plastic coverslip, anchor with nail polish, and place slide in aluminum "boat" directly on thermal cycler (Fig. 1).

8. Time delay file—82°C for 7 min.

9. At the onset of this file add 1.0 μl of Taq to tube on ice that contains 6 μl of the amplifying solution (this would be for 30 μl total and for three separate reactions).

10. At 55°C, lift one edge of the coverslip gently and add 2 μl of the Taq solution per tissue section; overlay with preheated mineral oil.

11. Switch to time delay file—94°C for 3 min.

12. Link this time delay file to a cycling file of 55°C for 2 min and 94°C for 1 min for 20–40 cycles. At conclusion link to soak file of 4°C. Remove mineral oil with xylene and ethanol washes. Air-dry.

13. Proceed to step 6 in Section A (standard *in situ* hybridization).

1. Use paraffin-embedded, formalin-fixed tissue or formalin-fixed cells, place on Silane slides; protease digestion

2. Add amplifying solution, plastic coverslip, and anchor with nail polish

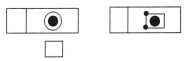

3. Place in aluminum boat, then on DNA thermal cycler

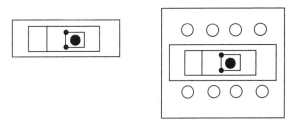

4. Add Taq DNA polymerase at 60 °C by gently lifting coverslip, overlay with mineral oil, cycle

FIGURE 1 PCR *in situ* hybridization protocol. PCR *in situ* hybridization done on the block of the DNA thermal cycler. The glass slides may be placed in an aluminum foil "boats." A plastic coverslip is placed over the amplifying solution. The coverslip may then be anchored with a drop of nail polish and overlaid with mineral oil during cycling. The boats and slides conduct the heat well and the boats retain the mineral oil during the PCR phase of the technique.

IV. Comments

The most commons problem encountered with *in situ* hybridization are background and the absence of a signal. Background may be defined as the presence of a hybridization signal with a specific probe in areas of the tissue where the target should not be present (i.e., normal endocervical cells or in basal cells with HPV). Of course, in some instances one may not be sure where the *in situ* signal should localize. A more strict definition of background would be a hybridization signal when the labeled plasmid vector is employed (the plasmid is the vehicle used to clone the probe of interest). Background is the result of nonspecific binding of the probe to nontarget molecules. Two simple and logical ways to deal with background are to decrease the concentration of the probe and to increase the stringency of the posthybridization wash. If background is a problem, first try increasing the temperature of the wash by 10° increments. If background remains a problem at 55°C, then decrease the concentration of the probe 10-fold.

Another potential problem with *in situ* hybridization is the absence of a hybridization signal. I recommend following a flowchart type of problem-solving tree, which is presented in Fig. 2. Note the importance of the *alu* probe, which serves as a positive control, i.e., as a way to check that the conditions are adequate for *in situ* hybridization, as this sequence is repeated many times in the human genome (Fig. 3).

The probe size for standard *in situ* hybridization is 100 to 250 base pairs (bp); however, one may want to use much smaller (20 to 40 bp) probes called oligoprobes.

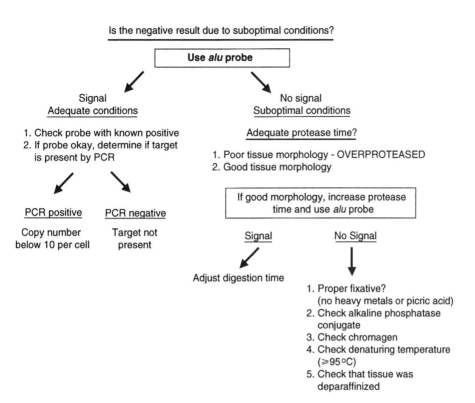

Is the negative result due to suboptimal conditions?

Use *alu* probe

Signal
Adequate conditions

1. Check probe with known positive
2. If probe okay, determine if target is present by PCR

PCR positive

Copy number below 10 per cell

PCR negative

Target not present

No signal
Suboptimal conditions

Adequate protease time?

1. Poor tissue morphology - OVERPROTEASED
2. Good tissue morphology

If good morphology, increase protease time and use *alu* probe

Signal

Adjust digestion time

No Signal

1. Proper fixative? (no heavy metals or picric acid)
2. Check alkaline phosphatase conjugate
3. Check chromagen
4. Check denaturing temperature (≥95°C)
5. Check that tissue was deparaffinized

FIGURE 2 Flowchart for a negative result with the *in situ* hybridization. The figure details a step-by-step approach to follow if a hybridization signal is not evident with *in situ* analysis.

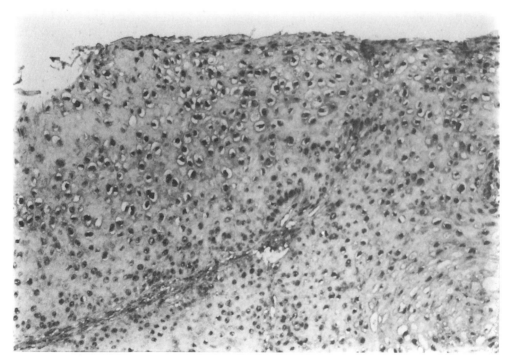

FIGURE 3 Usefulness of a positive control for *in situ* hybridization. The *alu* probe detects the *alu* family of highly repeated sequences in human DNA which make up about 5% of the human genome. The presence of a hybridization signal with the probe in most of the cells in the human tissue demonstrates that the various conditions for *in situ* hybridization, notably protease digestion, fixation, hybridization, and detection, are adequate.

There are two main reasons to use oligoprobes: first, they are more readily available than the larger probes, which require a cloned sequence of DNA. One only needs to know the sequence of the target of interest, readily available in the literature, to generate an oligoprobe. Second, one is obliged to use an oligoprobe internal to the sequence being amplified in PCR *in situ* hybridization to ensure that the signal is indeed the PCR product. Because oligoprobes are much shorter than a "standard" probe, there is a substantial reduction in the number of base pair matches and thus the strength of the hybridized complex compared with the larger probes. The practical consequence is that the wash conditions must be carefully chosen so as to minimize background but not to lose the signal. In practical terms, I have seen the signal lost for a 20mer oligoprobe with a posthybridization wash of 30 mM salt at 45°C; under these conditions the signal for a larger homologous probe would remain intact. Hence, I use different probe cocktail and posthybridization wash conditions for oligoprobes. Specifically, for the probe cocktail with an oligoprobe, I decrease the formamide concentration to 10% and the salt in the wash solution is increased to 300 mM (2× SSC).

Note that the Taq polymerase is not added to the tissue section until the temperature reaches 55°C. In any PCR reaction, several pathways compete with target-specific DNA synthesis. These include mispriming, DNA repair, and primer oligomerization. If the hot start modification is not employed, these "unwanted" pathways can overwhelm target-specific DNA synthesis such that a large amount of DNA is synthesized that is *mostly nonspecific!* This is not surprising when one considers that there is far more nontarget and primer DNA in a reaction mixture relative to target DNA. It has been shown that under nonhot start conditions that the detection threshold for the target of interest with standard PCR may be greater than several thousand copies, not the 1–100 copies most articles quote (Nuovo *et al.*, 1991b). Nonspecific DNA synthesis is, however, greatly curtailed by the hot start modification. The end result is that one can reliably detect one copy per tissue DNA extract with the hot start modification using PCR. For PCR *in situ* hybridization, it has been demonstrated that the hot start modification readily allows for the routine detection of one target per cell using a single primer pair (Fig. 4) (Nuovo *et al.*, 1991b; Nuovo, 1992).

To demonstrate the utility of PCR *in situ* hybridization for the analysis of HPV in tissue sections, let us examine two specific scenarios.

A. THE EQUIVOCAL PENILE OR VULVAR BIOPSY

About 40% of papillary lesions of the vulva or penis that are clinically suggestive of an HPV-induced condyloma (i.e., low-grade SIL) lack the diagnostic features of this lesion on histological examination (Nuovo, 1992). Terms such as equivocal for condyloma, suggestive of condyloma, or borderline condyloma may be used for such lesions. Although these terms reflect the difficulty inherent in making the histological diagnosis, they may be confusing to the clinician and, perhaps more importantly, to the patient who may be understandably confused as to whether he or she has a sexually transmitted disease.

About 10–20% of these equivocal penile and vulvar lesions are HPV positive as determined by either Southern blot hybridization or PCR (Nuovo *et al.*, 1990); however, the histological markers of HPV detection in such tissues cannot be ascertained as the DNA extraction prior to molecular analysis precludes histological correlation. This problem is eliminated with PCR *in situ* hybridization. Figure 5 shows a representative case. Note how a weak signal is evident with standard *in situ* hybridization for HPV 6/11. A much more intense signal is evident in many more cells if *in situ* hybridization is preceded by PCR. Such analyses have shown that about 10–20% of equivocal tissues contain HPV DNA as demonstrated by

A

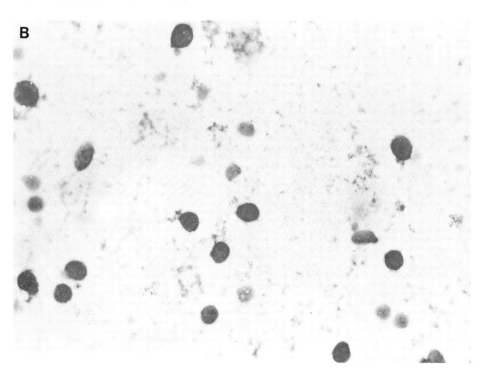

B

FIGURE 4 Detection of HPV DNA by PCR *in situ* and *in situ* hybridization. HPV DNA 16 was not detected in the SiHa cell line which contains one copy of the viral genome by *in situ* hybridization after PCR with a single primer pair under standard conditions (A). When, however, the hot start technique was used, viral DNA was detectable by PCR *in situ* hybridization with the single primer pair (B).

PCR *in situ* hybridization and that a focally thickened granular layer in conjunction with epithelial cervices and para- or hyperkeratosis is the marker for HPV detection in such equivocal cases (see Fig. 5) (Nuovo *et al.*, 1992a).

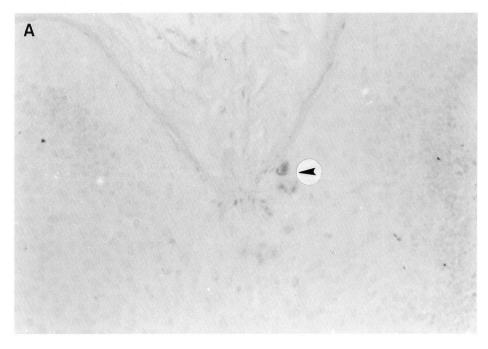

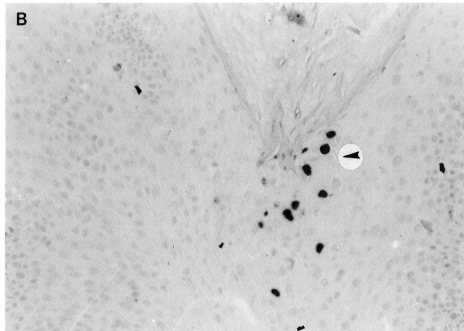

FIGURE 5 Histologic and molecular analysis of an equivocal penile lesion. This penile biopsy was taken from a lesion clinically suggestive of a condyloma. HPV DNA was detected in rare cells by standard *in situ* hybridization (A, note the weak signal). After PCR amplification of the serial section, many more cells had a detectable *in situ* hybridization signal (B, note that the signal is intense). Histologic analysis of such equivocal lesions positive for HPV DNA shows that the virus often localizes to a focally thickened granular layer at times found in epithelial crevices (C).

B. THE CERVICAL SQUAMOUS CELL OR ADENOCARCINOMA

Although most cervical carcinomas contain HPV DNA and RNA, the detection rate varies considerably with the detection method. While the rate of HPV detection

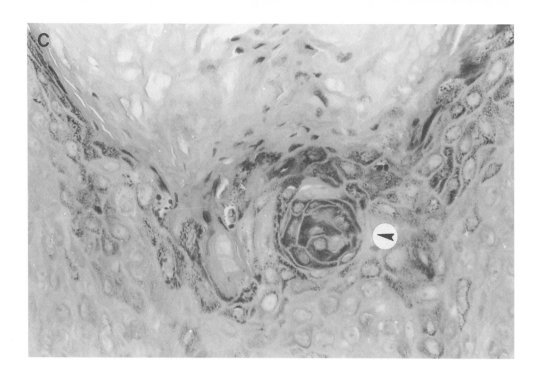

is greater than 90% with Southern blot hybridization or PCR, which have detection thresholds of about one virus per 100 to 10,000 cells, respectively, it is often about 30% with *in situ* hybridization, for which there must be 10 viruses per cell for a positive result. Even when viral nucleic acids are detected in cervical cancers by *in situ* hybridization, most cancer cells appear to be HPV negative. It is unclear whether these HPV-negative carcinoma cells contain low copy numbers of the virus or indeed contain no viral DNA or RNA. By using PCR *in situ* hybridization, we have shown that most cancer cells do contain HPV (Fig. 6) (Nuovo, submitted for publication). Further, we have modified the procedure to detect RNA by using a reverse transcriptase (RT) step (Nuovo *et al.*, 1993a,c). RT PCR *in situ* analysis of such lesions has shown that most cancer cells contain the E6 and E7–E1 spliced transcripts. This finding is consistent with the hypothesis that the malignancy develops from a subclone of HPV-infected cells where the transcriptionally active viral DNA has integrated into the host genome. Detailed protocols for RT PCR *in situ* hybridization are available (Nuovo, 1992).

V. Pitfalls

1. If tissue morphology is poor, the most likely explanation is protease overdigestion. Decrease the protease digestion time accordingly.

2. Always include an HPV-positive tissue with each experiment. Vulvar or penile biopsies that show the granular cell changes (perinuclear halos and nuclear atypia) of a condyloma invariably are HPV positive, usually for HPV 6 or 11.

3. Note that the optimal concentrations of the Mg^{2+} and Taq polymerase are greater than those for standard PCR. This may reflect difficulty in entry of these reagents to the site of DNA amplification and, in part, sequestration of the Mg^{2+} by cellular components. Consistent with this hypothesis is our observation that one may use 10-fold less Taq polymerase with the addition of 1 mg/ml bovine serum albumin (BSA) to the amplifying solution in PCR *in situ* hybridization;

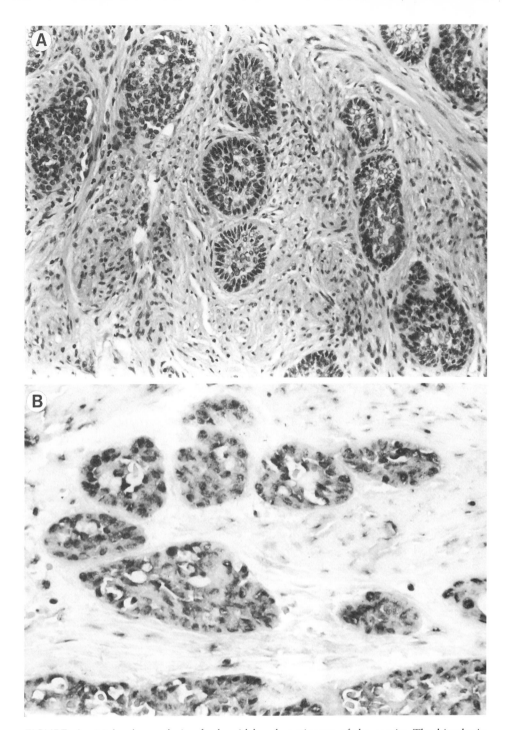

FIGURE 6 Molecular analysis of adenoid basal carcinoma of the cervix. The histologic features of this tumor are seen in A. HPV 18 RNA corresponding to the E6 ORF is detected in most of the cancer cells (B) using the RT *in situ* PCR technique.

BSA can block absorption of the enzyme to the glass slide or plastic coverslip (Nuovo *et al.*, 1993b).

4. Add mineral oil as needed to prevent evaporation of the amplifying solution during the PCR step of PCR *in situ* hybridization.

REFERENCES

Greer, C. E., Peterson, S. L., Kiviat, N. B., and Manos, M. M. (1991) PCR amplification from paraffin-embedded tissues: Effects of fixative and fixative times. *Am. J. Clin. Pathol.* **95,** 117–124.

Nuovo, G. J. (1992) "PCR *in situ* Hybridization. Protocols and Applications." Raven Press, New York.

Nuovo, G. J., and Silverstein, S. J. (1988) Comparison of formalin, buffered formalin, and Bouin's fixation on the detection of human papillomavirus DNA extracted from genital lesions. *Lab. Invest.* **59,** 720–724.

Nuovo, G. J., Hochman, H., Eliezri, Y. D., Comite, S., Lastarria, D., and Silvers, D. (1990) Human papillomavirus DNA in penile lesions histologically negative for condylomata: Analysis by *in situ* hybridization and the polymerase chain reaction. *Am. J. Surg. Pathol.* **14,** 829–836.

Nuovo, G. J., MacConnell, P., Forde, A., and Delvenne, P. (1991a) Detection of human papillomavirus DNA in formalin fixed tissues by *in situ* hybridization after amplification by the polymerase chain reaction. *Am. J. Pathol.* **139,** 847–854.

Nuovo, G. J., Gallery, F., MacConnell, P., Becker, J., and Bloch, W. (1991b) An improved technique for the detection of DNA by *in situ* hybridization after PCR-amplification. *Am. J. Pathol.* **139,** 1239–1244.

Nuovo, G. J., Becker, J., MacConnell, P., Margiotta, M., Comite, S., and Hochman, H. (1992) Histological distribution of PCR-amplified HPV 6 and 11 DNA in penile lesions. *Am. J. Surg. Pathol.* **16,** 269–275.

Nuovo, G. J., Lidonocci, K., MacConnell, P., and Lane, B. (1993a) Intracellular localization of PCR-amplified hepatitis C cDNA. *Am. J. Pathol.* **17,** 683–690.

Nuovo, G. J., Gallery, F., Hom, R., MacConnell, P., and Bloch, W. (1993b) Importance of different variables for optimizing *in situ* detection of PCR-amplified DNA. *PCR Method Appl.* **2,** 305–312.

Nuovo, G. J., Forde, A., MacConnell, P., and Fahrenwald, R. (1993c) *In situ* detection of PCR-amplified HIV-1 nucleic acids and tumor necrosis factor cDNA in cervical tissues. *Am. J. Pathol.* **143,** 40–48.

Accurate Quantitation of mRNA Species by Polymerase Chain Reaction and Solid-Phase Minisequencing

Ann-Christine Syvänen and Leena Peltonen

I. Introduction

Reliable quantitation of specific mRNA populations is of essential importance in numerous research problems, reaching from quantitation of rare mRNA species in human biopsy samples to the analysis of *in vitro*-expressed DNA constructs. Typically the presence of a mRNA population is sensitively detected using the polymerase chain reaction (PCR) after synthesis of a first-strand cDNA by reverse transcriptase (Kawasaki, 1990). A limitation of this approach is that it does not allow quantitation of the mRNA population of interest. The amount of PCR product obtained from a sample does not reflect the amount of RNA subjected to the amplification for two main reasons. First, the efficiency of a PCR cycle depends on the amount of template present in the reaction, the PCR being exponential only at low concentrations of template (Syvänen *et al.*, 1988). Second, small differences in the reaction conditions, e.g., impurities of the sample, may cause significant variation in the amount of PCR product obtained. For these reasons an accurate quantitative PCR analysis requires that a known amount of an internal standard is coamplified with the RNA to be quantified in the same reaction (Gilliland *et al.*, 1990). The sequence of the primers and the size of the PCR product also affect the efficiency of the amplification. Therefore, the internal standard should be as similar as possible to the sample RNA, but the two PCR products must differ from each other by some property so that their relative amounts can be determined after the amplification. For quantification of RNA, the internal standard should preferably be RNA included in the reaction before the reverse transcription reaction to control also the efficiency of the cDNA synthesis step.

In the present method an artificial RNA standard, prepared from a DNA template by transcription with an RNA polymerase (Melton *et al.*, 1984), which differs from the RNA species to be quantified only at a single nucleotide, is reverse transcribed and amplified together with the RNA to be quantified. After the amplification the ratio of the PCR products obtained from the two sequences is determined using the solid-phase minisequencing method, which detects single nucleotide variations (Syvänen *et al.*, 1990). Comparison of the ratio of the amounts of PCR products obtained from the standard RNA and the RNA in the sample with a standard curve prepared in parallel with mixtures of known amounts of the two RNA sequences allows accurate determination of the initial amount of the RNA molecules of interest in the initial sample (Fig. 1) (Ikonen *et al.*, 1992).

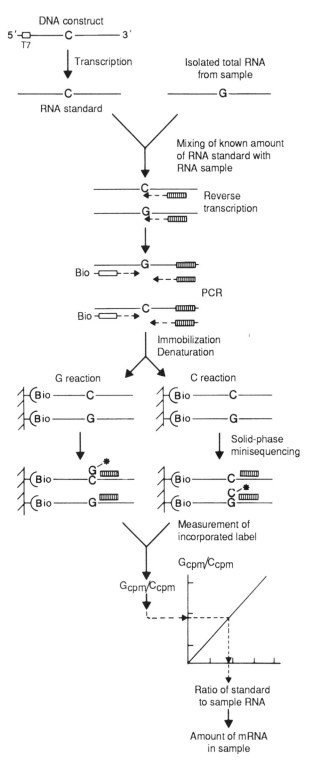

FIGURE 1 Principle of the method. A mixture of the standard and sample RNA is reverse transcribed and amplified using one biotinylated and one unbiotinylated PCR primer. The PCR product is captured in streptavidin-coated microtitration wells and denatured. The nucleotide that differs between the two sequences is detected in the captured DNA strand by two separate minisequencing reactions. In these reactions a detection step primer annealing immediately 3' of the variable nucleotide is elongated by Taq DNA polymerase with one single ^{3}H-labeled nucleoside triphosphate complementary to the nucleotide to be detected. The ratio of the incorporated labels reflects the initial ratio of the two RNA sequences. Adapted from Ikonen *et al.* (1992).

II. Materials and Instrumentation

T7 RNA polymerase (10–20 U/μl, Cat. No. P2075), DNase (RQ1 RNase free, 1U/μl, Cat. No. M6101), RNasin (20–40 U/μl, Cat. No. N2512), AMV reverse transcriptase (20–25 U/μl, Cat. No. M9004), and Taq DNA polymerase (2–5 U/μl, Cat. No. M1865) were from Promega Biotech. Ribonucleoside triphosphates ATP, CTP, GTP, and UTP (Cat. Nos. 1140956, 1140922, 1140957, and 1140949), deoxynucleoside triphosphates dATP, dCTP, dGTP, and dTTP (Cat. Nos. 1051440, 1051458, 1051466, and 195482), and yeast transfer RNA (Cat. No. 109495) were from Boehringer-Mannheim. The yeast transfer RNA was purified by phenol extraction and ethanol precipitation before use. ^{3}H-Labeled dATP, dCTP, dGTP, and dTTP (Cat. Nos. TRK 625, TRK 576 TRK 627, and TRK 633) were from Amersham. Bio-Gel P30 (Cat. No. 150-4150) and gelatin (Cat. No. 170-6537) were from Bio-Rad. Mineral oil (Cat. No. M-3516) was from Sigma. The reagents for the synthesis of the primers were from Applied Biosystems, except for the biotinyl phosphoramidite reagent (RPN 2012), which was from Amersham. The streptavidin-coated microtiter plates (Combiplate 8) were from Labsystems. Reagents of the highest purity grade from various sources were used for preparation of buffers and other solutions.

The following instruments are needed: centrifuge, spectrophotometer, shaker at 37°C, water bath for incubations at 37, 40, 42, and 50°C, programmable heat block for PCR, liquid scintillation counter, and, optionally, multichannel pipette or microtiter plate washer and access to oligonucleotide synthesis.

III. Procedures

A. DESIGN AND PREPARATION OF DNA TEMPLATES AND PRIMERS

1. DNA Templates

For preparation of the artificial RNA standards, two DNA fragments must be cloned into a plasmid vector (Gemini or Bluescript), which has the T7 (or SP6) RNA polymerase binding site. One of the plasmids should contain a DNA fragment with a sequence differing by one nucleotide from that of the RNA to be quantified, and the other plasmid should contain a sequence identical to the RNA to be analyzed. In the DNA template the variable nucleotide should preferably be preceded by a third nucleotide, so that only one labeled nucleotide will be incorporated into the minisequencing reaction. Prepare the DNA templates by standard cloning and site-directed mutagenesis techniques (Sambrook *et al.*, 1989) or with the aid of the PCR (Higuchi *et al.*, 1988). Linearize the plasmid DNA with a restriction enzyme that cleaves downstream of the site of the variable nucleotide and leaves a 5′ overhang sequence or a blunt end.

2. Primers

Design and synthesize the following three primers according to the sequence of the RNA to be quantified: a 3′ primer to serve as primer for the reverse transcription and as 3′-PCR primer, a 5′-PCR primer, which is biotinylated at its 5′ end, and a detection step primer for the minisequencing reaction. The PCR primers should preferably yield a short amplification product of about 80 to 200 bp spanning the site of the variable nucleotide. The primers should be 20–23 nucleotides long and have similar melting temperatures and noncomplementary 3′ ends (Innis and Gelfand, 1990). Introduce the biotin residue to the 5′-PCR primer using a biotinyl phosphoramidite reagent in the last step of the synthesis. The detection step primer should be complementary to the biotinylated strand of the PCR product immediately 3′ of the variable nucleotide and it should be 20 nucleotides long.

B. PREPARATION OF RNA STANDARDS BY *IN VITRO* TRANSCRIPTION

See Melton *et al.* (1984).

Solutions

1. *5× concentrated transcription buffer:* 200 mM Tris–HCl, pH 8.0, 30 mM MgCl$_2$, 10 mM spermidine, 50 mM NaCl. Store in aliquots at −20°C.

2. *rNTP mixture:* 2 mM ATP, 2 mM CTP, 2 mM GTP and 2 mM TTP in distilled autoclaved water. Store in aliquots at −20°C.

3. *100 mM dithiotheitol:* Store in aliquots at −20°C.

Steps

1. At room temperature add in the following order autoclaved water to give a final volume of 100 μl, 20 μl of 5× transcription buffer, 10 μl of 100 mM dithiothreitol, 25 μl of 2 mM rNTP mixture, 2 μg of linearized plasmid DNA, 100 units of RNasin, and 20 units of T7 RNA polymerase.

2. Incubate for 1.5 hr at 40°C.

3. Add 2 units of DNase.

4. Incubate for 15 min at 37°C.

5. Remove the excess rNTPs by gel filtration on a Bio-Gel P30 spin column prepared with autoclaved resin and RNase-free equipment (Sambrook *et al.*, 1989).

6. Extract once with phenol:chloroform and once with chloroform, and precipitate with ethanol (Sambrook *et al.*, 1989).

7. Dissolve the RNA preparation in 100 μl of autoclaved water and keep on ice. The RNA yield is typically 20–40 μg. Immediately measure the concentration of the synthesized RNA in a spectrophotometer at 260 nm and calculate the molecular concentration of the RNA according to the formula

$$\frac{A_{260 \text{ nm}} \times 0.033 \text{ g/liter} \times 6.023 \times 10^{23} \text{ molecules/mole}}{n \times 330 \text{ g/mole}}$$

where n = number of bases in the RNA.

8. Add RNasin to 1 unit/ml and store the RNAs at 4°C for a maximum of 4 weeks.

C. REVERSE TRANSCRIPTION AND PCR

Solutions

1. *Primers:* Dilute the 3′ primer to 20 μM, and the biotinylated 5′ primer to 4 μM in water. Store in aliquots at −20°C.

2. *RNA standards:* Dilute the RNA standards immediately prior to use in water containing 20 μg/ml yeast transfer RNA and 1 unit/ml RNasin (see step 1

TABLE I Preparation of the RNA Standard Mixtures [a]

RNA$_{st}$/RNA$_{sa}$	RNA$_{st}$		RNA$_{sa}$	
	μl	Molecules/μl	μl	Molecules/μl
0.04	10	400	10	10^4
0.1	10	10^3	10	10^4
0.4	10	4×10^3	10	10^4
1.0	10	10^4	10	10^4
4.0	10	4×10^4	10	10^4
10	10	10^5	10	10^4
—	10	10^4	—	—
—	—	—	10	10^4

[a] RNA$_{st}$ = artificial RNA with a sequence differing from that of the sample at one nucleotide. RNA$_{sa}$ = artificial RNA with a sequence identical to that of the sample RNA.

below). For the standard curve make mixtures with different molecular amounts of the RNA standards in 20 μl as shown in Table I. Keep the RNA dilutions on ice.

3. *dNTP mixture:* Prepare 2 m*M* dATP, 2 m*M* dCTP, 2 m*M* dGTP, and 2 m*M* dTTP in distilled water. Store in aliquots at $-20°$C.

4. *10× concentrated reverse transcription buffer:* Prepare 500 m*M* Tris–HCl, pH 8.1, 50 m*M* MgCl$_2$, 400 m*M* KCl, and 20 m*M* dithiothreitol. Store at $-20°$C.

5. *Reverse transcription mix:* Prepare a master mix by combining 5 μl of 10× reverse transcription buffer, 10 μl of 2 m*M* dNTP mixture, 2.5 μl of 20 μ*M* 3′ primer, 50 units of RNasin, 50 units of reverse transcriptase, and distilled water to 30 μl per reaction. Keep on ice until use.

6. *10× concentrated Taq DNA polymerase buffer:* Prepare 500 m*M* Tris–HCl, pH 8.8, 150 m*M* (NH$_4$)$_2$SO$_4$ 15 m*M* MgCl$_2$, 0.1% (v/v) Triton X-100, and 0.01% (w/v) gelatin. Store in aliquots at $-20°$C. Thaw completely before use.

7. *PCR mix:* Prepare a master mix by combining 5 μl of 10× Taq DNA polymerase buffer, 5 μl of 2 m*M* dNTP mixture, 2.5 μl of 20 μ*M* 3′ primer, 2.5 μl of 4 μ*M* biotinylated 5′ primer, and water to 25 μl per reaction. Keep at room temperature until use.

Steps

1. Add a known amount of diluted RNA standard to the samples from which the RNA is to be quantified. Note that the ratio of the amount of RNA standard to the amount of RNA in the sample should preferably be between 0.1 and 10. If the amount of RNA in the sample can vary over a wide range, it may be necessary to do the analysis using more than one amount of standard, e.g., 10^2, 10^4, and 10^6 molecules, or to perform a preliminary titration with a tenfold dilution series with between 10^2 and 10^8 molecules of the RNA standard. After addition of the standard, add water to 20 μl.

2. Add 30 μl of reverse transcription mix to the RNA samples and incubate for 10 min at room temperature followed by 60 min at 42°C. If necessary, the samples can be stored at $-20°$C after this step.

3. For PCR take a 20-μl aliquot of the reverse transcription reaction, add 25 μl of the PCR reaction mix, and overlay the sample with mineral oil. Include a

negative control with 20 μl of water in each series. Start the PCR by a "hot start" by first incubating the samples in the programmable heat block for 5 min at 95°C, followed by addition of 1.25 units of Taq DNA polymerase in 5 μl at 80°C. Carry out 30 PCR cycles of 1 min at 95°C, 1 min at an annealing temperature, which is determined by the sequence of the primers (usually between 50 and 60°C), and 1 min at 72°C. The amplified samples can be stored at −20°C.

D. SOLID-PHASE MINISEQUENCING

Solutions

1. *Buffer for the capturing reaction:* Prepare 20 mM sodium phosphate buffer, pH 7.5, 100 mM NaCl, and 0.1% (v/v) Tween 20. Store at 4°C.

2. *Wash solution:* Prepare 40 mM Tris–HCl, pH 8.8, 1 mM EDTA, 50 mM NaCl, and 0.1% Tween 20. Store at 4°C.

3. *Denaturing solution:* 50 mM NaOH. Store at room temperature.

4. *10× concentrated Taq DNA polymerase buffer:* See Section C, solution 6.

5. *Minisequencing reaction mix:* Prepare two master mixes, one for detection of the standard RNA sequence and the second for detection of the sample RNA sequence, by combining 5 μl of 10× Taq DNA polymerase buffer, 2 μl of 5 μM detection step primer, 0.1 μCi (usually 0.1 μl) of ^{3}H-labeled dNTP complementary to the nucleotide to be detected, 0.05 unit of Taq DNA polymerase, and distilled water to 50 μl per reaction. Prepare the mix during the capturing reaction, and store at room temperature until use.

Steps

1. Transfer two 10-μl aliquots of each amplified sample to streptavidin-coated microtiter wells. In each series include a negative control containing 10 μl of Taq DNA polymerase buffer for both minisequencing reactions. Add 40 μl of capturing buffer to each well. Seal the wells and incubate the plate for 1.5 hr at 37°C with gentle shaking.

2. Discard the contents of the wells. Wash the wells at room temperature three times by adding 200 μl of washing solution. Empty the wells thoroughly between the washes.

3. Add 100 μl of 50 mM NaOH to each well, and incubate at room temperature for 2–5 min.

4. Wash as in step 2.

5. For each sample, add 50 μl of minisequencing mix for detection of the standard sequence to one well and 50 μl of mix for detection of the template sequence to another well. Incubate at 50°C for 10 min.

6. Wash as in step 2.

7. Add 60 μl of 50 mM NaOH to each well and incubate for at least 2 min at room temperature.

8. Transfer the samples to liquid scintillation vials, add scintillation fluid, and measure the samples in a liquid scintillation counter.

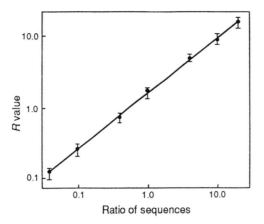

FIGURE 2 Solid-phase minisequencing standard curve prepared for quantification of human aspartylglucosaminidase mRNA. R value = ratio of the cpm values obtained in the reaction for detection of the standard RNA sequence to that in the reaction for detection of the sample RNA sequence. The mean value and variation range for three separate assays are shown. Adapted from Ikonen *et al.* (1992).

E. ANALYSIS OF THE RESULTS

Steps

1. For each sample calculate the ratio

$$\frac{\text{cpm in the reaction detecting the standard sequence}}{\text{cpm in the reaction detecting the sample sequence}}$$

2. Plot the cpm ratio obtained in the standard mixtures as a function of the initial ratio of the standard and sample RNA sequences on a log–log scale. Figure 2 shows an example of a standard curve (from Ikonen *et al.,* 1992).

3. Determine the initial ratio of the RNA standard to the RNA sample with the aid of the standard curve. Calculate the amount of RNA in the sample.

IV. Comments

As sample for the quantitative analysis we use total RNA isolated from tissues or cells, and relate the determined amount of mRNA to the amount of total RNA in the analyzed sample. It is also possible to reverse transcribe and amplify RNA from biological samples without complete purification (Kawasaki, 1990), but then information on some other parameter, e.g., the amount of total protein, mass of tissue, or number of cells in the sample, is required as a reference point for the determined amount of RNA.

The procedure presented in this chapter can be simplified if some loss of accuracy is acceptable. The preparation of RNA standards can be avoided by using a DNA standard added to the samples after the cDNA synthesis step (Suomalainen *et al.,* 1993). In this case the efficiency of the cDNA synthesis is assumed to be independent of the amount of RNA and the composition of the sample.

The amount of specific RNA in a sample can be determined without a standard curve directly from the ratio of the labels incorporated in the minisequencing reactions corresponding to the standard and sample RNA sequences, taking into account the specific activities and the number of labeled nucleotides incorporated (Syvänen *et al.,* 1993). In this case possible unspecific incorporation of labeled dNTP by the

DNA polymerase, which may be significant if one of the sequences is present in a small proportion of the other (<0.1), will not be accounted for.

The hybridization conditions for annealing of the detection step primer are non-stringent. Therefore the same reaction temperature (50°C) can be used for any 20-mer primer.

V. Pitfalls

1. The use of autoclaved water and an RNase inhibitor and the addition of a carrier RNA to the RNA dilutions are essential to keep the RNA standards undegraded.

2. A prerequisite for successful use of the solid-phase minisequencing method with ^{3}H, which has a low specific activity, as label is that the PCR amplification is efficient. Ten microliters of the PCR product should be clearly visible in an agarose gel by staining with ethidium bromide.

3. Precautions for avoiding DNA contaminations in the PCR should be taken (Orrego, 1990).

4. The biotin binding capacity of the microtitration wells set an upper limit to the amount of biotinylated PCR product (and excess of biotinylated primer) that can be present during the capturing reaction. The biotin binding capacity of the microtitration wells that we are using is about 2 pmole. Therefore we use 10 pmole of the biotinylated primer in the PCR and analyze one-fifth of the PCR product per minisequencing reaction.

5. It is important for the specificity of the minisequencing reaction that the excess dNTPs present during the PCR are completely removed by the washing steps preceding the capturing step. The use of an automatic microtiter plate washer saves time and improves the efficiency.

REFERENCES

Gilliland, G., Perrin, S., Blanchard, K., and Bunn, H. F. (1990) Analysis of cytokine mRNA and DNA: Detection and quantitation by competitive polymerase chain reaction. *Proc. Natl. Acad. Sci. USA* **86**, 2725–2729.

Higuchi, R., Krummel, B., and Saiki, R. K. (1988) A general method of in vitro preparation and specific mutagenesis of DNA fragments: Study of protein and DNA interactions. *Nucleic Acids Res.* **16**, 7351–7367.

Ikonen, E., Manninen, T., Peltonen, L., and Syvänen, A-C. (1992) Quantitative determination of rare mRNA species by PCR and solid-phase minisequencing. *PCR Methods Appl.* **1**, 234–240.

Innis, M. A., and Gelfand, D. H. (1990) Optimization of PCRs. *In* "PCR Protocols. A Guide to Methods and Applications" (M. A. Innis, D. H. Gelfand, J. J. Sninsky, and T. J. White, eds.), pp. 3–12. Academic Press, San Diego.

Kawasaki, E. S. (1990) Amplification of RNA. *In* "PCR Protocols. A Guide to Methods and Applications" (M. A. Innis, D. H. Gelfand, J. J. Sninsky, and T. J. White, eds.), pp. 21–27. Academic Press, San Diego.

Melton, D. A., Krieg, P. A., Rebagliati, M. R., Maniatis, T., Zinn, K., and Green, M. R. (1984) Efficient in vitro synthesis of biologically active RNA and RNA hybridization probes from plasmids containing a bacteriophage SP6 promoter. *Nucleic Acids Res.* **12**, 7035–7056.

Orrego, C. (1990) Organizing a laboratory for PCR work. *In* "PCR Protocols. A Guide to Methods and Applications" (M. A. Innis, D. H. Gelfand, J. J. Sninsky, and T. J. White, eds.), pp. 451–459. Academic Press, San Diego.

Sambrook, J., Fritsch, E. F., and Maniatis, T. (eds.) (1989) *"Molecular Cloning. A Laboratory Handbook,"* 2nd ed. Cold Spring Harbor Laboratory Press, Cold Spring Harbor, NY.

Suomalainen, A., Majander, A., Pihko, H., Peltonen, L., and Syvänen, A-C. (1993) Quantification of the $tRNA_{3243}^{Leu}$ point mutation in MELAS patients and its effect on mitochondrial transcription. *Hum. Mol. Genet.* **2,** 525–534.

Syvänen, A-C., Aalto-Setälä, K., Harju, L., Kontula, K., and Söderlund, H. (1990) A primer-guided nucleotide incorporation assay in the genotyping of apolipoprotein E. *Genomics* **8,** 684–692.

Syvänen, A-C., Bengstström, M., Tenhunen, J., and Söderlund, H. (1988) Quantification of polymerase chain reaction products by affinity-based hybrid collection. *Nucleic Acids Res.* **16,** 11327–11338.

Syvänen, A-C., Sajantila, A., and Lukka, M. (1993) Identification of individuals by analysis of biallelic DNA markers, using PCR and solid-phase minisequencing. *Am. J. Hum. Genet.* **52,** 46–59.